Hertfordshire
Geology and Landscape

John Catt
(editor)

To Inger Cooper, with best wishes,

John A. Catt

P H Banham

A. Allan Pherbire

Hayden W. Bailey.

Jack Gy Cy

Trevor James

Rob Sage

Christopher Green

Hertfordshire
Geology and Landscape

John Catt
(editor)

Hertfordshire Natural History Society 2010

To Percy and Enid Evans,
who began the work for this book

Text and maps copyright © the authors and the Hertfordshire Natural
History Society 2010

Photographs copyright © John Catt and the photographers as indicated

Published in 2010 by the Hertfordshire Natural History Society
Registered Charity number 218418
24 Mandeville Rise, Welwyn Garden City, Hertfordshire, AL8 7JU
www.hnhs.org

With generous assistance from:
Hertfordshire Geological Society, www.hertsgeolsoc.ology.org.uk/
Natural England through GeoEast – The East of England Geodiversity
    Partnership
The Curry Fund of the Geologists' Association,
    www.geologistsassociation.org.uk
Ver Valley Society, www.riverver.co.uk
St. Albans and District Footpaths Society
East Herts Geology Club

With thanks for generous donations from:
John Catt
Lynn Allen
Haydon Bailey
Linda Hamling
John Facer
Peter Allen
Peter Banham
Wendy Frost
Jack Hopgood
Margaret Selby
George Wells
Nikki Edwards
Max Roberts
Brian Warren
Mervyn Jones
Janet Howell

Designed by LTD Design Consultants,
54 Warwick Square, London SW1V 2AJ

Printed by Dolman Scott, www.dolmanscott.com

British Library Cataloguing-in-publication Data
A catalogue record for this book is available from the British Library

ISBN: 978-0-9521685-9-1

For information about all HNHS publications visit our website at
www.hnhs.org

Contents

Chapter heading images

Chapter 1: Woodoaks Farm, Maple Cross, Denham Village Terrace and bluff (photo Steve Carter).
Chapter 2: Strata under Shenley, extract from Figure 2.1.
Chapter 3: Chalk echinoid, *Micraster cortestudinarium* (photo Helen Baker).
Chapter 4: Puddingstone with iron stained joint, Wood Hall Stud Estate, Radlett, extract from plate 17.
Chapter 5: *Pholas (Barnea) cylindrica* from Red Crag at Rothamsted (copyright Rothamsted Research).
Chapter 6: Gravel of River Gade at Croxley Common Moor (photo Steve Carter).
Chapter 7: Barley.
Chapter 8: Hand axe from Folly Pit, Hitchin.
Chapter 9: Reflection in the Lee Navigation at Broxbourne (photo Helen Baker).
Chapter 10: Flints at St Peter Great Berkhamsted.

Preface and acknowledgements

Hertfordshire Geology and Landscape has suffered a long gestation period. The need for a book linking geology to other aspects of the county's natural history was originally suggested by the Council of the Hertfordshire Natural History Society in 1950, and the society has held a fund to meet the cost of publishing such a book since 1960, when W. H. Fordham donated £200 for that purpose. After Percy Evans retired from employment in petroleum exploration and moved to Berkhamsted in 1941, he took up the challenge, and began an intensive programme of fieldwork throughout the county to familiarize himself with its geology, mineral resources, building stones, landscape development, soils, flora and fauna. With the support of his wife Enid, the fieldwork extended through the 1950s and 1960s and, before his untimely death in 1973, they had together written first drafts of 30 chapters for a book 'designed for naturalists who are not geologists'.

Unfortunately, Percy was too good a geologist and too enthusiastic a research worker to complete the job to his own satisfaction in as short a period as the 10-20 years since he started writing. In particular, he was decades ahead of his time in realizing that the long sequence of terraces of the pre-glacial diversion proto-Thames in the Vale of St Albans and the post-diversion (modern) Thames through London provides a much more complete history of Quaternary events than could be obtained anywhere else in Britain. In his professional life in oil exploration, Percy had also been impressed by the work of Cesari Emiliani, who was showing in the 1960s that foraminiferal assemblages in sediment cores from the Caribbean and other deep ocean basins indicated a much more complex history of Quaternary (glacial-interglacial) temperature variation than had ever been suspected from studies of glacial sequences in the Alps, Germany, USA and UK. Linking Emiliani's datable oceanic sequence to the then undatable Thames terrace sequence was a challenge Percy couldn't resist. It led to a seminal and long, if understandably inconclusive, paper that was published by the London Geological Society in 1971. More importantly, it initiated a major international research programme by Nick (later Sir Nicholas) Shackleton at Cambridge investigating in ever increasing detail the oceanic evidence for the history of Quaternary global climatic change and its causes. So it was hardly surprising that the unfinished Hertfordshire book was 'put on the shelf' for a matter of years while Percy struggled with a new research programme of global significance that is still developing today.

After Percy's death, Enid asked me to complete the book. But, intimidated by its scope, I could only seek help from a range of experts who knew the county and had researched some of the subjects relevant to Percy's 30-chapter draft. Some agreed to revise chapters and others felt that a fresh start was required, but over the years progress was curtailed by more pressing priorities and by several unfortunate deaths. Deceased or otherwise inactive contributors were replaced by younger, but on many occasions I had to confess to Enid that progress was inadequate. Eventually, after retiring from Rothamsted Experimental Station (now Rothamsted Research), I was able to take advantage of an honorary position in the Geography Department at University College London to do the necessary self-education to cover most of the subject areas in Percy's original draft. Consequently, apart from Chapter 3, which has been in the safe hands of Haydon Bailey for a few years, all the present chapters have been based on Percy's or my own drafts. The other authors named at the head of each chapter have made many invaluable contributions and eliminated the worst of my erroneous ideas, and for that I am enormously grateful. Nevertheless, I accept full responsibility for any other errors and serious omissions that the reader may detect. In addition, I am especially grateful to Eric Robinson (Earth Sciences Department, University College London) and Peter Hopson (British Geological Survey), who diligently read and helpfully commented on the penultimate version of the whole book. Other friends who have helped in various ways are acknowledged below.

In revising Percy and Enid's earlier work, I have endeavoured to retain the breadth of approach they wisely initiated. I see this as the book's main strength, that is explaining the county's geology to local specialists in other subjects, and also explaining to geologists the links between their subject and other important aspects of the county's natural environment – its soils, ecology, agriculture, archaeology, water supply, waste disposal, civil engineering, mineral resources and building stones. I hope this will widen the book's appeal beyond a basic description of the county's geology.

However, the breadth of content has caused problems. Percy and Enid had devoted long sections of text to explaining simple geological principles. For the benefit of readers with no formal geological training, I have felt it appropriate to retain some aspects of this approach relevant to Hertfordshire, albeit in abbreviated form. They can be found in Chapter 1 and the Introductions to some later chapters. But a book covering first principles of what is any case a very broad subject and also explaining the numerous subtleties of Hertfordshire's complex geology would have been impossibly long and expensive and, like the Evans's first draft, might never have been completed in my lifetime! Also, I hope the book will be useful to academic and professional readers in Britain and abroad, and to the numerous enthusiatic amateur geologists who have acquired a sound basic knowledge from recent Open University and other television broadcasts. Thus *Hertfordshire Geology and Landscape* is a fairly comprehensive account of the county's geology and its influence on other aspects of natural history, but not a student introduction to basic geological principles. Readers who need the latter should first read one of the numerous introductory textbooks written for newcomers to the subject.

Finally, I must express my regret that publication has not preceded Enid's death. Throughout the years I have been writing and editing various parts or cajoling others to complete sections they had promised, I have been spurred on by expectation of the eventual pleasure she would have shown to see so much of her own work and that of her husband in print. Sadly I can never have that satisfaction, but I hope in time it will be replaced by the knowledge that others who love and study Hertfordshire will find the insights of Percy, Enid and the numerous other contributors both useful and stimulating.

Other acknowledgements

Liz Allsopp, Librarian at Rothamsted Research, for help with locating references.

Richard Bateman, Kew Gardens, for critically reading Chapter 4.

British Geological Survey, for permission to reproduce Figure 1.4.

The Curry Fund of the Geologists' Association, London, for an interest-free loan of £2000 towards the cost of drawing the figures.

John Facer, Earth Sciences Department, Birkbeck College London, for scanning old 35 mm colour slides and organizing the colour plates.

Margaret Glendining and Tony Scott, Rothamsted Research, for providing detailed records from the Rothamsted drain gauges.

Miles Irving, Geography Department, University College London, for completing the final versions of the diagrams and for expert advice in their preparation.

Nick Mann, Geography Department, University College London, for help with locating maps.

David Nowell, for invaluable help and advice with writing Chapter 2 and help with compiling Appendix 1.

Paul Poulton, Rothamsted Research, for detailed advice on Rothamsted classical experiments.

Hugh Prince, Geography Department, University College London, for advice on the history of Hertfordshire, especially the parks, and for commenting critically on Chapter 7.

Graham Shepherd, Rothamsted Research, for preparing Plate 23.

Linda Smith, Secretary, HNHS, for help with the production of the book.

Susan Stead, Deputy Rare Books Librarian, University College London, for help with locating references.

David Thorold, St Albans Museum Service, for locating the artefacts shown in Plates 34, 51 and 72.

Timothy Vickers, Museums Luton, for providing the photographs used in Plate 70.

Andy Webb and Jane Gardiner, Ver Valley Society, for useful comments on the text of Chapter 9.

John Catt
University College London
July 2010

Foreword

The story of our planet is undoubtedly the most compelling aspect of the study of geology. But in regional texts this rich history too often comes to an abrupt end somewhere within the Quaternary Period or, in far too many, even earlier. This is generally where the knowledge or interests of the author(s) wanes.

The volume represents a masterly compilation of all things Hertfordshire. It will take the reader through a full view of the evolution of that little piece of England that one often races through in the escape from London along the many significant radiating routes which pass through the county. Why are those natural corridors there? Well, this volume will provide a significant part of the answer to that question and so much more.

The story begins deep underground, hundreds of millions of years ago and thousands of miles to the south, in fact around the equator where the southern Gondwanan and northern Laurussian continents collided to form the supercontinent of Pangea. The deep rocks beneath Hertfordshire represent a complex basement of hard crystalline and metamorphosed sediments. These formed a stable part of the Laurussian continental plate, against which the small microplate of Avalonia was crushed along a margin termed the Variscan Front, just south of London as we know it, as Gondwana crashed into Laurussia. Quite a start! But in reality, it was only one episode in a long continuum of earlier earth events.

Above this hard basement, younger rocks accumulated in the tropical seas of the Cretaceous Period, most spectacularly represented by the Chalk that accumulated in a massively broad, almost world-wide sea. This is the true 'greenhouse world', where atmospheric carbon reached a peak and the dinosaurs were at their zenith in terms of numbers and diversity.

Later still, the reader is drawn through the 'Tertiary' Era when sediments were deposited in a more limited 'North Sea Basin' and climates initially reached a maximum then slowly declined towards the newly defined Quaternary Period.

Massive fluctuations in climate characterize this youngest period of the earth's history and show the first glimpses of the human interaction with our planet. Hertfordshire holds a significant part of that record, especially in relation to its landscape development. At first a small population of hunter-gatherers left a tantalizing record over a long period of occupation. Hominins migrated in and out of Britain as the climate fluctuated from full-glacial periods to very warm interglacials, each migratory cycle leaving its mark in Hertfordshire.

The Late Glacial Maximum, a time that saw Hertfordshire dominated again by periglacial conditions, was followed, as the climate ameliorated, by migration and re-colonization leading to a significant population growth that demanded a change in the interaction of man with the environment. Soils, the ease with which they could be worked with primitive tools, the availability of water and security of living, all became important as settlement became the norm. The reader will be treated to comprehensive descriptions of these aspects of human occupation.

Finally, the modern human interaction with the environment, the importance of soils for various agricultural purposes, our use of water and mineral resources and our creation of the built environment are all given a significant place in this volume, and bring the story of Hertfordshire geology and landscape to a comprehensive conclusion.

Remember those radial routeways? Well, after digesting the contents of this book, you will be able to answer that question for yourself. I thoroughly recommend this well illustrated and readable volume to both professional geological readers and to those amateur enthusiasts who need a geological background to their archaeological, historical and ecological studies. The authors are to be congratulated in bringing this book to completion after so many years in gestation, a time during which knowledge of the many aspects described have changed radically. It is a valuable contribution to our modern understanding of Hertfordshire.

Peter Hopson
British Geological Survey, Keyworth,
August 2010

List of authors and affiliations

B. W. Avery, formerly Deputy Director of Soil Survey of England and Wales

H. W. Bailey, Network Stratigraphic Consulting Ltd

P. H. Banham, formerly Geology Department, Royal Holloway, University of London

S. Bryant, County Archaeologist, Hertfordshire County Council

J. A. Catt, Honorary Professor, Geography Department, University College London; formerly Rothamsted Experimental Station, Harpenden

D. A. Cheshire, formerly Geology Department, University of Hertfordshire

J. C. Doyle, formerly Head of Geology, Hadham Hall School

C. Edmonds, Peter Brett Associates, Reading

C. P. Green, formerly Geography Department, Royal Holloway, University of London

T. J. James, formerly Keeper of Natural History, North Herts Museum, and Head of Ecology, Herts Biological Records Centre

B. T. Perry, formerly University of Hertfordshire

R. C. Sage, Water Resources Manager, Veolia Water Central, Hatfield

I. Thompson, Historic Environment Record Officer, Hertfordshire County Council

C. J. Wood, Scops Geology Ltd, formerly British Geological Survey

Chapter 1.

Introduction

John Catt

1.1. The character of Hertfordshire

Hertfordshire is one of the smaller counties of Great Britain. With an area of 1643 km² (634 square miles), the modern administrative county is only the 36th largest in the country. But, with a total human population of about 1,059,000 (645 per km²), it is more densely populated than almost any other. Because of minor changes to several parts of the county boundary, the total area has changed slightly since the late 19th century. But over the same period the population has increased approximately three times. Most of the long-established

towns and villages have slowly expanded their population, but during the 20th century the county also acquired several new towns, mainly to accommodate London's 'overspill' population. These were sited at Letchworth, Welwyn Garden City, Hatfield, Hemel Hempstead and Stevenage (Fig. 1.1). At the start of the 21st century there are plans for further expansion of housing across the county, so the population density is set to increase further in the near future, and this will put further pressure on local natural resources dependent on geology, such as building materials, water and soils.

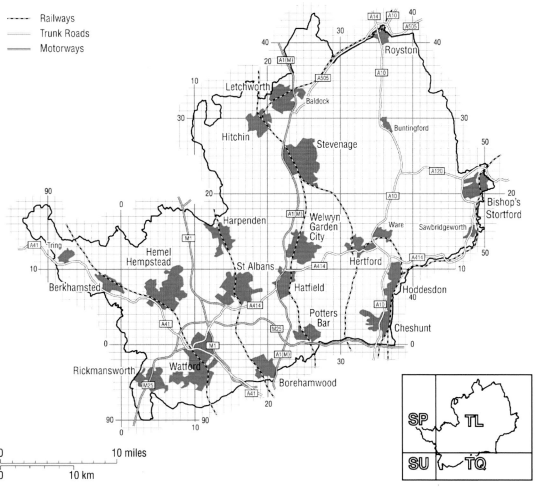

Fig. 1.1. Principal towns, railways and roads in Hertfordshire.

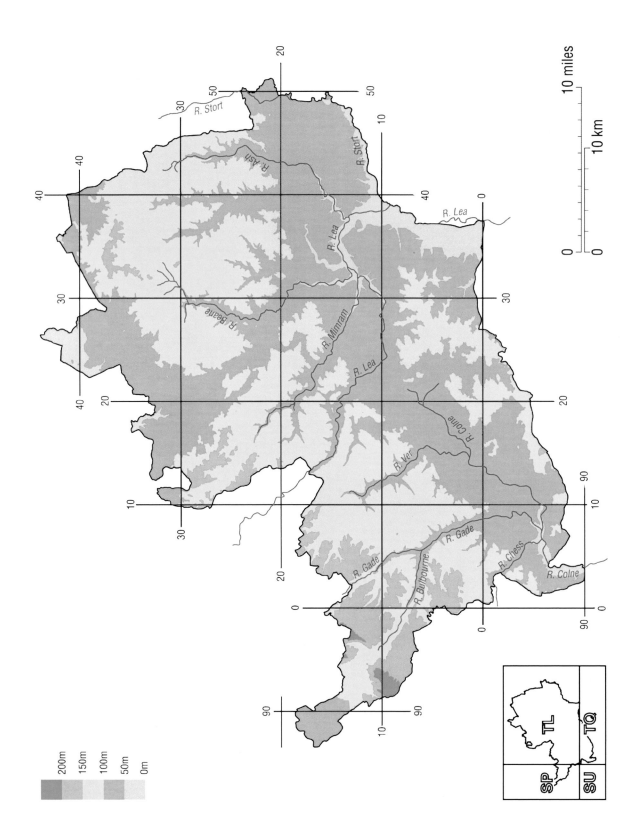

Fig. 1.2. Rivers and relief of Hertfordshire.

8

The county's southern border lies only 25-30 km north of the centre of London. This undoubtedly explains the changing population and many other aspects of the county's character, including the radial pattern of major railways, motorways and other roads spreading out from the capital (Fig. 1.1). To some extent, these reflect the pattern of roads built by the Romans to connect the crossing of the Thames at Londinium (Roman London) with centres to the north, such as Watling Street leading to Verulamium (now St Albans) and Durocobrivus (Dunstable), and Ermine Street leading to Lindum (Lincoln).

Despite the overshadowing influence of the capital, much of Hertfordshire retains, at least for the present, the charming rural character it has presented for at least a millennium. Anyone walking for example in the quiet fields, woods and narrow lanes close to St Albans would find it difficult to believe that the London Orbital Motorway (M25), the two main motorways carrying traffic from London to northern England and Scotland (the A1(M) and M1) and the major railways from London Euston (to Birmingham, Manchester and Glasgow), London St Pancras (to Leicester, Nottingham and Sheffield) and London Kings Cross (to York, Leeds, Durham and Edinburgh) are all within a few kilometres, even less that the modern suburbs of north London spread nearly as close. Despite its small total area, Hertfordshire claims to have more village greens than any other English county.

Hertfordshire's landscape is little different from most other parts of southeast England. Apart from the towns and lines of communication, it is dominated by gently rolling farmland with numerous small patches of woodland and a network of minor lowland rivers (Fig. 1.2), most of which eventually drain southwards into the Thames. The absence of heavy industry reflects the county's geology and complete lack of the mineral resources (coal, ironstone) that drove Britain's industrial revolution.

Almost all of the county lies between 50 m and 200 m above sea level, as defined by the British Ordnance Datum (OD). The highest point (244 m OD) is close to the western county boundary near the hamlet of Hastoe (SP 914092) on the Chiltern Hills south of Tring. It is a land-locked county with no coastline, no natural outcrops of hard bedrock and only the smallest areas of what might be classified, with some stretch of the imagination, as 'wilderness'. The effects of man on the landscape in both historic and prehistoric times are almost certainly ubiquitous; they are more obvious in some areas than others, but never completely obscure the influence of the underlying geology.

A characteristic feature of the Hertfordshire landscape over most of the last millennium has been the large number of privately owned parks, perhaps more than in any other English county (Prince, 2008; Rowe, 2009). In the late 13th century, there were at least 28 large deer parks, and by the late 16th century the number had increased to 36 (Norden, 1593). Subsequently the county attracted many ambitious newcomers, usually from London society, who modified the rural landscape by building large country houses surrounded by ornamental gardens and designed parkland (Williamson, 2007). By the late 19th century there were almost 250 large

Plate 1. The house (built 1670s) and park at Gorhambury (TL 113079) near St Albans. Published with permission from the Earl of Verulam.

and small estates of this type in the county (Prince, 2008, Table 6.3). The number decreased after 1880 because of the decline in land values, and many have since been sold for new uses, such as hotels, golf courses, colleges, schools and suburban housing development. Nevertheless, stately houses (Plate 1) and parkland remain an attractive aspect of Hertfordshire's scenery even today, and help preserve the county's rural aspect. Many of the house names were given the characteristic Hertfordshire suffix '-bury', which still occurs commonly on modern Ordnance Survey maps of the county. Also still evident are the numerous landscape modifications designed for many of the larger parks by Capability Brown and Humphry Repton, including for example the large ornamental lake (TL 2812) constructed in the Mimram valley in 1799-1800 for the Panshanger Estate (Prince, 1959).

Another housing venture for which Hertfordshire is famous is the garden city. The idea began in 1846 with Feargus O'Connor, a member of the Chartist Movement, who attempted to create, largely at his own expense, the first garden city at Heronsgate (TQ 0294) near Chorleywood. Unfortunately a Parliamentary Select Committee declared the scheme illegal, because the 35 smallholdings were allocated by lottery. As a result the company responsible was declared bankrupt in 1851. Nevertheless, it was a model for the more successful Garden City Pioneer Company, which was established by share capital in 1902 and inspired by the publications of Ebenezer Howard, a humanitarian who had lived among the slums of London's East End. The company's first venture, Letchworth Garden City, was established in 1903 on land purchased in the parishes of Letchworth, Norton and Willian northeast of Hitchin. Its spacious layout inspired many other suburban housing estates after World War I, including in Hertfordshire the new town of Welwyn Garden City, which was built in the early 1920s on land purchased by Howard from Hatfield and Panshanger Parks (Prince, 1959).

Although the Industrial Revolution had no direct impact on Hertfordshire, numerous lighter industries have added special character to its landscape over several centuries (Branch Johnson, 1970). The need to provide food and drink for the large population of nearby London explains the long-standing importance of agriculture as the county's dominant industry. Malting barley for beer production has been a major arable crop in Hertfordshire and nearby counties since at least the Middle Ages. By the early 19th century the number of maltings in the county had grown to at least 80, mainly in the towns of north Hertfordshire, such as Royston, Ashwell, Hitchin, Baldock, Bishop's Stortford and Tring. Later this industry became focussed on Ware, Bishop's Stortford, Hoddesdon and other towns with good transport connections to the capital using the River Lea. The supply of malt led naturally to a widespread brewing industry, and in the mid-19th century, more than 40 breweries were listed in the county, mainly in towns such as Hitchin, Royston, Baldock, Hatfield, Hertford, St Albans and Watford.

Wheat has also been grown widely in Hertfordshire, and gave rise to an important flour milling industry. By the mid-19th century there were almost 100 wind and water powered mills grinding corn in the county. After about 1870, steam and later electricity took over as sources of power, both for a small number of new mills and the modernization of existing ones. From the 17th to the early 20th centuries, wheat straw was the basis for a widespread cottage straw-plaiting industry in many Hertfordshire villages and towns, including Tring, Hemel Hempstead, Hitchin, Ashwell, Hertford and Harpenden. The straw plait was sold in town markets to factories in St Albans, Hatfield, Luton and Dunstable that produced mainly straw hats and bonnets. Grey (1977, Chapter 2) gave a detailed first-hand account of the role of this cottage industry in the daily lives of late 19th century people of Harpenden.

Some Hertfordshire water mills were also used for making paper from rags. The earliest known papermill in the county was at Hertford, and was owned in 1494 by John Tate, son of a Lord Mayor of London. In later periods, paper was produced at Sopwell Mill on the River Ver near St Albans (Plate 2), at Hatfield on the River Lea, at Standon on the River Rib, at Sarratt and several other sites on the River Chess, at Rickmansworth, Hamper and Bushey on the River Colne and at Apsley, Croxley, Nash and other sites on the River Gade. Other water mills in the county were used at various times for weaving silk (at Watford, Rickmansworth,

Plate 2. Sopwell Mill (TL 155054) on the River Ver near St Albans.

St Albans and Tring) and canvas (at Tring), for fulling wool (at Codicote, Braughing, Standon and Hemel Hempstead) or for dressing leather (at Hertford and Hitchin).

In the past, the county has also been famous for unusual horticultural crops, such as cherries grown on the Chiltern Hills around Frithsden in west Hertfordshire, watercress cultivated from the mid 19th to the late 20th centuries in many of the Chiltern chalkland streams and lavender for production of lavender water at Hitchin. In the late 19th century, there was also a rapid expansion in dairy farming, mainly in eastern Hertfordshire, but this declined when large areas of pasture were ploughed up for production of arable crops in World War II.

Until quite recently, no less than 18 Hertfordshire towns had held markets at weekly or more frequent intervals for several centuries, principally for the sale of farm and horticultural produce. Like the county of Kent on the opposite side of London, Hertfordshire has therefore been described as 'the garden of England for delight; men commonly say that such as buy a house in Hertfordshire pay two years' purchase for the aire thereof – a salubrity due to the geological condition of the greater part of the county, gravel upon chalk' (Clutterbuck, 1864). Clutterbuck's statement is of course a great over-simplification, but the well-drained nature of much of the county's land probably does contribute to the population's good health.

Hertfordshire includes much of the woodland-dominated Chilterns Area of Outstanding Natural Beauty (AONB), large areas of which are open to the public as they are owned by the National Trust. But even outside the Chilterns AONB, other non-urban parts of the county are almost as attractive to the country-lover and naturalist, and can be accessed using the county's dense network of minor roads, bridleways and footpaths. Through the efforts of the Herts and Middlesex Wildlife Trust, the county and adjacent areas of north London now has 45 nature reserves. These are also open to the public, and some (e.g. Reed, Barkway and Hillend chalk pits) were established for their geological interest. In addition, there are numerous local authority nature reserves well worth visiting. All of these areas attract millions of visitors each year, many of whom will wish to know more about what is under their feet and how it explains what they see around them.

The main purpose of this book is to provide this information by describing the geological history of the county and explaining how it has resulted in Hertfordshire's range of scenery, from the plateau woodlands and deeply incised dry chalkland valleys of the Chilterns in the north and west to the productive rolling arable farmland in the east. Ecological features, such as the various types of woodland and the distribution of heathland and flower-rich grasslands all depend on the county's geology, as expressed through soil types. In addition, major lines of communication and local industries using natural resources, such as chalk, gravel and brickearth, are determined by geological features. Geology also accounts for the distribution of many archaeological and historical features, and is vital for the county's water supply. All these aspects are discussed in later chapters.

However, before they can be considered, it is necessary to introduce some fundamental geological concepts for the benefit of readers with little or no training in the subject. Geology is probably the most multidisciplinary of all the sciences, in that some (though not a great) knowledge of chemistry, physics, mathematics, zoology and botany are all useful, and there are also important links with geomorphology, astronomy, pedology (soil science), ecology and archaeology. Indeed, once they delve into the subject, many people are fascinated by the range of interdisciplinary aspects that unfold. But, like other sciences, geology has its own peculiar vocabulary and thought processes, which need to be mastered before the practical value and indeed the aesthetic beauty of the subject can be appreciated.

1.2. Some basic geological facts and principles

Dating geological events

The first stumbling block for anyone, even the trained geologist, is grasping the concept of geological time. Even if one talks in terms of years rather than shorter periods such as days, time in geology is no easier to envisage than distances in astronomy. The enormous numbers involved cannot be appreciated from the experience gained during a human lifetime. To resolve this problem, geologists have developed various simplified ways of viewing the passage of time over the history of the Earth. The first of these involves quoting ages in millions of years, and throughout this book the abbreviation Ma is used for dating in this way; this at least removes the last six zeros from the ages of most rocks, fossils and geological events, and the approximation is justified because it is rarely possible to quote ages more precisely than 1 Ma. However, towards the present it is possible to date things with increasing precision, so that

within the later part of the Quaternary Period, over about the last 1 Ma, we can profitably use ka as an abbreviation for thousands of years. Ma and ka are used for dates before the present and also for intervals of time in the past. Even closer to the present, it is sometimes necessary to refer to yet more precise dates provided by archaeological and historical evidence over about the last 2500 years. Although it is conventional to refer to these as BC and AD, an attempt is made to treat Christian and non-Christian readers with equal respect by using BCE (Before the Common Era) and CE (Common Era). However, BCE dates are the same as those BC, and CE dates are the same as those AD.

As part of the solar system, planet Earth is thought to have originated about 4,600 Ma by accretion of cosmic debris. By about 3,800 Ma, the Earth had cooled sufficiently from an originally molten mass to acquire a hydrosphere, consisting of surface water (oceans, rivers and lakes) and groundwater (water held in rocks below the surface). The earliest forms of microbial life originating in the surface waters lived without oxygen, but by about 2600 Ma the appearance of green (chlorophyll-containing) micro-organisms, which obtain energy from gaseous carbon dioxide by the process of photosynthesis, resulted in a slow increase in the oxygen content of the atmosphere. This led to the start of the Proterozoic Aeon (Table 1.1). The previous 2000 Ma of Earth history before the appearance of photosynthesizing organisms constitutes the Archaean Aeon.

Through evolutionary processes, the oxygen-containing atmosphere supported an increasingly diverse range of plants, with the first animals (marine sponges) probably appearing about 750 Ma. For most of the Proterozoic Aeon these life forms were almost entirely soft-bodied, and as a result they are rarely preserved as recognizable fossils in the sediments in which they were buried. However, about 542 Ma a spurt of evolution led to the relatively sudden appearance of a wide range of hard-shelled animals, which are characteristic of the Phanerozoic Aeon. Their remains

Aeons	Eras	Sub-eras	Periods	Epochs	Dating
Phanerozoic	Caenozoic	Quaternary	Holocene		11.7 ka-present
			Pleistocene		2.6 Ma-11.7 ka
		Tertiary	Neogene	Pliocene	5.3-2.6 Ma
				Miocene	23.0-5.3 Ma
			Palaeogene	Oligocene	33.9-23.0 Ma
				Eocene	55.8-33.9 Ma
				Palaeocene	65.5-55.8 Ma
	Mesozoic or Secondary		Cretaceous		145-65.5 Ma
			Jurassic		200-145 Ma
			Triassic		251-200 Ma
	Palaeozoic or Primary		Permian		299-251 Ma
			Carboniferous		359-299 Ma
			Devonian		416-359 Ma
			Silurian		444-416 Ma
			Ordovician		488-444 Ma
			Cambrian		542-488 Ma
Proterozoic			Precambrian		2600-542 Ma
Archaean					4600-2600 Ma

Table 1.1 Subdivision of geological time (dating based on Gradstein et al., 2005).

are much more clearly preserved in sedimentary rocks and, as they could move around more easily in the early oceans, they are also more widely distributed. Because of further evolutionary changes over time, they can be used to date the Phanerozoic sediments much more precisely than the Proterozoic rocks, and also to correlate them from site to site. Correlation is the procedure by which sediments deposited in different areas or different environments (e.g. different seas or other surface waters, or on land areas in different climatic zones) are shown to be of the same age.

Another way of simplifying the passage of time over the history of the Earth is by reference to the forms of life, which can be recognized from fossil remains in the Phanerozoic sedimentary rocks. This view of geological time was developed long before it was possible to determine even approximately how many Ma ago the various life forms appeared or became extinct. However, extensive research over the last 70 years or so has determined these evolutionary events with increasing precision.

The Phanerozoic Aeon (542 Ma-present) is divided into three eras: the Palaeozoic or era of ancient life (542-251 Ma), the Mesozoic or era of middle life (251-65.5 Ma), and the Caenozoic or era of recent life (65.5 Ma-present). Each era has in turn been divided into periods, which are the most commonly used units of geological time. The Palaeozoic Era includes six periods (in chronological order, the Cambrian, Ordovician, Silurian, Devonian, Carboniferous and Permian Periods), the Mesozoic three periods (Triassic, Jurassic and Cretaceous) and the Caenozoic three periods (Palaeogene, Neogene and Quaternary). An alternative subdivision of the Caenozoic (used in Table 1.1) is into the Tertiary and Quaternary Sub-eras, the former comprising the Palaeogene and Neogene Periods, and the latter the Pleistocene and Holocene Periods. The boundaries between most of the periods have been established by major changes in fossil assemblages reflecting the appearance (evolution) of new animal groups or the disappearance (extinction) of others. The sediments exposed at the surface in Hertfordshire date entirely from the Cretaceous, Palaeogene, Neogene, Pleistocene and Holocene Periods. Those of some earlier periods occur at depth, but are known only from deep boreholes or indirectly from geophysical evidence (Chapter 2).

For further subdivision of Phanerozoic time, the periods are divided into epochs; for example, the Palaeogene Period is divided into three epochs (Palaeocene, Eocene and Oligocene) and the Neogene into two (Miocene and Pliocene). For yet further subdivision, epochs are divided into stages, which are typically a few Ma in duration in the Palaeozoic and Mesozoic, but decrease in length to a few ka in the later part of the Quaternary. Like the longer units of geological time, most stages are separated on evidence derived from the evolution of fossil groups. But in the Quaternary, when there were few true evolutionary changes, they are distinguished on fossil and other evidence for major climatic changes (glacials and interglacials).

The precise dating of time units, as given in Table 1.1, has been developed using a range of radiometric methods, which are based on the rates at which the radioactive isotopes

of certain elements decay (i.e. lose α and/or β particles) and form other isotopes. To obtain dates, the rate of decay must be known and the proportion of the radioactive 'parent' isotope originally present must be assumed, based on the amount remaining and the amount of daughter isotope present. Consequently, the material dated needs to be a closed system, with no losses or gains of parent and daughter isotopes. The amounts of the parent isotope remaining and of the daughter isotope produced from it are then measured very precisely with a mass spectrometer, and the date (t) calculated using the equation:

$$t = \frac{1}{\lambda} \log_e \left[1 + \frac{N_D}{N}\right]$$

where λ is the decay constant, N_D is the number of daughter isotope atoms and N is the number of radioactive parent isotope atoms originally present. Decay constants are derived from half-lives, that is the time taken for half of the parent isotope to decay to the daughter isotope (half-life = 0.693λ), and half-lives are calculated from laboratory measurements of daughter isotope production over a given time. The main decay series used in radiometric dating are summarized in Table 1.2.

Decay series	Half-life	Potential range
^{40}K to ^{40}A	11,900 Ma	0.03 to >4600 Ma
^{87}Rb to ^{87}Sr	50,000 Ma	20 to >4600 Ma
^{232}Th to ^{208}Pb	14,100 Ma	200 to >4600 Ma
^{235}U to ^{207}Pb	713 Ma	200 to >4600 Ma
^{238}U to ^{206}Pb	4,510 Ma	200 to >4600 Ma
^{14}C to ^{14}N	5,730 years	0-~70 ka (later Quaternary)

Table 1.2. Principal radioactive decay series used in radiometric dating.

Stratigraphy

Stratigraphy is the study of the three dimensional geometric relationships between rocks of different ages and types. In successions of sedimentary rocks, the simplest principle on which this is based is known as the Law of Superposition, which states that a sediment layer (B) overlying another rock (A) was deposited at some time after A. The exception to this law is of course where a sequence of deposits has been pushed beyond the vertical, as can happen locally in an episode of mountain building (orogeny) when rock sequences are strongly contorted by lateral compression. However, these circumstances can easily be identified from other evidence, including certain structures within the sediments themselves, and in any case do not apply to any sequences visible at the surface in Hertfordshire.

Hiatuses. Superposition does not necessarily imply continuity of deposition. Very often the plane between two deposits represents a gap in time, when either there was no deposition or unknown intervening deposits were lost by erosion before the later deposit was formed. Hiatuses or disconformities of this type can often be recognized by distinctly different dates for the two deposits, as indicated for example by the presence of fossils representing two widely separated periods of time. But in addition, a time gap may be represented by a plane of unconformity, with angular discordance between the bedding or fine layering in the deposits above and below the plane. Such planes may represent a short period of non-deposition, during which erosion cut a non-horizontal surface, such as the sloping side of a river valley or channel. Or they may represent quite long intervals of time, during which earlier marine deposits were raised above sea level and were then tilted by earth movements before they were eroded by the horizontal wave-cut platform of a later marine transgression that resulted in the overlying deposit. Where two deposits are some distance apart, so that the younger does not directly overlie the older, their age relationship can sometimes be demonstrated by the presence of fragments of the older rock enclosed within the younger.

Because of disconformities and unconformities, the geological record in many areas, including Hertfordshire, is very incomplete, sometimes with long time gaps of perhaps tens or even hundreds of Ma. Such gaps are often filled by rock sequences elsewhere, but exact correlation between the two areas may be uncertain because of different depositional environments or dating difficulties. In the rock sequence exposed at the surface in Hertfordshire, there are gaps several tens of Ma long between the youngest Cretaceous and oldest Palaeogene formations and between the youngest Palaeogene and oldest known Neogene deposits.

In geology, it is usual to distinguish between chronological units, i.e. the subdivisions of geological time such as those shown in Table 1.1, and chronostratigraphic units, which are the rocks formed during those time subdivisions. The distinction is preserved mainly at the period and epoch levels, all the rocks known to have been deposited during a particular period (e.g. the Cretaceous Period) being referred to as a System (the Cretaceous System), and all those deposited during a particular epoch (e.g. the Palaeocene Epoch) being referred to as a Series (the Palaeocene Series). However, these terms are now little used, and the word 'Series' is perhaps more widely employed as the fundamental unit of soil classification. To avoid confusion, neither chronostratigraphic term is used in this book and 'Series' is used only for soil types.

Lithostratigraphy. Rock units are distinguished primarily on lithological characteristics, such as overall chemical composition, particle size and type of stratification (e.g. strongly layered, weakly layered, unbedded or massive). Chemical composition is important for the identification of limestones (e.g. Chalk), which are composed mainly of calcium carbonate. Particle size is important in distinguishing gravels (particles mainly >2 mm across), sands (particles mainly 0.06-2.0 mm across), silts (particles mainly 0.002-0.06 mm) and clays (particles mainly <0.002 mm). Gravels consisting dominantly of rounded particles are termed conglomerates, and those with angular particles are known as breccias. Finer sediments which have been hardened by cementation or compaction are distinguished as sandstones, siltstones, mudstones, claystones, etc.

Lithostratigraphic units are classified according to a hierarchy, in which the smallest units with uniform lithological characteristics (chemical composition and particle size) are known as beds or laminae. They usually range in thickness from less than 1 cm to over 1 m, and as a result their outcrops (where they intersect the land surface) can usually be shown only as single lines on 1:10,000 to 1:50,000 maps. Associations of beds which can be traced laterally, are thick enough that their surface outcrops can be demarcated by two lines on such maps and show constant relationships to other associations of beds are defined as formations. These are the fundamental unit of lithostratigraphy. They are usually named after type localities (stratotypes), where they are well-exposed, preferably from top to bottom, and show typical characteristics. Some formations can be divided into members, each of which has a more limited lateral extent and includes beds of a particular type that differ from others in the formation (e.g. pebbly beds within a formation that is otherwise composed dominantly of sand).

Two or more associated formations that share certain lithological or fossil characteristics form a group, and two or more associated groups are sometimes linked as a supergroup. Groups and supergroups are usually bounded by major unconformities that can be traced over distances as great as tens or hundreds of kilometres. Consequently they are not commonly used in lithostratigraphic accounts of small areas such as a county. Where formations, members or beds are known (e.g. from borehole evidence) to intersect a plane of unconformity buried beneath younger deposits, their 'buried outcrops' on the unconformity are referred to as subcrops.

Lithostratigraphic units such as formations are not defined in terms of radiometric age or the presence of fossils indicative of age, though overall fossil content may be an important lithological characteristic (e.g. a shelly limestone). Some lithostratigraphic units with constant lithological properties may in fact vary in age from place to place. For example, as sea level rises so that the sea transgresses slowly over an earlier land surface, the coarse beach and shallow-water sediments deposited close to the land are older at the lower levels where the transgression started than at the higher levels eventually reached by the sea. Such units are described as diachronous. Units that are constant in age wherever they are found are said to be isochronous.

Mineralogy. Another sediment property commonly used to correlate and distinguish lithostratigraphic units such as formations is mineralogical composition. Rocks are composed of particles which range widely in chemical composition, but mainly include oxides (e.g. quartz – crystalline SiO_2), sulphides (e.g. pyrite – FeS_2), carbonates (e.g. calcite – $CaCO_3$), sulphates (e.g. gypsum – $CaSO_4.2H_2O$), phosphates (e.g. apatite – $3Ca_3(PO_4)_2$.

CaF$_2$) and complex silicates and alumino-silicates. The main sedimentary rock seen in Hertfordshire (the Chalk) is composed almost entirely of fine-grained calcite (Section 3.3), but in other less calcareous sediments (i.e. containing less carbonate) the particle size varies and with it the types of mineral present. The finest (clay) particles (<2 μm = <0.002 mm across), consist of a limited range of alumino-silicate minerals (layer- or sheet-silicates), which are thin and flat (platy), i.e. almost two-dimensional. In contrast, only a few of the coarser silt and sand grains are platy in shape; most are equant (three-dimensional), because they are composed of minerals with molecular structures that do not form thin layers or sheets. Quartz is the most common mineral in these particle size ranges, but numerous other non-platy minerals are also present in small or trace amounts. Using a heavy liquid, such as sodium polytungstate solution (specific gravity ~ 2.9 g cm^{-3}), it is possible to float off the lighter minerals (mainly quartz and alumino-silicates of K, Na and Ca, known as feldpars), thus separating them from the trace amounts of heavier minerals that sink in the liquid. The heavy mineral assemblages in sand and silt fractions can then be identified with a petrological (polarizing) microscope. They usually consist of hard, physically and chemically resistant minerals, which are characteristic of the source rocks from which the coarser fractions of the sediment were originally derived. Thus lithostratigraphic units, such as formations, which were deposited in single depositional episodes, are often characterized by a limited assemblage of heavy minerals occurring in approximately the same relative proportions throughout the unit. However, a few sand and silt minerals form in, and are characteristic of, the environment of deposition; in particular, the green microcrystalline pellets of glauconite form in shallow seas by reaction between clay minerals, iron oxides and seawater.

Fossils. Fossils are any remains indicating the former presence of life on Earth. They include body fossils and trace fossils. Most body fossils are the remains of hard and chemically fairly resistant body parts, such as the shells, bones, teeth and scales of animals, or the stems, roots, seeds, pollen and spores of plants. These may be preserved either in their original material, such as the calcium carbonate (CaCO$_3$) of mollusc shells, or as a new substance, which has replaced the original because of chemical changes after burial, and yet has retained sufficient detail that the original form of the fossil is still recognizable. Examples include the replacement of CaCO$_3$ with FeS$_2$ (pyritization) or SiO$_2$ (silicification). In fine-grained sediments, the soft fleshy parts are sometimes also preserved; these may include the muscles of animals, the feathers of birds, or the leaves and fruits of plants. Where body parts have been dissolved in groundwater but not replaced with any new substance, they are often preserved as casts or moulds within a sediment; most are external casts, but empty shells may first be filled with sediment and then dissolved to create internal casts.

Trace fossils provide evidence for the activity of organisms, but not for the organisms themselves. They include the tracks of mobile animals, such as footprints and worm trails, the burrows of molluscs or crustaceans, faecal pellets and borings made by animals into hard rock. The commonest plant trace fossils are the external casts of roots. For the majority of trace fossils, it is impossible to determine the species responsible, but the larger group (phylum or class) to which the species belonged is often indicated by morphological features of the trace fossil. Consequently, assemblages of trace fossil forms can be useful as broad indicators of depositional environment, such as water depth in the sea (Pemberton *et al.*, 1992).

Biostratigraphy. The study of fossils for dating and correlating deposits and for reconstructing changes in environment of deposition over time is known as biostratigraphy. Evolution is fundamentally a one-way process, that is changes leading to development of a new species from an older one are not reversed, and never result in reappearance of the old species. The two species may continue together, or one or both may become extinct when changing environmental conditions or competition from other organisms reduces reproductive ability and leads to a terminal decline in numbers. The fossil assemblages found in successions of sedimentary strata reflect the appearance and disappearance of species according to these evolutionary processes, but are also modified in response to changing environmental conditions.

If the times that species became extinct worldwide or new ones appeared have been determined (e.g. by radiometric dating), this information can then be used to date deposits at sites where the same changes in species can be recognized but no radiometric dating is available. However, changing environmental conditions in one area can lead to the local (but not worldwide) disappearance of a species, simply because it has emigrated to a more favourable area. Similarly, changing conditions may lead to the local appearance of a new immigrant species attracted from elsewhere. It is therefore necessary to distinguish true evolutionary changes in fossil assemblages from those caused purely by environmental change. The usual approach is to plot the abundance of all species identified through a vertical sequence of deposits, and then divide the sequence into assemblage biozones, each of which has a limited range of variation in fossil content. The reasons for differences between the biozones are then carefully assessed from what is known of evolutionary changes elsewhere and from evidence for environmental change from sediment properties such as chemical composition or particle size distribution. Assemblage biozones are usually based on single fossil groups (e.g. ammonite assemblage biozones), and are named after the most abundant species present in each biozone. However, the distinction between evolutionary and environmental causes of change is more satisfactory if two or more fossil groups are examined. In particular, an environmental change is identified more firmly if it is seen in several fossil groups than if it is suspected only in one.

Once the dates of the worldwide appearance and extinction of certain species (i.e. as a result of true evolutionary changes) have been established, they can be used to define interval biozones. For animal groups that evolved rapidly, with new species appearing at intervals of 1 Ma or less, the evolutionary range of one or more species allows deposits containing them to be dated quite precisely and correlated laterally without the need for isotopic dating. It is also useful if the species involved were abundant and able to spread rapidly into a wide range of environments, so that they are commonly found in various sediment types. In marine deposits of the Mesozoic Era, the fossil group that met these criteria best was the ammonites; other animal groups evolved more slowly or were restricted to certain environments, such as shallower parts of the oceans. Consequently, ammonites are the most universally useful group for subdividing, dating and correlating Mesozoic formations, such as the Gault Clay (Section 2.7).

In the Palaeogene, Neogene and Quaternary, after ammonites had become extinct, the most useful groups for establishing interval biozones are the microfossils, especially the rapidly evolving foraminifera, and the even smaller nannofossils, notably the primitive algae known as dinoflagellates. A major advantage of microfossils and nannofossils is that they occur in much larger numbers than macroscopic fossils, and can often be found in very small sediment samples. But special techniques such as electron microscopy are often required for their identification, and some of the most useful groups are restricted to the marine environment. For non-marine deposits, the most useful fossils for dating and correlating, especially in the Caenozoic Era, are the palynomorphs (pollen, spores and seeds of plants). Pollen and spores are widely distributed by insects or the wind, but identification at species level is often difficult and evolutionary changes were slower than in most animal groups. The vertebrates (fish, reptiles, mammals, etc) displayed rapid evolutionary development, and have been used for dating in various later periods; mammal remains are especially useful in the Quaternary.

Marine animal groups can be divided into those restricted to deeper parts of the sea floor (the benthonic organisms) and those floating freely in the surface waters (the planktonic organisms). Interval biozones based on planktonic species are more useful because these organisms are distributed in ocean currents more widely and also more rapidly than are the bottom-dwellers.

Various types of interval biozones are recognized. The most useful are taxon range biozones, which are based on the appearance and extinction of a single species, and concurrent range biozones, in which two species are used, the base of the zone being defined by the appearance of one species and the top by the extinction of the other. Less common is the lineage biozone (or consecutive range biozone), which is defined by the first and last appearance of one species, which can be shown to have followed another and preceded a third as part of a true evolutionary sequence.

Palaeotemperature determination

The temperature of the seawater in which marine animals lived in the past or the air temperature when terrestrial organisms inhabited the land surface can be estimated by assessing the environments inhabited by the same or closely related species today. This is most reliable for recent (especially Quaternary) fossils, many of which differ very little from those of the present day. But for species and assemblages of fossils found in progressively older deposits the technique becomes increasingly unreliable, because more and more of the species are now extinct and one has to assume, often incorrectly, that the environment in which the extinct species lived was the same as that of their nearest modern equivalents. Again, palaeoenvironmental assessments are more reliable if they are based on two or more species of fossil plants or animals.

A more precise method of assessing palaeotemperatures is based on the ratios of oxygen isotopes, notably in the calcium carbonate shells of marine molluscs and foraminifera. There are two common isotopes of oxygen with nuclear mass numbers of 16 and 18 (i.e. ^{16}O and ^{18}O). The commonest is ^{16}O (>99 %); ^{18}O forms about 0.2 %. Because the nuclei vary in mass, they react differently to phase and temperature changes. For example, the lightest isotope (^{16}O) is concentrated slightly in relation to ^{18}O in the water vapour produced when liquid water evaporates, and the remaining water becomes slightly enriched in the heavy isotope (^{18}O). The higher the temperature the more the water vapour becomes enriched in ^{16}O and the more the remaining water is enriched in ^{18}O. Consequently, the carbonate precipitated from warmer water (or concentrated from it in the shells of organisms) is also enriched slightly in ^{18}O. Thus, the water temperature at the time a fossil shell was alive can be determined if the $^{16}O/^{18}O$ ratio of the carbonate forming its shell is measured with a mass spectrometer and compared with the ratios in shells of the same species living today in waters with a range of temperatures.

During the Quaternary, when the sea surface temperature fluctuated fairly rapidly between glacial and interglacial stages, the oxygen isotope ratios of calcareous foraminifera in marine sediments have been used to establish an oxygen isotope stratigraphy. Changes in the ratio resulting from sea surface temperature fluctuations were in fact greatly amplified during the Quaternary by long-term storage of ^{16}O in the water of glaciers. This was because much of the ^{16}O-enriched water vapour lost from the oceans did not return immediately as rain during cold stages, but fell mainly as snow in high latitude and high altitude regions. Much of the snow was then compacted to create glaciers and, as these persisted for many thousands of years, the oceans were depleted in ^{16}O for long periods until the glaciers melted. Measurements of oxygen isotopes in cores of marine sediments have shown that there were approximately 50 separate cold stages (glacials) during the 2.6 Ma of the Quaternary.

Geological maps

Geological maps display the distribution of rocks of different types (lithostratigraphic units) and different ages occurring at the earth's surface. In Britain, they have been published by the British Geological Survey (BGS) since the early 19th century, originally at the scale of 1:63,360, but now metricated to 1:50,000. Each one covers

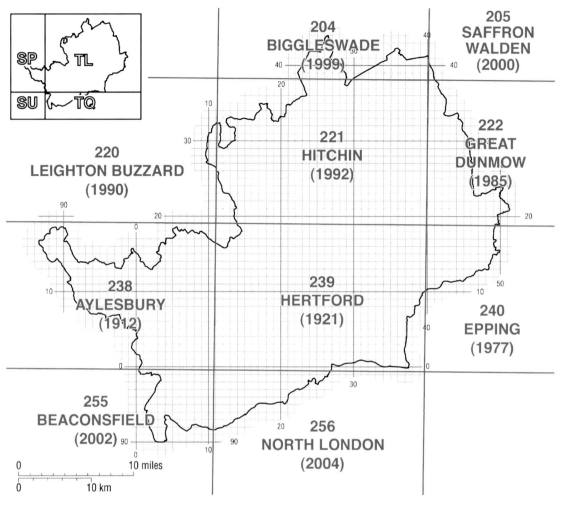

Fig. 1.3. British Geological Survey 1:50,000 map coverage for Hertfordshire (dates of latest field surveys given in brackets).

a rectangular area measuring 18 miles × 12 miles (29 km × 19 km approximately). Figure 1.3 shows the numbers, boundaries and dates of latest revision of the eight that cover Hertfordshire, and Figure 1.4 is a summary geological map of the whole county based on these. Each published 1:50,000 map is compiled from geological information recorded in the field on maps of 1:10,000 scale.

Nationally there are now five principal editions of 1:50,000 BGS maps:

1. **Solid (or Bedrock)**: these show only the pre-Quaternary bedrock formations stripped of all Quaternary deposits, however thick.
2. **Drift (or Superficial Deposits)**: these show only Quaternary deposits thicker than 1 m. Artificial (man-made) deposits are also shown. Pre-Quaternary bedrock appearing within 1 m of the surface is usually shown unclassified as a single colour.
3. **Solid and Drift (or Bedrock and Superficial Deposits)**: these show both pre-Quaternary and Quaternary deposits more than 1 m thick, merged to represent the 'surface' or underfoot geology. Boundaries between solid formations covered by the Quaternary deposits are shown as black lines, pecked where their

position is uncertain.

4. **Solid with Drift**: these also show pre-Quaternary formations and Quaternary deposits more than 1 m thick, but the latter are uncoloured or merely outlined in colour.
5. **Superficial Deposits and Simplified Bedrock**: where the Quaternary cover is complex, the underlying pre-Quaternary deposits are shown in less detail than in the other editions, usually by combining lithostratigraphic units at Group level.

Those currently available for Hertfordshire are Solid and Drift (Bedrock and Superficial Deposits for Sheet 256). They can be purchased from BGS headquarters at Keyworth, Nottingham NG12 5GG (Tel: 0115 936 3241, e-mail: sales@ bgs.ac.uk), or from BGS Information Office in the Earth Galleries of the Natural History Museum, Exhibition Road, South Kensington, London SW7 5BD (Tel: 0207 589 4090, e-mail: bgslondon@bgs.ac.uk). The 1:10,000 'field slips' can be consulted and often purchased at Keyworth.

In addition to the main map, most BGS 1:63,360 and 1:50,000 sheets provide a generalized vertical section to show formation thicknesses and the occurrence of unconformities. They also show cross sections indicating the subsurface relationships of formations based on borehole

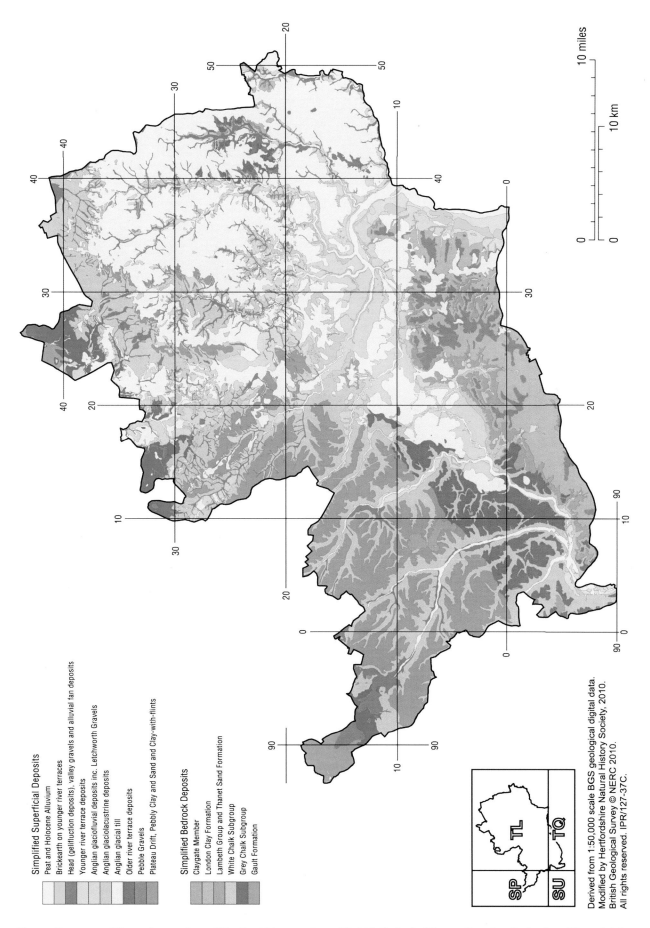

10 miles

10 km

Simplified Superficial Deposits

Peat and Holocene Alluvium
Brickearth on younger river terraces
Head (gelifluction deposits), valley gravels and alluvial fan deposits
Younger river terrace deposits
Anglian glaciofluvial deposits inc. Letchworth Gravels
Anglian glaciolacustrine deposits
Anglian glacial till
Older river terrace deposits
Pebble Gravels
Plateau Drift, Pebbly Clay and Sand and Clay-with-flints

Simplified Bedrock Deposits

Claygate Member
London Clay Formation
Lambeth Group and Thanet Sand Formation
White Chalk Subgroup
Grey Chalk Subgroup
Gault Formation

SP | TL

SU | TQ

Derived from 1:50,000 scale BGS geological digital data.
Modified by Hertfordshire Natural History Society, 2010.
British Geological Survey © NERC 2010.
All rights reserved. IPR/127-37C.

Fig. 1.4. Summary of the surface geology of Hertfordshire, courtesy of British Geological Survey (based on Bedrock and Superficial Deposits maps).

17

and geophysical evidence. Some of the more recently published maps also include a range of small summary maps showing geophysical properties and contours on important geological surfaces, such as major unconformities or the bedrock surface beneath Quaternary deposits (rockhead contours). Contour lines showing heights of buried geological surfaces above or below ordnance datum (present mean sea level) are known as structure contours. BGS also publish explanatory memoirs for most 1:50,000 maps and regional guides summarizing the geology of larger UK regions. The regional guide covering Hertfordshire is entitled London and Thames Valley (Sumbler, 1996).

Site locations on both geological and Ordnance Survey maps are indicated by national grid references. The land area of Britain is divided into squares measuring 100 km × 100 km, each of which is identified by two capital letters. Hertfordshire falls mainly within square TL, with some areas to the west and south in squares SP, SU and TQ. The boundaries between these squares are shown in Figure 1.1 and all subsequent maps of the county. The land within each 100 km square is divided into one hundred 10 km × 10 km squares, and each of these is further divided into one hundred 1 km × 1 km squares. These smaller squares are delineated by a grid of N-S and E-W lines, which are numbered 1 to 100 eastwards and northwards, respectively. The 10 km and 1 km squares are then identified by the numbered lines which intersect at their south-western corners. Thus 10 km squares are identified by two letters and two numbers and 1 km squares by two letters and four numbers. Sites within each 1 km square can be located to the nearest 100 m by two letters and six numbers, or to the nearest 10 m by two letters and eight numbers. It is conventional to quote the N-S numbered line (northing) first after the two letters, and the E-W numbered line (easting) after that.

1.3. Why study geology in Hertfordshire?

Because of the subdued relief and lack of natural rock exposures, anyone visiting Hertfordshire for the first time might well agree with many geologists, especially those hardened by hammering the resistant ancient rocks of the mountains in Wales, Scotland, the Lake District and Pennines, that the county has no geology worth speaking of. But 'the eyes of a fool are in the ends of the earth' (Proverbs 17, 24), because there are many reasons why the county is geologically famous. First, it is the home of Hertfordshire Puddingstone (Plate 3), a very hard silicified conglomerate (sedimentary rock composed mainly of rounded pebbles), which is sought by lapidarists throughout the world for the brilliant scratch-resistant polish it retains and the beautiful colours it displays. Second, it is the site of perhaps the best known example of river diversion by a glacier – that of the Thames, which about 450 ka was displaced by the Anglian ice sheet out of its original course through Hertfordshire and East Anglia into its present course through London. Third, there is a world famous assemblage of fossils found in the Hitchin area from part of the Chalk known as the Chalk

Rock; this assemblage includes heteromorph ammonites, which show the unusual evolutionary feature of partial or complete uncoiling. Fourth, the terrace gravels deposited by the Thames and its tributaries within Hertfordshire provide what is probably the most complete sequence of Quaternary deposits covering the last 2.6 Ma anywhere in Britain.

Certainly there are no rocks to be seen at the surface in Hertfordshire older than about 110 million years (Early Cretaceous). The oldest exposed deposit (the Gault Clay Formation) lies close to the surface only in the north-western extremities of the county, and even here this fossil-rich marine sediment can usually be seen in its original unaltered form only by digging down a metre or more through Quaternary deposits. The county's geological history, as inferred from deposits visible close to the land surface, thus begins at a time when that of many parts of upland Britain had long since come to an end. But the soft younger sediments from which the county's gentle landscape has been carved yield a detailed history of geologically recent changes in plant and animal communities, climate, sea level, river patterns and human environments that is difficult or impossible to obtain from exotic mountain areas of hard ancient rocks. This later geological history explains almost step by step how the county's landscape and natural modern environment originated. The links between geology and the present human environment are almost always much easier to discern in a lowland region such as Hertfordshire than in any upland area of more spectacular geology. In this way, the geology of Hertfordshire is representative of, and highly relevant to, most of southern England and even adjacent parts of northwest Europe.

To emphasize the links with present environment, this book is divided into two parts. Following the Introduction,

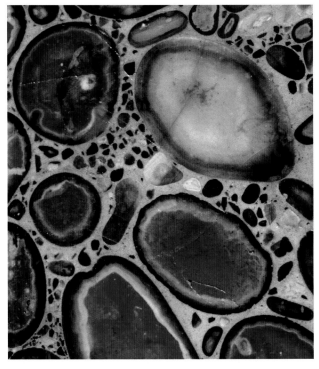

Plate 3. Cut surface of Hertfordshire Puddingstone, Abbots Langley.

Chapters 2-6 recount the geological history, often in increasing detail as the present is approached. Chapters 7-10 then consider the links with other subjects that illuminate our understanding of the present environment of the county, including its soils, agriculture, ecology, archaeology, water supply, waste disposal, environmental pollution, mineral resources and building stones.

1.4. Some famous inhabitants of Hertfordshire

The congenial countryside of Hertfordshire within a short distance of London has encouraged many famous politicians, writers and scientists to live in the county, including some notable geologists. Famous inhabitants of Hertfordshire have included:

Nicholas Breakspear (c. 1100-1159), who was born at Breakspear Farm, Bedmond, and was elected Pope Adrian IV in 1154, the only English-born pope. A spring close to his birthplace is often referred to as a holy well.

Sir Francis Bacon (1561-1626), who inherited the original Gorhambury House (TL 111077) near St Albans in 1601 and later became Lord Chancellor under James I. Although of dubious moral stature, his intellect was universally admired, and he is claimed to be the father of the experimental method in science and of the inductive method in philosophy.

Izaak Walton (1593-1683), though popularly associated with the River Dove in Derbyshire, in fact wrote his classic book on fishing (*The Compleat Angler*) from experience gained on a short angling holiday along the Lea valley around Hoddesdon and Ware in southeast Hertfordshire.

The poet **William Cowper** (1731-1800), who was the son of the rector of Berkhamsted.

John Scott (1731-1783), a Quaker poet and philanthropist, who lived at Amwell House (TL 357139) and designed and built a large grotto in the garden adorned with numerous geological specimens, including fossils, quartz crystals, Hertfordshire Puddingstone and seashells (Clarke, 2007).

Sir Abraham Hume II MP (1749-1838), who inherited Wormleybury (TL 355058) in 1772, and through his connection with the East India Company amassed an important collection of geological specimens, including many diamonds and other valuable minerals. He was a member of the first Council of the Geological Society of London, and also cultivated many rare exotic plants (Harwood, 2007).

Rev. Francis Egerton (1756-1829), who became the 8th Earl of Bridgwater in 1823 and inherited the Ashridge Estate. He gave £8000 to the Royal Society for the publication of the Bridgwater Treatises 'On the power, wisdom and goodness of God as manifested in the creation'. The fifth treatise, on 'Geology and mineralogy considered with reference to natural theology', written by Dean William Buckland, President of the London Geological Society, was published in 1836.

Thomas Robert Malthus (1766-1834), who was Professor of Political Economy at the East India College,

Haileybury, near Hertford. He wrote *An essay on the principle of population*, suggesting that population growth is checked naturally by the availability of food, which later influenced Charles Darwin in developing his theory of natural selection.

William Lamb (1779-1848), later Lord Melbourne, who lived at Brocket Hall (TL 212131) near Welwyn Garden City and was Prime Minister of the country from 1835 to 1841.

His brother-in-law **Lord Palmerston** (1784-1865), who inherited Brocket Hall in 1848, and was successively Secretary for War (1809-1828), Foreign Secretary (1830-1850), Home Secretary (1852-1855) and Prime Minister (1855-1865).

James Pulham (1788-1838), who established with William Lockwood a factory at Broxbourne to produce the cement-based artificial stone known as pulhamite. This stone was used to make rock gardens, memorials and garden furniture and was sold throughout the country, with many examples still visible in Hertfordshire churches and ornamental gardens (Banister, 2007).

Edward Bulwer-Lytton (1803-1873), who inherited Knebworth House (TL 230209) near Stevenage in 1843, became Lord Lytton in 1866 and was a famous playwright and novelist as well as Member of Parliament for three different constituencies.

The international banker **Baron Lionel de Rothschild** (1808-1879), who bought Tring Park (SP 9210) in 1872, where he kept a range of exotic animals. His son Walter (1868-1937), the Second Baron de Rothschild, established a zoological museum in Tring, which is now part of the Natural History Museum, South Kensington.

Sir Henry Bessemer (1813-1898), born at Charlton House (TL 179281) near Hitchin, was a famous engineer, mainly known for inventing an improved process for manufacture of steel that is still used today (Hine, 1932, pp. 262-273).

Sir John Lawes (1814-1900), who in 1822 inherited Rothamsted Farm and Manor (TL 125132) near Harpenden, and through a range of field experiments on the nutrition of arable crops made Rothamsted Experimental Station the most famous agricultural research institute in the world (Dyke, 1993).

Sir John Evans (1823-1908), who married into the Dickinson family of paper manufacturers and inherited Nash Mills House (TL 075047) near Hemel Hempstead in 1856. He was a pioneer palaeontologist, hydrogeologist, archaeologist and numismatologist (Macgregor, 2008), and his son Sir Arthur Evans became an equally famous archaeologist.

Alfred Russel Wallace (1823-1913), who attended Hertford Grammar School (1831-1836). He was a leading evolutionary thinker, who proposed a theory of natural selection independent of Charles Darwin, and became known as the father of biogeography.

Lord Robert Cecil (1830-1903), who inherited Hatfield House (TL 238084) and became the Third Marquess of Salisbury in 1868, later Foreign Secretary (1878-1880) and Prime Minister (1885-1892, 1895-1902). He was also Chancellor of the University of Oxford and something of a scientist, installing in Hatfield House his own very unreliable electric lighting system.

John Hopkinson (1844-1919), who inherited piano factories in Leeds and later in London, but lived in Watford and St Albans, spending most of his time recording the county's fossils, weather and hydrogeological features. He was a founder member of the Hertfordshire Natural History Society and its first secretary (1875-1900).

Cecil Rhodes (1853-1902), the son of the vicar of St Michael's, Bishop's Stortford, who was sent to Africa at an early age suffering with tuberculosis, and there formed De Beers Mining Company, became Prime Minister of the Cape and founded the country of Rhodesia.

The playwright **George Bernard Shaw** (1856-1950), who lived for 44 years in the rectory at Ayot St Lawrence.

Samuel Ryder (1858-1936), who developed a mail order seed business in St Albans, took up golf to improve his health and in 1926 presented the Ryder Cup to the Professional Golfers' Association for a competition between British and American golfers.

The novelist **Graham Greene** (1904-1991), who was the son of the headmaster of Berkhamsted School.

Further information on many of these and on other famous (and infamous) inhabitants of Hertfordshire can be obtained from the highly entertaining *Portrait of Hertfordshire* by B. J. Bailey (1978).

Chapter 2.

Concealed bedrock geology

John Catt

2.1. Introduction

The various bedrock (pre-Quaternary) formations occurring at the surface in Hertfordshire, which are described in Chapters 3-5, form part of a fairly thin cover of softer Mesozoic and Caenozoic sediments overlying a 'basement' of harder Palaeozoic and Precambrian rocks. The basement rocks rise closer to the land surface beneath the area stretching northwards from London towards Hertfordshire, Buckinghamshire, Bedfordshire and East Anglia than elsewhere in southeast England. In this area they form what is known as the London Platform, which is part of a larger basement massif (the Wales-London-Brabant Massif), extending westwards into Wales and eastwards into Belgium and other parts of continental Europe. Above the London Platform, the softer Mesozoic and Caenozoic bedrock formations are gently folded into a broad E-W syncline known as the London Basin (Fig. 2.1).

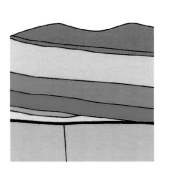

On the northern flank of the London Basin, the regional south-eastward dip of the Mesozoic/Caenozoic cover towards the axis of the London syncline allows older Mesozoic sedimentary rocks to emerge at the surface in counties to the northwest of Hertfordshire. However, many of these older Mesozoic formations do not extend beneath the whole of Hertfordshire. Most were never deposited over the London Platform, because it often formed a land mass surrounded by the Mesozoic seas. A few may have been deposited on rare occasions when the platform was briefly submerged, but even these were almost completely removed by erosion during the mid-Cretaceous marine transgression that led to deposition of the Gault Clay and Chalk. This chapter describes what is known about both the older basement and the concealed parts of the Mesozoic cover beneath the county.

Evidence for the nature and age of the basement rocks beneath the county has been obtained from the few deep boreholes that have penetrated its uppermost parts beneath the Mesozoic/Caenozoic cover (Fig. 2.2), and from a range of geophysical data. Only five boreholes have reached the basement beneath Hertfordshire itself, but further information relevant to the county can be inferred from others in neighbouring counties. Summary logs for all these boreholes are given in Appendix 1.

The deepest borehole yet drilled in the area was at Willesden (TQ 209848) in northwest London. It reached a depth of 816.9 m (-785.5 m OD) after penetrating 509 m of non-marine Devonian rocks lying immediately beneath the Lower Cretaceous Gault Clay (Falcon and Kent, 1960). Most of the other deep boreholes suggest that terrestrial Devonian sediments (Old Red Sandstone) are widespread beneath the region. However, they are absent locally, because marine Silurian deposits were encountered under the Mesozoic cover at Ware (TL 353140) and Little Missenden in Buckinghamshire (SU 901982), and steeply dipping mudstones of Tremadocian (Early Ordovician) age were reached in a borehole at Tattenhoe (SP 829344), west of Bletchley (Appendix 1). For further information on the distribution of these Palaeozoic rocks and on the presence of yet older rocks at greater depths beneath the Hertfordshire area, we must turn to geophysical studies, including seismic evidence and magnetic and gravity measurements.

2.2. Seismic evidence for deep structure

Earthquake waves propagated through the middle of the Earth and picked up on seismographs long distances from the epicentres of large earthquakes provide the main evidence for the very deep structure of the earth. They indicate that the planet has basically a three-fold structure: (a) at the earth's centre is the mainly iron core, which remains hot enough to be liquid at least in its outer part; this is surrounded by (b) a solid mantle, starting at a depth of approximately 2900 km below the earth's surface, and (c) a solid crust, which overlies the mantle at depths ranging from approximately 6 km below the oceans to 80 km beneath mountain ranges. The mantle is close to its melting point and much of it can flow very slowly over geological time. Together with the crust, its uppermost parts constitute the lithosphere, which is a geologically important unit because it can move in response to changes in distribution of mass at the surface of the planet resulting from erosion, deposition, formation of ice sheets and variations in sea level. These movements of the lithosphere are possible because lower parts of the mantle (the asthenosphere) are mobile and elastic.

The lithosphere consists of numerous plates, known as tectonic plates, which are dragged slowly over the asthenosphere, probably in response to convection

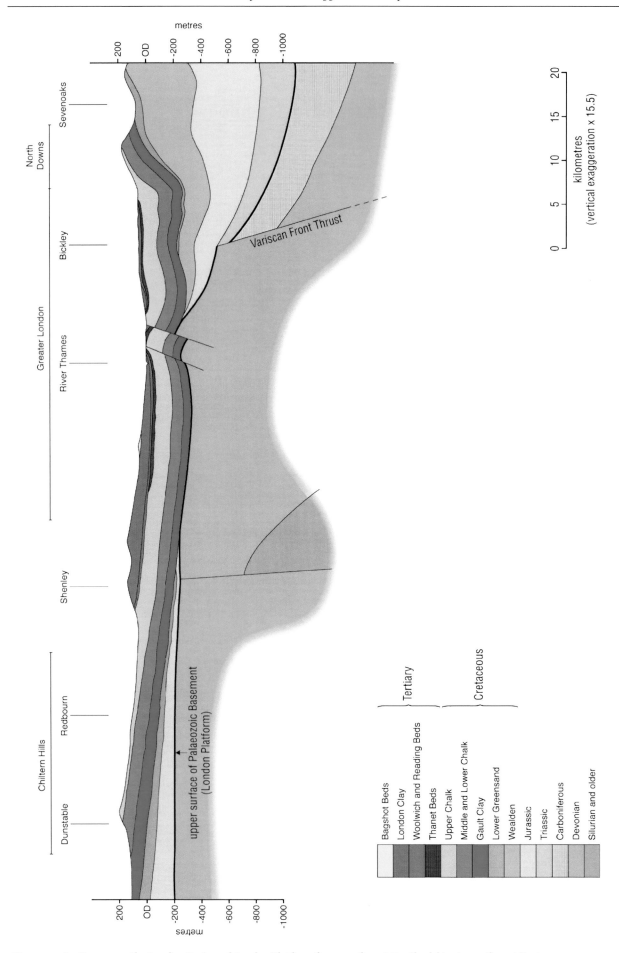

metres

200
OD
-200
-400
-600
-800
-1000

Sevenoaks

North Downs

Bickley

Greater London

River Thames

Variscan Front Thrust

Shenley

Chiltern Hills

Redbourn

upper surface of Palaeozoic Basement (London Platform)

Dunstable

200   OD   -200   -400   -600   -800   -1000
metres

0   5   10   15   20   kilometres
(vertical exaggeration x 15.5)

Bagshot Beds
London Clay
Woolwich and Reading Beds
Thanet Beds } Tertiary
Upper Chalk
Middle and Lower Chalk
Gault Clay
Lower Greensand
Wealden } Cretaceous
Jurassic
Triassic
Carboniferous
Devonian
Silurian and older

Figure 2.1. Section across the London Basin and London Platform from northwest Hertfordshire to northwest Kent.

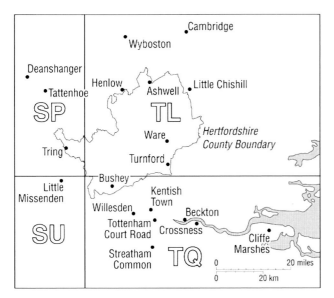

Figure 2.2. Location of deep boreholes providing evidence for pre-Mesozoic formations in the Hertfordshire area.

currents within the asthenosphere beneath. The plates are comparable to fragments of the solid hard skin of cooled sauce floating on the surface of liquid sauce heated in a saucepan on a stove. As they drift over the surface of the hot sauce, the solid fragments may divide or coalesce with others, as tectonic plates are known to have done. Strong currents in the underlying liquid may lead to collisions creating wrinkles in fragments that are less able to move because they are trapped between larger fragments. The wrinkles are equivalent to mountain chains, such as the Alps or Himalayas, formed by slow prolonged collisions between tectonic plates. Also, some of the sauce's skin fragments may slide beneath others, a process known as subduction where it has been shown to occur with tectonic plates on parts of the Earth's surface.

The base of the crust above the mantle is marked by a large increase in the velocity of earthquake or other seismic waves from about 7 to 8 km s^{-1}, and is known as the Mohorivicić Discontinuity or 'Moho' for short. It is thought to lie at a mean depth of 30 ± 5 km beneath the British Isles (Meissner *et al.*, 1986). Under the North Sea off the east coast of Norfolk, it is at 33 km depth (Cameron *et al.*, 1992), but it is difficult to detect beneath much of southeast England. However, it reappears in northern France at 35-38 km depth (Bois *et al.*, 1987, Fig. 3), suggesting that beneath Hertfordshire the crust is approximately 35 km thick, slightly more than average for Britain as a whole.

The lower part of the crust reached at depths of 15-20 km beneath continents has greater seismic velocities and a greater estimated mean density (~3000 kg m^{-3}) than the upper part. In many places the two parts can be distinguished by a sharp change in seismic velocities over what is known as the Conrad Discontinuity. The lower part is thought to consist mainly of the rock known as eclogite, which is composed of metamorphic minerals formed at very high pressures and temperatures, such as the red garnets pyrope and almandine and the green pyroxene omphacite. In contrast, the upper part of the crust consists mainly of

early Precambrian (Archaean) granite and gneiss overlain by late Precambrian (Proterozoic) and younger sediments, many of which have been penetrated by minor igneous intrusions and regionally metamorphosed within orogenic belts of various ages.

The structure of the crust can be investigated in more detail by generating artificial seismic (sound) waves on the surface, and detecting their reflections from subsurface geological boundaries (Bolt, 1993). In southern Britain, these surveys were done in the latter half of the 20th century in the search for oil trapped within deep Mesozoic sedimentary basins. However, Hertfordshire has poor seismic coverage compared with adjacent regions, because it has few such basins and consequently no oil reserves.

On land, seismic waves were originally generated by explosives such as dynamite, but more recently lorry-mounted vibrators, such as the Vibroseis equipment, have been used to produce a recognizable signal of known wave form. Reflections from the Moho, Conrad and other discontinuities between rock layers are then detected by a line of geophones on land or hydrophones at sea. These detectors measure very precisely the time elapsed between generation of the sound and its return to the surface, known as the two-way travel time (TWTT), which is measured in seconds (s). For example, a seismic wave generated by an air gun on the surface of the southern North Sea takes nearly 11 s to reach the Moho and return. The results are usually expressed graphically as two-dimensional profiles showing reflections from discontinuities at various TWTT values equivalent to calculated depths below the land or sea surface. Recently it has been possible to improve spatial resolution by three-dimensional data acquisition using an array of detectors, but as yet this technique has been used only in limited areas for evaluation of hydrocarbon reserves, such as the Wytch Farm oilfield in Dorset.

In southeast England, the signal reflections from the Moho and lower parts of the crust are masked by those from steeply dipping reflectors in the middle part of the crust at 3.5-7.0 s TWTT, which suggest the presence of intrusive igneous rocks and sediments strongly deformed (folded, cleaved and faulted) by Precambrian or Lower Palaeozoic (Caledonian) orogenesis (Cameron *et al.*, 1992). This type of structure in the middle crust is common in seismically stable regions within tectonic plates, known as cratons (Chadwick *et al.*, 1989). Hertfordshire lies near the southern margin of a small craton known as the Midlands Microcraton, which is thought to be composed of relatively undeformed Precambrian sediments intruded by Late Precambrian igneous rocks (Lee *et al.*, 1991; Tucker and Pharoah, 1991; Busby *et al.*, 1993). The Midlands Microcraton appears at the surface in Charnwood Forest, Leicestershire, and is thought to form an approximately triangular platform lying at no great depth beneath the London area, the east and west Midlands and southeast Wales, with an E-W boundary south of London and a SE-NW boundary extending from northwest Kent through east Hertfordshire (Fig. 2.3). As such it forms the lower part of the London Platform. Further south and east, Precambrian cratonic rocks probably extend at greater depth beneath most of southern England.

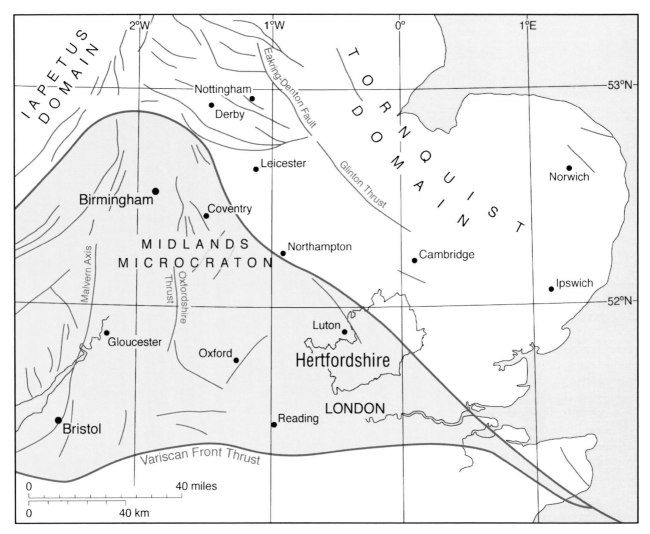

Figure 2.3. Map of Midlands Microcraton and other subsurface structural features in southeast England (redrawn from Chadwick and Evans, 2005, Figs 6 and 7).

Although a large number of seismic reflection lines were shot by oil companies and the British Geological Survey in the late 20th century, they were mainly in areas south of the Thames and to the north of Hertfordshire. The only one in the Hertfordshire area was by Shell (UK) Exploration along a NNW-SSE line east of Luton. This showed a strong reflector at approximately 1.8 s TWTT, equivalent to a depth of about 3 km, which according to Allsop (1985, Fig. 8) marked the top of the Precambrian on the eastern side of the Midlands Microcraton. Weaker reflectors closer to the surface, at 1.1 s and 0.2-0.3 s TWTT, i.e. within the upper part of the London Platform, were thought to indicate the Cambrian-Ordovician (basal Tremadocian) and basal Devonian boundaries, respectively.

2.3. Evidence from magnetic surveys

The Earth's magnetic field is generated by movement of partially molten iron in the outer core. Its strength varies mainly with latitude, increasing from about 0.3 gauss (G) or 24,000 nanoteslas (nT) near the equator to 0.6 G or 68,000 nT at the magnetic poles (1 Tesla = charge of 1 Coulomb moving with a speed of 1 m s^{-1} experiencing a force of 1 Newton; and 1G = 10^{-4} T) (Grant and Phillips, 1975, p. 125). At the surface, small variations result from the amounts of magnetic material in different rocks and their distance from the site of measurement. The strength of the magnetic field across an area can be measured with a hand-held magnetometer read at regular intervals along traverses over the land surface, but data are acquired much more rapidly from airborne instruments flown at a fixed height above sea level or at a constant height above the ground surface. The differences between measured values and the theoretical value for latitude, or one measured at a fixed location within the area, give either positive or negative magnetic anomalies. The anomalies indicate variations in the magnetization of rocks in the crust, negative values generally indicating sediments and larger positive values igneous rocks rich in iron minerals.

The aeromagnetic map of Britain published by Geological Survey of Great Britain (1965), shows magnetic anomaly values for Hertfordshire ranging from -30 nT to +60 nT, with the highest positive anomalies occurring near Bishop's Stortford, Stevenage and Harpenden, and the lowest negative values in the northeast of the county near Ashwell

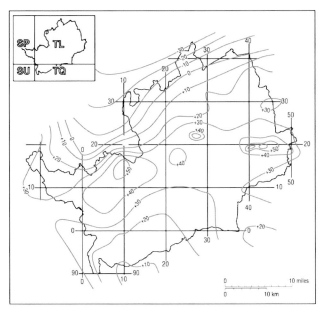

Figure 2.4. Aeromagnetic map of the Hertfordshire area with contours at 10 nT intervals (redrawn from Geological Survey of Great Britain, 1965).

(Fig. 2.4). From these values, Allsop (1985) derived depths to strongly magnetized rocks (the 'magnetic basement'). Beneath Hertfordshire, this generally occurs at depths greater than 4 km, the positive anomalies at Bishop's Stortford, etc indicating depths of 2.0-0.5 km. Depth to magnetic basement indicates the maximum thickness of the less magnetic Palaeozoic and Proterozoic sedimentary rocks forming the uppermost part of the crust. The peaks are areas where blocks of more magnetic basement, probably composed of igneous rocks within the southern part of the Midlands Microcraton, come closer to the surface, possibly because of faulting or folding. But as they lie near the northern margins of a large block of more magnetic basement that underlies the London Platform (Cornwell *et al.*, 1990), they could be extensions of it.

2.4. Evidence from gravity surveys

Gravity is measured with a gravimeter at points on the land surface known as gravity stations. For the national gravity survey of Britain, the measurements were taken at a spacing of about one per square kilometre; their locations are displayed on the BGS website. The measured values, in milligals (mGal; 1 mGal = 10 μm s^{-2}), are first corrected for any variations in the earth's gravitational field not resulting from differences in the density of the rocks underlying the station (Kearey and Brooks, 1994, pp. 127-131). These corrections include:

(a) the latitude correction, which is necessary because the earth is an oblate spheroid rather than a true sphere; consequently, points at sea level near the equator are further from the earth's centre than those near the poles, so that gravity at sea level decreases from pole to equator;

(b) the free-air correction, which allows for the decrease in gravity resulting from the height of the station in increasing

its distance from the centre of the Earth;

(c) the Bouguer correction, which removes the gravitational effect of the rock lying between the gravity station and sea level; as it equates this rock layer to a horizontal slab of infinite dimensions, it takes no account of the topographic relief around the station, which is then allowed for in:

(d) the terrain correction, in which valleys incised below the station's height increase the value of the slab correction and hills above it exert an upward attraction at the station, thus causing gravity to decrease (Nowell, 1999);

(e) the tidal correction, which allows for variation in the gravitational effects of the sun and moon resulting from their orbital motions; these cause the shape of the solid Earth to vary in a similar (though much smaller) way to oceanic tides, so that the distance between the measuring station and the centre of the Earth changes periodically by a few centimetres,

(f) the instrumental drift correction, which is calculated from repeated readings at a single station at recorded times, so that readings at other sites can be corrected according to the times they are taken.

For calculations on land, the differences between the measured and corrected values are known as Bouguer gravity anomalies. These reflect departures from measured densities of the rocks below and around each gravity station; negative anomalies indicate rocks with lower densities, and positive anomalies rocks with greater densities. The density of a sedimentary rock depends on its mineralogical composition (mean particle density, usually close to 2700 kg m^{-3}) and porosity, and tends to increase with depth as a result of progressive loss of porosity through compaction or cementation. Igneous and metamorphic rocks have very low porosities, and their densities mainly reflect mineral composition, so that they increase in value from acidic rocks, such as granite, through basic to ultrabasic types. The gravity anomalies for Hertfordshire, calculated at a uniform density of 2700 kg m^{-3} (British Geological Survey, 1986), range from less than -8 mGal to more than -16 mGal.

The effects of near-surface rocks, whose densities can be measured from surface or borehole samples, can then be removed – a process termed 'gravity stripping' – to give residual gravity anomalies, which indicate density variations in deeper rocks. The residual gravity field for the Hertfordshire area (stripped of effects attributable to the Mesozoic cover), as calculated by Allsop (1985, Fig. 5), shows values of -2.5 mGal to -7.5 mGal over most of the county, with minimum negative values (<-7.5 mGal) in the northeast around Barkway and in southwest Bedfordshire (west of Dunstable), and small positive values (0.0-+2.5 mGal) in south-eastern parts of the county near Sawbridgeworth and south-western parts near Rickmansworth and Kings Langley (Fig. 2.5). Allsop (1985, p. 375) interpreted this pattern as indicating a ridge of denser Palaeozoic rocks extending ENE-WSW beneath southern parts of the county, the ridge separating basins containing lower density Devonian sediments to the north (the Luton-Cambridge Basin) and south (the London-Canvey Island Basin). He estimated maximum thicknesses of the low density sediments of

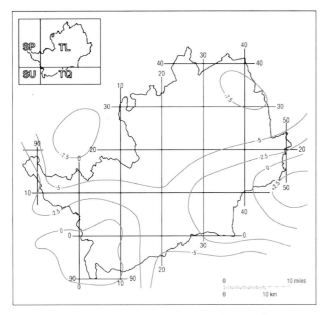

Figure 2.5. Residual Bouguer gravity anomaly map of Hertfordshire with contours at 2.5 mGal intervals (redrawn from Allsop, 1985, Fig. 5).

0.9 km in the Luton-Cambridge Basin and 1.4 km in the London-Canvey Island Basin. The latter estimate probably includes the 509 m (0.5 km) of non-marine Upper Devonian rocks (mudstones, limestones and sandstones) proved in the Willesden Borehole (House *et al.*, 1982). The ridge of denser rocks may consist of Silurian sediments uplifted by Variscan (Carboniferous) earth movements and underlain by igneous rocks (Allsop and Smith, 1988).

2.5. Evidence from deep boreholes

As mentioned previously (Section 2.1), most deep boreholes in Hertfordshire and the surrounding area have penetrated Devonian rocks (mainly non-marine alluvial sediments) beneath the Mesozoic cover. They were drilled mainly in the hope of obtaining water from the Lower Greensand (Lower Cretaceous), but often did not find this formation. Their approximate positions are shown in Figure 2.2, and summary logs with precise locations are given in Appendix 1. At seven of the sites (Turnford, Little Chishill, Bushey, Kentish Town, Willesden, Beckton and Crossness), the Devonian rocks were directly overlain by the late Early Cretaceous (Albian) Gault Clay (approximately 100-112 Ma), with little or no evidence of Lower Greensand, thus indicating non-deposition or extensive erosion of intervening (later Palaeozoic and early Mesozoic) deposits before or during the Albian marine transgression.

However, intervening sediments (Lower Greensand and various Jurassic deposits) were encountered in three boreholes, at Tring (22.8 m of Lower Greensand and 96.4 m of Middle and Upper Jurassic deposits), Ashwell (27.9 m of Lower Greensand and 18.2 m of Middle Jurassic), and Tottenham Court Road in central London (19.5 m of Lower Greensand). At two other sites (Henlow and Wyboston), the youngest deposits encountered beneath the Pleistocene

cover were older than Gault Clay. At Henlow, about 7 km north of Hitchin, 10.2 m of possible Lower Greensand and 10.8 m of limestone (Jurassic?) were penetrated beneath 107.9 m of Pleistocene deposits before Devonian rocks were reached at 129 m depth, and about 22 km further north at Wyboston, the Devonian was overlain by 104.6 m of Lower, Middle and Upper Jurassic beds beneath 6.1 m of Pleistocene deposits.

So, although the Lower Greensand and various Jurassic deposits are present beneath northern and western parts of Hertfordshire and thicken in these directions, they are absent beneath central and southern parts of the county. This suggests that the Palaeozoic basement formed a topographic ridge as part of the London Platform beneath central and southern Hertfordshire throughout the later Palaeozoic (Carboniferous and Permian) and earlier Mesozoic (Triassic, Jurassic and Early Cretaceous until the Albian transgression). Over this long period of time, the London Platform was either a land mass or was periodically covered by shallow seas, the deposits of which were later removed by marine transgressions or subaerial erosion. For this reason, Hertfordshire has never had any potential for the mining of coal from buried Carboniferous strata. The 19.5 m of Lower Greensand recorded in the Tottenham Court Road borehole was probably deposited by a marine transgression from the south onto the southern flank of the London Platform, as other boreholes in central and south London, for example at Richmond, Russell Hill, Carshalton and Warlingham (Ellison *et al.*, 2004), show that this formation thickens southwards towards its outcrop on the northern margin of the Weald.

The deep boreholes show that the top of the Devonian is closer to the surface in south Bedfordshire and north Hertfordshire, where it lies at only -78.6 OD at Henlow and -93.6 m OD at Ashwell, than in central and east London, where it is much deeper (-250 m to -300 m OD). This southward dipping sub-Mesozoic surface is polygenetic, in that it is unconformably overlain by Gault Clay in the south but by older Jurassic rocks to the north and west. Further north, it is level or declines gently northwards beneath the east Midlands (Allsop and Smith, 1988, Fig. 5); for example, it is at -95.1 m OD at Wyboston and -108.3 m OD in a borehole at Cambridge (TL 4316 5949). So it is likely that the southward dip of the sub-Mesozoic surface in Hertfordshire reflects continued uplift of the London Platform with southward tilting during the Early Cretaceous.

Based on palaeontological (including palynological) evidence (House *et al.*, 1982), it is likely that most of the Devonian strata occurring immediately beneath the Mesozoic cover of Hertfordshire, north London and East Anglia are of Late Devonian (Upper Old Red Sandstone) age. For example, in the Ashwell borehole, thin shelly marine limestones interbedded with grey and reddish brown mudstones contained brachiopods, such as *Ripidiorhynchus ferquensis*, *Retichonetes armatus* and *Cyrtospirifer verneuli*, and the lamellibranchs *Leptodesma spinigerum* and *Palaeoneilo constricta*, which are known from Frasnian (early Late Devonian, 385-375 Ma) beds elsewhere in Britain and from strata of similar age encountered in boreholes in northern France (Butler, 1981). Earlier Devonian beds are recorded only in areas to the south and west.

A few of the deep boreholes have indicated the presence of older (Early Palaeozoic) formations beneath the Mesozoic cover of the Hertfordshire area. For example, in the borehole near Ware (TL 3531 1398), the Gault Clay was immediately underlain at -209.2 m OD by 10.6 m of shallow marine Silurian (Wenlock, 428-423 Ma) shales and thin limestones (Etheridge, 1879; Hopkinson, 1880). The fossils obtained from approximately 1 m of core within the Wenlock deposits were:

Protozoa: *Ischadites koenigii*
Echinodermata: *Taxocrinus* sp., *Periechocrinus moniliformis*
Annelida: *Tentaculites ornatus*
Crustacea: *Phacops caudatus*
Brachiopoda: *Orthis canaliculata, O. elegantula, Meristella tumida, Cyrtia exporrecta, Spirifer elevata, Spirifer plicatella, Aythris* sp., *Crania implicata, Rhynchonella cuneata* (or *deflexa), Atrypa reticularis, Pentamerus galeatus, P. linguifer, Strophomena euglypha, S. reticulata, S. depressa* (= *rhomboidalis), S. antiquata, Chonetes* sp., *Leptaena sericea, L. transversalis*
Lamellibranchiata: *Pterinea* sp., *Mytilus mytilimeris, Ctenodonta* sp., *Orthonota rigida*
Gastropoda: *Euomphalus rugosus*
Cephalopoda: *Orthoceras attenuatum, O. angulatum*

Specimens of the core showing some of these fossils are stored in St Albans Museum and the Earth Sciences Department at Cambridge University. The Silurian strata immediately beneath the Mesozoic cover in this area occur within the ridge of denser rocks beneath south Hertfordshire reported by Allsop and Smith (1988). Allsop (1985, Fig. 5e) suggested that the Wenlock rocks are fault-bounded against Devonian on the northern side, but overlain by younger Silurian (Ludlow and Přídolí, 423-416 Ma) sediments to the south. Further afield, Silurian rocks have also been encountered beneath the Mesozoic cover in deep boreholes at Little Missenden (SU 901982), Buckinghamshire (Strahan, 1916), Streatham Common (TQ 296710) in south London (Whitaker, 1912) and Cliffe Marshes (TQ 719786) on the Isle of Grain, north Kent (Ellison *et al.*, 2004, p. 5). These probably indicate the presence of additional Silurian 'highs' similar to that beneath Ware.

Steeply dipping mudstones with graptolites and other fossils of Early Ordovician (Tremadocian, 488-479 Ma) age were encountered beneath Jurassic sediments in deep boreholes at Tattenhoe (SP 829344) and Deanshanger (SP 765388) in north Buckinghamshire (Shephard-Thorn *et al.*, 1994, pp. 6-9), and were also penetrated beneath 114 m of Devonian sediments at Wyboston (TL 176572), Bedfordshire. Using this sparse borehole evidence and geophysical data, Allsop and Smith (1988, Fig. 7) suggested that, beneath the sub-Devonian surface at -200 to -400 m OD, there are two gentle WSW-ENE synclines under south Bedfordshire and north London separated by an anticline beneath the central and southern parts of Hertfordshire.

Low density deposits of youngest Silurian age (Přídolí, 419-416 Ma, previously known in Britain as Downtonian) subcrop in the axial regions of the synclines, and older Silurian (Ludlow and Wenlock) rocks occur along the axis of the intervening anticline. Tremadocian and perhaps oldest Silurian (Llandovery) rocks subcrop on the northern flank of the northern syncline beneath north Bedfordshire, and their occurrence beneath the Devonian to the west under north Buckinghamshire suggests that this syncline plunges to the ENE.

Figure 2.6 shows approximate contours on the Sub-Mesozoic Surface (the Palaeozoic basement) beneath the Hertfordshire area and the ages of Palaeozoic rocks subcropping on that surface, both based on evidence from deep boreholes and various geophysical surveys. Apart from the Devonian strata underlying most of the area and the small subcrops of Silurian rocks beneath Ware and to the northeast and southwest of the county, Carboniferous, Ordovician and yet older rocks associated with the Midlands Microcraton occur to the north and west of Hertfordshire. South of London, the basement sinks rapidly to below -900 m OD along the Variscan Front, which is a major tectonic thrust on the northern margin of an area of late Carboniferous (Variscan) mountain building that resulted in folding of the Devonian and Carboniferous rocks of south Wales, the Mendips and southwest England.

2.6. Geological history before the Albian transgression

Palaeomagnetic data from rocks in various parts of the world indicate that, in Early Palaeozoic (Cambrian to Mid Ordovician) times, southern Britain, including Hertfordshire, formed part of a small, fairly uniform continental landmass (terrane) composed of Proterozoic (late Precambrian) rocks, which lay well south of the equator. Between 570 Ma and 550 Ma, the terrane broke away from a southern supercontinent named Gondwana or Rodinia, and started to drift northwards towards the equator. The separation from Gondwana created the Rheic Ocean, which by the Middle Ordovician extended from about 45° south of the equator almost to the south pole (Torsvik *et al.*, 1996). The terrane has been termed Cadomia (Cogné and Wright, 1980) or Eastern Avalonia (Soper, 1986; Soper *et al.*, 1987). The latter name is based on its geological similarity to the currently exposed Avalonian terrane of Newfoundland and maritime Canada. On its northern margin Eastern Avalonia was separated from the main (western) Avalonian landmass by the Iapetus Ocean.

In the Early Ordovician (488-478 Ma), when the Tremadocian graptolitic mudstones beneath Buckinghamshire and Bedfordshire were deposited on its rapidly subsiding margins, Eastern Avalonia lay near 50-60° S (Cocks and Fortey, 1982). Scotland then formed part of the Laurentian Precambrian Shield (the land mass of Laurentia), which was situated to the north in equatorial latitudes and was separated from Eastern Avalonia by several thousand kilometres of the Iapetus

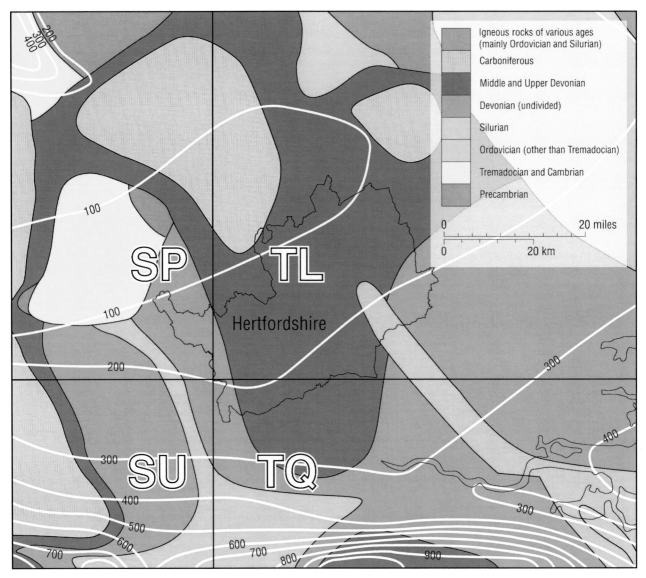

Figure 2.6. Structure contours (in m below OD) and subcrop geology for the Palaeozoic basement (Sub-Mesozoic Surface) in the Hertfordshire area (redrawn from Smith, 1985).

Ocean (Harland and Gayer, 1972). Scandinavia was part of another Precambrian shield (the Baltic Shield or Balthica), which was separated from Eastern Avalonia by the narrow Tornquist Sea. This sea linked the Iapetus and Rheic Oceans until it was closed by northward plate subduction late in the Ordovician (Cocks and Fortey, 1982; Ziegler, 1982). The western part of the Iapetus Ocean was also closed by subduction in the late Ordovician, thus uniting Eastern and Western Avalonia. As a result there are no late Ordovician deposits known in the area. The Silurian strata (shelly limestones and mudstones) encountered in the Ware, Little Missenden and Cliffe Marshes boreholes were deposited close to the equator in a shallow sea near the southern margin of the shrinking Iapetus Ocean (Woodcock and Pharoah, 1993). To the northeast, Silurian muds and fine sands (now slates and greywackes) were deposited in deeper water of a subsiding basin beneath East Anglia and the southern North Sea.

The collisions between Balthica, Laurentia and Avalonia in the early Palaeozoic led to various episodes of mountain building collectively known as the Caledonian Orogeny. The Silurian, Ordovician and older rocks were uplifted and deformed, creating a continent termed Laurussia, with highland areas on which the largely non-marine Devonian (Old Red Sandstone) accumulated in an arid subequatorial environment. Early Devonian sedimentation was probably confined to areas west and south of Hertfordshire, but a final phase of uplift in the Middle Devonian extended the area of deposition north-eastwards across Hertfordshire to East Anglia, where the Upper Old Red Sandstone oversteps unconformably onto deformed Silurian and Tremadocian strata. The Devonian beds consist mainly of red and purple silty mudstones, with greenish grey sandstones of mainly fluvial origin.

By mid Early Devonian times (about 400 Ma), closure of the Rheic Ocean during the later (Acadian) part of the Caledonian Orogeny had brought together lithospheric plates from the north (Laurentia) and south (Avalonia and Gondwana) to form a supercontinent known as Pangea (Anderton *et al.*, 1979). Most of the supercontinent still lay south of the equator, but northward movement carried the part that now includes Hertfordshire across the equator by the late Carboniferous.

Although the earlier Caledonian deformation had produced a strong NE-SW tectonic grain in the metamorphic rocks of the Scottish Highlands by the end of the Silurian, the Acadian deformation further south resulted in arcuate structures moulded around the rigid northern margin of the Midlands Microcraton (Soper *et al.*, 1987). To the west (the Iapetus Domain), these structures are orientated NE-SW, but on the northern margin, probably at a similar latitude to The Wash, the structures trend E-W, and on the eastern side of the microcraton, beneath eastern England and the southern North Sea (the Tornquist Domain), they swing southwards into a NW-SE orientation (Pharoah *et al.*, 1995).

During the late Carboniferous and Permian Periods (359-251 Ma), the southern parts of Pangea (now Africa, South America and Australia) became partially separated from northern parts (Laurussia, now North America, Greenland, Europe and Asia) by an expanding ocean known as Tethys, and northward subduction of oceanic crust beneath what is now Iberia and southern France resulted in the Variscan Orogeny. This led to formation of the Armorican mountain belt in Brittany and to NNW-directed compression and crustal shortening in southern Britain. The northern limit of significant Variscan deformation and metamorphism lay along the E-W Variscan Front to the south of the Midlands Microcraton between north Kent and south Wales (Fig. 2.3). Crustal extension (stretching) north of the Variscan Front caused the Laurussian continent to break into stable horsts (uplifted fault blocks) separated by subsiding grabens, in which thin condensed sediment sequences accumulated from the Carboniferous to the Jurassic and Early Cretaceous (Grayson and Oldham, 1987). The structures of this Variscan foreland have various orientations (Fig. 2.3), but are mainly similar to those of the older Acadian Orogeny, whose lines of weakness were probably reactivated by the Variscan extension (Corfield *et al.*, 1996).

The London Platform remained relatively stable during the Variscan earth movements, but to the west a zone of N-S thrusts about 4 km wide (the Oxfordshire Thrust) occurs beneath a Permo-Triassic cover (Chadwick and Evans, 2005, p. 99). On the north-eastern flank of the platform, the NNW-SSE trending Eakring-Denton Fault and Glinton Thrust are also concealed beneath Permian strata, though the Eakring-Denton Fault may be expressed at the surface as a normal fault with a downthrow of 60 m to the northeast resulting from reactivation after the Triassic Period. Because of the change in stress field from Caledonian compression to Variscan extension, the sense of movement on many of these long-established lines of weakness changed, so that Caledonian reversed faults became Variscan normal faults and vice-versa. Also, periodic movement continued over long intervals, often affecting the thickness of strata deposited on either side of these basement structures.

Although Carboniferous rocks were penetrated at a depth of -108.3 m OD beneath Lower Jurassic (Liassic) sediments in a deep borehole near Cambridge (TL 432595), and also occur to the west and north of Hertfordshire (Fig. 2.6) and at

much greater depths (>-1200 m OD) under north Surrey and Kent, they are absent from the London Platform beneath Hertfordshire, which was probably part of a horst block with little or no deposition throughout the Carboniferous. Also, apart from some minor marine transgressions from the north at various times in the Jurassic, the platform probably persisted as a landmass (part of the Laurasian continent) for most of the Mesozoic until it was progressively flooded in the Albian (late Early Cretaceous), and Gault Clay was deposited over the entire area.

As elsewhere on Laurasia, Permian or Triassic (New Red Sandstone) sediments probably accumulated on the London Platform in a hot arid environment, but subsequent erosion has removed them almost completely (Audley-Charles, 1970). The only possible evidence for deposits of this age near Hertfordshire is from the deep borehole at Little Missenden, where approximately 30 m of reddish terrestrial sediments were recorded between Silurian and Jurassic rocks, but these are as likely to be Devonian in age as Permo-Triassic. Further west, Triassic strata, comprising the Sherwood Sandstone Group (previously Bunter Sandstone) and the overlying Mercia Mudstone Group (previously Keuper Marl), increase in thickness beneath the Jurassic formations of Oxfordshire, Wiltshire and Gloucestershire, and emerge at the surface in the West Midlands and Worcestershire. The basal part of the Sherwood Sandstone Group includes the Kidderminster Conglomerate Formation (previously Bunter Pebble Beds), which consists mainly of coloured quartzite cobbles and pebbles brought by a large river flowing northwards from Cornwall and northwest France. Much later, in the Quaternary, Bunter quartzite pebbles were brought into Hertfordshire from the West Midlands by a precursor of the River Thames.

Tethys gradually expanded in the Triassic and early Jurassic, and by the Late Jurassic had fully separated the northern (Laurasia) and southern (Pangaea) continents. Jurassic sediments of various ages were deposited during minor marine transgressions from the Boreal Ocean to the north onto the margin of the London Platform (Fig. 2.7). The first such transgression occurred in the Early Jurassic or Liassic (200-176 Ma) as a result of a global rise in sea level and a phase of crustal extension that partially fragmented the Laurasian continent (Holloway, 1985). Thick sequences of Lias Group mudstones and limestones were deposited in basins north and west of the London Platform, but deposits of this age thin progressively south-eastwards as they overstep onto the platform and are unknown beneath most of Hertfordshire (Donovan *et al.*, 1979), suggesting that much of the platform probably persisted as a low relief landmass throughout the Early Jurassic. In the Tattenhoe borehole, the Lias Group was approximately 70 m thick, with a basal conglomerate nearly 7 m thick resting on the Tremadocian mudstones and overlain by 49 m of Lower Lias mudstones, then 6.5 m of Middle Lias mudstones, 1 m of Marlstone Rock (greenish limestone) and 6.9 m of Upper Lias mudstones with nodular limestones (Shephard-Thorn *et al.*, 1994, Fig. 5). Similar total thicknesses of Lower Jurassic mudstones were penetrated in the deep boreholes at Elstow and Wyboston northeast of Tattenhoe, but none is recorded in boreholes to the southeast in Hertfordshire.

During the Mid Jurassic (176-161 Ma), there were further, slightly more extensive transgressions onto the London Platform (Fig. 2.7), as deposits of this period directly overlie Devonian sediments with no intervening Liassic rocks in the deep boreholes at Tring, Henlow and Ashwell (Hopson *et al.*, 1996, pp. 12-13). They were also recorded above the Lias at Tattenhoe and Wyboston. In the Ashwell borehole, the Middle Jurassic sequence penetrated at depths of -75.2 m OD to -93.3 m OD consisted of (in descending order): Cornbrash (pale-coloured hard shelly limestone), Blisworth Clay, Blisworth Limestone, Rutland Formation and Grantham Formation (interbedded siltstones, sandstones and grey to black mudstones). The abundance of plant debris and infilled root channels in the Grantham Formation and Blisworth Clay indicates that many of the deposits accumulated in shallow brackish water, possibly an estuary on the northern margin of the London Platform landmass. Approximately similar incomplete sequences of Middle Jurassic deposits were encountered between -9.6 m and -26.8 m OD at Wyboston and between -108 m and -126 m OD at Tring, and in the Henlow borehole there was 10.8 m of 'white rock', probably shelly limestone of the Cornbrash, between -67.8 m and -78.6 m OD. However, the precise limits of what were probably several Mid Jurassic transgressions onto the London Platform (Fig. 2.7) are difficult to judge because of the lack of information from other boreholes.

A thick sequence of marine Upper Jurassic deposits (Kellaways Sands, Oxford Clay, Corallian Limestone, Ampthill Clay, Kimmeridge Clay and Portland Limestone) is exposed at the surface in Bedfordshire, Buckinghamshire and other counties northwest of Hertfordshire (Shephard-Thorn *et al.*, 1994), but like the Lower and Middle Jurassic sequences, these deposits are strongly attenuated south-eastwards against the rising surface of the London Platform. Thin representatives of the older of these Upper Jurassic formations have been recorded in the deep boreholes at

Wyboston, Tattenhoe and Tring, indicating further marine transgressions onto the northern part of the London Platform (Fig. 2.7) in the period between approximately 161 Ma and 156 Ma. The sequence in these three boreholes consists of 0.7-5.6 m of Kellaways Sand overlain by 13.4-68.8 m of Oxford Clay, with 5m of Corallian limestone above the Oxford Clay at Tring. As with the Mid Jurassic transgressions, the exact geographical limits and duration of Late Jurassic marine invasions of the London Platform are unknown until more deep borehole information becomes available.

Despite the lack of borehole evidence for yet younger Jurassic deposits, Chadwick (1985) speculated that, because of high global sea levels later in the Late Jurassic (Haq *et al.*, 1987), a thin layer of Kimmeridge Clay was deposited over most of the London Platform at approximately 156-151 Ma. But even if this did happen, the subsequent decline in global sea level at the close of the Jurassic and during the Early Cretaceous led to erosion and loss of most if not all of this clay layer. It also precluded further marine transgressions until the Aptian and Albian Stages (125-100 Ma) of the later Early Cretaceous.

No marine Cretaceous deposits older than Aptian are known in southern England, but a thick sequence of Early Cretaceous non-marine (deltaic) sediments accumulated over what is now the Weald while marine sediments were deposited further north in Lincolnshire and eastern Yorkshire in a shallow shelf sea that had at least periodic connections to the east with Germany and Russia. For much of the pre-Aptian Early Cretaceous (145-125 Ma), erosion of the London Platform may have supplied sediment to a subsiding Wealden Basin to the south. However, early in the succeeding Aptian Stage (125-112 Ma), rising global sea level resulted in a marine transgression northwards across the Weald to deposit the Atherfield Clay and Hythe Beds in southern counties of England. Part of the London Platform persisted at this time as a land mass separating this shallow sea from the northern marine basin, which probably

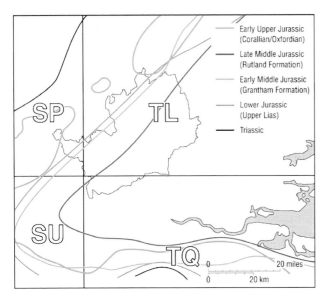

Figure 2.7. Limits of Jurassic marine transgressions in the Hertfordshire area (redrawn from Whittaker, 1985).

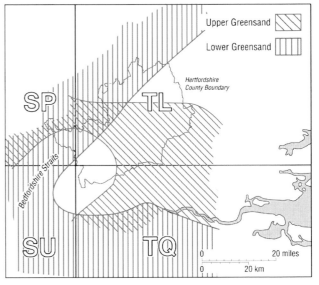

Figure 2.8. Subsurface extents of Lower Greensand and Upper Greensand in the Hertfordshire area.

extended as far south as Upware, Cambridgeshire. Later in the Aptian, further sea level rise caused the two seas to join around the western flank of the London Platform through a narrow 'Bedfordshire Straits' (Fig. 2.8). The Sandgate and Folkestone Formations of the Lower Greensand were then deposited to the south of the platform and the Woburn Sands to the north.

For at least a century, the Woburn Sands Formation has been exposed in numerous pits near Leighton Buzzard (Shephard-Thorn *et al.*, 1994), where it is probably up to 120 m thick, and forms a prominent northwest-facing scarp overlooking the broad vale of Upper Jurassic clay formations around Milton Keynes. The maximum recorded thickness is 88.7 m in a borehole at Potsgrove (Shephard-Thorn *et al.*, 1994, p. 118), but an unknown thickness was missing here because of erosion before deposition of overlying Quaternary deposits. The sands range in colour from white through brown to red, with cross-bedding indicating a range of current directions. A basal bed containing phosphatic nodules was previously dug for use as phosphate fertilizer at the scarp foot in the area between Little Brickhill and Great Brickhill, Buckinghamshire (Ford and O'Connor, 2002), and pebbles of white quartzite, vein quartz and shiny black 'lydite' occur at various levels within the sand. Many of the lydites probably originated by rolling, rounding and polishing of phosphatic nodules, but one examined in thin section by Catt *et al.* (1975) was a quartz-tourmaline hornfels, a fine-grained metamorphic rock similar to some from the contact aureoles of the granite intrusions in southwest England.

Within lower parts of the Woburn Sands at Old Wavendon Heath (SP 930344), Aspley Wood and other areas near Woburn, there are layers of dark grey or paler yellowish green clay ranging in thickness from a few centimetres to almost 4 m. As they are composed almost entirely of the highly absorbent expanding clay mineral smectite, these beds have been extensively quarried for several centuries (Cox, 1979a), originally as 'fuller's earth' for removing grease from wool, but more recently for a wide range of uses, including refining edible oils, as a bonding agent for foundry sands, as a filler in papermaking, for production of well drilling fluids, as pet litter and in the manufacture of cosmetics and cattle foods. The fuller's earth beds contain euhedral crystals of typical volcanic minerals, such as sphene, biotite, feldspar and zircon, so the smectite probably originated by alteration of volcanic ash on the floor of the shallow Woburn Sands sea (Jeans *et al.*, 1977). Cowperthwaite *et al.* (1972) suggested the Wolf Rock off Cornwall as a possible source for the ash, but later work indicated that it came from the North Sea area (Dixon *et al.*, 1981).

South-eastwards from its outcrop in Bedfordshire, the Woburn Sands Formation dips beneath the Gault Clay and becomes gradually thinner as it overlaps the Jurassic formations onto the Palaeozoic basement of the London Platform. A minimum thickness of 42 m was proved in a borehole at Fairfield Hospital (TL 204353) near Arlesey (Hopson *et al.*, 1996, p. 16), and full thicknesses of 10.2-27.9 m were penetrated in the deep boreholes at Henlow,

Ashwell and Tring (Appendix 1) and in shallower boreholes at Radwell (TL 231362) and Bygrave (TL 256366) (Hopson *et al.*, 1996, pp. 18-19). However, no Lower Greensand has been recorded in boreholes to the southeast in other parts of Hertfordshire.

2.7. The Gault Clay and Upper Greensand

Following deposition of the Lower Greensand in the Aptian Stage, there was an extensive marine transgression in the succeeding Albian Stage (soon after 112 Ma) that resulted in deposition of the Gault Clay over the whole of southeast England, including the London Platform. The Gault Clay is divided into Lower Gault (Middle Albian) and Upper Gault (Upper Albian). The Upper Greensand, occurring between the Gault and Chalk from Dunstable south-westwards, is a sandy and strongly glauconitic shallow-water lateral equivalent of the uppermost Gault. The transgression of the Albian sea onto the London Platform was progressive, as the Lower Gault is attenuated against its northern flank (Gallois and Morter, 1982, Fig. 5), and it was probably only in the Late Albian that the sea eventually flooded the platform completely. In the Leighton Buzzard area, the Gault is separated from silty beds at the top of the Woburn Sands beneath by a thin and variable sequence of sands, clays, shelly limestones, gritty ironstones and phosphatic nodules known as the Junction Bed, which is of Early Albian age.

The Gault Clay is the oldest deposit outcropping at the surface in Hertfordshire. Although it forms a belt several kilometres wide northwest of the Chiltern scarp foot, only two small parts of this actually lie within the county boundary (Fig. 3.1), one north of Ashwell and the other around Wilstone and Long Marston, and even here it is partly hidden beneath thin Quaternary deposits. Beneath most of the county it is deeply buried by the Chalk and younger deposits so, as far as Hertfordshire is concerned, it is appropriate to consider the Gault as the youngest of the concealed bedrock formations.

Near the north-western margin of the Chalk outcrop, where the maximum thickness of Gault Clay is likely to be preserved, a total of about 65 m has been recorded, for example in boreholes at Hitchin Brewery (Hill, 1908) and Fairfield Hospital (TL 204353) (Hopson *et al.*, 1996, p. 19). Greater thicknesses have been recorded in some older boreholes in the region, such as those at Tring (91.5 m) and Bushey (93.9 m), but these values may be unreliable because, without detailed lithological or palaeontological evidence, it is difficult to place the boundary between the strongly calcareous Upper Gault and the marly Lower Chalk. Although it is continuous over the London Platform, the total thickness of Gault Clay decreases slightly south-eastwards, with 61.6 m recorded at Little Chishill (Duddenhoe End), 55 m at Ashwell, 52 m at Willesden, 51 m at Ware, 46 m at Turnford and 40 m at Kentish Town.

At various past exposures in the Leighton Buzzard area, including Southcott Mill (SP 901245), Littleworth (SP 881233), Mundays Hill (SP 937282), Tiddenfoot (SP 911424), Grovebury (SP 923229), Billington Crossing (SP

930241), Stone Lane (SP 930289), Chamberlain Barn (SP 931268) and New Trees (SP 931275), the Junction Bed has included lenticular and fragmentary masses of fossiliferous limestone, known as the Shenley Limestone. This bed became famous because of a controversy between Lamplugh (Lamplugh and Walker, 1903; Lamplugh, 1920, 1921, 1922), who maintained that the sequence at sites near Shenley Hill (SP 9327) is undisturbed, and Kitchin and Pringle (1920, 1922), who suggested that it had been overturned by glacial action in the Pleistocene. The controversy was later resolved in favour of Lamplugh when Toombs (1935) found a Lower Albian ammonite (*Leymeriella* aff. *tardefurcata*) in the limestone at Mundays Hill and Middle Albian fossils in the overlying Lower Gault Clay. More recently, Eyers (1992) has suggested that the limestone in the Shenley Hill area was deposited as a clastic carbonate infilling hollows in a wave-cut platform of Aptian ironstone. In the BGS Arlesey borehole (TL 189346) near Hitchin, a limestone in the same stratigraphic position takes the form of a laminated mat of intertidal algal remains (Woods *et al.*, 1995). In addition to *L. tardefurcata*, the Shenley Limestone fauna includes brachiopods, bryozoans, belemnites, gastropods, bivalves (oysters), echinoids and casts of serpulid worms. The Junction Bed as a whole probably represents a condensed Lower Albian sequence resulting from a marine regression followed by a transgression during which earlier sediments were eroded and reworked.

Most of the Gault Formation consists of stiff calcareous grey clay, with brown phosphatic nodules, either scattered throughout or sometimes concentrated in layers of darker polished concretions. Although they were originally known as 'coprolites', the phosphatic nodules are in fact rarely if ever fossil faeces. Similar nodules occurring in the Glauconitic Marl at the base of the Chalk in other parts of southern England are thought to have had complex histories, involving infilling of dead shells, post-burial diagenetic cementation of the mud infilling, dissolution of the carbonate shells, exhumation, rolling and abrasion of the concretions by sea-floor currents, replacement with phosphate and glauconite by prolonged reaction with seawater, boring and encrustation by a later generation of marine organisms and finally reburial in fresh sediment (Kennedy and Garrison, 1975). Repeated cycles of reworking and exposure of the nodules to seawater resulted in progressive enrichment in phosphate and sometimes the amalgamation of single into compound nodules.

There are occasional sandy layers in the Gault, especially near the base of the formation, but stratification in the main bulk of the clay has been lost by bioturbation during deposition. Pyrite (FeS_2) is disseminated throughout as small crystals and locally occurs also as nodules. Where the clay has been oxidized, small gypsum crystals have been formed by reaction between calcium carbonate and the sulphuric acid produced by oxidation of pyrite. Analyses by Prior *et al.* (1993) of unweathered samples from boreholes in northeast Hertfordshire indicated that the carbonate content ranges from 31 % to 42 %, and that the clay (<2 μm) fraction is composed of about 10 % mica, with kaolinite increasing from near 20 % at the top to 60 % near the base,

and smectite decreasing in the same direction from about 80 to 30 %. Because of the upward increase in carbonate, the Upper Gault is paler in colour than the Lower Gault.

Both macrofossils and microfossils are abundant, the former including ammonites, lamellibranchs, gastropods, echinoids and the characteristic small belemnite *Neohibolites minimus*. The main lamellibranchs are *Birostrina* (previously *Inoceramus*), *Anomia* and *Aucellina* spp., some species of which seem to have local stratigraphic significance. *Birostrina concentrica* occurs mainly in the Lower Gault and the strongly ribbed *Birostrina sulcata* at the base of the Upper Gault. Higher parts of the Upper Gault are poorly fossiliferous, containing mainly various species of *Aucellina*.

In numerous cored boreholes through the Gault Clay in East Anglia, Gallois and Morter (1982) identified 19 lithological units, each with a burrowed erosion surface overlain by a thin lag deposit of rounded phosphatic nodules in a silty matrix, followed by a thicker layer of calcareous bioturbated clay. These subdivisions can be traced over long distances, and many have been identified in, for example, the Gault of the Arlesey borehole (Hopson *et al.*, 1996, Fig. 6). They indicate rhythmic cycles of shallowing and deepening of the Gault sea, probably as a result of global (eustatic) changes of sea level. The 11th cycle (Bed G11) can be traced westwards into Wessex, and its base is used as the boundary between lower and upper divisions of the Gault.

Based on the work of Spath (1923-1943) and Owen (1972, 1975), the Albian Stage has also been subdivided into ammonite zones and subzones (Table 2.1), which have been correlated with foraminiferal assemblage biozones (Hart, 1973a; Hart *et al.*, 1989). Ostracods (Wilkinson and Morter 1981; Wilkinson, 1990a) and calcareous nannofossils (Crux, 1991) have also been used to subdivide the sequence. The nannofossil assemblages suggest that the sea was cooler in the Mid and early Late Albian than later in the Late Albian. Bed by bed collection of ammonites in the Leighton Buzzard area (Owen, 1972) has shown that episodes of erosion have resulted in many local gaps in the sequence, derived ammonites from the missing zones often being incorporated into the lag deposits of polished phosphatic nodules. For example, after deposition of the Junction Bed in the *Leymeriella (Leymeriella) regularis* and *Sonneratia kitchini* subzones, three periods of erosion produced three separate beds of nodules at Chamberlain Barn, each with a mixed derived fauna containing both *L. regularis* and *S. kitchini*. Although sedimentation resumed in the *Hoplites (Isohoplites) eodentatus* subzone, erosion in the *Lyelliceras lyelli* subzone produced another bed of nodules containing derived *H. eodentatus* at Billington Crossing. In the later *Hoplites (Hoplites) spathi*, *Anahoplites intermedius* and *Dimorphoplites niobe* subzones, deposition of clay continued uninterrupted, but erosion early in the subsequent *Dipoloceras cristatum* subzone then extensively removed higher parts of the Lower Gault. Because of gaps in the sequence, the total thickness of Lower Gault preserved in the Leighton Buzzard area is only about 10 m.

Another period of uninterrupted sedimentation throughout the later *Dipoloceras cristatum, Hysteroceras*

Stage subdivisions	Zones	Subzones
Upper Albian (Upper Gault)	Stoliczkaia dispar	Mortoniceras (Durnovarites) perinflatum
		Mortoniceras (Mortoniceras) rostratum
	Mortoniceras (Mortoniceras) inflatum	Callihoplites auritus
		Hysteroceras varicosum
		Hysteroceras orbignyi
		Dipoloceras cristatum
Middle Albian (Lower Gault)	Euhoplites lautus	Anahoplites daviesi
		Euhoplites nitidus
	Euhoplites loricatus	Euhoplites meandrinus
		Mojsisovicsia subdelaruei
		Dimorphoplites niobe
		Anahoplites intermedius
	Hoplites (Hoplites) dentatus	**Hoplites (Hoplites) spathi**
		Lyelliceras lyelli
		Hoplites (Isohoplites) eodentatus
Lower Albian (Junction Beds)	Douvilleiceras mammillatum	Protohoplites (Hemisonneratia) puzosianus
		Otohoplites raulinianus
		Cleoniceras (Cleoniceras) floridum
		Sonneratia kitchini
	Leymeriella (Leymeriella) tardefurcata	**Leymeriella (Leymeriella) regularis**
		Hypacanthoplites milletioides
		Farnhamia farnhamensis

Table 2.1. Ammonite zones and subzones of the Albian Stage (112-100 Ma). Subzones identified in the Leighton Buzzard area shown in bold.

orbignyi and *Hysteroceras varicosum* subzones then led to deposition of Upper Gault equivalent to Beds G11-G14 of Gallois and Morter (1982). Finally, a further erosive episode removed any remaining Upper Albian subzones, so that the Upper Gault near Leighton Buzzard is also only about 10 m thick. Beds G15-G18 of Gallois and Morter (1982), belonging to the *Callihoplites auritus* and *Mortoniceras (Mortoniceras) rostratum* subzones of the Upper Albian, were probably deposited in southern Bedfordshire, as they were identified in the BGS Arlesey borehole (Hopson *et al.*, 1996, Fig. 6) close to the south-eastern margin of the Gault outcrop. Bed G19 (also *rostratum* subzone) is probably absent in the Arlesey borehole sequence, but has been recorded further east.

Lower parts of the Gault Clay have been exposed near Leighton Buzzard in the overburden of several quarries exploiting the Woburn Sands, including Mundays Hill, Chamberlain Barn and New Trees. Lower Gault was also previously exposed at Clophill (TL 091388) and Gamlingay (TL 237530) in southeast Bedfordshire (Woods *et al.*, 1995). Closer to Hertfordshire, the only permanent exposures have been at (a) Arlesey Pit (TL 188347) north of Hitchin (Hill, 1911a), where a 15 m section of Upper Gault is equivalent to the higher part of the nearby Arlesey borehole, and (b) beneath the Chalk in the south-eastern part of the College Lake pit (SP 933138) near Bulbourne. At College Lake, now a BBOWT nature reserve, the clay was mixed with

chalk excavated nearby to manufacture cement. In the late 19th and early 20th centuries, Arlesey Pit was a source of clay for brickmaking, and there were other exposures in south Bedfordshire at Meppershall Hoo and Harlington Brickworks (Bloom and Harper, 1938).

The Gault Clay thins northwards across East Anglia, and eventually disappears in Norfolk, where the Albian Red Chalk Formation overlies the Aptian Carstone (Lower Greensand). Woods *et al.* (1995) suggested that the synclinal basin proposed by Allsop (1985) in the sub-Devonian Palaeozoic basement between Luton and Cambridge (Section 2.4) was reactivated in the Albian, so that a greater thickness of Gault was deposited in north Hertfordshire and south Bedfordshire than in areas further north.

Where it is exposed (between clay of the Upper Gault and the lowest Chalk in southwest Bedfordshire, southeast Buckinghamshire and the Hertfordshire salient northwest of Tring), the Upper Greensand is probably equivalent to Beds G15-G19 of Gallois and Morter (1982), that is to the *varicosum, auritus, rostratum* and *perinflatum* subzones of the Upper Albian. For example, in a BGS borehole sited on the floor of the now infilled chalk quarry at Sundon (TL 041272), it consisted of 3.4 m of dark greenish grey calcareous and non-calcareous glauconite-rich siltstones with phosphatic nodules and various types of infilled burrows, and the microfauna indicated a Late Albian age equivalent to the *varicosum* and later substages (Fletcher,

1989). Upper Greensand was temporarily exposed in the 1990 excavations for the Leighton Buzzard by-pass, and in the Stanbridge-Tilsworth area it is represented by two units of siltstone, the upper of which contains abundant glauconite and phosphatic nodules (Shephard-Thorn *et al.*, 1994, p. 55).

Across southern England, the thickness of the Upper Greensand increases westwards, and its base is diachronous as it progressively replaces more and more of the Gault Clay. This suggests that the sand was derived from land areas to the west and was deposited in shallower nearshore water, which gradually migrated eastwards as the basin of deposition was infilled. The sandy facies is completely absent east of a line drawn approximately between Dunstable and Eastbourne (Rawson, 1992, Map K3); any Upper Greensand deposited beyond this was probably removed by erosion in the slightly later marine transgression early in the succeeding Cenomanian Stage. Figure 2.8 shows the approximate extent of Upper Greensand beneath the Chalk in the Hertfordshire area, based on the borehole evidence given in Appendix 1.

2.8. The Cambridge Greensand

At the beginning of the Late Cretaceous (99.6 Ma), there was another extensive marine transgression across Britain. The first deposit of this Cenomanian transgression in the Hertfordshire area was a thin greenish-grey sandy glauconitic marl containing brown phosphatic nodules ('coprolites'), which is now known as the Cambridge Greensand. In parts of Bedfordshire northeast of Harlington and in southern Cambridgeshire, it is the basal member of the West Melbury Marly Chalk Formation (the lowest part of the Upper Cretaceous Chalk sequence), and rests on an irregular erosion surface truncating various beds of the Upper Gault and also infilling burrows penetrating as much as 1 m into the Gault. Consequently, Jukes-Browne (1875) concluded that it was Early Cenomanian in age rather than Late Albian.

However, the lithological similarity and apparently similar stratigraphic position of the Cambridge Greensand and Upper Greensand have led to confusion between the two in the past, and this is compounded by the presence in the Cambridge Greensand of abundant fossils derived from Albian deposits (Jukes-Browne and Hill, 1903; Spath, 1932; Morter and Wood, 1983) and by typical Upper Albian ostracods in the basal part further east (Wilkinson, 1988). In addition, the two deposits occur in different areas, so that there is no exposure or borehole clarifying their stratigraphic relationship; the Upper Greensand is preserved only southwest of Dunstable, whereas the area of original deposition of the Cambridge Greensand was apparently limited to the southwest by uplift along a monoclinal structure that coincides approximately with the Lilley Bottom valley east of Luton (Hopson *et al.*, 1996). Much of the confusion arose because, in the Cambridge area, the deposit was previously known as the 'Upper Greensand of Cambridge' (Sollas, 1873a, 1873b) or the 'Cambridge Upper

Greensand' (Sollas and Jukes-Browne, 1873). However, the conclusion of Jukes-Browne (1875) that it is entirely Early Cenomanian may be an over-simplification, as the indigenous Upper Albian microfossils suggest that the Cenomanian transgression actually began to the east in the Late Albian.

In southeast Bedfordshire, northeast Hertfordshire and southwest Cambridgeshire, the Cambridge Greensand is usually less than 1 m thick, and is consequently too thin for its outcrop to be shown separately on the 1:50,000 geological maps of these areas. A thin (0.6 m) layer was previously exposed between the Gault Clay and Chalk at Arlesey Brickworks (Bloom and Harper, 1938). Where it thickens slightly to the northeast, it has been divided into two, a lower part rich in glauconite and phosphatic nodules and containing phosphatized shells of *Aucellina* spp., and an upper part lacking phosphatic nodules and rich in non-phosphatized *Aucellina* shells (Morter and Wood, 1983). Elsewhere in southeast England, including for example along the foot of the Chiltern scarp southwest of Dunstable, the Cambridge Greensand is replaced at the base of the West Melbury Marly Chalk Formation by a thin bed of greenish-grey clay. This was known originally as the Chloritic Marl (Penning and Jukes-Browne, 1881), but is now more accurately termed the Glauconitic Marl Member.

Because of the abundance, especially near its base, of 'coprolite' nodules up to 10 cm across and containing 55-60% calcium phosphate (25 % P_2O_5), the Cambridge Greensand was extensively worked in northeast Hertfordshire and south Cambridgeshire during the 19th century (Grove, 1974; Ford and O'Connor, 2002) for production of superphosphate fertilizer (Section 7.7). The deposits exposed by these workings were described by Bonney (1874), Fisher (1873), Sollas (1873b) and others, and became famous for a rich assemblage of fossils, including gastropods, lamellibranchs, crustacea, echinoids, crinoids, brachiopods, polyzoa, annelid worms, sponges, corals, ammonites, foraminifera, ostracoda, fish teeth and scales, reptile bones and bird bones, almost all of which were preserved in phosphatic nodules and derived from the Upper Gault Clay or Upper Greensand (Jukes-Browne, 1875; Spath, 1932). Peake and Hancock (1961) concluded that some of the brachiopods are indigenous rather than derived, and that they indicate a Cenomanian age, but Casey (1965) felt that the brachiopod faunas in this part of the Cretaceous are too poorly known to justify their use for such precise dating. Together with Breistroffer (1947), Casey concluded that the fauna of the Cambridge Greensand is entirely Upper Albian in age, implying (probably incorrectly) that it is equivalent to the Upper Greensand.

An Early Cenomanian age for the deposit at Arlesey and Barrington (Cambridgeshire) is clearly indicated by the foraminifera (Hart, 1973b). In the more complete Upper Albian-Lower Cenomanian sequences at East Wear Bay, Folkestone (Kent) and other sites in southern England, there are distinct changes in both planktonic and benthonic foraminiferal assemblages across the stage boundary, and comparison with the assemblage from the Cambridge Greensand indicates that the latter was deposited late in the first Cenomanian subzone (the *Hypoturrilites carcitanensis* subzone) after erosion of at least 13 m of Upper Gault Clay (the *Stoliczkaia dispar* zone). Hart (1973b) also noted that numerous juvenile oyster shells ('spat') colonized the upper surfaces of many of the phosphatic nodules, suggesting that initial deposition of the greensand after the Early Cenomanian erosion episode was very rapid, preventing development of more mature shells before the nodules were buried.

Faunal lists for the Cambridge Greensand have been compiled by Bonney (1874), Jukes-Browne and Hill (1903, pp. 202-205) and White (1932, pp. 16-17). Spath (1932) gave a partially revised list of the ammonites derived from the Albian. Most of the fossils found in the 19th century were housed in the Woodwardian Museum, Cambridge (now part of the Sedgwick Museum, Downing Street).

As the coprolites were excavated by opencast methods on almost flat ground adjacent to and beneath the lowest part of the West Melbury Marly Chalk Formation, the workings left a belt of disturbed ground up to several hundred metres wide (Grove, 1974). In the late 19th century, the nodules were transported to factories for treatment with sulphuric acid and conversion to superphosphate fertilizer. One of the factories was situated between Royston and Bassingbourn, and another near Ashwell station.

In addition to fossils, the coprolite workings also yielded rounded pebbles, angular fragments and boulders up to 30 cm across of a wide range of far-travelled rocks, including granite, rhyolite, schist, gneiss, hornfels, obsidian, basalt, quartz porphyry, essexite and various Palaeozoic sandstones, conglomerates, greywackes, slates, quartzites and limestones, including Permian Magnesian Limestone (Sollas and Jukes-Browne, 1873; Bonney, 1874; Jukes-Browne and Hill, 1903; White, 1932; Hawkes, 1943). Because of the angularity of some of these 'erratics', Jukes-Browne and Hill (1903, Chapter 16) suggested that they were ice-rafted from the north, but there is no other known evidence for a Late Cretaceous glaciation in Europe, and it is more likely that they were carried into the Early Cenomanian sea attached to the floating roots of trees derived from land to the west (Bonney, 1874; White, 1932). They can often be distinguished from lithologically similar Pleistocene glacial erratics, which are common in the same parts of Cambridgeshire and northeast Hertfordshire, by partial surface coatings of spat.

Chapter 3.

The Upper Cretaceous Chalk

Haydon Bailey and Chris Wood

3.1. Introduction

Along the northern margin of
Hertfordshire, the route of the ancient
Icknield Way runs north-eastwards
from Tring along the present-day B488
and A505 following the foot of a major
regional geomorphological feature, the
Chalk escarpment. Because of the south-
eastward dip of the Mesozoic strata, almost
the whole of the county is underlain by the Chalk (Fig. 3.1).
This distinctive limestone is responsible for the undulating
topography and frequent dry valleys so characteristic
of much of the county. In spite of the importance of
the Chalk in Hertfordshire, exposures are rare and the
detailed succession has to be pieced together from isolated
quarry sections, road and railway cuttings and temporary
exposures. Jukes-Browne and Hill (1904) noted that 'Chalk
... is exposed along many of the valleys which open to the
eastward and south-eastward, and in some of these inlying
tracts large quarries have been opened'. But a hundred years
later only two quarries are still being worked and many
other man-made exposures have been lost. However, it is
possible to establish details of the Upper Cretaceous geology
of the county from records of the isolated past and present
exposures.

Before describing the Upper Cretaceous succession in
detail, it is necessary to clarify the stratigraphic terminology
used in this chapter and describe the nature and origin of the
Chalk sediment and the associated marls and flints.

3.2. Lithostratigraphic terminology

Jukes-Browne and Hill (1903, 1904) formally recognized
a three-fold division of the English Chalk into Lower,
Middle and Upper, which approximated to the three
divisions previously established in France as Cenomanian,
Turonian and Senonian, respectively (Barrois, 1876). Their
terminology was used widely for almost a century, but in
the late 20th century it was recognized that, for mapping
purposes, it would be more logical to divide the Chalk Group
into two Sub-Groups, with the Grey Chalk Sub-Group (the
old Lower Chalk) overlain by the White Chalk Sub-Group
(previously the Middle and Upper Chalk). Between the
two there is a well-defined boundary recognized across the
whole of southern England at the erosion surface located at

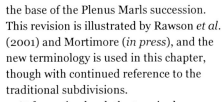

the base of the Plenus Marls succession.
This revision is illustrated by Rawson *et al.*
(2001) and Mortimore (*in press*), and the
new terminology is used in this chapter,
though with continued reference to the
traditional subdivisions.

At formation level, the terminology
introduced by Mortimore (1986) is ideal
(Figs 3.1 and 3.2). Although defined along
the Sussex coast, it is applicable to the
whole of southern England, including Hertfordshire. It was
adopted by the British Geological Survey (BGS) following
discussions in 1997, which were subsequently reviewed
in Rawson *et al.* (2001) and Rawson (2006). Many of the
lithostratigraphic marker horizons identified and named
in Sussex by Mortimore (1986), including flint bands
and marl seams, are traceable across southern England
into Hertfordshire. The palaeogeographic location of
Hertfordshire during deposition of the Chalk is important,
as it lies within the Transitional Province defined by
Mortimore (1983), which links a Southern Province typified
by the Anglo-Paris Basin and the Northern Province of
Lincolnshire, Yorkshire and the North Sea Basin.

3.3. The nature of Chalk and its origins

Towards the close of Early Cretaceous times, a major
eustatic rise in sea level led to the near-global Cenomanian
transgression that progressively inundated the whole
of Europe. As sea level rose, decreasing amounts of
terrigenous material were supplied from the shrinking
land-masses, so that the marine deposits that became the
Chalk were composed increasingly of calcium carbonate.
The occurrence in the Chalk of skeletons of organisms that
cannot tolerate lower salinities, such as corals, brachiopods
and echinoderms, indicate that the Late Cretaceous sea
was of normal salinity. At its maximum the sea depth was
probably 200-600 m (Hancock, 1975), though near its
margin and over submerged massifs it was considerably less
than this. Stable isotope studies of calcite from fossils such
as planktonic foraminifera (Hart and Carter, 1975) suggest
that sea-surface temperatures were significantly warmer
than at present (>17°C); Skelton (2003) suggested than in
tropical areas they were higher than 30°C, reflecting the firm
establishment of a 'greenhouse' world.

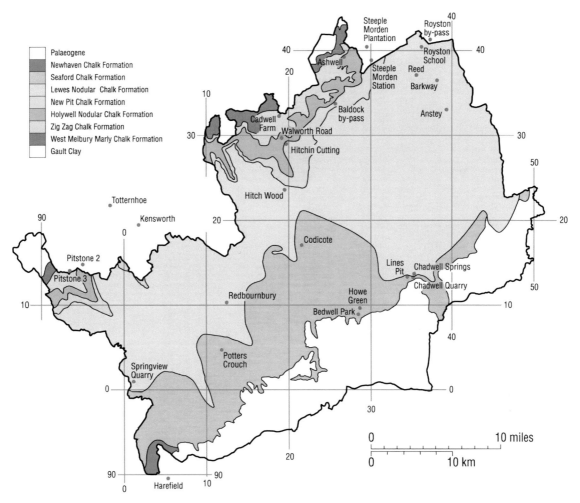

Figure 3.1. Simplified outcrop map of the Chalk formations exposed in Hertfordshire (superficial deposits and Palaeogene outliers omitted) and location of sites described in the text. Boundaries between formations based mainly on BGS maps.

Composition of Chalk

The familiar white Chalk seen in quarries and other exposures across Hertfordshire is a very fine-grained, extremely pure (>98% $CaCO_3$) and fairly soft white limestone. The calcium carbonate is in the form of the mineral low-magnesian calcite. The acid-insoluble (non-carbonate) residue comprises clay minerals such as smectite and illite and subordinate slightly coarser detritus, mainly quartz. The white colour of most of the Chalk reflects the insignificant content of clay and iron-containing minerals, and the commercially important brightness or reflectivity is a function of the fine grain size (Hancock, 1975).

Although the Chalk was previously thought to be either a deep-sea deposit like the modern *Globigerina* Ooze, or a shallow-water inorganic aragonite precipitate of Bahama Banks type, electron microscopy has shown that up to 90% of the sediment is composed of tiny calcite crystals, a few microns across, derived from the disintegration of complex, ring-like structures known as coccoliths. These are secreted by the Coccolithophoridae, a family of highly specialized unicellular golden-brown algae. Larger particles of biogenic calcite are suspended within this coccolith 'flour'. These comprise nannofossils such as complete coccoliths and, at some levels, the enigmatic *Nannoconus*,

microfossils including calcispheres (dinoflagellates with calcareous skeletons, such as *Pithonella*), foraminiferal tests and ostracod valves, and bryozoan, shell and echinoderm debris. Silica-walled microfossils such as radiolarians are only rarely preserved in the Chalk of Hertfordshire (Hill and Jukes-Browne, 1886; Hill and Monckton, 1896), but must have been present, albeit in lower numbers than recently discovered in Chalk samples from beneath the North Sea floor (Hampton *et al.*, 2010). Especially important components are small calcite prisms derived from the mechanical breakdown of shells of the bivalve *Inoceramus*. At current-winnowed horizons, these reach rock-building proportions, producing Chalk that is gritty to the touch. Other macrofossils are an insignificant proportion of the total sediment and tend to be concentrated at particular horizons.

Rhythmic sedimentation

Much of the Chalk displays rhythmic sedimentation on a decimetre scale (Robinson, 1986; Gale 1990, 1995), giving repeated successions of darker (grey) more argillaceous beds that grade up into increasingly paler more carbonate-rich layers. The more calcareous layers of such rhythmic couplets often resist erosion and project slightly from older

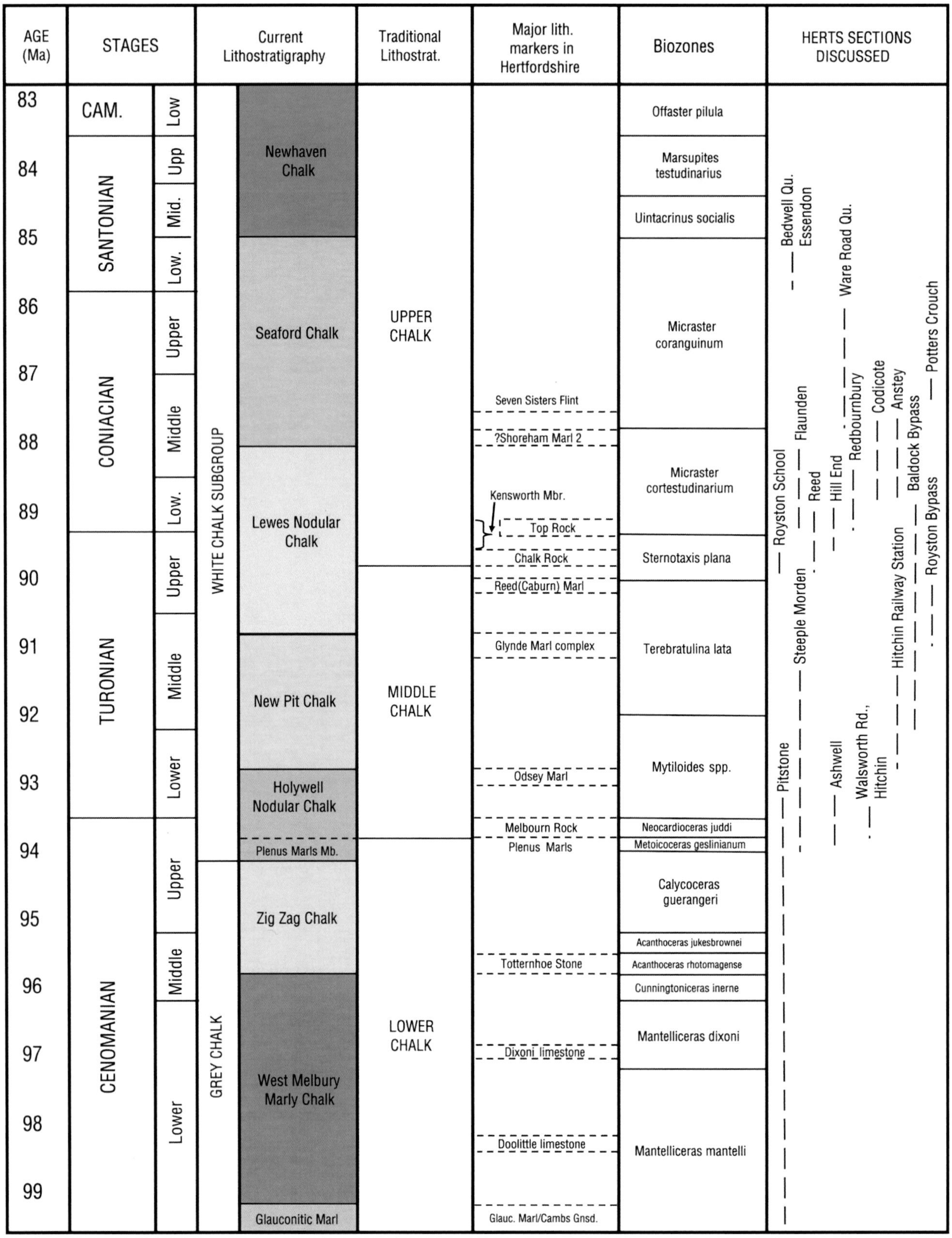

AGE (Ma)	STAGES		Current Lithostratigraphy	Traditional Lithostrat.	Major lith. markers in Hertfordshire	Biozones	HERTS SECTIONS DISCUSSED
83	CAM.	Low	Newhaven Chalk	UPPER CHALK		Offaster pilula	
84	SANTONIAN	Upp	Newhaven Chalk			Marsupites testudinarius	
85	SANTONIAN	Mid. / Low.	Seaford Chalk			Uintacrinus socialis	
86–87	CONIACIAN	Upper	Seaford Chalk			Micraster coranguinum	
88	CONIACIAN	Middle	Lewes Nodular Chalk		Seven Sisters Flint / ?Shoreham Marl 2	Micraster cortestudinarium	
89	CONIACIAN	Low.	Lewes Nodular Chalk		Kensworth Mbr. / Top Rock	Micraster cortestudinarium	
90	TURONIAN	Upper	Lewes Nodular Chalk	MIDDLE CHALK	Chalk Rock / Reed (Caburn) Marl	Sternotaxis plana	
91	TURONIAN	Middle	New Pit Chalk		Glynde Marl complex	Terebratulina lata	
92	TURONIAN	Lower	New Pit Chalk			Mytiloides spp.	
93	TURONIAN	Lower	Holywell Nodular Chalk		Odsey Marl	Mytiloides spp.	
94	CENOMANIAN	Upper	Holywell Nodular Chalk / Plenus Marls Mb.	LOWER CHALK	Melbourn Rock / Plenus Marls	Neocardioceras juddi / Metoicoceras geslinianum	
95	CENOMANIAN	Upper	Zig Zag Chalk			Calycoceras guerangeri	
96	CENOMANIAN	Middle	Zig Zag Chalk		Totternhoe Stone	Acanthoceras jukesbrownei / Acanthoceras rhotomagense / Cunningtoniceras inerne	
97	CENOMANIAN	Lower	West Melbury Marly Chalk		Dixoni limestone	Mantelliceras dixoni	
98	CENOMANIAN	Lower	West Melbury Marly Chalk		Doolittle limestone	Mantelliceras mantelli	
99	CENOMANIAN	Lower	Glauconitic Marl		Glauc. Marl/Cambs Gnsd.	Mantelliceras mantelli	

Current Lithostratigraphy subgroups: WHITE CHALK SUBGROUP (upper part) and GREY CHALK (lower part).

HERTS SECTIONS DISCUSSED (sites listed): Bedwell Qu., Essendon, Ware Road Qu., Flaunden, Redbournbury, Codicote, Anstey, Potters Crouch, Royston School, Reed, Hill End, Baldock Bypass, Royston Bypass, Steeple Morden, Hitchin Railway Station, Pitstone, Ashwell, Walsworth Rd., Hitchin.

Figure 3.2. Summary of the Chalk formations, lithostratigraphic markers, macrofossil zones and successions exposed at important sites in and near Hertfordshire (dating from Gradstein et al., 2005; CAM. = Campanian).

cut faces, especially if they are slightly lithified. Rhythmicity is most clearly seen in the relatively clay-rich 'Chalk Marl', a unit within the lower part of the traditional Lower Chalk (principally the West Melbury Marly Chalk Formation of the Grey Chalk Sub-Group), in which the distinction between the marly and more carbonate-rich beds is emphasized by the colour contrast. It is less obvious, but still present, in the overlying White Chalk Sub-Group, which has much lower overall clay contents. The Chalk Marl couplets can be traced from England throughout the Anglo-Paris Basin and as far as northern Germany and the Caucasus (Gale, 1990, 1995; Gale *et al.*, 1999).

The rhythmicity is generally attributed to climatic oscillations resulting from variations in the amount of solar energy reaching the surface of the earth, due to periodic changes in the distance between the earth and the sun and in the tilt and axis of rotation of the earth. These orbital periodicities are known as Milankovitch Cycles (House, 1995), the rhythmic couplets in the Chalk probably reflecting the 20-21 ka cycle of precession of the equinoxes, often abbreviated to 'the precession cycle'. During the warmer periods of increased solar influence, there is greater organic productivity at the sea surface. Production of nannoplankton is then greater, and the amounts of calcium carbonate reaching the sea floor are more than during periods of lower solar influence. Increased deposition of carbonate then dilutes the concentration of clay minerals in the seafloor sediment.

Marl seams

In addition to the marl (clay) component of the rhythmic couplets, discrete clay-rich beds ranging in thickness from less than 1 cm to several cm occur in some parts of the Chalk succession, especially in the (traditional) Middle Chalk. These so-called marl seams bear no relationship to the sedimentary rhythmicity, as they are episodic rather than periodic. Their origin is not clearly understood, but the most favoured explanation at present is one of increased supply of detrital material at times of falling sea level (Wray and Gale, 1993). However, from their rare earth element geochemistry, some marl seams in the Turonian of England and north Germany have a definite volcanic origin, the ash from volcanoes being altered to clay minerals including bentonite (a type of smectite) on contact with seawater or water circulating within the sediment after deposition (Wray, 1995, 1999; Wray and Wood, 1995, 1998; Mortimore *et al.*, 2001, Fig. 1.12).

In the higher part of the White Chalk Sub-Group, there is a broad alternation of units composed of (a) poorly flinty, relatively marly chalk with marl seams, and (b) more calcareous chalk almost devoid of marl seams but containing large flints. This is particularly well seen in the succession comprising the New Pit (with marl seams) and the Lewes and Seaford (marl-free) Formations.

Individual marl seams provide conspicuous marker horizons in exposures of the White Chalk Sub-Group. They are especially useful in long-range correlation, because they are represented by low-value electrical resistivity peaks in wireline geophysical logs of wells and boreholes. Each marl seam has its own trace-element geochemistry, providing a 'finger print' that serves as a useful correlation tool. They are essentially a feature of the thicker basinal successions, and lose their identity when traced into the condensed successions of more marginal situations and over submerged massifs.

Very fine, hair-like wispy clay seams, often referred to as 'horsetails' in the early literature, also occur in parts of the Chalk. They resemble the flaser bedding seen in many other marine deposits, and are probably of primary sedimentary origin (Mortimore, *in press*). Where such clay-rich seams anastomose and form thicker beds, they are often associated with the development of nodular chalks, and sometimes resemble the 'griotte textures' originally described from Devonian limestones (Hancock, 1975).

Omission surfaces, nodular chalks and hardgrounds

Brief interruptions in Chalk sedimentation are marked by omission surfaces, which may be imperceptible apart from a slight yellow or orange coloration from iron minerals. With longer exposure to seawater, the superficial levels of the seafloor sediment underwent progressive cementation. Initially this involved localized deposition of secondary calcite in the pore spaces within chalk between animal burrows, leading to the formation of nodular chalks. Exhumation of these hardened nodules by current action sometimes resulted in an intraformational conglomerate. With further exposure, the cementation spread from the original centres, progressively converting the patchily hardened chalk into a more or less homogeneous limestone or chalkstone. This hardening generally extends down for some 30 cm from the top of the bed, the lower limit being ill-defined. The cemented seafloor provided a hard substrate for encrusting and boring organisms and may itself undergo mineralization, including formation of the yellow iron oxide geothite, green glauconite and brown complexes of iron and phosphate. Such a hardened seafloor is known as a hardground, though this term is often loosely (but incorrectly) applied to both the surface and the underlying chalkstone. Hardgrounds form in relatively shallow water and characterize the condensed sequences near basin margins and over submerged massifs; basinwards they grade into increasingly poorly defined nodular chalks and finally into omission surfaces. South of the Thames, there is a classic example of this transition in the closely stacked hardgrounds comprising the Chalk Rock of the Marlborough Downs and its coeval nodular chalk correlative in the North Downs. The Chalk Rock, earlier taken by BGS as the base of the traditional Upper Chalk, is a classic hardground, which has also been exposed in quarries in and near Hertfordshire, for example at Kensworth (Bromley, 1967a, Plate 7a).

A deep structural line (fault or monocline) known as the Lilley Bottom Structure, which is orientated NW-SE, perpendicular to the strike of the Chalk in northern Hertfordshire, probably occurs over part of the north-eastern margin of the Midlands Microcraton (Mortimore, 1983; Mortimore *et al.*, 2001). Along with other lineaments beneath the county, its position is indicated on Bouguer Gravity Anomaly maps (Hopson *et al.*, 1996). Uplift along these lineaments may account for lateral variations in thickness of parts of the county's Chalk succession, including local condensation and hardground development, for example in the Chalk Rock sequence (Bromley and Gale, 1982). But in addition there may have been eustatic changes in sea level during the Late Cretaceous. Most of the inferred episodes of low sea level in the Late Cretaceous (Haq *et al.*, 1987) occurred at approximately the same times as the Cretaceous tectonic phases known in northern Europe as Subhercynian (Mortimore *et al.*, 1998, 2001). As the latter can often be related to major structural readjustments on intra-plate margins, they could have affected ocean volumes and caused changes in sea level.

Flints

Also present in the Chalk, but generally only in pure white chalks with an insignificant clay content, are irregular nodules and sheets of flint. Flint is a form of chert (SiO_2) with a well developed conchoidal fracture. It is an aggregate of ultramicroscopic quartz crystals, which are similar in size to the coccolith plates constituting the chalk itself and are set in a matrix of amorphous (opaline) silica. Beds of flint nodules occur at regular intervals related to the sedimentary rhythmicity and are aligned parallel to the bedding. The most strongly developed and semi-continuous flint beds provide correlatable marker horizons, such as the East Cliff Semi-tabular or Seven Sisters Flint and the Whitaker's 3-inch Flint in the *Micraster coranguinum* Zone of the traditional Upper Chalk.

Most flints are intimately related to trace fossils, such as the large burrow-trace *Thalassinoides* and, to a lesser extent, the feeding-trace *Zoophycos*. The former can be regarded as replacements of the sedimentary fill of burrows as, when dissected out from the surrounding chalk, they typically exhibit either the original form of the burrow or some modification of it. Less commonly, flints formed around burrows, and are annular in cross section. An extreme form of this is provided by the vertical flints up to several metres long known as paramoudras, which have formed around the tiny burrow-trace *Bathichnus*. Paramoudras are commonly found in the highest part of the Chalk, and are therefore rare in Hertfordshire, although there is one in the Potters Crouch chalk pit near St Albans (TL 116046). Better developed examples occur at the level of the Bedwell's Columnar Flint Band of the *Micraster coranguinum* Zone in quarries between Purfleet and Grays, Essex.

The formation of flint was a multistage process (Clayton, 1984, 1986), which took place within the chalk sediment immediately beneath the seafloor, and was completed as a syn-sedimentary process by the end of the Cretaceous, because derived flints are found widely at the base of the overlying Palaeogene deposits. The silica is believed to have come from the skeletons of siliceous sponges, radiolaria and diatoms. On burial, this biogenic silica rapidly passed into solution. With greater depth of burial, anaerobic decomposition of organic matter in the sediment under the action of sulphate-reducing bacteria released hydrogen sulphide, which diffused upwards to the boundary between the reduced and oxidized zones in the chalk sediment. Here it was oxidized to sulphate and thus liberated hydrogen ions, which initiated acidic dissolution of calcium carbonate and the simultaneous precipitation of silica to replace it. These processes took place preferentially within the fill of larger burrows such as *Thalassinoides*. The silica was

initially precipitated as minute spherical aggregates of microcrystalline cristobalite known as lepispheres, which provided nuclei for the accretion of more silica from solution. The embryonic flints composed of cristobalite, opal and possibly other silica minerals eventually underwent partial late-stage (diagenetic) recrystallization to quartz. Early diagenetic mobility of silica within the chalk sediment and its redeposition replacing calcite is also indicated by the partial silicification of many types of macrofossils in the Hertfordshire Chalk (Brown *et al.*, 1969). The existence of angular flint shards, notably at horizons of bedding plane shear in the *Micraster cortestudinarium* Zone of the traditional Upper Chalk, provides evidence that the embryonic flints were hard enough to fracture rather than deform plastically under shearing stress.

Sheet flints that cross the bedding at a high angle are clearly of later origin. They are not completely solid, but often contain a central fill of soft chalk (meal), suggesting that they represent the linings of fractures resulting from compaction or shearing. Sheet flints orientated approximately parallel to beds of nodular flints were formed similarly by redeposition of silica from solutions passing along subhorizontal shear fractures.

Fauna

The invertebrate fauna of the relatively deep water White Chalk is of low diversity and largely restricted to organisms with calcite skeletons, such as brachiopods, echinoderms and some bivalves. Molluscs with shells originally composed of aragonite, such as gastropods, ammonites and many bivalves, have very low preservation potential in the colder deep water environment close to the sea floor, because of the preferential solubility of aragonite in cold water. Such fossils are generally preserved only in the more argillaceous, shallower water chalks (e.g. the Chalk Marl) and in hardgrounds such as the Chalk Rock, where they are represented by hollow moulds.

Because ammonites are rarely preserved in the White Chalk, the traditional macrofossil zonation is based on a combination of calcitic fossils, such as brachiopods, bivalves, belemnites, crinoids and echinoids (Fig. 3.2). Consequently, identification of the international Late Cretaceous ammonite zones has proved difficult in the British post-Turonian sequence, but latterly inoceramid bivalves have provided an alternative zonation. Inoceramids have the dual advantage of an almost worldwide distribution and, because of the calcite part of their shells, a high preservation potential.

Microfaunal remains are common in the Chalk. The coccoliths of which the chalk is almost entirely composed provide useful zonal markers for international correlation. Coccolith zonal schemes developed for the southern English Chalk (Burnett, 1998; Hampton *et al.*, 2007) allow very precise comparisons with more argillaceous successions encountered in deeper water basins elsewhere in Europe. The tests (shells) of other microfaunal remains, such as foraminifera and ostracods, are also very common in the Chalk of southern England, where they provide both biostratigraphic and palaeoenvironmental information (Hart *et al.*, 1989; Hampton *et al.*, 2007). Siliceous microfossils, particularly radiolaria, are very rare in the onshore English Chalk; the few records that exist come exclusively from Hertfordshire (Hill and Jukes-Browne, 1886; Quennell, *pers. comm.*).

3.4. The Chalk succession in Hertfordshire

Figure 3.2 summarizes the Chalk succession exposed at various sites in Hertfordshire, and shows the lithostratigraphic units, macrofossil zonation scheme and important lithological marker beds used for correlation from site to site. Although the county is almost entirely underlain by the Chalk, there are rather few scattered exposures, most of which have been small and temporary. The largest and most useful are the deep quarry sections, such as Pitstone, and the roadside sections along the Chiltern scarp, such as the recently cut Baldock by-pass. On the south-eastern dip-slope of the Chilterns, there are several small quarries, which were formerly used for agricultural lime and are now preserved for their importance as Sites of Special Scientific Interest (SSSIs) or Regionally Important Geological Sites (RIGSs). The former have statutory protection under the Countryside Act 1949. The latter are not formally protected in the same way, but many have protection provided by Hertfordshire County Council under their Structure and Local Plans (Hertfordshire RIGS Group, 2003).

The oldest Chalk exposed in the county is the Grey Chalk sequence seen in Pitstone Quarry #2 (SP 947148), which lies astride the county boundary with Buckinghamshire. The Plenus Marls and immediately overlying Melbourn Rock (the lowest members within the Holywell Nodular Chalk Formation at the base of the White Chalk Sub-Group) are also exposed here on the north-eastern margin of Quarry #2 (SP 949149), and are again exposed in quarries near Ashwell (TL 269394) and Steeple Morden (TL 297402) in northeast Hertfordshire, where the succession extends up into the basal part of the overlying White Chalk Sub-Group. The Plenus Marl succession was also exposed temporarily in the Walsworth Road section (TL 193297) adjacent to Hitchin railway cutting (Hopson *et al.*, 1996, p. 42).

The cutting for the tunnelled part of the Baldock by-pass (TL 259339) dug in 2004-5 exposed the lower part of the White Chalk (the traditional Middle Chalk) from a level within the New Pit Formation to just above the Top Rock. Although subsequently back-filled, this valuable section allowed calibration of wireline log data from boreholes at Worsted Lane near Hare Street (TL 399292) and Hamels Mill, Braughing (TL 386247) (Hopson *et al.*, 1996, p. 143) through to the Royston by-pass sections.

The Chalk Rock to Top Rock succession (the Kensworth Nodular Chalk Member) at the base of the traditional Upper Chalk (Lewes Formation) is important throughout Hertfordshire, particularly with reference to the very fossiliferous sites at Reed (TL 359371), Hill End (Hitch Wood) (TL 197239), Redbournbury (TL 124104) and Kensworth (TL 015197) discussed below. It represents probably the most important period of relatively low sea

level in the Late Cretaceous (Hancock, 1975; Bromley and Gale, 1982). The hardground surface of the Top Rock has often formed the lower limit for quarrying of White Chalk. Many of the small pits, which were opened across the county in Victorian times for the production of agricultural lime and are still extant, are floored by this distinctive nodular and mineralized chalk. They include Redbournbury (TL 124104), Flaunden (TL 007010) and Anstey (TL 395329) Quarries.

What is probably the youngest chalk in Hertfordshire, the lower part of the Upper Santonian Newhaven Chalk Formation, outcrops in the extreme southwest of the county near Harefield, but there is only one small exposure, in the largely backfilled Harefield Quarry (TQ 050898) just outside the county boundary (Hampton, *pers. comm.*). Elsewhere, the youngest exposed chalk, within the topmost Lewes and lower Seaford Formations, is seen in several scattered locations throughout the county, including Codicote Quarry (TL 214171), Bedwell Park Quarry (TL 284090) near Essendon, Potter's Crouch Pit (TL 116046) near St Albans and Springwell Quarry (TQ 045931) in the Colne Valley south of Rickmansworth. In east Hertfordshire, the presence of Lower Santonian Seaford Chalk Formation is also indicated by a single specimen of the echinoid *Conulus albogalerus* (Plate 13) found by J. C. Doyle in the old Bishop's Stortford Limeworks quarry (TL 489234). The top Chalk unconformity (Sub-Palaeogene Surface) is currently best exposed at Harefield Quarry (TQ 050898), where the Newhaven Chalk Formation is overlain by glauconitic sediments of the Palaeocene Upnor Formation (Daley and Balson, 1999) (Section 4.4).

The Upper Cretaceous sequence represented in Hertfordshire is thus fairly restricted, ranging from the Cenomanian Grey Chalk through to the Late Santonian White Chalk. Many of the sections described below lie within the range Late Turonian-Early Coniacian.

3.5. Chalk exposures within the county

It is important to document each of the exposures across Hertfordshire in some detail, as it is likely than many will disappear in the near future because of back-filling and landscaping. They are described below in approximate stratigraphic order from the base upwards.

Grey Chalk Sub-Group (Lower Chalk)

Pitstone Quarries. Much of the now disused cement works at Pitstone is cleared and the land developed for housing. This includes the original Quarry #1, which has been backfilled. Quarry #3 (SP 932144), which lies within south-eastern Buckinghamshire, is partially flooded and the lake forms the central feature of the BBOWT College Lake nature reserve. A section of the West Melbury Marly Chalk Formation of the Grey Chalk Sub-Group exposed in Quarry #3, originally described and measured by Professor A. S. Gale, is included as part of the sequence illustrated in Figure 3.3.

Pitstone Quarry #2 has not been backfilled at present, despite attempts by the site owners to utilize it for landfill.

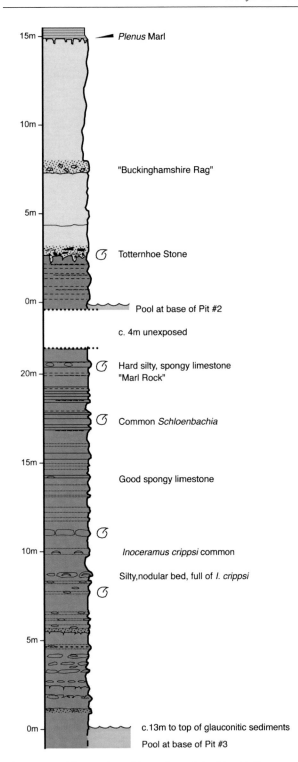

Figure 3.3. Lithostratigraphic sections of the West Melbury Marly Chalk and Zig Zag Chalk Formations exposed in Pitstone Quarries #2 (SP 947148) and #3 (SP 932144).

Partial restoration may well happen in the future, but with the preservation of certain important geological features outlined below. Quarry #2 exposes the upper part of the Grey Chalk Sub-Group and the Plenus Marls at the base of the White Chalk Sub-Group (Fig. 3.3). The former is described here and the White Chalk sequence later in this section. The deep north-western corner of Quarry #2 contains a small permanent lake obscuring the sequence to just above the level of the 'Marl Rock'. About 4 m above water level there is a 0.5 m development of the Totternhoe Stone, a curious channel-filling deposit showing significant regional variations in thickness.

About 5.5 m above the base of the Totternhoe Stone, there is a localized development of the 'Buckinghamshire Rag'. Because of the gentle dip, this bed is exposed just above water level at the south-eastern end of the lake. It was originally described from Buckinghamshire by Jukes-Browne and Hill (1903) and later in greater detail by Sherlock (1922), but there have been few subsequent exposures, so that at Pitstone is of considerable importance. The Rag comprises a lenticular glauconitized and phosphatized pebble bed containing fish teeth and scales in a calcarenitic matrix. At Pitstone, it dies out laterally over approximately 100 m. It may correlate laterally with a hardground level developed approximately the same distance above the Totternhoe Stone at Totternhoe Quarry in Bedfordshire (Shephard-Thorn *et al.*, 1994), but this relationship remains unproven. Regional correlation would make it the local equivalent of Jukes-Browne Bed 7 in the south coast succession seen at Folkestone (Mortimore *et al.*, 2001, and references therein).

About 7.5 m of Zig Zag Chalk Formation is poorly exposed above the Rag. It is composed of mid to light grey argillaceous chalk with occasional beds of gritty, sparsely glauconitic argillaceous mudstone. This is capped by a distinctive orange-stained hardground seen at the base of a low cliff on the eastern edge of Quarry #2, and a bed of *Thalassinoides* bioturbated chalk with common wispy marls occurs above the hardground. The uppermost part of this unit is intensely burrowed and truncated by the sub-Plenus Marl erosion surface, which marks the major lithostratigraphic boundary between the Grey Chalk Sub-Group and White Chalk Sub-Group.

Sections in the Plenus Marls Member

Pitstone. The Plenus Marls are clearly exposed in a prominent small cliff at the eastern edge of Pitstone Quarry #2 (SP 948248). Here they comprise just over 1 m of alternating calcareous claystone/marl beds and light grey limestones (Fig. 3.4); detailed measurements, following the bed definitions of Jefferies (1963), are:

Bed 8: 10 cm dark grey marly claystone
Bed 7: 12 cm hard light grey limestone
Bed 6: 4 cm dark grey marly claystone
Bed 5: 10 cm hard light grey limestone, with slightly undulating upper surface
Bed 4. 10 cm pale greenish grey marly claystone, with the belemnite *Praeactinocamax plenus*
Bed 3: 20 cm hard grey limestone with common burrows, particularly in the upper part of the bed
Bed 2: 6 cm mid-dark grey marly claystone
Bed 1: 30 cm clay rich mudstone grading up into a gritty limestone

This sequence is capped by a prominent hard non-nodular

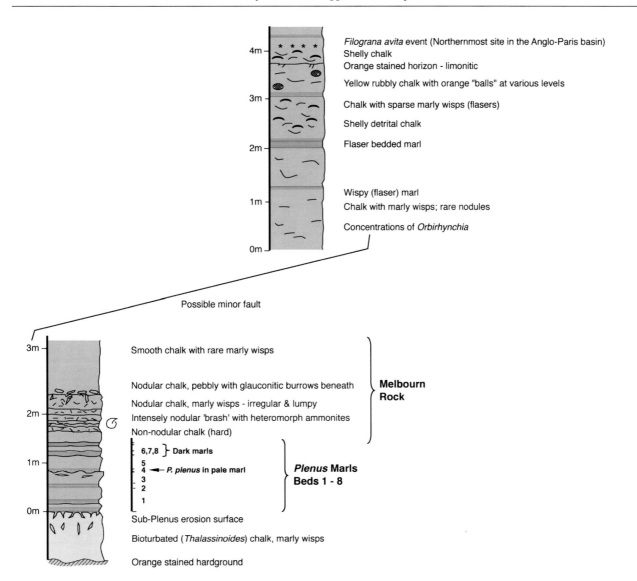

4m — *Filograna avita* event (Northernmost site in the Anglo-Paris basin)
Shelly chalk
Orange stained horizon - limonitic
Yellow rubbly chalk with orange "balls" at various levels

3m — Chalk with sparse marly wisps (flasers)

Shelly detrital chalk

Flaser bedded marl

2m —

Wispy (flaser) marl

1m — Chalk with marly wisps; rare nodules

Concentrations of *Orbirhynchia*

0m —

Possible minor fault

3m — Smooth chalk with rare marly wisps

Nodular chalk, pebbly with glauconitic burrows beneath   **Melbourn**
Rock
Nodular chalk, marly wisps - irregular & lumpy
2m — Intensely nodular 'brash' with heteromorph ammonites
Non-nodular chalk (hard)

6,7,8 } Dark marls
5
4 ← *P. plenus* in pale marl   ***Plenus* Marls**
1m — 3   **Beds 1 - 8**
2
1

0m — Sub-Plenus erosion surface

Bioturbated (*Thalassinoides*) chalk, marly wisps

Orange stained hardground

Figure 3.4. Lithological section of Plenus Marls (base of the Holywell Nodular Chalk Formation) exposed in Pitstone Quarry #2 (SP 948148).

limestone, which forms the base of the Melbourn Rock.

Ashwell Quarry (TL 269394). The Plenus Marls are exposed in this small, partly back-filled quarry, which is now an orchard. The exposure was recorded in detail by Hopson *et al.* (1996, p. 41). The total sequence of Beds 1-8 is less than 1 m thick. Even so, all the beds seen at Pitstone are distinguishable, though Bed 4 is reduced to a thin clay parting.

Cadwell Farm (TL 189327). The thickest development of the Plenus Marls in the county is that recorded from this small roadside pit close to the Hertfordshire-Bedfordshire county boundary. Here Hopson *et al.* (1996, p. 42) described a 1.77 m sequence resting unconformably on the top of the Grey Chalk Sub-Group. Well-developed clay beds occur at the base of Beds 1 and 2 and form Beds 4, 6 and 8. Bed 4 has yielded specimens of *Praeactinocamax plenus*.

Walsworth Road (TL 193297). A temporary section of Plenus Marls 0.96 m thick was recorded at this site near Hitchin

Station by Hopson *et al.* (1996, p. 43). Bed 3 was a hard splintery chalk similar to the basal bed of the Melbourn Rock, and Beds 4-8 were condensed to a total thickness of 0.16 m.

White Chalk Sub-Group (Middle and Upper Chalk)

Anstey Quarry (TL 395329). This is one of the last working chalk quarries in Hertfordshire, and at present is being steadily back-filled following planned restoration, which should be complete by 2020. This plan agreed with the County Council includes the preservation of the western faces of the existing quarry, which are illustrated in the lower half of Figure 3.5. The section, in the lower part of the traditional Upper Chalk, was described in detail by Hopson *et al.* (1996, p. 61), though without a graphic log. It comprises white chalk with a series of 15 strong nodular flint bands. One of these, described as an 'impersistent large nodular flint' is directly underlain by 3 m of flintless chalk. Approximately 3 m above this nodular flint is a tabular flint, which migrates obliquely across the section over a depth of

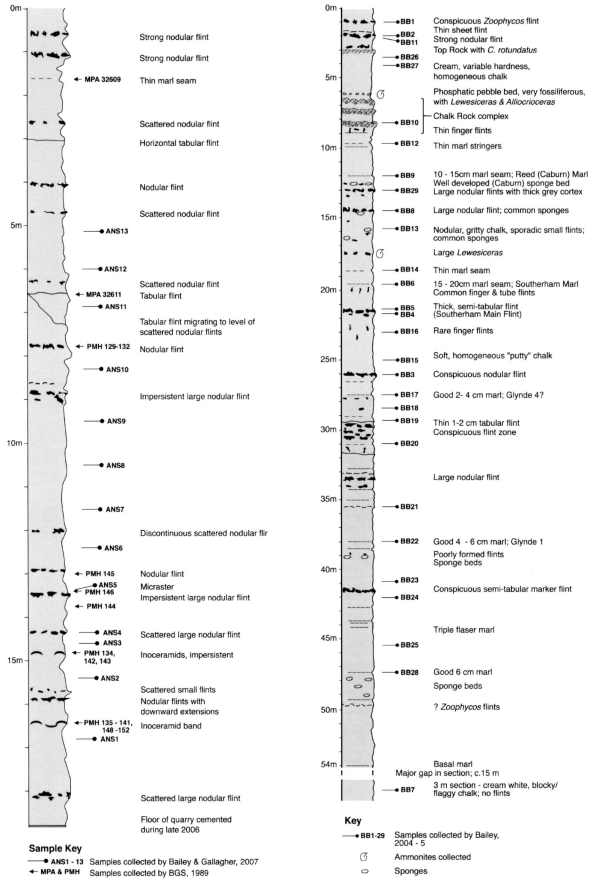

0m

Strong nodular flint

Strong nodular flint

← MPA 32609   Thin marl seam

Scattered nodular flint

Horizontal tabular flint

Nodular flint

Scattered nodular flint

5m

— ANS13

— ANS12

Scattered nodular flint

← MPA 32611   Tabular flint

— ANS11

Tabular flint migrating to level of
scattered nodular flints

← PMH 129-132   Nodular flint

— ANS10

Impersistent large nodular flint

— ANS9

— ANS8

10m

— ANS7

Discontinuous scattered nodular flir

— ANS6

← PMH 145   Nodular flint
— ANS5   Micraster
PMH 146
Impersistent large nodular flint
← PMH 144

— ANS4   Scattered large nodular flint
— ANS3
← PMH 134,   Inoceramids, impersistent
142, 143

— ANS2

Scattered small flints
Nodular flints with
downward extensions

15m

← PMH 135 - 141,   Inoceramid band
148 -152
— ANS1

Scattered large nodular flint

Floor of quarry cemented
during late 2006

Sample Key

——● ANS1 - 13   Samples collected by Bailey & Gallagher, 2007
← MPA & PMH   Samples collected by BGS, 1989

*Figure 3.5. Lithological section of Lewes Nodular Chalk exposed
at Anstey Quarry (TL 395329).*

0m

—● BB1   Conspicuous *Zoophycos* flint
—● BB2   Thin sheet flint
●BB11   Strong nodular flint
Top Rock with *C. rotundatus*
—●BB26
—●BB27   Cream, variable hardness,
5m   homogeneous chalk

Phosphatic pebble bed, very fossiliferous,
with *Lewesiceras* & *Alliocrioceras*

—● BB10   Chalk Rock complex

Thin finger flints

—● BB12   Thin marl stringers

10m

—● BB9   10 - 15cm marl seam; Reed (Caburn) Marl
Well developed (Caburn) sponge bed
—● BB29   Large nodular flints with thick grey cortex

—● BB8   Large nodular flint; common sponges

15m

—● BB13   Nodular, gritty chalk, sporadic small flints;
common sponges

Large *Lewesiceras*

—● BB14   Thin marl seam

—● BB6   15 - 20cm marl seam; Southerham Marl
Common finger & tube flints

20m

—● BB5   Thick, semi-tabular flint
●BB4   (Southerham Main Flint)

—● BB16   Rare finger flints

25m

—● BB15   Soft, homogeneous "putty" chalk

—● BB3   Conspicuous nodular flint

—● BB17   Good 2- 4 cm marl; Glynde 4?

—● BB18

—● BB19   Thin 1-2 cm tabular flint
Conspicuous flint zone

30m

—● BB20

Large nodular flint

35m

—● BB21

—● BB22   Good 4 - 6 cm marl; Glynde 1
Poorly formed flints
Sponge beds

40m

—● BB23   Conspicuous semi-tabular marker flint

—● BB24

Triple flaser marl

45m

—● BB25

—● BB28   Good 6 cm marl

Sponge beds

? *Zoophycos* flints

50m

Basal marl

54m   Major gap in section; c.15 m

—● BB7   3 m section - cream white, blocky/
flaggy chalk; no flints

Key

——● BB1-29   Samples collected by Bailey,
2004 - 5

⟲   Ammonites collected

⊂⊃   Sponges

*Figure 3.6. Lithological section of New Pit and Lewes Nodular
Chalk Formations measured in 2004-2005 during construction
of the Baldock by-pass (TL 259339). The section is now largely
backfilled around the tunnel.*

44

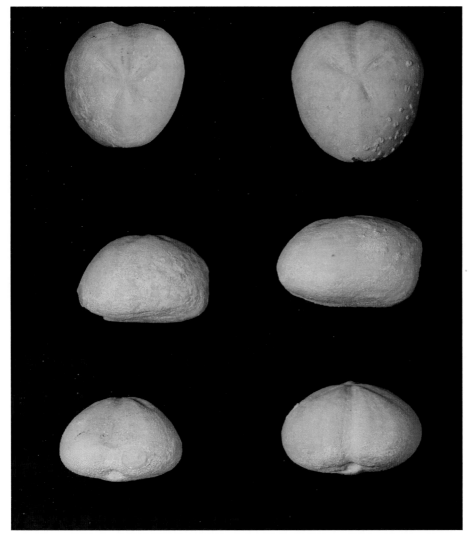

B. parca expansa, B. signata, *Eprolithus floralis*, *Helicolithus turonicus*, *H. trabeculatus*, *Lithastrinus cayeuxii*, *Micula staurophora*, *Quadrum eptabrachium*, *Q. gartneri* and *Zeugrhabdotus biperforatus*. The very rare occurrences of *M. staurophora* throughout the section imply a lower Middle Coniacian age (Subzone UC10i of Burnett, 1998).

Baldock by-pass (TL 259339). The deep road cutting (Plate 5) excavated at this point in 2004-2005 for the A505 Baldock by-pass is now fenced off or covered by the backfill over the Weston Hills Tunnel, but was measured in detail (Fig. 3.6) when fully exposed. Two distinctive marl seams exposed at the base of the section are believed to equate with the New Pit Marls 1 and 2 in the Sussex succession (Mortimore, *pers. comm.*). The boundary between the New Pit Formation and the overlying Lewes Nodular Chalk Formation is drawn 23.5 m higher at a 2-4 cm marl seam believed to represent the highest of the Glynde Marls (Glynde 4) in Sussex. The whole of the New Pit Chalk Formation comprises chalk mudstones with at least ten discrete marl

Plate 4. A small Micraster cortestudinarium *from Anstey Quarry (left) and* Micraster corbovis *from nodular chalk above the Top Rock at Reed (right). Viewed from above (upper photos), the* M. cortestudinarium *is 40 mm across and the* M. corbovis *45 mm.*

1 m. The uppermost 4 m of the section illustrated in Figure 3.5 are taken from measurements made in 1989 (CJW), as this interval is no longer exposed.

Macrofossils, including inoceramid bivalves and echinoderms, collected during the BGS investigation of the site are housed at BGS Keyworth. A small *Micraster cortestudinarium* (Plate 4) was collected by HWB, and macrofaunal evidence summarized by Hopson *et al.* (1996, p. 61) suggests that most of the quarry is within the upper part of the *Micraster cortestudinarium* Zone. This conclusion is supported by the results of microfossil analyses by BGS (Wilkinson, 1990b), which indicate that the thin marl seam close to the top of the quarry section (now covered by backfilling) probably equates with Shoreham Marl 2 in Sussex (Mortimore, 1986; Mortimore *et al.*, 2001) and the Upper East Cliff Marl in Kent, both of which mark the base of the *Micraster coranguinum* Zone (Bailey *et al.*, 1983). This age is also indicated by calcareous nannofossils recovered from samples collected throughout the Anstey section. These all yielded broadly similar assemblages, including the important marker species *Broinsonia enormis*,

seams and very rare nodular flints.

Nodular flints occur more regularly throughout the lower part of the Lewes Nodular Chalk Formation, and approximately 4.25 m above Glynde Marl 4 a well developed nodular (locally tabular) flint is recognized as the Southerham Main Flint. A thick (12-15 cm) marl seam 1.25 m above this flint probably equates with the volcanic Southerham Marl 1 (Mortimore, 1986) because, as in the Sussex succession (Hart, 1993), it contains common specimens of the large agglutinating foraminiferid *Labyrinthidoma southerhamensis*.

A large fragmented *Lewesiceras* was found 2.5 m above the Southerham Marl within a nodular gritty chalk containing many iron-stained sponges. A further marl seam occurring 6.5 m above the Southerham Marl 1 is equated with the Reed Marl of the Chiltern succession and the volcanic Caburn Marl of Sussex, and the strongly developed Caburn Sponge Bed occurs just below it. The Caburn Marl is visible from the road as a thin white-weathering band just beyond the western end of the Weston Hills Tunnel. Between 2 and 4 m above the marl at least three fossiliferous

Plate 5. *Section of Chalk exposed in the cutting for the tunnelled section of the Baldock by-pass (TL 259339), 2004.*

Plate 6. *Section of glaciotectonically disturbed Chalk Rock with till layer at Barkway (TL 381366)*

mineralized hardgrounds with common phosphatic pebbles are developed as the local representative of the Chalk Rock. Glauconitized ammonites and other fossils are succeeded upwards by phosphatized fossils. This is similar to the sequence described at Reed (TL 359370) by Bromley and Gale (1982).

The Top Rock was recorded 3.5 m above the Chalk Rock in a section exposed in the pit dug for the foundations of the footbridge over the road to the west of the tunnel (TL 252322). It comprised a glauconitized burrowed surface, and the 0.5 m thick chalkstone beneath contained fine (mm scale) vertical tubular burrows and pebbles with glauconitized surfaces. A very large flint between the Top Rock and a minor omission surface 0.5 m above it may correspond to a distinctive flint horizon present at a similar stratigraphic level in the sections at Clothall Bury (TL

274325), Wallington (TL 288337) and Reed (Hopson *et al.*, 1996, Fig. 17). The highest 3 m of chalk exposed in the road cutting contains two flint bands, the upper of which includes *Zoophycos* flints. Nannoplankton analyses of samples from Baldock confirm the early Coniacian age of the chalk immediately above the Top Rock (Wyton *et al.*, 2007).

Newsells Bury Pit, Barkway (TL 381366). The chalk section here was originally logged (in 1877) by Jukes-Browne and Hill (1904). They described two layers of 'hard, cream-coloured nodular limestone' identified as 'Chalk Rock Beds' separated by 'rubbly whitish chalk with a thin layer of whitish marl', all dipping to the north at 60° (Plate 6). This description was confirmed by Hopson *et al.* (1996, p. 60). A sketch of the section was given by Whitaker *et al.* (1878, p. 8). The steep dip was originally attributed to glacial disturbance by Woodward (1903a, 1903b). This was later confirmed by Bromley (1967b), who recognized that the two hard limestones are repeated units including the Chalk Rock, which are superimposed on one another as glaciotectonic thrust slices separated by chalky clay till of glacial origin. Hopson (1995) and Hopson *et al.* (1996, pp. 85-88) recognized several other rafts along a swathe of the degraded Chalk scarp-slope measuring 7 km × 1 km from Therfield (TL 3337) to just east of Barkway (TL 3836), and described the origin of these thrust slices in detail (Section 6.6).

Codicote Quarry (TL 214171). This working quarry was described by the Hertfordshire RIGS Group (2003) as exposing 'upper Lewes Nodular Chalk Formation (Lower Coniacian, *Micraster cortestudinarium* Zone) overlain by basal Seaford Chalk Formation (Middle Coniacian, *Micraster coranguinum* Zone)'. Later the sections exposed on the north and southeast faces were measured in detail (Fig. 3.7). The two marl seams cited by the Hertfordshire RIGS Group (2003) at the top of the sequence are in fact a thin well-defined tabular flint with a marl seam 1.20 m above and a nodular flint 0.5 m above that. These beds probably correspond to a similar succession at the top of the Anstey Quarry section (Figs 3.5 and 3.8), where a single marl seam, the regionally persistent Shoreham Marl 2, is present. Samples collected in 2006 and analysed for foraminifera and nannoplankton confirmed this correlation.

Below the well-defined tabular flint band identified at Codicote, there is a 5.6 m succession of chalk with four nodular flint bands each just over 1 m apart. The section below this was difficult to measure precisely because of breaks in the quarry faces, but there seems to be a bed of flintless chalk approximately 3.5 m thick at the base of the western face, which may equate with a similar bed at Anstey (Fig. 3.5). The south-eastern face at Codicote exposes 2.85 m of chalk with three nodular flint bands, topped by an impersistent thin marl seam and a tabular flint. In all, a total of just over 12 m is exposed at Codicote Quarry, the floor of which may be formed by the Top Rock.

Bedwell Park Quarry (TL 284090). Any exposures in this quarry near Essendon are temporary, as back-filling with inert waste is continuing and any pits excavated by the

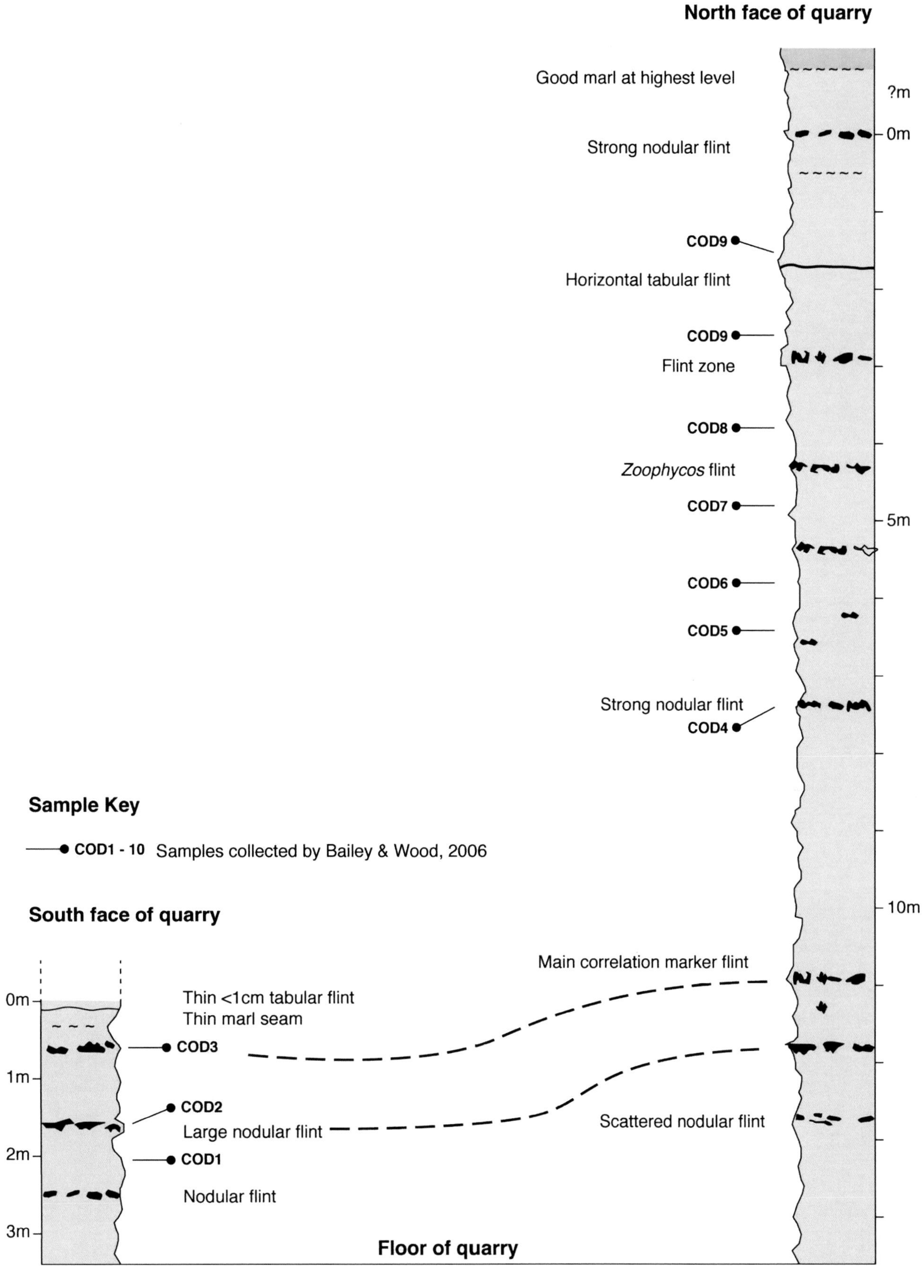

North face of quarry

Good marl at highest level — ?m

Strong nodular flint — 0m

COD9

Horizontal tabular flint

COD9

Flint zone

COD8

Zoophycos flint

COD7 — 5m

COD6

COD5

Strong nodular flint
COD4

Sample Key

●COD1 - 10   Samples collected by Bailey & Wood, 2006

South face of quarry

— 10m

Main correlation marker flint

Thin <1cm tabular flint
Thin marl seam

0m

COD3

1m

COD2

Large nodular flint

Scattered nodular flint

2m COD1

Nodular flint

3m

Floor of quarry

Figure 3.7. Lithological sections of Lewes Nodular Chalk Formation measured at Codicote Quarry (TL 214171).

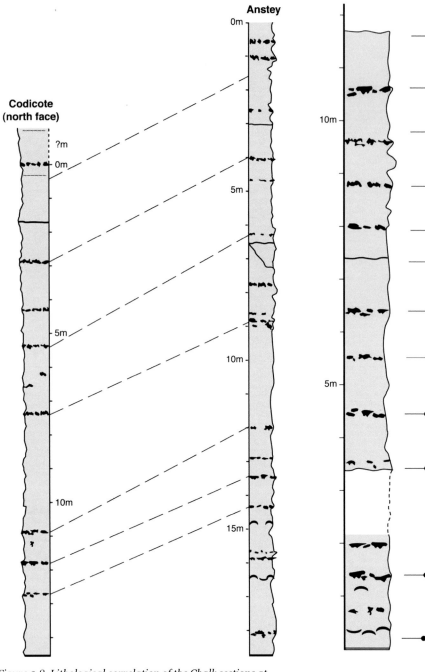

Figure 3.8. Lithological correlation of the Chalk sections at Codicote and Anstey, illustrating persistence of flint bands between the two sites.

Sample Key

BQ1 - 12   Samples collected by Bailey & Wood, 2002

Figure 3.9. Lithological section of Seaford Chalk Formation measured at Bedwell Park Quarry (TL 284090) in 2003. Section now obscured by inert waste.

current owners are rapidly infilled. A 12 m section of White Chalk Group with conspicuous nodular and tabular flints was measured and sampled in 2003 (Fig. 3.9). Large platy fragments of *Cladoceramus* near the base of the measured section indicate a high level in the Seaford Chalk Formation. Eleven regularly spaced nodular flint bands *c.* 1 m apart were logged in the section, together with two tabular flints, the upper being approximately 2 cm thick and the lower, 4.05 m below the first, thin and impersistent. No other macrofossils were found in the fresh vertical faces.

A distinctive assemblage of benthic foraminifera from samples collected at the base of the pit included *Stensioeina granulata granulata, Gavelinella arnagerensis* and

Gavelinella eriksdalensis. Just above the *Cladoceramus* level, rare specimens of *Stensioeina granulata polonica* were identified, indicating an early Santonian age for this section. This dating was confirmed by nannoplankton recovered from the same samples (Liam Gallagher, *pers. comm.*), which included common *Helicolithus trabeculatus,* an abundance level recognized throughout southern England in chalk of earliest Santonian age (Hampton *et al.*, 2007).

Howe Green Pit (TL 286096). A 10 m section exposed in this pit near Essendon was logged in 1971. It comprised white chalk with 11 nodular flint bands and a single tabular flint 2.5 cm thick. The similarity of this succession to that described above from Bedwell Park Quarry suggests that it is the same sequence of Santonian age. Before the pit was back-filled, rare *Micraster* were recorded (J. C. Doyle, *pers. comm.*).

Springview Quarry (TL 007010). This pit near Flaunden is hidden in a narrow belt of woodland on a steep west-facing valley side close to the county boundary with Buckinghamshire. It exposes 13 m of Chalk with characteristics typical of the upper part of the Lewes Nodular Chalk Formation (Lower Coniacian, *Micraster cortestudinarium* Zone). Two nodular hardgrounds occur 10 m apart in the face, and the floor of the quarry is probably formed by the Top Rock hardground (Fig. 3.10). Neither of the nodular hardgrounds is well mineralized

Plate 7. 'Bank' in Chalk sequence at Springview Quarry (TL 007010), Flaunden.

or glauconitized, suggesting that they do not represent the Top Rock. Just below the upper hardground, there is a distinctive purplish nodular flint, and immediately below this specimens of the regular echinoid *Tylocidaris clavigera* have been found. Through binoculars, the highest (inaccessible) part of the section seems to contain marl seams, and may correlate with beds across the boundary between the *Micraster cortestudinarium* and *Micraster coranguinum* Zones.

Of particular note within the western quarry face are well developed anastomosing sheet, tabular and nodular flints, which follow a low amplitude bank structure (mound with channels on either side) within the Chalk (Plate 7), the layers of chalk between the flints expanding on either side of the bank. The precise nature and origin of this bedform are disputed (Mortimore, *in press*). It is unique in England north of the south coast (R. N. Mortimore, *pers. comm.*), but similar to larger features exposed along the north French coast at Etretat (Kennedy and Juignet, 1974; Quine and Bosence, 1991), which are also developed in Lower Coniacian chalk. Late-stage high-angle shearing occurs in one of the tabular flints about 4.5 m above the quarry floor. The highest

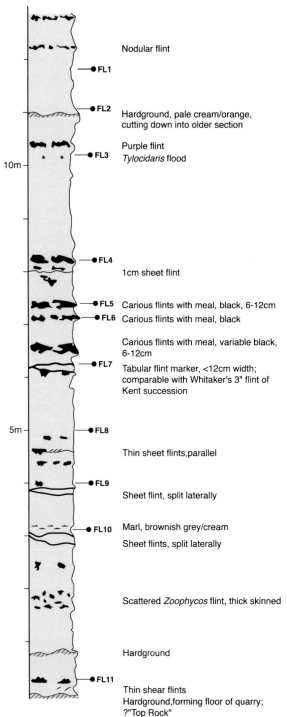

Nodular flint

●FL1

●FL2 Hardground, pale cream/orange, cutting down into older section

Purple flint
●FL3 *Tylocidaris* flood

10m

●FL4
1cm sheet flint

●FL5 Carious flints with meal, black, 6-12cm
●FL6 Carious flints with meal, black

Carious flints with meal, variable black, 6-12cm
●FL7 Tabular flint marker, <12cm width; comparable with Whitaker's 3" flint of Kent succession

5m ●FL8

Thin sheet flints, parallel

●FL9

Sheet flint, split laterally

●FL10 Marl, brownish grey/cream
Sheet flints, split laterally

Scattered *Zoophycos* flint, thick skinned

Hardground

●FL11
Thin shear flints
Hardground, forming floor of quarry; ?"Top Rock"

Sample Key

●─ FL1 - FL11 Samples collected by Bailey & Wood, 2002

Figure 3.10. Lithological section of Chalk exposed at Springview Quarry (TL 007010), Flaunden. Now partly backfilled, this section shows the most expanded post-Top Rock sequence in the county. The uppermost hardground at 11 m cuts across underlying beds.

of the three hardground surfaces cuts down obliquely across the quarry face from north to south, progressively removing older parts of the section.

Because of the bank structure, this secluded site is of considerable geological importance in Hertfordshire. It is

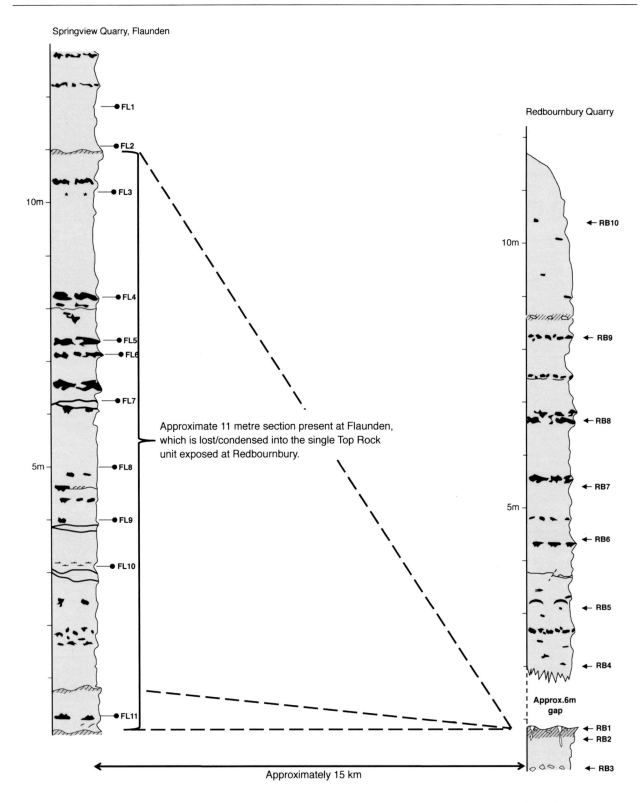

Figure 3.11. Lithological correlation of the Lewes Nodular Chalk successions at Flaunden (TL 007010) and Redbournbury (TL 124105), illustrating the loss of section overlying the Top Rock at Flaunden, which becomes part of the Top Rock complex at Redbournbury

also regionally important as it provides one of the thickest exposures of the highest Lewes Nodular Chalk Formation; comparable sections elsewhere in Hertfordshire (e.g. Redbournbury Quarry) show condensation or partial loss of the succession above the Top Rock. The two visible hardground surfaces and the third that almost certainly forms the quarry floor probably amalgamate to the east and

are represented by the single hardground found in the floor of Redbournbury Quarry. i.e. more than 11 m of section at Flaunden are condensed to a single hardground bed 1.5 m thick at Redbournbury (Fig. 3.11).

Chalk samples collected from the site in 2002 for analysis of calcareous nannoplankton indicated the extinction points within the section of *Quadrum intermedium*,

Q. eptapetalus, *Helicolithus turonicus* and *Retecapsa ficula*, and the inception points of *Broinsonia parca expansa*, *Micula staurophora* and *Lithastrinus grillii* (Liam Gallagher, *pers. comm.*). These species indicate that the important boundary between Nannoplankton Zones UC9 and UC10 of Burnett (1998) occurs close to the upper hardground. This allows correlation with sites at similar stratigraphic levels throughout Europe.

Samples of 'flint meal' (the siliceous powder containing foraminifera and other microfossils that is often found in cavities within flint nodules) were studied by Curry (1982) from Flaunden and 18 other sites in southern England. This work, reviewed by Bailey and Clayton (*in press*), is being continued by the analysis of foraminifera from the chalk samples collected from Flaunden in 2002.

Hill End Farm Pit (= Hitch Wood Pit) (TL 197239). This site is of national stratigraphic and palaeontological importance, but has become very degraded in recent years and has lost its SSSI status. It is the type locality of the Hitch Wood Hardground at the top of the Chalk Rock. The pebble bed associated with the hardground is unusually fossiliferous, and has yielded more fossils of all groups, including ammonites, bivalves and gastropods, than any other Chalk Rock locality in the county (Bromley and Gale, 1982; Gale, 1996). The currently poorly exposed section of the Lewes Nodular Chalk Formation spans the *Sternotaxis plana* Zone and the lower part of the *Micraster cortestudinarium* Zone. It extends from the Chalk Rock, which is 0.7 m thick excluding the overlying pebble bed, to 1.6 m above the Top Rock (Hopson *et al.*, 1996, p. 58). Beds beneath the Chalk Rock are covered by talus and need to be re-exposed by trenching, but they are known to include the Reed (Caburn) Marl and probably the Southerham Marl (J. C. Doyle, *pers. comm.*).

The fossiliferous pebble bed of the Hitch Wood Hardground provides the type locality of the siliceous sponge *Hillendia*, which is part of a rich sponge fauna described by Reid (1962). The occurrence of very well preserved ammonites was first recorded by Billinghurst (1927), a schoolmaster at Hitchin Grammar School, who described as new species *Prionocyclus* (now *Subprionocyclus*) *hitchinensis* and *Prionotropis cristatus* (now *Subprionocyclus branneri*). These figured specimens and many others from Hill End Farm Pit are housed in the Natural History Museum, London, and Billinghurst's plate of these ammonites was reproduced by Bloom (1934). In total, the site has yielded 22 of the 24 different species of ammonite described nationally from the Chalk Rock, including the holotype and paratypes of *Allocrioceras strangulatum*, the holotype of *Anisoceras reidi* (now *Allocrioceras schlueteri*), the holotype of *Lewesiceras woodi*, a paratype of *Otoscaphites reidi* (now *Yezoites bladenensis*), paratypes of *Scaphites diana*, the holotype of *Scaphites kieslingswaldensis doylei* and figured specimens of *Pseudojacobites farmeryi* and *Tongoboryoceras rhodanicum* (Wright, 1979; Kaplan *et al.*, 1987; Kaplan, 1989). The fauna also includes the heteromorph (uncoiled) ammonite *Hyphantoceras reussianum* (Wright and

Kennedy, 1987, Plate 36, Fig. 1 and Plate 37, Fig. 5), whose specific name is often used internationally for the whole ammonite fauna of the Chalk Rock (i.e. the *reussianum* fauna). Hopson *et al.* (1996, p. 58) recorded non-mineralized specimens of *Micraster cortestudinarium* from immediately above the Top Rock hardground. This morphotype is typical of those noted elsewhere from high in the *M. cortestudinarium* Zone, implying considerable condensation of section at the hardground surface.

Hitchin Railway Cutting (TL 196295). This was formerly a SSSI and is now designated a RIGS (Hertfordshire RIGS Group, 2003). It was first described in detail by Hill and Jukes-Browne (1886) and subsequently redescribed by Jukes-Browne and Hill (1903). Fossils from this location described in these and subsequent publications have been a valuable resource in understanding the Chalk sequence in southern England. In 1993, the section in the cutting on the south-western side of the railway was remeasured by CJW on behalf of BGS, and the description is included in Hopson *et al.* (1996, Fig. 15). The locality includes chalk faces on either side of the railway tracks and also a former quarry from which railway tracks previously connected with the main line, but this is now the site of a small industrial estate.

The site was again examined and measured by CJW and HWB in 2006 as part of a site investigation prior to the possible construction of a pedestrian ramp across the chalk face. This provided details similar to Section 2 of Hopson *et al.* (1996) and is presented here as Figure 3.12. A second stratigraphically higher section was also measured approximately 38 m southeast of Section 2; this is believed to equate with Section 1 in Hopson *et al.* (1996).

The chalk exposed is part of the White Chalk Subgroup (traditional Middle Chalk), principally within the New Pit Chalk Formation, though the highest c. 1 m of the Holywell Nodular Chalk Formation is exposed at the base of Section 2. Together Sections 1 and 2 indicate the presence of approximately 5.6 m of white chalk with occasional patchy iron-staining and an iron-stained marl seam 2.45 m below the top of the section. This succession overlies a grey anastomosing marl seam, the Odsey Marl of Hopson *et al.* (1996), which marks the boundary between the coarse shell-detrital chalk of the Holywell Nodular Chalk Formation and the overlying smooth powdery white chalk of the New Pit Chalk Formation. Approximately 1 m of shell-detrital chalk with minor wavy grey marl flasers and small nodular finger-shaped flints is visible in Section 2 below the Odsey Marl down to the top of the talus slope.

The recognition of the Odsey Marl at Hitchin permits correlation with other Chalk exposures of similar age to the northeast at the Steeple Morden Plantation and Station Quarries near Ashwell. Comparison with these active quarry sections suggests that soft shell-detrital chalk below the talus slope at Hitchin Station should change to a unit of strongly indurated shell-detrital chalk approximately 6 m below the Odsey Marl. This hard bed, the Morden Rock, varies in thickness (1.0-1.5 m at Steeple Morden), and a further 1 m below it is a thin marl seam, which in turn lies less than 1 m above the Melbourn Rock. In the Walsworth Road

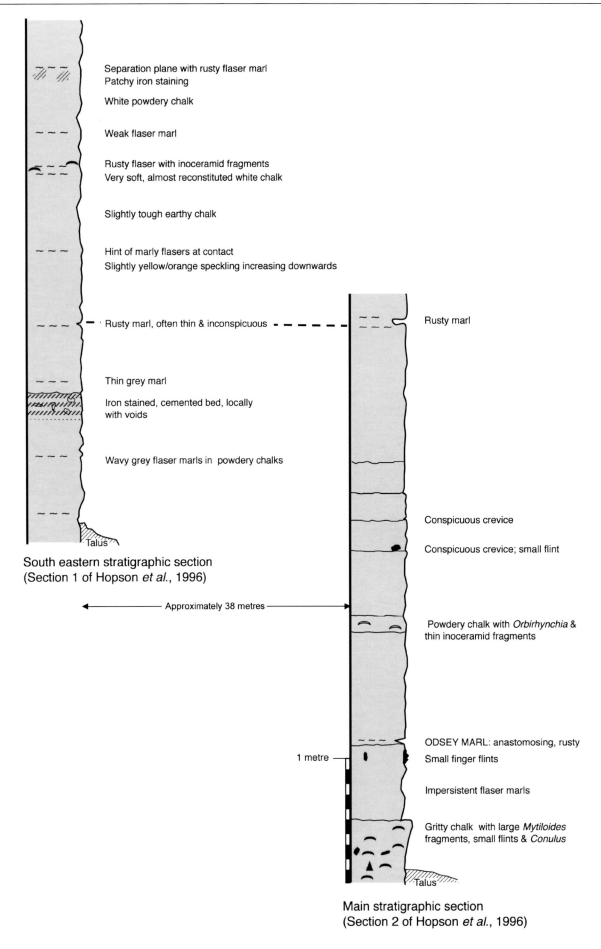

Separation plane with rusty flaser marl
Patchy iron staining

White powdery chalk

Weak flaser marl

Rusty flaser with inoceramid fragments
Very soft, almost reconstituted white chalk

Slightly tough earthy chalk

Hint of marly flasers at contact
Slightly yellow/orange speckling increasing downwards

Rusty marl, often thin & inconspicuous

Rusty marl

Thin grey marl

Iron stained, cemented bed, locally
with voids

Wavy grey flaser marls in powdery chalks

Conspicuous crevice

Conspicuous crevice; small flint

South eastern stratigraphic section
(Section 1 of Hopson *et al.*, 1996)

◄———— Approximately 38 metres ————►

Powdery chalk with *Orbirhynchia* &
thin inoceramid fragments

ODSEY MARL: anastomosing, rusty

1 metre

Small finger flints

Impersistent flaser marls

Gritty chalk with large *Mytiloides*
fragments, small flints & *Conulus*

Talus

Main stratigraphic section
(Section 2 of Hopson *et al.*, 1996)

Figure 3.12. Lithological sections of New Pit Chalk Formation measured at Hitchin Railway Cutting (TL 196295), 2006.

section (Hopson *et al.*, 1996, Fig. 13) near Hitchin Station, the Melbourn Rock comprises approximately 3 m of hard, off-white non-shelly chalk with rare very thin marl seams; its top is often poorly defined and the lowest 0.5 m unit is a very hard, partly nodular, splintery limestone, which would be difficult to remove if the excavation for the pedestrian ramp reaches this level. Also water may be encountered within the Melbourn Rock. The total thickness from the Odsey Marl to the top of the Plenus Marls Member immediately beneath the Melbourn Rock would be 16-17.5 m.

The original section at Hitchin Station was one of three type sections for the Melbourn Rock described by Hill and Jukes-Browne (1886), the others being at Ashwell and Melbourn itself. As both the Melbourn and Hitchin Station sections are no longer available, the Ashwell Section now becomes the stratotype. Four photomicrographs of thin sections of the Melbourn Rock illustrated by Jukes-Browne and Hill (1903, Vol. II, Plate VI, Fig. 2; Plate VII, Figs. 1 and 2; and Plate VIII, Fig. 1) are almost certainly from the Hitchin Railway Cutting or the adjacent quarry.

Over the last 120 years, many important fossils have been found in the Hitchin Railway Cutting. Two collections made by Jukes-Browne are stored at BGS Keyworth, Nottinghamshire. The specimens from Hitchin Station include the bivalve *Pycnodonte vesiculare* and the echinoid *Conulus subrotundus* (Registration Nos Ze 1485-1486 and 1538-1539). From 'Hitchin' (no other locality details given) the collection includes 19 specimens of the brachiopod *Orbirhynchia*, including *O. cuvieri* and a coarsely ribbed *Orbirhynchia* sp. (Nos Ze 1506-1524). These brachiopods almost certainly came from the Holywell Nodular Chalk Formation, probably from the very fossiliferous Morden Rock.

In addition to the BGS collections, Hitchin (probably the railway cutting) is the source of the specimen of the bivalve *Inoceramus lamarcki* var. *apicalis*, which is housed in the Sedgwick Museum, Cambridge. Woods illustrated this specimen (1912, Plate 53, Figs 4a & 4b), which was subsequently designated the lectotype of *Inoceramus apicalis*. Two specimens of the terebratulid brachiopod *Concinnithyris bulla* figured by Sahni (1929, Plate 1, Figs. 21-23 & 24-26), which are currently held by the Natural History Museum in London, are known to have originated at Hitchin, probably either from the railway cutting or the adjacent quarry. They probably came from the Holywell Nodular Chalk Formation. Finally, it is notable that the only published record of radiolaria from the English Chalk is that made by Hill and Jukes-Browne (1886) from Hitchin Railway Cutting. As such, it is a unique site, because these microfossils have not subsequently been recognized in any other *in situ* chalk sections despite extensive research.

Little Hadham Crossroads Pit (TL 440229). Two small sections are exposed in the old chalk pit north of the crossroads. The smaller face shows a 2 m section of firm white chalk with two small nodular flint bands 1 m apart. The main (upper) section in the western face of the pit is just less than 3.5 m high, and shows soft, blocky white chalk with scattered black nodular flints. A major nodular flint band

occurs at the base of the section and another about 1.25 m higher. A third occurs just below the top of the section, with a very large nodule approximately 70 cm across at the top of the face. The site was becoming very overgrown and difficult to access when visited in 2007.

Pitstone Quarry #2 (SP 949149). This Melbourn Rock section (Fig. 3.4) is important, as it provides a location in the Chiltern region that assists correlation between the Melbourn Rock succession in southeast England and that to the northeast in Cambridgeshire. Above the basal hard non-nodular limestone, there are four irregularly lumpy chalk beds or 'brash', each approximately 30 cm thick, the top one of which has a pebble bed developed on its upper glauconitic burrowed surface. Specimens of the heteromorph ammonite *Sciponoceras* have been recovered from these nodular chalks, which are separated from each other by wispy marl seams.

Above this, the section is disrupted, probably by a minor fault, then a further 4 m of marly chalk are exposed. At the base of this upper section, specimens of *Orbirhynchia* are recorded. At the top of the accessible section, the *Filograna evita* event has been identified. This is a level at which serpulid-covered bivalves have been recorded in many sections across the Anglo-Paris Basin. As Pitstone is the northernmost site where it has been seen, it provides a useful link for correlation of the Transitional and Southern Chalk Provinces.

Potters Crouch (TL 116046). Although it is small and overgrown, this pit is listed as deserving preservation (Hertfordshire RIGS Group, 2003), because paramoudra and marl seams have been recorded there. It is thought to expose the lower part of the Seaford Chalk Formation (Middle Coniacian, *Micraster coranguinum* Zone).

Redbournbury Quarry (TL 124105). This disused pit, now occupied by an active waste chemical treatment plant, has RIGS status (Hertfordshire RIGS Group, 2003). The exposed section extends from a level just above the Top Rock to almost the top of the Lewes Nodular Chalk Formation (Fig. 3.13). The Top Rock and approximately 1 m of the underlying, relatively soft nodular chalk (*Sternotaxis plana* Zone) are visible in a trench cut into the floor of the quarry. Above the Top Rock there is an estimated 5 m gap in the section, which is covered by talus from the higher quarry level. Above the gap the exposed beds contain the trace fossil *Zoophycos*, and have been assigned to the Beachy Head *Zoophycos* horizon in the higher part of the *Micraster cortestudinarium* Zone. Partially silicified echinoids and inoceramid bivalves were recorded from this part of the section by Brown *et al.* (1969).

The Top Rock contains phosphatized inoceramid bivalves typical of both the basal Coniacian *Cremnoceramus deformis* Zone and the overlying *Cremnoceramus waltersdorfensis hannovrensis* Zone, demonstrating that the hardground represents a condensed sequence. Specimens of *Cremnoceramus crassus crassus* (formerly *C. schloenbachi*) and *Tethyoceramus* sp., indicating

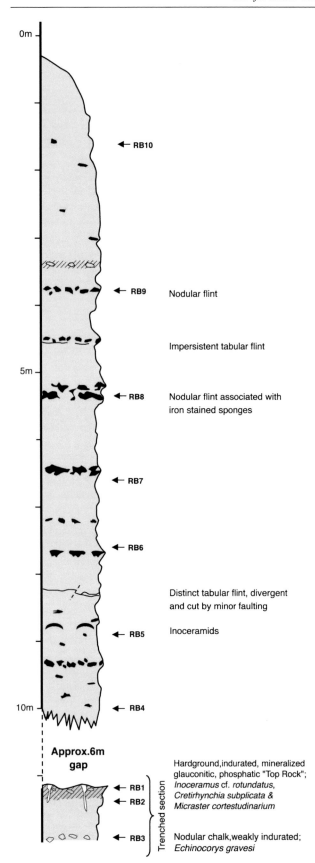

0m

← RB10

← RB9   Nodular flint

Impersistent tabular flint

5m

← RB8   Nodular flint associated with iron stained sponges

← RB7

← RB6

Distinct tabular flint, divergent and cut by minor faulting

← RB5   Inoceramids

10m

← RB4

Approx.6m gap

← RB1
← RB2

Hardground,indurated, mineralized glauconitic, phosphatic "Top Rock"; *Inoceramus* cf. *rotundatus*, *Cretirhynchia subplicata* & *Micraster cortestudinarium*

← RB3   Nodular chalk,weakly indurated; *Echinocorys gravesi*

Trenched section

Figure 3.13. Lithological section of Lewes Nodular Chalk Formation exposed at Redbournbury (TL 124105).

the succeeding *Cremnoceramus crassus crassus* – *Cremnoceramus deformis deformis* Zone (also Early Coniacian), have been found in the white chalk with flints just above.

Foraminifera from the Redbournbury section include a single specimen of the important benthic marker *Stensioeina granulata levis*, which was found in soft chalk within a burrow penetrating the Top Rock hardground (Bailey *et al.*, 1984). This subspecies, typical of the Lower Coniacian (probably *Micraster cortestudinarium* Zone), is the oldest representative of the *Stensioeina* genus yet found in England. By contrast, in other parts of northern Europe *Stensioeina* is known from sediments as old as Late Cenomanian (Koch, 1977).

Reed Pit (TL 359370). This disused chalk pit is a Hertfordshire and Middlesex Wildlife Trust Nature Reserve and has RIGS status, but has lost its original SSSI status. The section exposes 4+ m of the upper part of the Lewes Nodular Chalk Formation, and has a dip of 21° to the north (Jukes-Browne and Hill, 1904, Fig. 57), because the quarry has been cut into a glaciotectonic thrust slice (Plate 8). The slice includes Chalk Rock, which in the past has yielded numerous ammonites, brachiopods, echinoids and sponges. The pit also provides the type section for the Reed Marl, which is now known to be a lateral equivalent of the volcanic Caburn Marl in Sussex (Mortimore, 1986), and has also been exposed at Kensworth Quarry (Mortimore *et al.*, 2001), Royston School Pit (Hopson *et al.*, 1996, Fig. 16) and in the Baldock by-pass section. However, the Reed Marl is now covered by talus below the quarry face. The Chalk Rock comprises approximately 2.5 m of hard, partly mineralized chalk containing five separate hardground surfaces (Bromley and Gale, 1982; Hopson *et al.*, 1996, Fig. 17). Close to its base is a nodular flint band, and the Reed Marl is estimated to be 1.6 m below this.

Near the top of the section there are two further nodular flint bands and beneath them a sheet flint, recorded as the Reed Tabular Flint by Hopson *et al.* (1996, Plate 6). This is approximately 1.5 m above the omission surface at the top of the Top Rock. The sequence from the top of the Chalk Rock to nodular chalk overlying the Top Rock was defined by Hopson *et al.* (1996) as the Kensworth Nodular Chalk Member, named after Kensworth Quarry, Bedfordshire. Specimens of the echinoid *Micraster corbovis* from the nodular chalk above the Top Rock show the form typical of late stages in the development of this species (Plate 4). Specimens of an earlier form, typical of the *Terebratulina lata* Zone, were collected by CJW from chalk between the Chalk Rock and the Reed Marl and are now in the BGS collections.

Although Reed lacks the duplication of the Chalk Rock section seen at Newsells Bury Pit Barkway, it is nevertheless important in illustrating the range of glaciotectonic effects in this area. Its conservation is therefore important.

Royston by-pass (TL 373410). The sequence in this roadside cutting was illustrated by Hopson *et al.* (1996, Fig. 16) based on measurements made earlier by Mortimore and Wood

Plate 8. Glaciotectonic thrust slice of Lewes Nodular Chalk Formation at Reed (TL 359370).

(1986). In total approximately 26 m is exposed, including 16 m of marly chalk typical of the New Pit Chalk Formation, above which there are 10 m of blocky chalk with rare nodular flints and shell debris. Within the blocky chalk are three marl seams, which Hopson *et al.* (1996) tentatively correlated with the Glynde Marl complex in Sussex.

The recent detailed logging of the Baldock by-pass section, and confirmation of the New Pit Chalk Formation at that site (Wyton *et al.*, 2007), suggest that correlation with the Glynde Marls is correct. The top marl at Royston is similar in thickness and its relationships with other lithological markers to the marl identified as Glynde Marl 4, 35.5 m below the top of the Baldock by-pass section. In both by-pass sections there is a flint just below this marl and a further wispy marl below that. Also, distinctive 'finger flints' were identified by Mortimore and Wood (1986) 7 m above the top marl at Royston, and at Baldock the similar 'Southerham Finger and Tube Flints' are again 7 m above the top Glynde Marl. The two lower marls at Royston are 1 m apart, and are thought to correspond with the two marls (Glynde Marls 1 and 2) at 40.5 m and 41.5 m below the top of the Baldock section (Fig. 3.6). Three further marl seams occur at the base of the Royston section. They are similar distances apart to the three New Pit Marls lying between 46 m and

52.5 m below the top of the section at Baldock, thus further supporting the correlation between the two sections.

Royston School Pit (TL 364405). This small overgrown quarry exposes approximately 12 m of chalk, including what Hopson *et al.* (1996, p. 51, Fig. 16) regarded as the best exposure of the Reed Marl in Hertfordshire. As this bed is no longer exposed at Reed, Royston School Pit was designated its type locality by Bromley and Gale (1982). In contrast, the Chalk Rock is poorly developed. Hopson *et al.* (1996) suggested that the base of this unit is represented by a band of scattered black flints above a bed rich in *Inoceramus*. This flint band may be the same as that recorded at the base of the Chalk Rock at Reed, though in the 5 m + of chalk above it there are no hardgrounds, suggesting that this is an expanded section and that the Chalk Rock hardgrounds and nodular beds are located above the top of the exposed section.

Chadwell Springs Quarry (TL 352137). This disused and degraded pit close to the Ware Road on the eastern side of Hertford is thought to represent the uppermost part of the Lewes Nodular Chalk Formation within the *Micraster cortestudinarium* Zone. The Top Rock probably crops out at the foot of the slope leading down to the Chadwell Springs.

Chadwell Quarry (TL 351136). This small overgrown quarry, hidden behind two bungalows beside Ware Road, provides access to an extensive chalk mine system, the roof of which is formed by a very thick tabular *Thalassinoides* flint believed to be the Seven Sisters Flint (Plate 9) in the lower part of the Seaford Chalk Formation. This is supported by nannoplankton analyses indicating that the chalk below is of early Late Coniacian age. Approximately 1 m below the *Thalassinoides* flint is a thin (*c.* 2 cm) tabular flint, which can be followed in the walls of the mine for at least 250 m. Numerous large inoceramid bivalves occur at and just below the level of the Seven Sisters Flint. They include *Volviceramus* and *Platyceramus*, which are regionally characteristic of the Coniacian (*Micraster coranguinum* Zone) chalk below the Seven Sisters Flint elsewhere in southern England.

The Hertfordshire RIGS Group (2003) suggested that Chadwell Quarry is probably the Barrowfield Limekiln Quarry of Sherlock and Pocock (1924, p. 17), where they recognized the basal *Micraster coranguinum* Zone. But identification of the Seven Sisters Flint suggests a level slightly higher in the succession (uppermost Belle Tout Beds), though still within the Seaford Formation. CJW previously noted a section of typical shell-detrital and marl-rich Belle Tout Beds at the base of the quarry face on its eastern side.

Plate 9. The Seven Sisters Flint exposed in the roof of the chalk mine at Chadwell Quarry (TL 351136).

Lines Pit and Greens Pit (TL 346134). These disused quarries behind garages further east along Ware Road expose sections of chalk with nodular and thin tabular flint bands. These sections probably correspond to the Cuckmere Beds in the Upper Coniacian part of the Seaford Chalk Formation (*Micraster coranguinum* Zone), but they are inaccessible and have not been studied further.

3.6. Important Chalk exposures at nearby localities outside the county

Several important chalk quarries lying just outside the Hertfordshire county boundary deserve mention because of their relevance to successions within nearby parts of the county.

Steeple Morden Station Quarry (TL 301388). Like the nearby Plantation Quarry, both currently operated by Omya UK, this quarry is in westernmost Cambridgeshire. The Station Quarry currently exploits up to 11 m of Holywell Nodular Chalk Formation overlain in the south-eastern corner by up to 9 m of New Pit Chalk Formation (Fig. 3.14). The basal beds of the Holywell Nodular Chalk, comprising the Plenus Marls Member (*c.* 1 m thick) and the overlying Melbourn Rock (*c.* 3 m thick) have been proved in a trench in the northeast corner of the quarry, adjacent to the current working face. The Plenus Marls Member is composed of alternations of relatively soft marls and marly chalks, which are dark coloured because of a high clay content and have a greenish tinge due to the presence of glauconite or chlorite. In the middle is a bed of very indurated chalk comparable in hardness to the basal beds of the overlying Melbourn Rock. The Plenus Marls are underlain by soft, relatively carbonate-rich off-white chalks, traditionally called the 'White Bed', which forms a local aquifer.

The Melbourn Rock consists of impure indurated chalk with many irregular anastomosing green-stained clay-rich surfaces, which are especially well developed in the lower part. The basal 0.5 m is an unusually hard yellowish splintery limestone. Above this is massively bedded chalk followed by a thin (<5 cm) bed of brownish coarse grained rather sandy chalk (the 'Arenite Bed'), which grades up into flaggy chalk (the 'Flaggy Bed'). Further details of this sequence are given by Hopson *et al.* (1996, Fig. 14). In contrast to the remainder of the Holywell Nodular Chalk Formation, much of the Melbourn Rock, particularly the yellowish basal bed, is not conspicuously shell-detrital.

Above the Melbourn Rock, the Holywell Nodular Chalk Formation comprises tough, gritty textured chalk usually with a moderate content of inoceramid shell detritus. Shell fragments first appear immediately above the Melbourn Rock and increase upwards over 4-5 m to a variably developed unit of very hard, cemented, richly shell-detrital chalk known as the Morden Rock. This is 1.5 m thick and, because of its hardness, protrudes slightly from old eroded faces. Its position in fresh quarried faces can be identified from a conspicuous dark marl bed several cm thick, which lies between it and the Melbourn Rock. The remainder of the Holywell Nodular Chalk Formation above the Morden Rock consists of alternations of more and less shell-rich chalks with several thin variably developed marl seams.

The top of the Holywell Nodular Chalk Formation is marked by the lower and thinner of two marl seams, which are 15-30 cm apart. The upper seam (generally <1 cm thick) is the Odsey Marl. Most of the shell detritus terminates upwards at the lower marl seam, although there is a little immediately above it. The chalk between the two marls

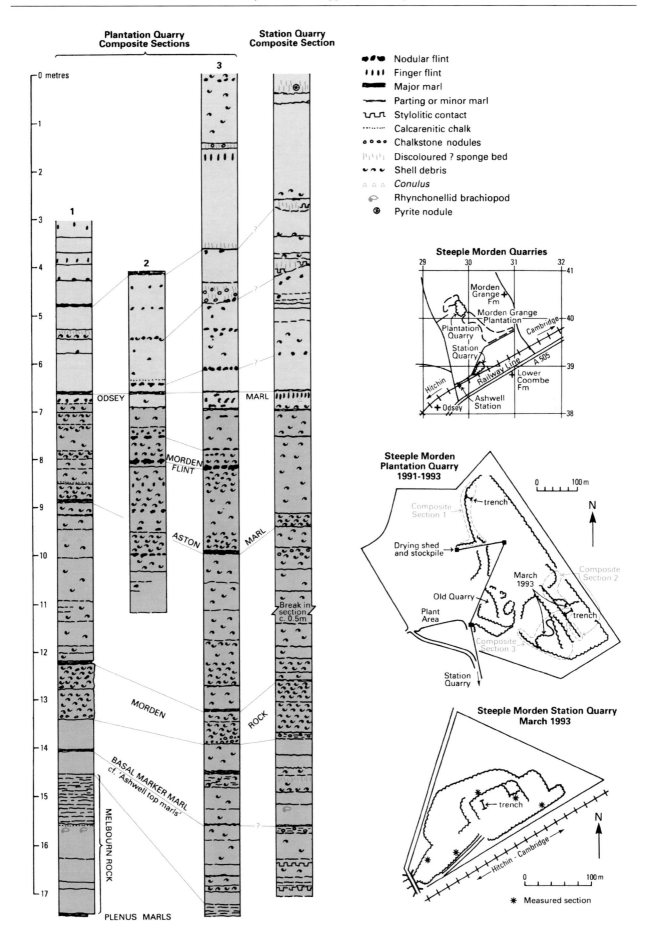

Figure 3.14. Correlation of Chalk beds above the Melbourn Rock seen in composite sections in Steeple Morden Quarries, Cambridgeshire (from Hopson et al., 1996).

forms the base of the New Pit Chalk Formation, and contains inconspicuous small, predominantly vertical, white-skinned 'finger flints' (the Glyndebourne Flints), which are burrowfill replacements. In many of the older parts of Station Quarry, these are the only flints in the Holywell Nodular Chalk. However, at either end of the current working face, there is a weak development of shell-rich black nodular flints less than 1 m beneath the marl seam that marks the top of the Holywell Nodular Chalk. This development of nodular flint suggests some thickening of the succession close to the working face and the existence of a synclinal structure similar to that seen in the Plantation Quarry (see below). A dip of *c.* 1° SE is typical of the working face of Station Quarry, but away from the centre of this face towards the southeast corner of the quarry there are anomalous dips of up to 5°.

The basal 9 m of the New Pit Chalk Formation in Station Quarry consists of white chalk which, in contrast to the underlying hard shell-detrital chalk of the Holywell Nodular Chalk Formation, is soft and smooth to touch. Although generally white, the succession includes several impersistent horizons of yellow iron-stained (limonitic) chalk containing fossil sponges. There are also some marl seams less than 1 cm thick and several marly surfaces. The succession is generally devoid of flint, apart from the Glyndebourne Flints, a conspicuous band of black nodular flints *c.* 1 m above the Odsey Marl and a few small scattered flints which do not form distinct beds.

Steeple Morden Plantation Quarry (TL 298402). This quarry exposes a weak anticline and syncline, which plunge south-eastwards. Within the syncline at the southern end of the quarry, the highest part of the Holywell Nodular Chalk contains several bands of nodular flint, the most conspicuous and laterally persistent of which is the Morden Flint. This is readily identifiable from the abundance of fragments and more or less complete shells of inoceramid bivalves on its upper and lower surfaces. The lower limit of flints in this succession is marked by a thin marl seam that is tentatively correlated with the Aston Marl at Chiltern sites to the southwest outside Hertfordshire. There is an overall thinning of the succession onto the anticline and all of the flints progressively disappear north-westwards within a short distance until, in the section adjacent to the conveyor belt, only the Glyndebourne Flints remain. There is also a progressive loss of flint north-eastwards towards the eastern side of the quarry.

The absence of flint other than the Glyndebourne Flints and rare subspherical flints some distance below in parts of Station Quarry near the entrance (now quarried away), and the reappearance of flint in the present working face of this quarry may be related to further weak fold structures. The shelly nature of the subspherical flints below the Glyndebourne Flints suggest they equate with the Morden Flint.

Totternhoe Stone Quarries (SP 9822). This famous group of quarries lying just beyond the northern margin of the county in southern Bedfordshire is the type section of the Cenomanian Totternhoe Stone. It has recently been purchased as a nature reserve, partly because of its geological importance, so access and visible outcrop are likely to improve in the near future. Detailed descriptions of the various quarry sections in the area were given by Shephard-Thorn *et al.* (1994, p. 70-74). Roberts (1974) and Curran (2005) have described the history of stone excavation and its use as a building stone in Hertfordshire and adjacent counties (Section 10.3).

Totternhoe Stone is developed in two distinct lithofacies. The first, referred to as the shelf facies, was described by Mortimore *et al.* (2001, p. 340) as 'a thin (less than 1 metre thick) highly fossiliferous bed, with numerous *Orbirhynchia mantelliana* and small phosphatic intraclasts scattered throughout'. This facies was recorded in the flooded section of Pitstone Quarry #2. It has also been recorded at Totternhoe, but here the second lithofacies, the channel facies, is developed to a thickness of 4.7 m only 200 m away. The channel facies comprises a succession of weakly glauconitic calcarenites and calcisiltites (sandy and silty limestones, respectively), again with phosphatic intraclasts and fossil debris. It is intensely bioturbated, principally by *Planolites* and *Chondrites*, but also with *Thalassinoides* burrow systems present at the top.

The Channel Facies at Totternhoe has an erosional base cutting down into the underlying Chalk Marl (West Melbury Marly Chalk Formation). From foraminiferal evidence (Carter and Hart, 1977), it is of lowest Middle Cenomanian age (*Acanthoceras rhotomagense* ammonite Zone). However, at some localities the channels cut below the Lower Cenomanian Doolittle Limestone within the *Mantelliceras mantelli* ammonite Zone (Shephard-Thorn *et al.*, 1994, Fig. 26). This is true at Totternhoe itself where, in the present Stone Pit (SP 988222), the underlying beds are dark grey marlstones containing *Inoceramus crippsi* and the thin-shelled bivalve *Aucellina*, indicating that the erosion may have cut down to even the lowest (*Neostlingoceras carcitanense*) subzone of the Cenomanian succession.

The Totternhoe Stone is a lateral equivalent of the 'Cast Bed' in the Chalk succession of the Folkestone-Dover area in Kent. This is a stratigraphic level associated with a fall in sea level, the Mid-Cenomanian break of Carter and Hart (1977). However, a regional or even global shallowing event does not alone account for the sudden increase in thickness of the channel facies at Totternhoe. This may reflect a deeper underlying structural control on sedimentation. Although there is no direct evidence for this, Shephard-Thorn *et al.* (1994, Fig. 30 and p. 84) suggest a weak NE-SW anticline associated with a gravity anomaly through the Totternhoe area, which could have affected local chalk sedimentation.

Kensworth Quarry (TL 015197). This lies just 4.5 km southeast of Totternhoe, again just north of the Hertfordshire-Bedfordshire boundary. At present it is the largest active chalk quarry in Britain. Chalk quarried here is reduced to slurry on site and the slurry is pumped by pipeline to the cement works at Rugby. The quarry exposes a unique, if condensed, section encompassing the boundary between the Turonian (traditional Middle Chalk) and the

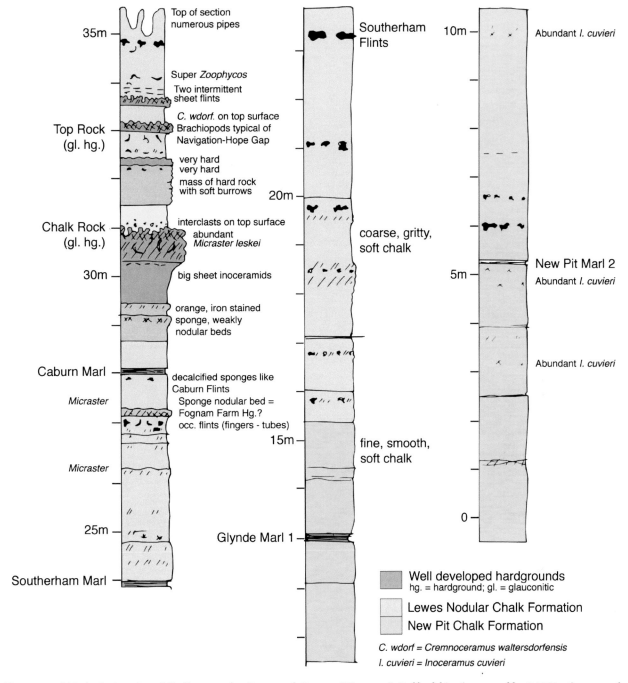

Figure 3.15. Lithological section of Chalk exposed at Kensworth Quarry (TL 015197), Bedfordshire (measured by R.N.Mortimore, and reproduced with his permission).

Coniacian (traditional Upper Chalk) Stages (Fig. 3.15). It is the stratotype section for the Kensworth Nodular Chalk Member (Hopson *et al.*, 1996), which is used by BGS for mapping purposes. The Kensworth section was fully described by Mortimore *et al.* (2001, pp. 342-347) and discussed in detail with photographs by Shephard-Thorn *et al.* (1994, pp. 74-78). Mortimore *et al.* (2001) stress the importance of the site, as it is the best section in southern England where the marl seams defined on the Sussex coast can be clearly related to the complex hardground sequence present in the Chiltern area. Locally, it can also be correlated with the sequences exposed at Redbournbury and the Baldock by-pass.

The basal part of the section consists of approximately 15 m of fine smooth soft chalk of the New Pit Chalk Formation, which is characterized by numerous marl seams. Two of these were recognized by Mortimore *et al.* (2001) as the detrital New Pit Marl 2 and the volcanic Glynde Marl 1. Three additional less well developed marl seams occur over approximately 2 m of section above Glynde Marl 1, and these are interpreted as Glynde Marls 2, 3 and 4. The highest of these is used to define the top of the New Pit Formation. From Glynde Marl 4 to the top of the exposed section, the chalk becomes more gritty, typical of the Lewes Nodular Chalk Formation. Bands of nodular flints occur throughout this unit, and two greenish marl seams important for regional correlation are recognized. About 8.5 m above Glynde Marl 4, a 10 cm marl seam contains many specimens of the distinctive large agglutinating foraminiferid *Labyrinthidoma southerhamensis*. This also occurs in Southerham Marl 1 in Sussex, and the same marl was exposed in the cutting for the tunnel section of the Baldock by-pass, where it was again equated with Southerham Marl 1. In both Sussex and Hertfordshire, this marl is underlain by chalks with characteristic finger and tubular flints (Mortimore *et al.*, 2001, Fig. 4.21). The second greenish marl seam, 5 cm thick, occurs just over 4 m above the Southerham Marl 1. This was defined as the Caburn Marl by Mortimore and Wood (1986), and is equated with the Reed Marl in north Hertfordshire. Mortimore *et al.* (2001, p. 346) gave details of the fossils found between the two marls.

Probably the most distinctive level at Kensworth is the Chalk Rock, which is clearly exposed about 2 m above the Reed Marl in the Nature Reserve section at the northern edge of the quarry (TL 011200) (Plate 10). At first sight, this prominent chalkstone appears to be a massive homogeneous nodular bed, but it is in fact a complex condensed unit probably comprising three or more hardgrounds (Bromley and Gale, 1982). It is intensely bioturbated by *Thalassinoides* burrow systems, which are often filled with softer chalk, though some are hollow, as illustrated by Bromley (1967a). It is at the base of the *Sternotaxis plana* Zone and is often very fossiliferous, yielding a rich *reussianum* fauna, similar to that from Hitch Wood, of shells preserved in aragonite. In addition to sponges and corals, the terminal pebble bed of the Chalk Rock here contains brachiopods (*Cretirhynhia cuneiformis* and *Gibbithyris subrotunda*), echinoids (*Sternotaxis plana* and *Micraster leskei*), inoceramid bivalves (*Inoceramus perplexus, Mytiloides costellatus* and *M. incertus*) and ammonites typical of the *Subprionocyclus neptuni* Zone. Ammonites were previously common in the area of the Nature Reserve section, where the Chalk Rock was unusually fossiliferous, and there are extensive collections made by J. C. Doyle at BGS Keyworth, including some figured material. By contrast, the Chalk Rock fauna in the main part of the present working face is poor. The ammonite association from the Chalk Rock at Kensworth was described in detail by Shephard-Thorn *et al.* (1994, p. 77), who compared the sequence with the expanded *Scaphiten-Schichten* in Germany (Kaplan, 1986), emphasizing the international importance of Kensworth.

Plate 10. Section in Chalk Rock exposed in the Nature Reserve at Kensworth Quarry (TL 015197), preserved by the Bedfordshire and Luton Geology Group.

The section from the top of the Chalk Rock to the top of the Top Rock comprises the Kensworth Nodular Chalk Member, which includes several glauconitized hardgrounds and poorly fossiliferous hard stone horizons. The Top Rock is the higher of two distinctive glauconitized hardgrounds exposed in many parts of the quarry and occurring at the top of the Nature Reserve section. The stratigraphically important (latest Turonian) inoceramid zonal index fossil *Cremnoceramus waltersdorfensis* has been recorded from Kensworth (Mortimore *et al.*, 2001, p. 347), confirming the site's importance in international correlation. Approximately 1 m above the Top Rock echinoids, particularly *Echinocorys gravesi*, are abundant.

Chapter 4.

The Palaeogene Period

John Catt and Jack Doyle

4.1. Introduction

The time elapsed since the end of the Cretaceous Period is termed the Caenozoic, Cenozoic or Cainozoic Era (Table 4.1). This is divided into two Sub-eras, the Tertiary (65.5-2.6 Ma) and the Quaternary (2.6 Ma-present), and the Tertiary is further divided into two Periods, the Palaeogene (65.5-23.0 Ma) and Neogene (23.0-2.6 Ma).

The Palaeogene is in turn divided into three Epochs, the Palaeocene (65.5-55.8 Ma), Eocene (55.8-33.9 Ma) and Oligocene (33.9-23.0 Ma). Apart from that of the Tertiary-Quaternary boundary (discussed in Section 5.1), the dates quoted approximate to those most recently agreed by the International Commission on Stratigraphy or ICS (Gradstein *et al.*, 2005), part of the International Union of Geological Sciences. In Hertfordshire the only deposits attributable to the Palaeogene Period are of late Palaeocene and early Eocene age. In Britain Oligocene sediments are present mainly in the Isle of Wight, but do not extend northwards to Hertfordshire.

Until recently there was no internationally recognized sequence of stages for the Caenozoic. Previously, many local names had been proposed in Europe (Adams, 1981), but detailed dating of deposits using various microfossil groups, including foraminifera, dinoflagellates, calcareous nannoplankton, pollen and spores (Curry, 1965; Curry *et al.*, 1978; Aubry, 1986; Jolley, 1992; Powell, 1992), and also by palaeomagnetic methods (Aubry *et al.*, 1986), has shown that there are many gaps and overlaps between stages recognized in different regions and many examples of stages incorrectly correlated from area to area. Some stage boundaries have now been redefined (Berggren *et al.*, 1995) and ratified internationally by ICS, but others are still under discussion. For the moment, it is therefore best to avoid the use of stage names, and instead describe the Palaeogene deposits of Hertfordshire in terms of the now fairly well-dated lithostratigraphic formations (Table 4.1).

The boundary between the Mesozoic and Caenozoic (base of the Palaeogene) is dated fairly precisely to 65.5 Ma at sites outside Britain, but the oldest Caenozoic (Palaeocene) deposits in southeast England are somewhat younger than this, about 58 Ma. As the youngest Chalk in the region dates from at least 80 Ma, there is a long time gap of more than 20 Ma at the base of the Palaeogene. This gap includes the important K/T boundary when many fossil groups including the dinosaurs, ammonites and belemnites became extinct worldwide.

The climate of the Palaeocene was probably almost as warm as that of the Late Cretaceous, with little or no evidence for polar ice caps. The Palaeocene-Eocene boundary is now defined by ICS at a very brief but even hotter interval designated the Palaeocene-Eocene Thermal Maximum or PETM, which is dated to approximately 55.8 Ma. The PETM probably resulted from a large release of 'greenhouse gases' into the atmosphere, either of methane

Sub-eras	Periods	Epochs	Formations
Tertiary (65.5-2.6 Ma)	Quaternary (2.58 Ma to present)	Holocene (11,700 BP to present)	See Chapter 6
		Pleistocene (2.58 Ma to 11,700 BP)	
	Neogene (23.0-2.6 Ma)	Pliocene (5.3-2.6 Ma)	Only local deposits in Hertfordshire (see Chapter 5)
		Miocene (23.0-5.3 Ma)	
	Palaeogene (65.5-23.0 Ma)	Oligocene (33.9-23.0 Ma)	None in Herts
		Eocene (55.8-33.9 Ma)	Bagshot
			London Clay (including Claygate Member) (54-51 Ma)
			Harwich 54.5-54 Ma
			Woolwich and Reading (55.8-55 Ma)
		Palaeocene (65.5-55.8 Ma)	Upnor (56-55.8 Ma
			Thanet Sand (58-57 Ma)

Table 4.1. Subdivision of the Caenozoic Era (dating based mainly on Gradstein et al.*, 2005) and main formations in Hertfordshire.*

(CH_4) from ocean floor (continental shelf) sediments (Schmitz *et al.*, 2000) that were disturbed by uplift in the north Atlantic region (MacLennan and Jones, 2006), or of carbon dioxide (CO_2) from wildfires that burned large areas of late Palaeocene vegetation (Collinson *et al.*, 2007). The extreme warmth over a period of only *c*. 30 ka led to a massive growth of the dinoflagellate *Apectodinium*, the extinction of many benthonic foraminifera and a major change in land mammal assemblages.

The thickest and most famous Palaeogene deposit in southeast England is the London Clay Formation. Together with the underlying Harwich Formation, previously known as the 'Basement-bed of the London Clay' (Prestwich, 1850), this constitutes the Thames Group (Ellison *et al.*, 1994), which is Early Eocene in age. Both the Harwich and London Clay Formations occur in Hertfordshire, mainly in southern and eastern parts of the county. Prestwich (1852) introduced the term 'Lower London Tertiaries' for the various thinner deposits lying between the Chalk and the London Clay Basement Bed. These are now thought to be Late Palaeocene and earliest Eocene in age, and have been divided into five formations (Ellison *et al.*, 1994): in ascending order, the Ormesby Clay, Thanet Sand, Upnor, Woolwich and Reading Formations. The last three of these form the Lambeth Group. Only three of these formations (the Thanet Sand, Upnor and Reading formations) occur in Hertfordshire. The Ormesby Clay is restricted to northern parts of East Anglia, and the Woolwich Formation is the lateral equivalent of the Reading Formation in areas east of the county. Pebbly sands overlying the London Clay comprise the Bagshot Formation, which is Early to Mid Eocene in age. It is absent from Hertfordshire, but forms small patches in north London, capping the high ground of Hampstead, Highgate and Harrow on the Hill.

This chapter deals with the Palaeogene formations present in Hertfordshire – their distribution (Fig. 4.1), lithology, mineralogy, fossils and environment of deposition. Chapter 5 describes the few possible Neogene deposits in the county, but is principally concerned with earth movements affecting the Mesozoic and Palaeogene formations, and with processes leading to development of the county's main landscape features.

4.2. Palaeogeographic and tectonic setting of Hertfordshire in the Palaeogene

After moving northwards to straddle the equator, the great southern continent of Pangea began to separate into two plates, now Africa and South America, towards the end of the Jurassic (about 150 Ma). Continued separation by seafloor spreading through the Cretaceous and Tertiary produced an ever widening south Atlantic Ocean, which extended northwards in the early Tertiary to form the north Atlantic. This had the effect of separating the great northern continent of Laurentia into two plates, North America to the west and Eurasia to the east. Later in the Tertiary Sub-Era, the northward movement of the African Plate towards Eurasia resulted in the Alpine Orogeny, with formation of the Alpine and Himalayan mountain chains on the southern margin of Eurasia.

Sea level was much higher in the Late Cretaceous than today and probably at any time since the Cambrian. In the Maastrichtian Stage of the Late Cretaceous it was more than 250 m higher than at present (Hardenbol *et al.*, 1998), and only 18 % of the earth's surface was land, compared with 28 % today. Subsequently, in the Palaeocene, sea level declined slightly worldwide and there was also uplift of much of northwest Europe on the western margin of the Eurasian Plate (Hancock, 1989). The uplift affecting Britain was probably not, as previously thought, an early effect of the Alpine Orogeny to the south, but is now attributed to doming over an anomalously hot, low-density mantle plume or 'hotspot' at depths of 50-200 km beneath what is now western Britain and the Irish Sea (Cope, 1994). From the recorded velocities of recent earthquake waves, Bott and Bott (2004) suggested that, beneath western Britain and an area projecting eastwards under the English Midlands, the temperature at about 100 km depth is still approximately 150°C above the normal for that depth (1250°C). Much of southern England was probably uplifted by as much as 350 m, but the effect in northern England was several times greater than this (Chadwick *et al.*, 1994). Because the doming was centred in the west, it resulted in eastward tilting of Britain.

The combined effects of Palaeocene uplift and falling sea level resulted in many new land areas, which included Hertfordshire and other parts of southeast England, but also extended to southwest England, northwest France, Wales and Scotland. The existence of these persistent land areas accounts for the long absence of marine sediments on either side of the K/T boundary in northwest Europe. When marine sedimentation did recommence in the late Palaeocene, the erosion of rocks older than the Chalk in areas such as Scotland and southwest England and the greatly decreased abundance of planktonic calcareous organisms resulted in essentially clastic sediments, which contrast strongly with the almost pure carbonate deposits of the Late Cretaceous.

The worldwide (eustatic) sea level changes probably resulted from changes in the shape and depth of ocean basins, especially the developing Atlantic and Indian Oceans. Seafloor spreading in the north Atlantic was especially rapid, so that this ocean had reached about 75 % of its present width by the end of the Palaeocene. The spreading probably resulted from another 'hotspot' centred beneath Iceland or southern Greenland, which also led to late Palaeocene and early Eocene igneous activity in western Scotland and repeated falls of volcanic ash in the North Sea area.

The crustal compression resulting from collision of the African and Eurasian Plates during the Caenozoic led mainly to formation of the Alps, though some important effects were also felt in southern England. For example, the London Platform subsided and major structures, such as the London Syncline and Wealden Anticline, were probably created in Mesozoic basinal sediments deformed over reactivated Variscan faults that cut deep into the crust (Blundell, 2002). Numerous smaller folds and minor faults also affected the Chalk and Caenozoic deposits (Section 5.7). Although

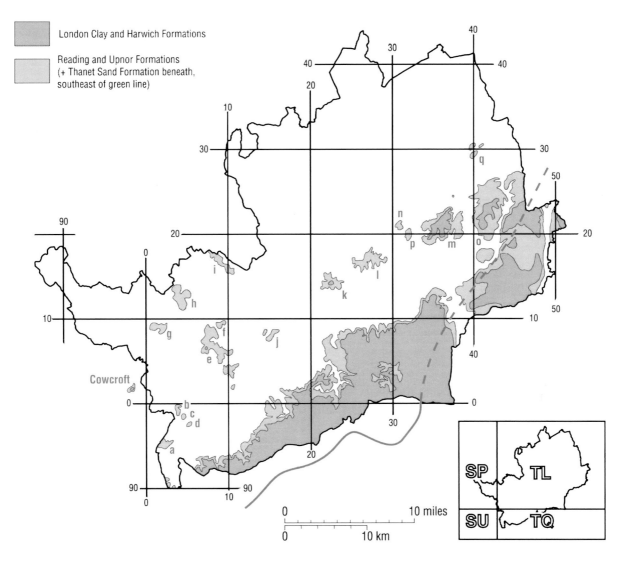

London Clay and Harwich Formations

Reading and Upnor Formations
(+ Thanet Sand Formation beneath,
southeast of green line)

Cowcroft

SP   TL

SU   TQ

0   10 miles

0   10 km

Figure 4.1. Outcrops of Palaeogene formations in Hertfordshire and location of outliers a-q listed in the text. Redrawn from British Geological Survey 1:50,000 sheets 221, 222, 238, 239, 240, 255 and 256.

this tectonic activity probably reached its maximum in the early Neogene (Miocene), it extended over a much longer period, commencing even as early as the Cretaceous and continuing to the present day. The occasional earthquakes recorded historically in parts of southern England, including Hertfordshire (Section 5.8), may provide evidence for some, albeit slight, tectonic activity even continuing today.

Throughout the Caenozoic, Britain was on the western margin of a slowly subsiding area (the proto-North Sea), which formed a southward projecting arm of the eastern North Atlantic. In the Palaeogene, the proto-North Sea covered much of the Netherlands, Denmark, north Germany and Poland, and periodically it extended even further south-eastwards. The history of the Palaeogene in southeast England is essentially one of repeated transgressions and regressions of this sea, which at times was confined to areas east of the present British coast (Vandenberghe *et al.*, 1998), but occasionally extended westwards as far as southwest England. According to Knox (1996), the transgression-regression cycles mainly resulted from continuing episodic uplift of the lithosphere across southern England, though

further minor eustatic changes of sea level cannot be completely ruled out. Recent work on late Palaeocene-early Eocene successions in the northern North Sea and other areas on the eastern flank of the north Atlantic (White and Lovell, 1997; Rudge *et al.*, 2008) has suggested that short periods of regional uplift lasting 2 Ma or less at this time resulted from transient phases of continuing convective flow over mantle plumes. As the proto-North Sea was often partially isolated from the Atlantic, its fossil faunas did not evolve in exactly the same ways, so that biostratigraphic correlations between the two are often uncertain.

4.3. The Ormesby Clay and Thanet Sand Formations

The Ormesby Clay Formation is the lowest part of the Palaeogene succession in northern parts of East Anglia (Knox *et al.*, 1990). It reaches a maximum thickness of 27.45 m in a borehole at Ormesby St Margaret, Norfolk, but thins southwards against a rising surface of Chalk in the Ipswich-Felixstowe area, Suffolk (Ellison *et al.*,

1994). Further south, its upper part passes laterally into the Thanet Sand Formation, which extends southwards from the Ipswich-Felixstowe High into north Kent and westwards into eastern Hertfordshire. Both formations rest unconformably on an erosion surface cut across the Chalk, the Sub-Palaeogene Surface, which represents the long time gap in deposition on either side of the K/T boundary. Both have a basal bed of largely unworn flint nodules set in a dark greyish-green, glauconite-rich sand or sandy clay matrix. The flint nodule bed at the base of the Thanet Sand Formation is up to 30 cm thick, and has long been known as the Bullhead Bed, probably because many of the flint nodules have projections (horns) and thus crudely resemble a bull's head. The similar nodule bed at the base of the Ormesby Clay Formation is probably diachronous (younger in Suffolk than Norfolk) because of the slow transgression of the sea onto the Ipswich-Felixstowe High and, for a similar reason, the Bullhead Bed may also be diachronous (younger in Hertfordshire than in areas further east).

The numerous boreholes that penetrate to the Chalk in the London area show that the Thanet Sand Formation thins westwards from about 30 m in Essex and north Kent to zero along a line extending north-eastwards from Harrow through Stanmore, Edgware and Barnet (Ellison *et al.*, 2004, Fig. 9) to Southgate and Forty Hill near Enfield (Bromehead, 1925). In east Hertfordshire, it is 5-9 m thick near Sawbridgeworth, but thins westwards to <1 m and disappears within a few kilometres of the Stort valley (Millward *et al.*, 1987, Fig. 4) (Fig.4.2). However, this may not have been the furthest west that the sea reached during deposition of the Thanet Sand Formation; it could have extended westwards to cover much of Hertfordshire, but any deposits it left there were probably thin and almost entirely removed by subsequent erosion before deposition of the Lambeth Group. Disturbed remnants of the Bullhead Bed and other basal parts of the Thanet Sand Formation may be preserved in pipes and solution hollows in the Chalk of the Chilterns. For example, from mineralogical evidence, Thorez *et al.* (1971) suggested that a very thin layer was preserved in this way at Castle Lime Works near South Mimms (TL 230025), more than 20 km west of the line along which the Thanet Sand Formation feathers out. Unfortunately, this quarry with its numerous spectacular pipes has since been infilled.

Above the Bullhead Bed, the Thanet Sand Formation consists mainly of grey fine-grained glauconitic sand or silty sand. Exposures in eastern Hertfordshire are rare because there is a thick cover of younger Palaeogene and Quaternary deposits. The borehole records for this area describe the formation as homogeneous grey and loose 'running' sand, though some vertical variation in particle size distribution was noted by Hildreth (1972) in boreholes drilled through 6-9 m of Thanet Sand Formation in the valley of Cobbin's Brook west of Epping in Essex. The homogeneity and lack of bedding probably result from bioturbation by marine animals burrowing in the sand during deposition.

On the basis of palaeomagnetic studies and nannoplankton assemblages (Siesser *et al.*, 1987) from various parts of southeast England, the Thanet Sand

Formation as a whole is thought to date from about 58 Ma to 57 Ma. Less precise estimates in the range 60-56 Ma are indicated by potassium-argon dating of glauconite from the Thanet Sand Formation in east Kent (Fitch *et al.*, 1978). Molluscs are the main macrofossils, but they are found mainly in north Kent (Cooper, 1934) and are often poorly preserved. They include the lamellibranchs *Arctica morrisi, Astarte tenera, Ostrea bellovacina, Cucullaea decussata, Nemocardium plumstedianum, N. semigranulatum, Corbula regulbiensis, Thracia oblata, Cyrtodaria rutupiensis, Pholadomya konincki* and *Eutylus cuneatus* and the much rarer gastropods *Sigatica abducta, Euspira bassae, Aporrhais sowerbyi* and *Siphonalia subnodosa*. Together with the foraminifera, these suggest deposition in a rather cool sea less than 50 m deep, though the finer sediments of the Ormesby Clay Formation probably accumulated in slightly deeper water offshore. The low water temperature and somewhat restricted fauna probably reflect a high latitude connection and limited water-mass exchange with the opening Atlantic and other oceans (King, 2006).

The heavy mineral assemblage of the Thanet Sand Formation is fairly diverse, containing epidote, garnet and amphiboles, possibly from a northerly source such as the Moine and Dalradian metamorphosed sediments in northern Scotland (Hallsworth, 1993), and also more resistant minerals, such as tourmaline, rutile, staurolite, kyanite, sphene and zircon, thought to indicate either a south-westerly source in southwest England or northwest France (Weir and Catt, 1969) or a south-easterly source in the Ardennes. Morton (1982) attributed an apparent decline in less resistant minerals in higher parts of the formation south of the Thames valley to deep-reaching acidic weathering before deposition of overlying formations, but this inference was questioned by Moffat and Bateman (1983).

4.4. The Upnor Formation

After deposition of the Thanet Sand Formation, an uplift episode caused the sea to recede eastwards beyond the present English coastline for approximately 1 Ma. Then, at about 56 Ma (Knox, 1996), it briefly reinvaded much of southeast England, including most of Hertfordshire, to deposit the Upnor Formation (Ellison *et al.*, 1994), which was previously known as the 'Woolwich and Reading Bottom Bed' (Hester, 1965; Bateman and Moffat, 1987; Bateman, 1988). During this second Palaeocene marine transgression, the Thanet Sand and Ormesby Clay formations and much of the Chalk beyond were extensively bevelled before a few metres of dark green (glauconitic) sands or clayey sands with seams and stringers of well-rounded black-coated flint pebbles were deposited in shallow water (Plates 11 and 12). The sand component of this sediment is often slightly coarser and less well sorted than the Thanet Sand Formation (Ellison *et al.*, 1994).

At the base of the Upnor Formation there is often a thin bed of green-coated flint pebbles and unworn flint nodules in a matrix of brown glauconitic sand or sandy clay. This

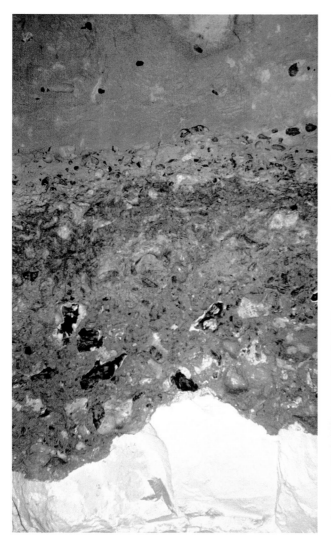

Plate 12. *Pebbly sand of the marine Upnor Formation overlying Chalk and overlain by non-marine Reading Formation, exposed when A120 was widened at Chalk Pit Hill (TL 402226) near Standon, 1965.*

Plate 11. *Brown and dark green glauconitic Upnor Formation overlying Chalk and overlain by pale sands of Reading Formation, roof of Pinner Chalk Mine, north London.*

Plate 13. *Specimens of the echinoid* Conulus albogalerus *preserved in black flint, Upnor Formation, Church End Farm (TL 448229), Little Hadham, and in original white chalk, Bishop's Stortford Limeworks Quarry (TL 489234).*

resembles the Bullhead Bed at the base of the Thanet Sands Formation, and where it overlies chalk the two have frequently been confused. The unworn flint nodules become more abundant westwards and are probably derived from the underlying Upper Chalk, though Bateman (1988) showed that very little of the fine matrix between the flints was derived from the Chalk. Chalk fossils preserved in flint can sometimes be found in basal parts of the Upnor Formation. For example, a specimen of the Chalk echinoid *Conulus albogalerus* (Plate 13) found at Church End Farm (TL 448229), Little Hadham, indicates that during the Upnor transgression the upper part of the Seaford Chalk Formation (lower Santonian) was being eroded in this part of Hertfordshire. At the junction between the Upnor Formation and Chalk exposed in the valley of the Northaw Brook (TL 2902), there is a thin layer composed mainly of the clay mineral allophane (a hydrated silicate of aluminium), which probably formed *in situ* long after deposition by precipitation of silica and alumina where percolating acidic water was neutralized on contact with the Chalk (Whitaker, 1889, p. 207).

As the marine transgression of the Upnor Formation removed the Thanet Sand Formation from many areas and then bevelled the Chalk beneath, the Sub-Palaeogene Surface is polygenetic, that is pre-Thanet Sand Formation to the east but pre-Upnor Formation further west. Later Tertiary transgressions may also have trimmed the Chalk in areas beyond Hertfordshire, so that the Sub-Palaeogene Surface across southern England as a whole is probably a complex of erosion facets of various ages (Fig. 4.2). Where Chalk is exposed beneath unweathered Upnor Formation, the eroded sub-Upnor facet is usually a flat plane, though Irving (1899a) recorded a site in the Stort valley exposing a channel cut 2-3 m into the Chalk.

Impersistent beds dominated by small black-coated flint pebbles, the 'upper conglomerate' of Bateman and Moffat (1987), are also common near the top of the Upnor Formation, and shattered pebbles of bleached (white) or red flint occur locally (Hester, 1942). Beds several metres thick composed of small, well-rounded black-coated flint pebbles were recorded in the Upnor Formation where it was previously exposed at Orsett, near Grays in Essex (Sumbler,

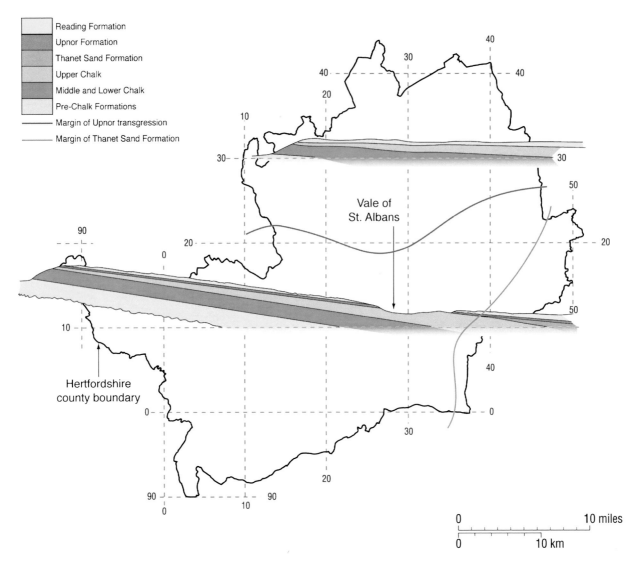

Reading Formation
Upnor Formation
Thanet Sand Formation
Upper Chalk
Middle and Lower Chalk
Pre-Chalk Formations
Margin of Upnor transgression
Margin of Thanet Sand Formation

Vale of
St. Albans

Hertfordshire
county boundary

0   10 miles
0   10 km

Figure 4.2. Sections across Hertfordshire to show relationship of different Palaeogene formations to the polygenetic Sub-Palaeogene Surface.

1996, Plate 16). Many of these pebble beds probably originated as marine beach gravels, deposited during either transgression or regression of the Upnor sea.

East of London the Upnor Formation is up to 8 m thick, and boreholes in central London indicate 5-6 m (Ellison *et al.*, 1994). Almost 5 m were exposed in the railway cutting south of Bushey Station (TQ 1194) (Whitaker, 1889, p. 198) and 4 m in a brickpit at Chorleywood (TQ 028953) (Whitaker, 1889, p. 193; Hopkinson, 1910, p. 27). But elsewhere in Hertfordshire, numerous exposures over the last century or so in brickpits exploiting the Reading Beds or in the overburden of Chalk quarries, have shown that it is slightly thinner (usually <3 m) and oxidized in part or throughout to a reddish brown or yellowish brown sandy clay. In south-eastern parts of the county, this weathered zone (including the bleached and reddened flint pebbles) extends beneath a thick cover of the Reading and later formations, indicating that some soil development occurred as a result of emergence and exposure to the atmosphere before deposition of the Reading Formation. However, to the northwest a veneer of Upnor and basal Reading formations

has contributed to the Plateau Drift overlying Chalk of the Chiltern plateau, and here the weathering is thought to date partly from the Neogene Period (Section 5.3) or even warm stages of the Quaternary.

Where it emerges from beneath the thicker Reading, Harwich and London Clay formations in south-eastern parts of the county, the Upnor Formation has a very narrow outcrop (too narrow to be shown on the 1:50,000 BGS maps or in Fig. 4.1) on the north-western margin of the main Reading Formation outcrop southeast of Watford, St Albans, Hatfield, Hertford, Ware and Bishop's Stortford. Southeast of this line the Upnor and overlying formations are continuous and dip at a low angle SSE towards the axis of the syncline beneath London. For example, in the Ash Valley near Little Hadham (TL 4422) and Furneux Pelham (TL 4327), outcrops of the Upnor Formation in the overburden of disused chalk quarries and temporary exposures indicate a dip of 0.3° in this direction (Hornett, 1998; Fegan, 1999).

Northwest of the Watford-Bishop's Stortford line, the same formations have been partially removed by erosion at various times in the late Neogene and Quaternary, so that the Chalk is covered only by outliers (outlying isolated patches), the Upnor and basal Reading formation components of which have been extensively transformed into Plateau Drift. The various BGS maps of the Chilterns and Berkshire Downs show numerous small outliers where the basal Palaeogene sediments are still recognizable because they are too thick to have been completely transformed into Plateau Drift. In Hertfordshire the main outliers on the Chiltern plateau are shown in the following seventeen areas (Fig. 4.1):

a) In the southern part of Chorleywood (TQ 0194,TQ 0195, TQ 0294, TQ 0295)
b) West of Sarratt (TQ 0499)
c) West of Micklefield Green (TQ 0498)
d) North of Loudwater at Micklefield Hall (TQ 0597)
e) East of Hemel Hempstead, between Hyde Meadow Farm (TL 089043) and Cupid Green (TL 0709); at Bennetts End (TL 073064), the Palaeogene beds are downfaulted into the Chalk in a small graben (Section 5.7); to the south, there is also a line of five small subsidiary outliers largely buried by proto-Thames terrace gravels between Bedmond (TL 0903) and Home Farm (TL 105019) near Abbots Langley
f) Between Cherry Tree Lane (TL 0809) and the M1 north of Punchbowl Lane (TL 0909)
g) North of Berkhamsted, between Little Heath (TL 0108), Potten End (TL 0109) and Gutteridge Farm (TL 0008)
h) Northeast of Great Gaddesden, between Briden's Camp (TL 0411) and Jockey End (TL 0313)
i) Northwest of Harpenden, between Kinsbourne Green (TL 1015) and Caddington (TL 0718)
j) On the northern side of St Albans, between the City Hall (TL 149073) and Bernard's Heath (TL 1508), with a small separate outlier beneath St Albans City Hospital (TL 144082)
k) On the western side of Welwyn Garden City, between Sherrardspark (TL 2313) and Ayot St Peter (TL 2115)
l) At Burnham Green, between Harmer Green (TL 2515), Hawkins Hall Farm (TL 2718) and Bright's Hill (TL 2916)
m) At Colliers End, between Sandon (TL 3822) and Sacombe Green (TL 3418)
n) Southeast of Stevenage, between Arbury Wood (TL 3020) and Cutting Hill Farm (TL 3121)
o) East of Puckeridge, between Braughing (TL 3924) and Albury Lodge (TL 4424)
p) At Sacombe Hill Farm (TL 323198)
q) East of Hare Street, between Little Hormead (TL 4028) and Great Hormead (TL 4029).

Beneath the highest central parts of four of these outliers (e, k, m and o), the total original thickness of the Reading Formation is preserved beneath a thin cover of Harwich and London Clay formations, but most of them consist only of the Upnor Formation and lower parts of the Reading Formation. In southeast Buckinghamshire close to the Hertfordshire border, another important outlier at Cowcroft (SP 9801) also shows the full thickness of the Reading Formation, though the succession here is much disturbed (Anon., 1898a).

There are numerous earlier descriptions of the Upnor Formation in Hertfordshire, usually under the name 'Woolwich and Reading Bottom Bed', in other BGS publications (Whitaker, 1889; Sherlock, 1922; Sherlock and Noble, 1922; Sherlock and Pocock, 1924). More recently, detailed successions recorded in surface exposures and boreholes through the Upnor Formation were given in outlier k by Bateman (1984) and outliers m and p by Hopson *et al.* (1996, pp. 68-70). At Bishop's Stortford Lime Works (TL 488235), a section seen in 1971 above the Chalk consisted of a 15 cm layer of black-coated flint pebbles (sometimes green-coated), overlain by 2 m of dark greenish grey glauconitic clay with a thin (15 cm) pale yellowish grey clay stripe about 50 cm above the base. The deep road cutting dug nearby in 1976 for the Bishop's Stortford by-pass (A120) (TL 492234) exposed a similar succession, but here overlain by Reading Beds, which consisted of a thin basal bed of flint pebbles followed by greyish yellow sandy clay and pale yellow current bedded sands.

The main effect of the two Palaeocene marine erosion episodes before deposition of the Upnor Formation was to remove more of the Chalk in north-western than south-eastern parts of the Hertfordshire area. Consequently, the thickness of the Upper Chalk (Lewes and overlying formations) in areas still covered by the Upnor Formation, i.e. where it has not been thinned by later (Neogene and Quaternary) erosion, increases progressively south-eastwards (Fig. 4.2). Beneath the Cowcroft outlier near Chesham, Buckinghamshire (SP 983017), it is only 35 m thick (Sherlock, 1922, p. 21), but it reaches 74 m at Barnet (Bromehead, 1925, p. 10), 79 m in the Turnford borehole near Cheshunt (Appendix 1), 84 m at Waltham Cross (Whitaker, 1921, p. 207) and as much as 140 m at Slough (Whitaker, 1921, p. 158). Further southeast, beneath north London, there seems to be no further increase in thickness of the Upper Chalk, as the full range indicated by deep boreholes is 73 m (at Stanmore) to 113 m (at Willesden), though it is generally less than 80 m.

At the base of the Upnor Formation there is local evidence for burrowing into the upper surface of either the Thanet Sand Formation or the Upper Chalk. The burrows are circular in cross section, 5-15 mm across, descend steeply at 50-90°, reach a maximum depth of approximately 50 cm and are filled with green glauconite-rich sand from the Upnor Formation. In the Chalk, their walls often show bioglyphs, a criss-cross pattern of grooves or striations created by the burrowing organism. Originally this was thought to be a marine annelid worm named *Terebella harefieldensis* (White, 1923), but the burrows are now grouped with trace fossils of crustacean origin, and have been renamed *Glyphicnus harefieldensis* (Bromley and Goldring, 1992). In the Hertfordshire area, the burrows are best exposed in a section (Plate 14) preserved in the largely infilled Cement Works Pit SSSI at Harefield Quarry (TQ 049898), north London, where they were originally illustrated in a photograph by De Salis (1914). At this site, sands and pebble beds of the Upnor Formation rest on

Plate 14. Crustacean burrows (Glyphicnus harefieldensis) *in Chalk beneath Upnor Formation exposed at Harefield (TQ 049898).*

Newhaven Chalk and are overlain by grey and brown silty sands at the base of the Reading Formation, followed by the Harwich and London Clay Formations (Whitaker, 1889; Green, 1895; Wooldridge and Wrigley, 1929; Hester, 1940, 1967). The burrows have also been recorded at Cowcroft (Sherlock, 1922, p. 31) and Pincent's Kiln, Theale (SU 651721), near Reading (Bromley and Goldring, 1992). Similar burrows are also present in Essex where sands of the Upnor Formation overlie the Thanet Sands (Ellison *et al.*, 2004).

The heavy mineral assemblage of the Upnor Formation is diverse and broadly similar to that of the Thanet Sand Formation, though it shows considerable geographic and stratigraphic variation in the numerous outliers on the Chilterns (Bateman and Moffat, 1987). The sediment was therefore derived mainly from the Thanet Sand Formation or from the same distant sources as the Thanet Sand Formation, though Hallsworth (1993) found pyrope garnets different in composition from the garnets in the Thanet Beds, which suggest derivation partly from other unknown sources. On the north Kent coast and in boreholes in northeast London, Thomas (2007) found that the heavy mineral assemblage consistently differs from that of the Thanet Sand Formation in containing more zircon but less tourmaline.

4.5. The Woolwich and Reading Formations

These two formations were deposited over approximately the same period of time. According to Knox (1996), this was between about 55.5 Ma and 55 Ma, which places them in the earliest Eocene now that the Palaeocene-Eocene boundary is dated to 55.8 Ma, though previously they were regarded as the youngest Palaeocene formations in southeast England. The Woolwich Formation consists of essentially shallow-water marine deposits in northwest Kent and southeast London, and the Reading Formation of non-marine clays and sands deposited further west. The two formations overlap with some interdigitation beneath central London (Ellison *et al.*, 2004), suggesting repeated oscillation of the coastline. However, the extreme western limit of marine (Woolwich) deposits is uncertain, because the sediments are sparsely fossiliferous and were also modified by repeated episodes of emergence and soil development, either during deposition or before the transgression that led to deposition of the Harwich Formation. Consequently, it is unclear whether or not a representative of the Woolwich Formation extends into southeast Hertfordshire. Similarly, the eastern limit of the Reading Formation is uncertain, though almost certainly it lies east and southeast of the Hertfordshire county boundary. This suggests we need consider only the Reading Formation in Hertfordshire.

Over the last century or so, numerous exposures of the Reading Formation in the Hertfordshire area have been described in BGS publications and reports of local excursions of the Geologists' Association and Hertfordshire Natural History Society and Field Club. Many of the sections included the Upnor Formation (often described as the 'Woolwich and Reading Bottom Bed'), and were in the numerous pits where Reading Beds clay was dug for brickmaking or in the overburden of quarries where chalk was worked for lime production. There were good descriptions in the 19th century of sections at:

Rush Green, Hertford (Morris, 1878),
Hatfield Park Kiln (TL 252083) (Morris, 1878; Hopkinson, 1910, p. 17),
Bushey (Blake 1900; Hopkinson, 1910, p. 20),
Watford Heath Kiln (Whitaker, 1889, p. 202; Hopkinson, 1873; 1910, p. 21),
on either side of the Stort valley near Bishop's Stortford (Irving, 1899a, 1899b),
in the railway cutting south of Bushey Station (TQ 1194) (Morris, 1878) and
in the cutting in Sherrardspark Wood (TL 226141) on the now disused Hatfield-Dunstable line (Hopkinson, 1887b; Hopkinson and Salter, 1899).

At some sites, clay and sand from the Reading Formation were mixed and used for brick-making, for example at:

Cowcroft (SP 9801) in southeast Buckinghamshire (Prestwich 1854; Anon., 1898a; Barrow, 1915; Sherlock, 1922, pp. 31-32),
Bennetts End (TL 076065) in the outlier (e) east of Hemel

Hempstead (Whitaker, 1889, Vol. 1, p. 208; Anon. 1892b; Green, 1900; Sherlock, 1922, p. 32),

Woodcock Hill, Rickmansworth (TQ 062925) (Whitaker and Hopkinson, 1900),

Ayot Green (TL 222139) in outlier (k) (Wooldridge, 1928), and

Bernards Heath (TL 1508) on the northern side of the St Albans outlier (j) (Whitaker, 1889, Vol. 1, p. 210; Hopkinson and Whitaker, 1892).

From these numerous accounts, it seems that the Reading Formation originated mainly as early Eocene alluvium (Ellison *et al.*, 1994), which was deposited by a braided river system feeding eastwards into a swampy delta (Hester, 1965) bordering the sea in which the Woolwich Formation accumulated. Brightly coloured mottled clays predominate, but beds of brown, pale yellow, grey or white sand, sometimes with thin (<2 cm) grey or brown clay laminae, are also common. The total thickness is usually less than 16 m, though in a borehole at Hillingdon it reached 30 m (Sherlock and Noble 1922, p. 28). The sands often occur at the base of the formation and the mottled clays above, but locally this relationship is reversed or the formation is sandy throughout.

Recently the Reading Formation has been seen only in temporary exposures in various parts of the county. For example, in 1968 a cutting near the foot of Bells Hill, Bishop's Stortford (TL 484213) exposed about 2.5 m of purple, red and grey mottled silty clays (Plate 15), which were probably near the base of the formation, as they overlay greenish glauconitic clay, probably the upper part of the Upnor Formation. Approximately 200 m to the south, in the playing field of St Mary's Roman Catholic School, sixth form students from Hadham Hall School augered in 1983 through the lowest 2 m of the London Clay Formation into a bed of black flint pebbles containing a tooth of the shark *Odontaspis* sp. and a pyritized seed, possibly of *Magnolia*. As this pebble bed was probably the local equivalent of the Harwich Formation, the total thickness of the Reading Formation here was no more than 5 m.

At several sites in Hertfordshire, there is evidence at the base of the Reading Beds for channel erosion, which has locally cut into the Upnor Formation, and perhaps even through it into the underlying Chalk. For example, in 1971, when the A120 was widened on the hill west of Standon (TL 385225), shallow channels containing pale grey flint pebbles were cut into greenish grey sandy clays of the Upnor Formation (Plate 16).

A similar pebble bed at the base of the Reading Formation was seen in 1976 in a cutting for the Bishop's Stortford by-pass (TL 482243); the section here exposed the following beds:

Reading Formation
   Pale yellow sand, red stained, clayey at base and current bedded above, 100 cm
   Bed of small grey flint pebbles, 12 cm
Upnor Formation
   Dark greenish glauconitic silty clay, 50 cm

Pale yellowish clay, 20 cm
   Dark greenish glauconitic silty clay, 50 cm
   Basal flint pebble bed of Upnor Formation, 40 cm
Chalk, seen to 60 cm.

In parts of southeast Buckinghamshire, the Reading Beds sands are pure white and from a distance can easily be mistaken for chalk. Slump structures, probably attributable to localized dissolution of the underlying chalk, have been recorded in past exposures of these sands at Lane End

Plate 15. Section in multicoloured silty clays of Reading Formation, Bells Hill (TL 484213), Bishop's Stortford.

Plate 16. Section showing channels containing flint pebbles of basal Reading Formation cut into Upnor Formation, exposed when A120 west of Standon (TL 385225) was widened in 1971.

(Wooldridge and Ewing, 1935) and Chesland (SP 917060) near Dundridge Manor (Ollier and Thomasson, 1956).

Beneath central London, the Reading Formation can be divided into Upper and Lower Mottled Clays separated by shelly clay of the Woolwich Formation (Ellison *et al.*, 2004). But probably only the Lower Mottled Clay extends into Hertfordshire, as the Upper Mottled Clay, up to 8 m thick in the Westminster area, is identifiable from borehole evidence only in a crescentic area extending from Edmonton in the north to Merton in the south (Ellison *et al.*, 2004, Fig. 20). Bateman (1984) suggested that the sands were washed from the sea into lagoons associated with the delta and that the overlying clays were transported eastwards by the braided river system following a period of uplift and erosion of land to the north and west.

Beds of usually small (20-50 mm) black-coated flint pebbles in a sandy matrix also occur sporadically at various levels in the Reading Formation. Many of these could be derived from the local Upnor Formation, but at some localities (e.g. Standon and Bishop's Stortford) they are pale grey and probably from some other source. The thickest (up to 40 cm) and most persistent pebble beds occur within the sandy facies, but scattered pebbles, usually less than 25 mm across, are also common in the mottled clays. Most of the pebbles show quite highly polished surfaces, which probably resulted from transportation and repeated reworking in a sandy environment; transportation of pebbles alone, without a sandy matrix, would create surfaces with numerous crescentic 'chatter-marks' rather than a uniformly smooth patina.

On many parts of the Chalk dip-slope of the Chilterns, a pebbly sand facies associated with some of the Palaeogene outliers and also occurring as patches within the Plateau Drift (Section 5.3) is separated on BGS 1:50,000 sheets 238, 239 and 255 as 'Pebbly Clay and Sand'. This is almost certainly equivalent to the sandy facies of the Reading Formation. On higher parts of the dip-slope near Stevenage and Baldock, as seen for example in the deep cutting dug in 2003-4 for the Baldock by-pass, it forms the bulk of the Plateau Drift, and many of the flint pebbles are larger (>100 mm) than elsewhere. The Baldock by-pass and other exposures near Stevenage have provided no evidence for an underlying layer of Upnor Formation, suggesting that the Upnor marine transgression never reached this area (Fig. 4.2).

As in the Isle of Wight (Buurman, 1980), the grey, green, red and purple mottling of the clays is attributable to repeated episodes of intraformational soil development (pedogenesis) in a warm, humid environment. Grey and green colours resulted from mobilization of iron in solution under locally reducing conditions, and the red and purple mottles from redeposition of the iron from solution as haematite in oxidizing situations. Exposure to the atmosphere leading to soil formation occurred as the river or rivers depositing the clay migrated laterally over what must have been a very broad floodplain extending roughly west-east across southeast England. The soils are probably intraformational, that is they formed locally during relatively short periods of non-deposition within accumulation

of the Reading Formation. In these circumstances one might expect to find abundant remains of plants that lived in the floodplain soils, but none has been recorded in Hertfordshire and they are rare outside the county. The commonest are elongate and often bifurcating blackened root impressions, but leaves of willow (*Salix* sp.) have been reported at Harefield, north London (Whitaker, 1889, Vol. 1, p. 196; Bateman, 1988). Elsewhere, plant remains were probably lost by microbial oxidation in the warm, humid climate of the late Palaeocene.

Pedoturbation (disturbance) processes during soil development, including penetration by plant roots and seasonal shrink-swell movements in clays, have almost completely destroyed any original sedimentary structures such as bedding in the Reading Formation. Instead, they have imposed new, mainly subsoil, structures on the deposits. In the clay-rich sediments this accounts for the widespread development of angular and subangular aggregates bounded by a network of planar fractures. The aggregates range in size from a few millimetres to several centimetres across. Downward illuviation of clay in percolating water (a soil-forming process described in Section 7.2) and its redeposition as clay coatings on the walls of the fissures probably strengthened the aggregates so that they have survived subsequent burial beneath a considerable thickness of later Palaeogene deposits. In the sands, similar clay illuviation and redeposition at levels determined by temporary water tables may also account for the repeated thin clay laminae, but the sands were much less affected by pedogenesis than the clays, probably because they were deposited in lagoons and remained submerged.

Another process that was at least partly related to pedogenesis in the Palaeocene was silica cementation (silicification) of the coarser deposits (pebble beds and sands) in the Upnor and Reading Formations. In the pebble beds this created the rock for which Hertfordshire is famous worldwide, namely Hertfordshire Puddingstone, and in the sandy deposits it resulted in formation of the very hard, silica-cemented sandstone often known as sarsenstone. Puddingstone and sarsenstone are examples of silcretes – sediments cemented into hard rock by deposition of silica from solution (Summerfield, 1983a). This is thought to have occurred in one of three ways (Ullyott *et al.*, 1998): (a) by dissolution and redeposition of silica close to the land surface in soils that developed during breaks in deposition (i.e. as intraformational pedogenetic silcretes), (b) by much later deposition of silica from groundwater after burial of the sediments to a considerable depth below the land surface (i.e. as post-depositional diagenetic silcretes), or (c) by deposition of silica from shallow groundwater emerging along drainage lines, such as inland basins or river valleys (drainage-line silcretes). However, even the silica redeposited from groundwaters (types b and c) would probably have originated by weathering of silica or silicate minerals in soils associated with contemporary land surfaces under a warm humid climate.

Silcretes have been recorded *in situ* in undisturbed Palaeocene sequences at only a few sites. In Hertfordshire *in situ* puddingstone was reported by Whitaker (1889, Vol. 1,

Plate 17. Exposure of in situ Hertfordshire Puddingstone within Reading Formation at Wood Hall Stud Estate (TQ 175994) near Radlett.

Plate 18. Hertfordshire Puddingstone block at Hertford Castle, brought from Colliers End Palaeogene outlier by East Hertfordshire Geology Club.

p. 200) within the Reading Formation between Radlett and Batlers Green (TQ 1598), and a 0.8 m-thick seam was also seen in Reading Beds exposed in Grover's Brickpit off Lower Paddock Road (TQ 1295) in Oxhey (Anon., 1908a; Hopkinson, 1910, p. 19). In the latter exposure, the puddingstone was seen to pass laterally into loose pebbly sand. In the St Albans outlier it was recorded within the Reading Formation exposed in pits near the workhouse (later part of St Albans City Hospital) (Hopkinson and Whitaker, 1892). More recently *in situ* puddingstone was recorded nearby in St Albans in a temporary exposure of the Reading Formation when the Seventh Day Adventist Church (TL 151079) was built (Catt and Moffat, 1980). There is a permanent exposure of puddingstone on private land of the Wood Hall Stud Estate (TQ 175994) east of Radlett (Plate 17), previously part of Newberries Park. Here it is underlain by an uncemented pebble bed and typical Reading Beds sand (Hopkinson, 1885, 1911c; Green, 1891; Evans, 1947; Ward, 1975; Robinson, 1994). The Wood Hall Stud site and a nearby field (TL 174999), in which fragments of puddingstone are especially abundant in the soil, are designated RIGSs (Hertfordshire RIGS Group, 2003).

Puddingstone also occurs at the base of the Reading Formation, where flint pebble beds are common, or in the

upper part of the Upnor Formation, where it could have resulted from interformational soil development on a land surface following deposition of the Upnor Formation. Perhaps the most famous example at this stratigraphic level is at Pinner Green (TQ 116904), north London, where a raft about 20 cm thick is penetrated by a vertical shaft through the Reading Formation into the Pinner Chalk Mine (Whitaker, 1889, Vol. 1, p. 206; Kirkman, 1992; Gallois, 1993). During the construction of a new section of the A10 between Thundridge and Puckeridge, which cut through the Colliers End outlier (l), large amounts of puddingstone were exposed in the Upnor Formation (Lovell and Tubb, 2006), or possibly in a sub-Reading Beds channel cut into the Upnor Formation. Thanks to the efforts of local farmers and the East Hertfordshire Geology Club, a fine specimen from this site has since been displayed in the grounds of Hertford Castle (Plate 18).

There are no records of *in situ* sarsenstone in Hertfordshire, but in the former county of Middlesex (now part of Greater London) examples have been recorded in sand of the Reading Formation exposed in the railway cutting east of Siblet's Wood (SU 9889) near Gerrard's Cross (Hopkinson, 1910, p. 24; Sherlock and Noble,1922, p. 25), in a trench beside the A4180 through Ruislip Common (TQ

0888) (Whitaker, 1889, p. 197), and at Northwood Golf Club House (Hester, 1942, p. 308).

The few recorded exposures of *in situ* silcretes in the Hertfordshire area therefore suggest that silicification of suitable coarse sandy or pebbly beds occurred at various times in the Palaeogene: (a) after deposition of the Upnor Formation but before accumulation of the alluvium of the Reading Formation, (b) soon after deposition of the basal pebble bed of the Reading Formation, and (c) in later breaks during deposition of the alluvial Reading Formation. It is unlikely that there is a single silcrete horizon within the Palaeogene sequence.

Much more widespread in Hertfordshire and adjacent parts of Essex, Greater London and Buckinghamshire are disturbed blocks of puddingstone and (less commonly) of sarsenstone. Many of these are found in or on the present soil, and derivation from the Palaeogene deposits is often suggested by their frequent occurrence on the outcrops of the Upnor and Reading Formations, for example in the valley of the Cuffley Brook on the northern side of Northaw Great Wood (TL 2904) (Sage, 1966). However, they are also common in the Plateau Drift overlying the Chalk of the Chilterns and in many of the other Quaternary deposits of Hertfordshire and counties to the west, south and east. These secondary occurrences and the nature of the silicification process will be discussed further in Chapter 5, but it is likely that all the blocks north of the Thames were derived by disruption of silcrete rafts originally formed in the coarser sediments of the Upnor and Reading Formations.

South of the Thames, from Kent to at least as far west as Dorset, silcretes may also have formed at other levels in the Palaeogene succession, for example in the Thanet Sand Formation (Dines *et al.*, 1954, p. 78), in the Blackheath Beds, which are probably part of the Harwich Formation, and in the Bagshot Formation (Dewey and Bromehead, 1915, p. 37). Isolated blocks of a much rarer type of puddingstone, in which small black-coated flint pebbles are cemented with brown iron oxide (Plate 19), can also be found occasionally in Hertfordshire. Like the silcretes, this form of ferricrete

probably originated as laterite in the contemporaneous soils that developed during breaks in deposition, though later diagenetic precipitation of iron from groundwater is also possible. The term 'ferricrete' and others like it was originally proposed by Lamplugh (1902), who lived for many years in Beaconsfield Road, St Albans while working for the BGS in London.

Because of original deposition in an alluvial environment with constant migration of the river channel and the various pedogenetic modifications of the sediments, the Reading Formation is very variable in lithology. Even within the limits of a small temporary exposure, rapid vertical and horizontal changes in texture, pebble content, colour and the extent of development of pedogenetic aggregates are all common. Subdivision of the formation is consequently difficult and detailed site-to-site correlation virtually impossible. Nevertheless, Bateman (1984) argued that, as the sands and clays were deposited in different environments and are usually separated by sharp textural discontinuities, they should be treated as separate members within the Reading Formation. Northwest of the main Reading Formation outcrop, it is also difficult to map the extent of outliers at all precisely, because the transformation of thinner layers into Plateau Drift by further pedogenesis in the Neogene or Quaternary, and downslope mass movement (gelifluction) under periglacial conditions in the Quaternary have made their boundaries rather diffuse.

The non-opaque heavy mineral assemblage of the Reading Formation is usually more restricted than those of the Thanet and Upnor formations. Zircon and tourmaline are the most abundant minerals and rutile, staurolite and kyanite are also common. These five minerals, which are very resistant to weathering, dominate most samples analysed from the Hertfordshire area (Moffat and Bateman, 1983; Bateman and Moffat, 1987; Bateman and Catt, 2007). Anatase, brookite, andalusite, garnet, epidote and amphiboles also occur sporadically in small amounts. Weir and Catt (1969) and Morton (1982) suggested that the dominant minerals represent an Armorican (northwest France) assemblage, though Walder (1964) and Blondeau and Pomerol (1968) argued that they came from Cornubia (southwest England). It is possible that less resistant minerals, such as garnet, amphiboles and apatite, which are more common in the Thanet and Upnor Formations, were originally present in the Reading Formation but were lost by weathering during the episodes of intraformational soil development. If so, the original assemblage could have been derived partly from the Thanet and Upnor Formations (Thomas, 2007). The clay (<2 μm) fraction of the Reading Formation consists mainly of smectite and mica, with subordinate (<20 %) kaolinite, but in some samples smectite is the only identifiable clay mineral (Perrin, 1971).

At present the only brickworks exploiting the Reading Formation is at Dunton Brickpit near Ley Hill (SP 987012) on the south-eastern side of the Cowcroft Outlier. The sequence here is very disturbed, probably by slumping into solution hollows in the underlying Chalk, and includes Upnor Formation and Quaternary brickearth as well as mottled clay of the Reading Formation (Plate 20).

Plate 19. Puddingstone with soft brown iron oxide (ferricrete) matrix instead of hard silica matrix (silcrete).

Plate 20. General view of Dunton Brickpit (SP 987012) exposing disturbed Upnor and Reading Formations and Quaternary brickearth, south-eastern side of Cowcroft outlier, Buckinghamshire.

4.6. The Harwich Formation

Originally defined by Prestwich (1854) as the 'Basement-bed of the London Clay', this formation overlies the Reading Formation in Hertfordshire and the Woolwich Formation (locally the Thanet Formation) in areas further east, and is overlain everywhere by the London Clay Formation. Locally in southern Essex and north Kent, it rests directly on the Upnor Formation (Sumbler, 1996, p. 102), indicating complete removal of the Woolwich Formation by erosion before deposition recommenced. Deposition of the Harwich Formation therefore followed another marine regression/transgression cycle early in the Eocene Epoch, dating to about 54.5-54 Ma (Knox, 1996). Erosion before or during this transgression may also account for the north-westward thinning of the Reading Formation as a whole and for the loss of the Upper Mottled Clay unit in north London and Hertfordshire.

In east Kent the Harwich Formation probably includes fine glauconitic shallow-water marine sands known as the Oldhaven Beds (Whitaker, 1866) or Herne Bay Member (King, 1981). In southeast London and northwest Kent, a bed of black-coated flint pebbles (the Blackheath Beds of Whitaker, 1872), up to 12 m thick near Lewisham, may be attributable to the same episode. In the deeper water area close to Harwich and other parts of the East Anglian coast, it comprises 15-20 m of silty and sandy clays with over 40 thin beds of bentonitic clay (decomposed volcanic ash) in

its upper part (Ellison *et al.*, 1994). But in the Hertfordshire area, it is less than 3 m thick and consists of greyish brown glauconitic sandy clay or sand containing small black-coated flint pebbles and sometimes also layers of hard yellowish grey calcareous (septarian) nodules. Because it is so thin in Hertfordshire, the outcrop of the Harwich Formation is not shown separately on the BGS 1:50,000 maps or in Figure 4.1.

In the 19th century, there were important exposures of the 'Basement-bed of the London Clay' at Hedgerley, Lane End, Coleshill and Tyler's Hill (= Cowcroft) in south Buckinghamshire (Whitaker, 1889) and at Batchworth Heath, Bennetts End (Hemel Hempstead), Bushey railway cutting, Woodcock Hill (Rickmansworth), Watford Heath (Hopkinson, 1873), Hatfield Park, and Rush Green (Hopkinson, 1887a) in Hertfordshire. Later, Kidner and Woodhead (1911) and Kidner (1915) described sections exposing basal London Clay Formation, Harwich Formation and mottled clay of the Reading Formation at Bushey and Oxhey Lane bridge (TQ 122925), approximately 1 km south of Carpenders Park Station, during widening of the railway south of Bushey. Another exposure at Harefield (TQ 049898) was described by White (1923), and sections in the outlier at Ayot Green were described by Wooldridge (1928). In north London, for example at Lower Heath, Hampstead, it was also encountered in wells drilled for water through Palaeogene formations into the Chalk.

At all these sites the Harwich Formation was notably

rich in fossils, including numerous bivalves (e.g. *Ostrea bellovacina, Arctica morrisi*), gastropods (e.g. *Aporrhais sowerbyi, Rostellaria lucida*), plant remains (fossil wood, impressions of leaves), fish teeth and bones (especially rootless teeth of sharks such as *Odontaspis teretidens* and *Lamna obliqua*), occasional mammal (*Hyracotherium*) and reptile (turtle) bones, and casts of the marine annelid worm *Ditrupa plana* (Whitaker, 1889, Vol. 1, pp. 264-265). Among many other species at Harefield, Wooldridge and Wrigley (1929) recorded abundant shells of the burrowing mollusc *Panopaea* and numerous borings of *Martesia saxorum* in carbonate concretions. Shallow water with minor episodes of erosion was indicated by evidence that the concretions had been bored by *Martesia*, then rolled over and rebored, and by some *Panopaea* shells lying on their sides while others were still in their original vertical burrows.

The section in a disused pit on the western side of the Palaeogene outlier at Cowcroft (SP 982015), south Buckinghamshire, previously described by Prestwich (1854, p. 90), Evans and Hopkinson (1878) and Green (1899), is still visible (Fig. 4.3). However, talus from the overlying London Clay Formation usually needs to be removed to provide an interpretable section.

Plate 21 shows a temporary section that exposed a thin representative of the Harwich Formation above the Reading Formation in 1984 when the A120 was widened at Standon Hill (TL 403225). The section was logged as follows:

Dark grey chalky till	1.0 m
Harwich Formation	
Mottled brown sandy clay	0.5 m
Grey sandy clay, with fragments of fossil wood	0.5 m
Bed of black flint pebbles	0.1 m
Reading Formation	
Pale brown clay with grey mottles	0.5 m
Pale clay	0.05 m
Dark brown clay with grey mottles	2.8 m
Purplish grey silty clay	0.3 m

The Harwich Formation was also exposed in the early 1970s during construction of the Ware by-pass (A10). At the Hailey Interchange (TL 365115) near Hoddesdon, about 5 m of dark, pyritic silty clays containing lenticular septarian nodules and scattered patches of crushed bivalves were exposed, and at Hoe Lane (TL 356128) a basal bed consisting mainly of black-coated flint pebbles and yielding bivalves and sharks' teeth was overlain by pale grey silty clays. The pebble bed at Hoe Lane overlay pale yellowish grey stiff plastic clay of the Reading Formation. More recently, an excavation at Eastwick Lodge Farm (TL 441118) near Harlow revealed unweathered grey sandy clay of the Harwich Formation beneath a thick cover of chalky till and proto-Thames gravel (Lower Westmill Gravel). At this site the Harwich Formation has yielded teeth of *Odontaspis*, pyritized wood fragments of indeterminate genera and small clasts resembling amber. Poorly preserved bivalves were recorded from lenticular masses of siltstone within fine sands and pebbly clays of the Harwich Formation exposed in a roadside trench dug near the junction of Cricket Field Lane

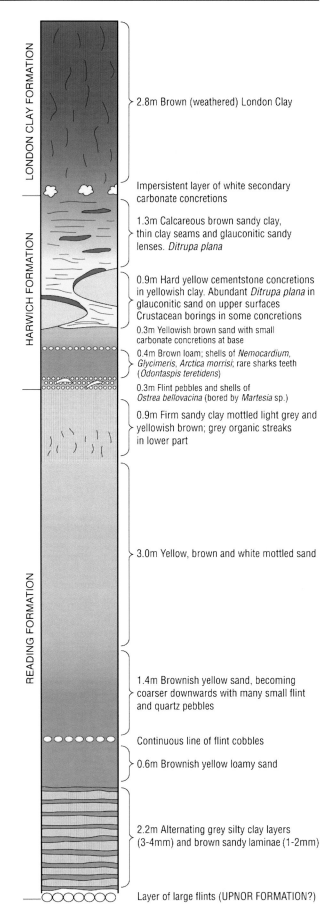

LONDON CLAY FORMATION

2.8m Brown (weathered) London Clay

Impersistent layer of white secondary carbonate concretions

1.3m Calcareous brown sandy clay, thin clay seams and glauconitic sandy lenses. *Ditrupa plana*

HARWICH FORMATION

0.9m Hard yellow cementstone concretions in yellowish clay. Abundant *Ditrupa plana* in glauconitic sand on upper surfaces Crustacean borings in some concretions

0.3m Yellowish brown sand with small carbonate concretions at base

0.4m Brown loam; shells of *Nemocardium, Glycimeris, Arctica morrisi*; rare sharks teeth (*Odontaspis teretidens*)

0.3m Flint pebbles and shells of *Ostrea bellovacina* (bored by *Martesia* sp.)

0.9m Firm sandy clay mottled light grey and yellowish brown; grey organic streaks in lower part

READING FORMATION

3.0m Yellow, brown and white mottled sand

1.4m Brownish yellow sand, becoming coarser downwards with many small flint and quartz pebbles

Continuous line of flint cobbles

0.6m Brownish yellow loamy sand

2.2m Alternating grey silty clay layers (3-4mm) and brown sandy laminae (1-2mm)

Layer of large flints (UPNOR FORMATION?)

Figure 4.3. Section in Reading, Harwich and basal London Clay formations at Cowcroft (SP 982015), Buckinghamshire.

Plate 21. Thin (1.1 m) Harwich Formation above Reading Formation and overlain by till exposed at Standon Hill (TL 403225) when A120 was widened in 1984.

and Graylands (TL 480220) in Bishop's Stortford (Lake and Wilson, 1990, p. 11).

In north Kent, the Harwich Formation (including the Herne Bay Member) contains abundant molluscs (Cooper, 1934) and fish remains, including sharks' teeth. Its detrital sand mineral assemblage is similar to that of the Thanet Beds, but with the addition of chlorite, green biotite and muscovite (Weir and Catt, 1969). The provenance of these three new minerals is unknown, but they probably have a different (third) source from the two groups of minerals present in earlier Palaeogene formations.

4.7. The London Clay Formation

Evidence for a break in deposition between the Harwich and London Clay formations is weaker than at lower levels in the Palaeogene succession of southeast England, and the base of the London Clay Formation is dated to approximately 54 Ma, little younger than the Harwich Formation (Knox, 1996). Nevertheless, in parts of central and south London the Harwich Formation is absent and the London Clay Formation rests on either the Reading or the Woolwich Formation (Ellison *et al.*, 2004), suggesting some localized erosion during a minor break between deposition of the Harwich and London Clay formations.

On the southern boundary of Hertfordshire near Bushey Heath, Elstree and Arkley, the maximum thickness of the London Clay Formation is probably about 90 m, though

beneath central London (e.g. in the BGS Crystal Palace borehole) it is at least 130 m (Ellison *et al.*, 2004) and in Essex and north Kent even greater thicknesses are recorded (Davis and Elliott, 1957). Because of post-Palaeogene erosion it thins rapidly north-westwards across Hertfordshire. Wells for water supply indicate maximum thicknesses of 67 m at Monkhams Hall (TL 386028) near Waltham Abbey (Whitaker *et al.*, 1916, p. 288), 83 m at Chipping Barnet and High Barnet, 52 m at Cheshunt and Elstree, 47 m at Little Berkhamsted, 44 m at Hertford, 43 m at Hatfield, 32 m at Essendon, 30 m at Aldenham and Bushey, 13 m at Sawbridgeworth and 7 m at Wormley (Whitaker, 1921). Exposures in the outliers at Cowcroft and Ayot St Peter (k) have shown less than 5 m. However, the BGS Dowsett's Farm borehole through the Colliers End outlier (m) proved a surprisingly thick 12.7 m of London Clay Formation (Hopson *et al.*, 1996, p. 67).

Most of the formation consists of unbedded (strongly bioturbated), grey, slightly calcareous clay or silty clay containing pyrite (FeS_2). Thin beds slightly richer in silt or fine sand (<125 µm), and usually richer also in glauconite, become gradually thicker and more abundant westwards towards the presumed shoreline. The pyrite indicates anaerobic bottom conditions, and partly replaces plant remains such as twigs, seeds and fruits, which must have been rafted from nearby land. It also forms small framboidal aggregates, irregular concretions up to 5 cm across and narrow tubes, which may have been created by algae. Lens-shaped carbonate concretions up to 50 cm in diameter, often showing radial fractures filled with calcite (septarian nodules), also occur at certain horizons.

Upper parts of the clay close to the land surface or beneath coarse Quaternary deposits have often been oxidized to a uniform dark brown colour and are partly decalcified. In these layers, sulphuric acid produced by oxidation of the pyrite has reacted with fine disseminated carbonate to form gypsum, which often occurs as characteristic 'arrowhead' twinned crystals up to 15 cm long. In lower parts of the brown weathered zone, carbonate has also been reprecipitated as small (2-5 cm) secondary 'race' nodules and as powdery accumulations on fissure faces. The brown colour indicates the presence of hydrated iron oxides, which are residual from the oxidation of pyrite. Sulphuric acid has also reacted with potassium-containing alumino-silicate clay minerals and with iron oxides to produce the yellow mineral jarosite ($KFe_3(OH)_6(SO_4)_2$), which often forms a powdery coating on desiccation cracks and other planar voids in the clay.

Within the London Clay Formation of southeast England, King (1981) recognized five lithological subdivisions (A-E in ascending order), which he related to slightly different depositional environments. The uppermost subdivision (E) included sandy beds, which were originally identified in Surrey (Dewey, 1912) and, from exposures in Essex, were later defined by Bristow *et al.* (1980) as the Claygate Member of the London Clay Formation. All the other subdivisions are thought to have begun with a sudden deepening of the sea, followed by gradual shallowing. Some of King's subdivisions are also characterized by macrofossils with apparently short time ranges; for example, the brachiopod *Terebratulina wardenensis* occurs only in C and D and the crinoid *Balanocrinus subbasaltiformis* is confined to the middle of B. Based on later BGS boreholes in the London area, Ellison *et al.* (2004) also recognized five units, the lowest four of which were again labelled A-D in ascending order (though with boundaries at different horizons from King's subdivisions A-D) and the fifth was equated with the Claygate Member.

In Hertfordshire, the Claygate Member has been mapped separately from the remainder of the London Clay Formation as three small outliers (British Geological Survey, 1993), which straddle the southern county boundary at Borehamwood (TQ 1995), Elstree (TQ 1795) and Bushey Heath (TQ 1594) (Fig. 4.1). All three are partly covered by the Early Pleistocene Pebble Gravel Formation (Stanmore Gravels). The Claygate Member in these outliers consists of finely stratified sands with thin, irregularly spaced clay and silt laminae. There is no evidence that it was separated from the remainder of the London Clay Formation by a marine regression-transgression cycle, but the base of the sandy beds is often marked by a bed of hollow ironstone concretions (boxstones) and by occasional iron-depositing chalybeate springs, such as Lady Rachel's Well at Moat Mount (TQ 216941), south of Borehamwood.

The remaining parts of the London Clay Formation (units A-D of Ellison *et al.*, 2004) are distinguished on relatively minor lithological differences. At the base, Unit A (7-14 m thick) is slightly sandier than the remainder and

often contains large fragments of fossil wood and clusters of flattened fragments of agglutinating foraminifera (white silt tubes up to 30 mm long), but calcareous concretions are rarer than in higher units. Unit B (7-18 m thick) is mainly silty clay with a few thin sandy horizons and layers of septarian nodules and flattened siderite concretions less than 5 cm thick. Unit C (40-52 m thick) is dominated by homogeneous, strongly bioturbated clay, again with layers of large septarian nodules, and some silty beds containing small (1-2 cm) phosphatic nodules. Unit D (30-45 m thick) consists of alternating beds of sandy silt and clayey silt, each up to 5 m in thickness though with diffuse boundaries; smaller septarian nodules and phosphatic concretions are again present.

Fossils are fairly common throughout the formation, though they are rarer in Unit A and the Claygate Member than other parts of the succession. In the wider area of southeast England, they include plant remains, molluscs (gastropods, bivalves, scaphopods, pteropods), brachiopods, crinoids, echinoids, asteroids, ophiuroids, crustacea (decapods, ostracods), corals, reptile bones, bird bones, mammalian bones, fish bones and teeth, annelid worms, bryozoa, sponge spicules, foraminifera, dinoflagellate cysts, diatoms and radiolaria. The most frequent records are from coastal exposures in north Kent (Sheppey) and Essex (Harwich, Walton-on-the-Naze). The plant remains include logs, some several metres long, which are often bored by the long, cylindrical carbonate-lined tubes of Teredinidae or shipworms (Huggett and Gale, 1995). Apart from molluscs there are few records of fossils from Hertfordshire, probably because there have never been many good exposures of the unweathered clay in the county.

In the 19th century the popularity of fossil collecting and the abundance of macrofossils in the London Clay Formation led to formation of a 'London Clay Club'. A prominent member of the club was Frederick E. Edwards, who specialized in Eocene molluscs, and began the preparation of a monograph on Eocene cephalopods and univalves for the Palaeontographical Society (Edwards and Wood, 1849-1877). When the original Potters Bar railway tunnel (TQ 256004–TQ 260993) was dug through the London Clay Formation in 1848-1850, a local collector, Henry Keeping, paid the workmen for any fossils that they found, and passed them to Edwards. Further London Clay fossils found later in construction of the the Elstree railway tunnel (TQ 193956–TQ 197948) (Blake, 1895) and Ponsbourne Tunnel (TL 076315-TL 053309) between Hertford North and Cuffley (Pocock, 1914a) were added to the collection, which was purchased by the Natural History Museum and is stored in their Palaeontology Department. Molluscs (gastropods and lamellibranchs) from the Potters Bar tunnel held in the Natural History Museum's collection were listed and in part figured by Warren (2006). Although it covers only two groups, Warren's is the most comprehensive and accessible list of London Clay fossils available for Hertfordshire. Lists for other sites in the London area have been compiled by Elliott (1963), Rundle and Cooper (1970), Kirby (1974) and Tracey *et al.* (2002).

Plant remains have been recorded from numerous sites

Plate 22. Scarp formed by basal Palaeogene clays near Salisbury Hall (TL 1902), London Colney.

in southeast England (Collinson, 1983), though none of them in Hertfordshire. The assemblage as a whole includes more than 500 plant types, and represents one of the world's most varied fossil floras. Plant macroremains such as fruits and seeds (Bowerbank, 1840; Reid and Chandler, 1933) have been studied most intensively, but there are also accounts of some components of the microflora, including pollen (Sein, 1961; Kedves, 1967; Gruas Cavagnetto, 1976) and dinoflagellate cysts (Costa and Downie, 1976; Costa *et al.*, 1978; Bujak *et al.*, 1980). Although all the plant species are probably now extinct, many of them belong to genera with fairly close modern equivalents, such as the *Nipa* palm and (more rarely) members of the Rhizophoraceae or mangrove family (Chandler, 1951), which today grow only in the mangrove swamps of tropical coasts and estuaries. The abundance of these and other plant remains suggest that coastal swamps must have occurred at no great distance to the west of Hertfordshire, but the exact position of the coastline is unknown. The foraminiferal (Murray and Wright, 1974) and ostracod (Keen, 1978) assemblages in the clay-rich part of the formation indicate deposition in a moderately deep (50-200 m) shelf sea, but the sandiness of the Claygate Member suggests that the sea had by then become much shallower, probably less than 30 m deep.

In addition to the tropical indicators in the London Clay flora, there are many subtropical and temperate genera, including ferns and the angiosperms *Betula*, *Magnolia* and gymnosperms such as *Metasequoia*, *Cedrus* and *Engelhardtia*, which are also strongly represented in the numerous twig fragments. The pollen assemblages also include many groups indicating cooler conditions (Sein, 1961). Temperate plants might have grown on cooler, higher ground inland from the coastal swamps, but the dominantly clay-rich sediment suggests that there was no such high land close enough for temperate wood fragments to reach the coast. Palaeogeographic reconstructions in fact indicate that southern England lay close to 40° N in the Early Eocene, so the different climatic zones indicated by the overall flora are perhaps best explained by seasonal or longer-term climatic variation. Despite the occurrence of some temperate genera, the overall climate of London Clay times was certainly warmer than during deposition of the Thanet Sand Formation. The warming cannot be explained by movement of the Eurasian tectonic plate, which would have been small over the intervening 3 Ma and in any case was away from rather than towards the equator. Instead, it is likely that the sudden global warming of the Palaeocene-Eocene Thermal Maximum (PETM) at 55.8 Ma tailed off slowly over the next 1-2 million years.

In Kent the small amounts of sand in lower parts of the London Clay Formation contain a fairly diverse heavy mineral assemblage similar to that of the Harwich Formation, including the chlorite-biotite-muscovite group (Weir and Catt, 1969). This group persists into higher parts of the formation, including the Claygate Member, but the zircon-tourmaline-kyanite-staurolite (Armorican?) group becomes less abundant upwards and the garnet-epidote-amphibole (Scottish?) group more abundant. This change suggests an increasing predominance over time of sediment inputs from northerly rivers into the London Clay sea.

The clay fraction (<2 μm) of the London Clay is dominated by mica and smectite, with smaller amounts of kaolinite, which were probably also derived from land areas to the west and north. As in the Reading Formation, the smectite component probably came from wet, low-lying land areas bordering the sea. It is important as it shrinks and swells with changes in the water content of the clay, and thus influences the engineering behaviour of the deposit in horizons close to the land surface (Section 9.6).

Between the Colne and Lea valleys in south Hertfordshire, the lower part of the London Clay and the underlying Reading Formation form a fairly prominent scarp overlooking the Vale of St Albans (proto-Thames valley) to the north (Plate 22). To the south the Palaeogene outcrop in south Hertfordshire and north London is dissected by numerous deep valleys containing small misfit streams, such as the Monken Mead Brook, Salmon's Brook, Leeging Beech Gutter and Merryhills Brook in the Enfield Chase area, and the Cuffley Brook, Turkey Brook and Theobald's Brook between Enfield and Goffs Oak. Between these valleys, whose floors are as low as 60 m OD, the interfluves rise to 133 m OD at Shenley (TL 193008) and 128 m OD at Queenswood School (TL 268036), Coldharbour Farm (TL 285055) and Brookmans Park (TL 258048). Near the southern county boundary at Elstree (TQ 183951), Borehamwood (TQ 198954) and Arkley (TQ 222959) the outcrops of the Claygate Member rise even higher, to 147 m, 139 m and 144 m OD, respectively. For comparison, the floor of the Vale of St Albans lies at 65-75 m OD. The Palaeogene scarp could have resulted from undercutting by the proto-Thames before the Anglian glaciation (see Chapter 6), but this does not explain the elevated and deeply dissected land to the south, which is quite unlike the subdued topography of clay outcrops elsewhere in southeast England. Also it is unlikely that the scarp would have persisted over the long period (>0.5 Ma) since before the Anglian. Instead, the geomorphological features of this area are perhaps better explained in terms of fluvial erosion during post-Anglian uplift. The most likely cause of such uplift is glacio-isostatic rebound after melting of the Anglian glacier, which spread southwards across this area from the proto-Thames valley as far south as Finchley.

4.8. Later Palaeogene formations

Deposition of the London Clay Formation probably continued until about 51 Ma and the coarser nature of the Claygate Member suggests shallowing of the sea over southeast England at this time. The overlying Bagshot Formation is dominantly sandy, again suggesting shallow marine conditions. However, it locally rests on an erosion surface cutting across the Claygate Member (Dewey and Bromehead, 1921), so the sea probably receded for a short period before transgressing again across parts of southeast England. It could well have reached parts of Hertfordshire during deposition of the Bagshot Formation, but any deposits here have been completely removed by later erosion. In north London (e.g. at Hampstead Heath), the Bagshot Formation is up to 18 m thick (Ellison *et al.*, 2004, p. 50). A total of 27.5 m was recorded further east in a borehole at Stock in Essex (Bristow, 1985), though at the top this included 4 m of flint pebble beds (the 'Bagshot Pebble Bed'), which have been recorded elsewhere but could have been confused with the lithologically similar but much younger, Early Pleistocene, Pebble Gravels (Stanmore Gravel). The lower and upper age limits of the Bagshot Formation are unknown, but it is unlikely that the formation represents more than 1-2 Ma, so it is probably no younger than Mid-Eocene.

No later Palaeogene deposits are known in the London Basin, but in the Hampshire Basin (mainly the Isle of Wight) the Barton Group and Solent Group probably date from a period including the Late Eocene, Early Oligocene and Mid Oligocene (44 Ma–34 Ma approximately) (Curry *et al.*, 1978). It is unlikely that these were ever deposited over Hertfordshire. Sedimentation also continued in the central North Sea, where there is a concentric pattern of sediments with different depth-related microfaunas (King, 1983).

Chapter 5.

Neogene deposits and early landscape development

John Catt

5.1. Introduction

Following deposition of the Bagshot Formation, there is a long time gap of approximately 45 Ma in the sedimentary record of Hertfordshire and surrounding areas. There are no deposits that can definitely be attributed to the later Palaeogene or earlier parts of the Neogene, and the next youngest datable  sediments are either very late Neogene (Pliocene) or earliest Pleistocene. For most of this long hiatus, there were almost certainly no further marine transgressions across the county, though marine deposits did accumulate fairly continuously on the floor of the North Sea, and also in coastal areas of East Anglia periodically in the later Neogene. Following the Late Cretaceous and Palaeocene uplift of the land, there was undoubtedly extensive subaerial (mainly fluvial) erosion of the Palaeogene formations and possibly also of the Upper Chalk in Hertfordshire, and this resulted in development of the county's landscape into something approximating to its present form. During uplift, the Chalk and Palaeogene formations were gently folded, locally faulted and further eroded as a result of earth movements, including those that created the Alpine Mountains. This tectonic activity is the only tangible evidence for a late Palaeogene-early Neogene geological history in the strata preserved in the county, though the dating of these earth movements is impossible to determine precisely from the evidence preserved locally.

The Palaeogene-Neogene boundary is placed at 23.0 Ma (Gradstein *et al.*, 2005), and the Neogene is divided into two Epochs, the Miocene (23.0-5.3 Ma) and Pliocene (5.3-2.6 Ma) (Table 4.1). At the beginning of the Neogene all the continents were close to their present positions.

The climate of the Early Miocene was almost as warm as that of the Palaeogene. But there was a progressive cooling after the Mid Miocene (about 15 Ma), when the Antarctic ice cap, which had probably begun to form early in the Oligocene, expanded considerably in size. Slight warming occurred in the Mid Pliocene, but was followed by further global cooling through the later Pliocene, when the Arctic ice cap was initiated. The overall cooling of the earth through the later Neogene has been attributed to the progressive intensification of Alpine tectonic uplift, leading to the formation of extensive mountains such as the Alps, Himalayas, Andes, the western North American coastal ranges and those associated with the Great Rift Valley in East Africa (Raymo and Ruddiman, 1992). In addition to lowering mean temperatures by creating extensive cold high-altitude areas, the mountains increased the earth's total snow cover, and the resulting increase in albedo (reflectance) caused more solar radiation to be returned to space. The mountains also modified circulation in the atmosphere, intensifying monsoonal rainfall; this accelerated rates of the chemical weathering of silicate minerals, which in turn increased cooling by depleting the amount of the 'greenhouse gas' carbon dioxide in the atmosphere. By the Late Pliocene the orogenic (mountain-building) activity had brought the earth's climate to a critical threshold, at which the Quaternary glacial-interglacial cycle became established as a result of changes in solar radiation resulting from the perturbations in the earth's orbit around the sun, known as the Milankovitch cycles (Maslin *et al.*, 1998).

Although the base of the Pleistocene and Quaternary was previously placed at 1.61 Ma (Aguirre and Pasini, 1985), a date accepted by Gradstein *et al.* (2005) though corrected to 1.81 Ma, it is now agreed that it would be better drawn at the Gauss/Matuyama palaeomagnetic polarity reversal (Gibbard *et al.*, 2005, 2010), which is dated to 2.58 Ma. At this time there was another major global cooling episode that led to further expansion of the polar ice sheets, an increase in ice-rafted debris into the North Atlantic, large changes in oceanic, shallow marine and terrestrial faunas, the first appearance of a cold climate vegetation in northwest Europe, the initiation of widespread loess (periglacial windblown silt) deposition in Asia and evolutionary changes in hominins leading to the first appearance of early man (*Homo habilis*) in Africa. Following a proposal by the International Quaternary Association (INQUA), this date was formally ratified by the International Union of Geological Sciences (IUGS) in June 2009. The Plio-Pleistocene boundary is therefore now placed at 2.58 Ma, when the earth experienced the main worldwide change to a typical Quaternary environmental regime resulting from glacial-interglacial climatic cycles.

5.2. Possible late Neogene deposits in Hertfordshire

In Hertfordshire, the only deposits attributable to the late Neogene (or possibly the earliest Pleistocene) have been found on Rothamsted Experimental Farm near Harpenden and in gravel pits at Little Heath near Berkhamsted. Outside the county, deposits thought to be approximately similar in age were previously exposed at Lane End, near High Wycombe, Buckinghamshire (where they overlie another Palaeogene outlier), on the North Downs at Netley Heath and Headley Heath in Surrey, at Lenham in east Kent and near Beachy Head on the South Downs in Sussex.

Rothamsted

The deposits at Rothamsted were discovered in 1926, when shallow trenches were dug across the Experimental Farm to install a system of water pipes for irrigation purposes. The trenches mainly exposed Plateau Drift, which in this area consists partly of sand or sandy clay that contains flint pebbles but no flint nodules or fragments of nodules like those in the more usual flinty clay type of Plateau Drift (Section 5.3). In several places the sandy Plateau Drift contained isolated, disturbed blocks of ferruginous sandstone, and on the field called West Barnfield (TL 118142) a deeper pit was dug to excavate and remove two of the blocks, which were several metres long and about 0.5 m

thick. The blocks contained more than 400 casts and moulds of molluscs (Dines and Chatwin, 1930), mainly *Mytilus edulis* and *Pholas (Barnea) cylindrica*. Other molluscs recorded were *Modiola barbata, Ensis ensis, Pectunculus glycimeris, Cardium parkinsoni, Cardium (Cerastoderma edule), Modiolaria costulata, Nassa granulata, Natica* sp. and *Tellina*? There were also casts of isolated plates of the barnacle *Balanus* sp. All the original specimens are stored in the Natural History Museum, South Kensington, but wax impressions were donated to Rothamsted Experimental Station, and are held in the archive there. Some of the fossils from Rothamsted are illustrated in Plate 23.

Using geophysical methods and deep augering, Moffat (1980) attempted to locate more of the fossiliferous sandstone on West Barnfield at Rothamsted, but without success. This and adjacent fields have many ironstone blocks in the surface soil, which could be derived from the same source, but none of these has yielded any recognizable fossils.

Dines and Chatwin (1930) stated that the fossil assemblage at Rothamsted indicates 'no difficulty in accepting a Red Crag age for the sandstone'. The Red Crag Formation occurs mainly in East Anglia from Essex

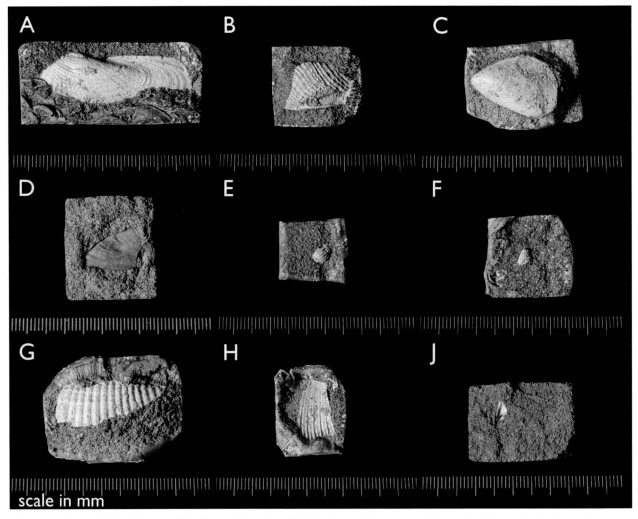

Plate 23. Red Crag (Plio-Pleistocene) fossils from West Barnfield, Rothamsted Farm, near Harpenden (Copyright Rothamsted Research). A. Pholas (Barnea) cylindrica J. Sowerby; B. ditto; C. Mytilus edulis L.; D. ditto; E. Nassa granulata J. Sowerby; F. ditto; G. Cardium parkinsoni J. Sowerby; H. ditto; I. plate of Balanus sp. Scales in mm.

to eastern Norfolk, where it is up to 40 m thick on the coast and rests on the London Clay and other Palaeogene formations close to or below sea level. Inland it forms a slowly thinning but continuous sheet of sand, whose base rises gradually to approximately 90 m OD near Stansted Mountfitchet in western Essex (Hopson, 1981; Mathers and Zalasiewicz, 1988; Lake and Wilson, 1990, Fig. 4). At Rothamsted, the isolated sandstone blocks are close to 132 m OD. But beneath the Netherlands and southern North Sea, where the lower part of the Red Crag Formation, the Sizewell Member of Zalasiewicz *et al.* (1988), is correlated with the Westkapelle Ground Formation (Cameron *et al.*, 1992), its base sinks to at least -600 m, so the total height range of the deposit is at least 700 m.

Boswell (1952) proposed that the base of the Quaternary and Pleistocene in Britain should be drawn at the base of the Red Crag as seen at Walton-on-the-Naze (TM 266236), Essex. This has been followed by most general accounts of the British Quaternary (e.g. Bowen, 1999; Catt *et al.*, 2006), but has been questioned by Zagwijn (1974), Cameron *et al.* (1984) and others. The disagreement can be explained by the fact that, from palaeomagnetic and palaeontological evidence, the Red Crag may actually be partly late Pliocene and partly early Pleistocene (as defined in Section 5.1). In deposits penetrated in the Stradbroke borehole (Suffolk), Beck *et al.* (1972) distinguished lower (Waltonian) and upper (Butleyan) units in the Red Crag. In other Suffolk boreholes, Zalasiewicz *et al.* (1988) also recognized two units, a lower Sizewell Member and an upper Thorpeness Member, both consisting dominantly of shallow-water shelly sands. Foraminiferal and dinoflagellate assemblages suggested further division of the Sizewell Member into the same (Waltonian and Butleyan) units as recognized at Stradbroke, and Zalasiewicz *et al.* (1988) suggested that the Sizewell Member is equivalent to the Reuverian C Stage of The Netherlands, which is normally magnetized and therefore predates the Gauss-Matuyama palaeomagnetic polarity reversal, i.e. it is Late Pliocene. However, they regarded the later Thorpeness Member as Early Pleistocene, equivalent to the temperate Ludhamian Stage of the Ludham borehole in Norfolk (West, 1961). From the presence of pollen of exotic (relict Neogene) plant genera, Hunt (1989) also concluded that the Red Crag at Walton is older than parts of the formation elsewhere in East Anglia, and should be correlated with the late Pliocene (Reuverian C) of The Netherlands. Recent palaeomagnetic studies of the Red Crag in East Anglia (Maher and Hallam, 2005) have confirmed that, although parts of the deposit may be as young as 2.2 Ma (early Matuyama and therefore early Pleistocene), some parts are older than 2.6 Ma (late Gauss and therefore late Pliocene). So, as precise correlation of the Rothamsted Red Crag with the various parts of the Red Crag in East Anglia remains uncertain, it could be either very late Pliocene or very early Pleistocene.

The extensive fauna of the late Pliocene Sizewell Member of the Red Crag in Suffolk suggests a relatively cool climate, as does the flora of the Reuverian C deposits of The Netherlands. In these conditions, sea level would if anything have been declining eustatically and the sea regressing from southern England. The fact that it was actually transgressing westwards at this time therefore suggests that coastal parts of East Englia were subsiding tectonically at a greater rate than sea level was falling (Jones, 1999).

Little Heath

The deposits at Little Heath (TL 017082) near Berkhamsted (not to be confused with Little Heath near Potters Bar), are approximately 12 km WSW of Rothamsted and at an even greater height (160-170 m OD). Unfortunately they are unfossiliferous, so correlation with the Red Crag is uncertain. The sands and gravels here were originally noticed by Prestwich (1890), but the first detailed descriptions were by Gilbert (1920, 1924) when the deposits were being worked for road-metal and to fill sandbags for protection from First World War bombs. Since the various pits fell into disuse, the area has been invaded by woodland and is now owned and managed by The National Trust. However, there are still numerous shallow exposures of the uppermost deposits, and in 1978 the section described by Gilbert (1920) was re-excavated and studied by Moffat and Catt (1983). Both accounts described 5-6 m of coarse stratified flint gravels overlying sand and the 'Reading Beds Bottom Bed' (i.e. Upnor Formation) with Chalk beneath. The gravels were overlain by 2-3 m of reddish yellow well-sorted coarse sand (Fig. 5.1, Plate 24). At the surface the sands were overlain by 0.4 m of angular flint gravel with a reddish brown and grey mottled silty clay matrix, a deposit visible

Plate 24. Section (shown diagrammatically in Fig. 5.1) in Plio-Pleistocene marine gravels and sands, Little Heath (TL 017082) near Berkhamsted, 1978.

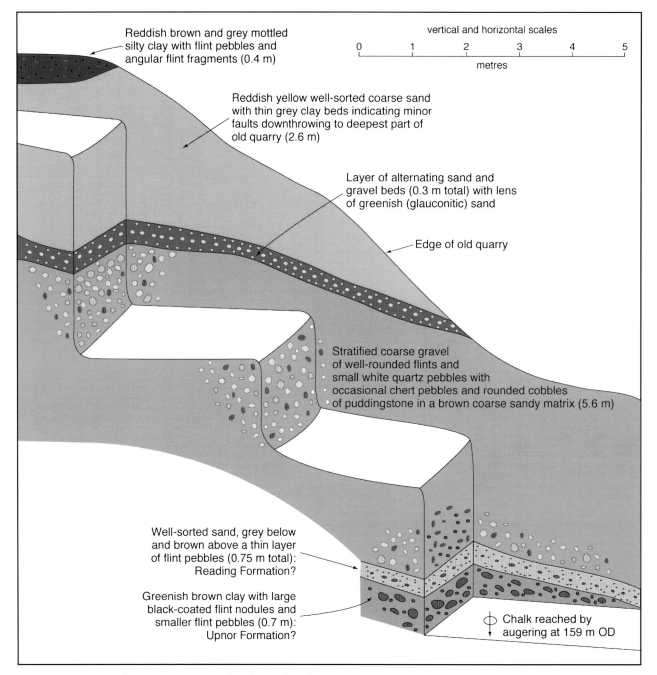

Reddish brown and grey mottled silty clay with flint pebbles and angular flint fragments (0.4 m)

vertical and horizontal scales

metres

Reddish yellow well-sorted coarse sand with thin grey clay beds indicating minor faults downthrowing to deepest part of old quarry (2.6 m)

Layer of alternating sand and gravel beds (0.3 m total) with lens of greenish (glauconitic) sand

Edge of old quarry

Stratified coarse gravel of well-rounded flints and small white quartz pebbles with occasional chert pebbles and rounded cobbles of puddingstone in a brown coarse sandy matrix (5.6 m)

Well-sorted sand, grey below and brown above a thin layer of flint pebbles (0.75 m total): Reading Formation?

Greenish brown clay with large black-coated flint nodules and smaller flint pebbles (0.7 m): Upnor Formation?

Chalk reached by augering at 159 m OD

Figure 5.1. Section in Plio-Pleistocene marine beach gravels and sands exposed at Little Heath (TL 017082) near Berkhamsted, 1978; redrawn from Moffat and Catt (1983). A photo of the section is shown in Plate 24.

and often thicker in many of the other shallow excavations in the area. This was described as 'glacial gravel' by Gilbert (1920), but was reinterpreted as a Pleistocene periglacial slope (gelifluction) deposit by Moffat and Catt (1983).

The heavy mineral assemblage in the flint gravels and reddish-yellow coarse sand at Little Heath differs slightly from those in the underlying Upnor Formation and the Reading Formation at other Hertfordshire sites in containing more zircon, rutile, anatase and andalusite, but less tourmaline and staurolite (Wooldridge, 1927; Moffat and Catt, 1986a). In these respects it resembles the sandy ironstone at Rothamsted, so correlation with the Red Crag is likely, though Sherlock (1930) suggested that the differences noted by Wooldridge (1927) between the Reading Beds and

Little Heath sands can be explained by natural mineralogical variation in the Reading Beds. In addition to well rounded flint cobbles and pebbles, the flint gravels also contain small white quartz or quartzite pebbles, which were reported as abundant in gravels originally thought to be part of the Reading Formation at Lane End near High Wycombe (White, 1906; Wooldridge and Gill, 1925). Consequently, Sherlock (1922, pp. 37-38; 1924) attributed the Little Heath gravels to the Reading Formation. However, for the same reason, Barrow (1919a) had earlier suggested that the Lane End and Little Heath deposits are similar in age and younger than the Reading Formation, possibly Pliocene. He emphasized that white quartz/quartzite pebbles are absent from the Reading Formation elsewhere, even from a thick pebble bed of the Reading Formation exposed in 1870 at Bolter End close to Lane End (Whitaker, 1889, Vol. 1, p. 183). Both Barrow (1919a, pp. 36-39) and Gilbert (1920) believed that the vein quartz/quartzite pebbles were derived from the Lower Greensand (Woburn Sand Formation) of the Leighton Buzzard area via the Wendover Gap, as a layer of similar pebbles was recorded beneath flinty valley gravels exposed in a railway cutting in the Misbourne valley about 2 km south of Wendover (Barrow and Green, 1921a; Sherlock, 1922, p. 37).

Based on sedimentological and mineralogical studies, Moffat and Catt (1983) agreed with Gilbert's suggestion (1920) that the gravels and overlying sands at Little Heath represent, respectively, a marine beach and shallow water, possibly intertidal, sands. The gravel is coarse (mean size 34 mm) and also well sorted, a combination of features commonly found in marine beach gravels. In the sand fraction, it also contains the mineral glauconite, which forms in the marine environment by interaction between seawater and detrital clay and iron oxide particles. At one level in the upper part of the gravel, a thin layer of sand containing 28% of this mineral was recorded in the 1978 excavation. In addition, Gilbert (1920) reported ripple marks, suncracks and rainspots in the overlying sands. All these features are certainly compatible with deposition at or near the margin of a sea that transgressed higher parts of the Chilterns.

Although there is no direct evidence for the exact age of the marine transgression, it bevelled and therefore must postdate the Upnor and Reading Formations. It could be attributed to a later Palaeogene formation, such as the Bagshot Formation, but the similarity in heavy mineral assemblage to the Rothamsted Red Crag indicates that a late Pliocene or early Pleistocene date is more likely. Isotopic (K-Ar) dating of the glauconite in the gravel could clarify the age, but loss of Ar from the microcrystalline structure of glauconite can render this method unreliable.

In addition, the gravels at Little Heath have yielded a few well rounded boulders composed of Hertfordshire Puddingstone (Gilbert, 1920, p. 38; Moffat and Catt, 1983). These also indicate that the gravels are younger than the Reading Formation, because at least one episode of erosion resulting in disruption of a puddingstone layer and severe rounding of the fragments must have intervened between them.

In several temporary excavations near Little Heath, Gilbert (1920) reported gravels similar in composition and thickness to those described above; he also suggested that they cover much of Berkhamsted Common. There is also some evidence that remnants of the Red Crag Formation are more extensive on other parts of the Chilterns than existing records suggest. Well rounded boulders composed of puddingstone like those encountered in the Little Heath excavations, but somewhat larger, were found by members of the Hertfordshire Geological Society (Bettina Seale and Avis Evans) on the surface at Marshalls Heath (TL 1615) near Harpenden, about 4.5 km east of Rothamsted Farm, and Sherlock and Pocock (1924, p. 30) recorded another near Hedges Farm (TL 135111), 3 km south of Rothamsted. Both of these localities are at a similar height to the Rothamsted Red Crag site. A further well-rounded boulder composed of puddingstone was found by Judith Everett, another member of the Hertfordshire Geological Society, at Rosehall Wood (TL 032004) near Chipperfield. This site is 16 km southwest of Rothamsted but only a few metres lower (approximately 125 m OD), so it could indicate the presence nearby of a gravel similar to that at Little Heath. Plate 25 shows well rounded puddingstone boulders from two of these sites. Further discoveries of well rounded puddingstone boulders on the Chilterns might therefore indicate other parts of the county where shoreline deposits of the Red Crag sea are preserved.

Using the heights of the Rothamsted, Little Heath and Lane End deposits and those of presumed equivalent shallow marine deposits on the North Downs at Netley Heath and Headley Heath, it is possible to draw a contour map for the Sub-Red Crag Surface in south-east England (Fig. 5.2). Jones (1999, p. 15) drew a similar map using in addition the evidence from fossiliferous deposits at Lenham in east Kent, though the Lenham Beds are probably much older (late Miocene or early Pliocene) than the other sites (Worssam, 1963), suggesting that in southeast England as a whole there could have been two different transgressions in the late Neogene. Nevertheless, both maps indicate a synclinal axis plunging north-eastwards from the Reading area, where the base of the Red Crag lies at or above 180 m OD, towards the Suffolk coast near Ipswich, where it is close to OD.

Although the Red Crag must have been deposited during

Plate 25. *Well rounded boulders of Hertfordshire Puddingstone from Marshall's Heath (TL 1615) near Harpenden (above), and Rosehall Wood (TL 032004) near Chipperfield (below).*

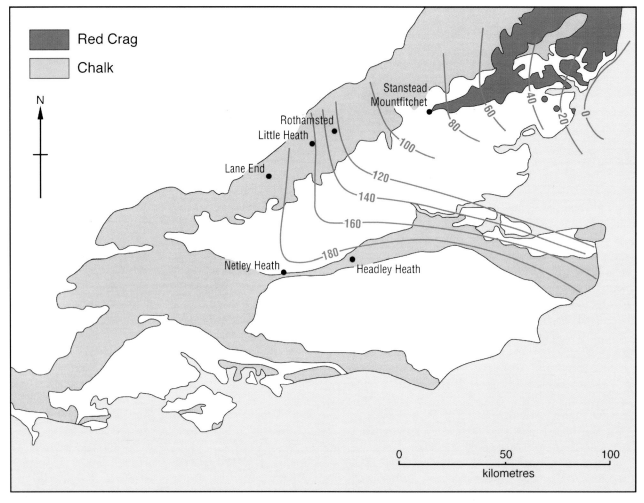

Figure 5.2. Occurrence of the Plio-Pleistocene Red Crag in southeast England and structure contours (m OD) on the folded Sub-Red Crag Surface, redrawn from Moffat et al. (1986) and Mathers and Zalasiewicz (1988).

another westward transgression of the North Sea like those of the Palaeogene, the marked westward increase in the elevation of its base cannot reflect the original depositional slope. The sediments all accumulated in shallow water (probably <25 m), and a change in sea level of more than 700 m (between Little Heath and the lowest part of the Westkapelle Ground Formation (-600 m OD) beneath the North Sea) is impossible in a short period. Also, Haq *et al.* (1987) estimated that the late Pliocene sea level was only about 20 m higher than present. Instead the slope of the Sub-Red Crag surface must have resulted from crustal earth movements after deposition. Such movements would certainly have included continuing subsidence of the North Sea Basin, but the onshore height difference of at least 160 m between the East Anglian coast and the western Chilterns suggests Quaternary tilting of southeast England by uplift in the west (Mathers and Zalasiewicz, 1988). The present East Anglian coastline in fact seems to have been a hinge line between uplift to the west and subsidence to the east (Westaway, 2009). The eastward decline of surfaces beneath Palaeogene deposits, such as the London Clay Formation, from the main Chiltern outliers to the East Anglian coast is little greater than 160 m, so most of the eastward tilting has occurred in the 2-3 Ma since deposition of the Red Crag,

with less in the earlier Neogene and later Palaeogene.

As discussed in Section 4.2, the south-easterly regional dip of the Mesozoic in the English Midlands is now attributed to doming caused by a long-lived mantle plume or 'hotspot' centred under the Irish Sea (Cope, 1994; Bott and Bott, 2004). As the doming began in the late Cretaceous or early Palaeogene (Cope, 1994), it probably accounts for the episodes of uplift that led to repeated marine regressions in the Palaeogene as well as the post-Red Crag tilting of southeast England. Alternatively, Watts *et al.* (2000, 2005) have suggested that the regional dip resulted from isostatic uplift of the west Midlands following unloading due to meltwater erosion in the valleys of the Severn and Warwickshire Avon during Mid Pleistocene glaciation. Their theory explains why most of the tilting seems to have occurred in the Quaternary, but cannot account for Palaeogene movements. Nor does it explain the height of the Red Crag in Hertfordshire, because their modelling of crustal movement showed that the uplift caused by erosion was limited to areas west of the present Chiltern scarp.

5.3. The Plateau Drift and Clay-with-flints *sensu stricto* of the Chiltern dip-slope

These drift materials overlying the Chalk are much more extensive than the very restricted deposits of late Pliocene or earliest Pleistocene age described in Section 5.2. In western Hertfordshire they occur on higher parts of the Chiltern dip-slope plateau, which declines gently south-eastwards from the crest of the escarpment between Hitchin and Tring (Fig. 5.3). Like other parts of the southwest Chilterns, this area is deeply dissected by a complex pattern of dry valleys (Moffat and Catt, 1986a) and by a series of NW-SE 'through-valleys' occupied by minor rivers, including in Hertfordshire the Mimram, Lea, Ver, Gade, Bulbourne and Chess. The interfluvial areas of the plateau separating both valley types are covered by up to 15 m of weathered, non-calcareous materials, which are identified as Clay-with-flints and coloured brown on current BGS maps of the area. However, on the original (pre-1900) Geological Survey 'Old Series' maps of the Chilterns and many other chalkland areas in southern England, the same materials were divided into a thick and very variable upper layer known as 'Brickearth' or 'Loam' and a thinner, more uniform lower layer lying immediately over the Chalk and termed 'Clay-with-flints' (Hull and Whitaker, 1861). The later decision to amalgamate the two under the name 'Clay-with-flints' was justified mainly because the lower layer is very thin (usually <1 m, though sometimes up to 3 m), so that its outcrop could not be shown separately at the 1:63,360 scale of the 'Old Series' maps. However, it means that BGS now uses 'Clay-with-flints' for some deposits that are neither clayey nor especially flint-rich. Also, the use of the term in two different senses has unfortunately led to considerable confusion.

Barrow (1919a) suggested reinstating the original division into two layers, and for the south-western Chilterns Loveday (1962) defined the upper layer as Plateau Drift and the lower as Clay-with-flints *sensu stricto*. Although 'Plateau Drift' has been used elsewhere for deposits that are lithologically similar, but often genetically different, from the Chiltern Plateau Drift, in this book Loveday's distinction is retained and the two terms are used as he defined them.

Clay-with-flints *sensu stricto*. This material is a clay containing large unworn flint nodules (or broken fragments thereof) similar to those in the chalk which always lies immediately beneath (Plate 26). The clay between the flint nodules is usually uniform reddish brown in colour (close to 5YR 5/6 of the Munsell Colour Chart), though it is often stained dark brown or black with iron and manganese oxides and hydrated oxides, which have mainly been redeposited from acidic water percolating downwards from soil horizons above. These two elements are probably carried in solution in the acidic water but precipitated where the pH increases on meeting the chalk (Thorez *et al.*, 1971). Black Clay-with-flints *sensu stricto* is often visible immediately above the chalk in Dunton brickpit at Ley Hill (SP 987012).

The clay is usually plastic when kneaded between the fingers, and contains very little sand or silt (>2 µm); up to 95% of the <2 mm fraction consists of particles less than

Plate 26. Clay-with-flints sensu stricto *over irregular surface of Chalk, Hillock Wood (SP 828027), Buckinghamshire.*

(usually much less than) 2 µm in size. In mineralogical terms, these clay particles are dominantly smectite, though small amounts (<10%) of kaolinite and mica-like clay minerals may also occur. The small amounts of sand and silt consist mainly of flint fragments, with subsidiary quartz grains (sometimes in euhedral bipyramidal crystals), glauconite and collophane (mainly fish scales, teeth and bones composed of calcium phosphate), all of which can be found in the minute quantities of insoluble residue (<1%) remaining after laboratory dissolution of chalk in weak (acetic or carbonic) acid. Smectite is also the dominant clay mineral in non-carbonate residues from the Chalk (Perrin, 1971).

In thin section the clay is almost completely birefringent, indicating a preferred orientation of the platy particles, which suggests it is illuvial clay (i.e. deposited particle by particle from percolating water). As with the precipitation of iron and manganese, the increase in pH at the junction with the chalk probably plays an important role in redeposition of illuvial clay, because the presence of Ca^{2+} ions flocculates the colloidal clay particles. However, redeposition can also occur where the percolating water reaches drier or more permeable layers and does not go deeper because it seeps into them; this filtering effect happens mainly where the more permeable chalk is reached, but may also occur at higher levels in the Plateau Drift during dry periods. The birefringent clay of the Clay-with-flints *sensu stricto* is usually laminated, with yellow and brown layers containing different amounts of iron, though the laminations and the birefringence itself may be masked by strong, often nodular concentrations of iron and manganese oxides. The layering often picks out the presence of flow structures, suggesting downward slumping of the clay into cavities. Immediately adjacent to the very irregular chalk surface there are often incompletely filled cavities up to 2 cm across, which give the clay an unusually low bulk density (Thorez *et al.*, 1971). The illuvial clay is often deposited also in fissures penetrating the chalk to depths of several metres. Where a network of variously orientated fissures have been widened by dissolution and progressively infilled with illuvial clay, small irregular blocks of chalk may be preserved within the Clay-with-flints *sensu stricto*, giving rise to what Kirkaldy (1950a) described as 'stoping' effects in the chalk quarry at Castle Lime Works, South Mimms (TL 230025).

This combination of features has been interpreted (Loveday, 1962; Thorez *et al.*, 1971; Catt, 1986) as indicating that the Clay-with-flints *sensu stricto* originated by prolonged downward illuviation of fine clay through the Plateau Drift and its redeposition in cavities produced by dissolution of chalk beneath the Plateau Drift cover. Flint nodules and other acid-insoluble residues released from the chalk, including fragments of silicified shells of echinoids and inoceramids similar to those described by Brown *et al.* (1969), also accumulated in the cavities and became mixed with the illuvial clay by slumping and possibly also by frost disturbance (cryoturbation) during cold stages of the Quaternary. The abundant smectite in the fine clay component of Clay-with-flints *sensu stricto* may be partly derived from the natural insoluble residue of the Chalk, but most is probably illuvial in origin, as it is mainly the finest clay particles that are moved by illuviation and in soils smectite tends to occur dominantly in the finest clay fraction.

A thin layer of Clay-with-flints *sensu stricto* also occurs commonly between the Chalk and other permeable overlying deposits, which have been weathered throughout, such as the older terrace sands and gravels deposited by the River Thames during the Quaternary (Section 6.2). Unlike the Plateau Drift, these deposits originally contained very little clay, but once they had been decalcified, the weakly acidic water percolating through them could slowly wash the small

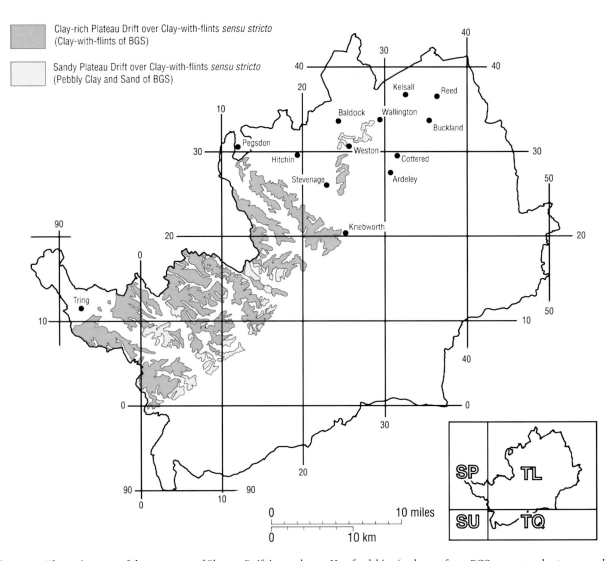

Figure 5.3. The main areas of the two types of Plateau Drift in northwest Hertfordshire (redrawn from BGS 1:50,000 sheets 221 and 239 and Soil Survey 1:63,360 sheet 238). Smaller patches also occur in northeast Hertfordshire near the named villages.

amounts downwards, together with any additional clay produced by weathering of coarser particles, and concentrate it by redeposition as an illuvial layer at the chalk surface where the pH increases.

Plateau Drift. The properties of the Plateau Drift overlying the Clay-with-flints *sensu stricto* were originally defined by Loveday (1962) on higher parts of the Chilterns dip-slope near Henley-on-Thames. Here it is a yellowish brown (10YR 5/6), yellowish red (5YR 5/6) and occasionally red (2.5YR 5/6) mottled clay, sandy clay or sandy clay loam, containing variable amounts of angular flint fragments and small black-coated flint pebbles resembling those in the Reading and Upnor Formations. The flint pebbles have a patchy distribution, occurring mainly in sandier forms of the Plateau Drift that correspond with areas shown on BGS maps as 'Pebbly Clay and Sand' (Sherlock and Noble, 1922; Sherlock, 1947; also shown in Fig. 5.3). Over the range of Plateau Drift types, sand (20 µm – 2 mm) forms 30-70%, clay (<2 µm) 20-60%, and silt (2-20 µm) usually about 15%. Vertical channels and cracks often occur in the upper 2-3 m, and are usually lined with light grey (10YR 7/2) or black clay. In addition to flint fragments and pebbles, the clasts also include occasional blocks of silcrete (silica-cemented puddingstone and sarsenstone), which range in size up to several metres across. For example, large sarsens were previously quarried in deep pits exposing Plateau Drift at Walter's Ash, Buckinghamshire (SU 8398) (Spicer, 1905; Woodward and Herries, 1905; Sherlock and Noble, 1922, p. 35), where they were used mainly to make paving setts and kerbstones. A photograph of the pit at Walter's Ash showing large sarsen blocks in Plateau Drift was published by Davies and Baines (1953, Plate 1).

The sand fraction of the Plateau Drift consists mainly of subangular to subrounded quartz grains, with minor amounts of flint, muscovite and feldspars; the heavy mineral assemblage consists principally of zircon, tourmaline, rutile, staurolite and kyanite with sporadic anatase, brookite, garnet, epidote, andalusite and hornblende. This assemblage is very similar to that of the Upnor and Reading formations

occurring in outliers on the Chiltern dip-slope. The clay mineralogy (mainly smectite and mica with subsidiary kaolinite and vermiculite) is also like that of these two formations.

In thin section, the Plateau Drift is much more heterogeneous than the Clay-with-flints *sensu stricto*. In the more clay-rich varieties, the sand and occasional silt particles are unevenly distributed through the clay matrix, and most of the latter is much less birefringent than in the Clay-with-flints *sensu stricto*. Strongly birefringent (oriented) clay occurs only locally as thin laminated infillings or coats lining channels conducting water, such as desiccation cracks, root or earthworm channels.

A similar range of clast content, micromorphological and mineralogical features has been reported in the Plateau Drift subsoil at Rothamsted Farm (Weir *et al.*, 1969; Catt, 1969; Avery *et al.*, 1972), and indicates derivation mainly from a cover of the Reading and Upnor formations over the Chalk. The three main types of sediment in these formations (sand, silty clay and flint pebble beds, Sections 4.4 and 4.5) largely explain the range in composition of the Plateau Drift from the common clay-rich variety to the rarer 'Pebbly Clay and Sand'. The main feature that they do not explain is the abundance of angular flint fragments, which must have been incorporated from the Chalk beneath (or from Clay-with-flints *sensu stricto*) by processes of mixing and disturbance, such as cryoturbation or mass downslope movement (gelifluction) under periglacial conditions during the Quaternary. Gelifraction (frost-shattering) under periglacial conditions could also explain why most of the flints occur as broken angular fragments rather than complete nodules (as in the Clay-with-flints *sensu stricto*). The size of the fragments usually decreases towards the surface, where the effects of gelifraction would have been strongest.

The thickest Plateau Drift, locally reaching 15 m, for example at Walter's Ash in Buckinghamshire (Sherlock and Noble, 1922, p. 35), occurs on parts of the Chiltern dip-slope interfluves furthest from the valleys. In these areas it often surrounds and seems to pass laterally into recognizable outliers of Reading and Upnor formations (Fig. 5.4). Some

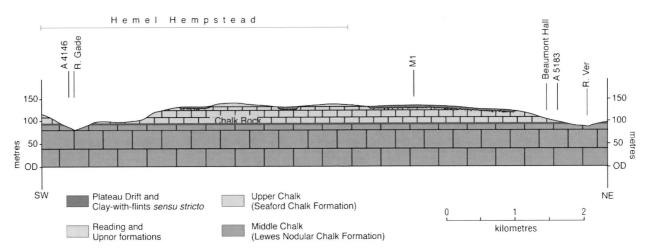

Figure 5.4. Section across Palaeogene outlier at Hemel Hempstead, showing relationship to Plateau Drift and Clay-with-flints sensu stricto.

Plate 27. Pipes in Chalk containing reddish brown Plateau Drift and lined with darker brown Clay-with-flints sensu stricto *exposed when the M25 near Chorleywood (TQ 040957) was widened in 2009.*

deeper exposures, for example on Aldbury Common (SP 974119) (Kidner, 1908; Anon., 1908b), have shown that it also covers and conceals patches of clay or sand attributable to the Reading Formation.

On the shoulders of the valleys and scarp-slope, the Plateau Drift feathers out to expose the underlying Clay-with-flints *sensu stricto*. The chalk surface beneath the Plateau Drift and Clay-with-flints *sensu stricto* is much more irregular than under the Palaeogene outliers (Plate 26); pinnacles project upwards into the Plateau Drift and pipes descend downwards, sometimes many metres below the mean level of the chalk surface. Though variable in thickness, the Clay-with-flints *sensu stricto* forms a fairly continuous layer following the chalk surface, and even occurs on the near-vertical walls of solution pipes that descend deeply into this rock (Plate 27). This is probably because water percolating through Plateau Drift that had collapsed into the pipes eventually reached a drier layer, and then seeped laterally into the surrounding chalk after depositing its load of illuvial clay. An oblique section of a pipe filled with Pebbly Clay and Sand and lined with Clay-with-flints *sensu stricto* exposed when the roundabout at the junction of Martins Way, Grace Way and Canterbury Way, Stevenage (TL 244262) was constructed was designated a RIGS by the Hertfordshire RIGS Group (2003).

These relationships suggest that, once the original cover of Reading and Upnor formations over the Chalk was reduced by subaerial erosion to a certain thickness, perhaps about

15 m, it no longer remained impermeable. The slightly acidic water percolating through the veneer from surface soils could then dissolve chalk adjacent to joints or other cracks and also carry illuvial clay particles downwards and redeposit them in the cavities and fissures formed by dissolution. The summit level of the chalk pinnacles consequently approximates to the local sub-Palaeogene surface, though even the pinnacle tops may have been lowered somewhat by loss of chalk.

Because of their unusual origins, it is difficult to place the Plateau Drift and Clay-with-flints *sensu stricto* in the geological history of the Chilterns. Essentially the Plateau Drift is derived from the oldest Palaeogene formations in the area, but many of its important characteristics and all those of the Clay-with-flints *sensu stricto* are the result of complex and quite deep-reaching pedogenetic modifications that occurred subsequently, in the late Palaeogene, Neogene or Quaternary. However, the dating of important events in their development after deposition of the original Upnor and Reading Formations is very difficult. Consequently, they cannot be described simply as Palaeogene sediments, nor as monogenetic soil units formed in a single climatic interval, nor as Quaternary ('drift') deposits, though undoubtedly they have aspects of all these in their complex histories. As Bateman (1988) pointed out, the question arises of 'what criteria must be fulfilled before a modified Tertiary deposit becomes a legitimate Quaternary deposit, and demoted to the ignominy of drift!'

Plate 28. Deep wide pipes containing yellow Pebbly Clay and Sand and lined with a thick layer of dark brown Clay-with-flints sensu stricto, *exposed when the Baldock by-pass (TL 249316) was constructed in 2004.*

In Hertfordshire, the Plateau Drift is most extensive on interfluve areas of the Chalk dip-slope southwest of a line between Pegsdon and Knebworth (Fig. 5.3) on the south-western side of the broad valley known as the Hitchin-Stevenage Gap. This gap is underlain by two buried valleys cut deeply into the Chalk and extending NNW-SSE beneath Hitchin, which were probably cut subglacially during the Anglian Stage of the Quaternary (Section 6.6). East of the Hitchin-Stevenage Gap, the Plateau Drift is much thinner and more patchy in occurrence, and is overlain by an increasing thickness of glacial deposits (tills and gravels) of the Anglian Stage. Quite large patches, occurring as inliers surrounded by Anglian till or glaciofluvial gravels, are shown (as Clay-with-flints) on the BGS Hitchin map (Sheet 221) between Baldock and Stevenage, in a strip from Weston north-eastwards to Wallington. Smaller ones were also mapped even further east, mainly near the villages of Kelshall, Ardeley, Cottered, Buckland and Reed (Fig. 5.3). A borehole at Ardeley (TL 310271) penetrated over 9 m of Plateau Drift over Chalk, and ploughed topsoil at Church Farm on the southern side of the village contains the assemblage of stones (large fragments of flint nodules and small flint pebbles) typical of Plateau Drift elsewhere. This contrasts with the assemblage in soils on the glacial deposits, which consist essentially of small flint fragments, quartzite pebbles, sandstones and occasional igneous rocks. Shallow temporary exposures for housing development in northeast Stevenage have often shown a thin (<2 m) cover of dark

brown silty and clay-rich Plateau Drift over Clay-with-flints *sensu stricto.*

In addition to the indication provided by stones exposed on the surface of cultivated soil, the outcrops of Plateau Drift can often also be identified in these parts of northeast Hertfordshire by the occurrence of acidophilous plant assemblages, which are absent from the till outcrop (James, 2009). Typical species of this assemblage include rough hawk's-beard (*Crepis biennis*), sweet vernal grass (*Anthoxanthum odoratum*) and pignut (*Conopodium majus*).

The deep cutting dug in 2003-4 for the Baldock by-pass across the crest of the Chalk scarp between Baldock and Weston indicated that the Plateau Drift here consists mainly of yellow Pebbly Clay and Sand containing abundant flint pebbles, which is similar to the material exposed at the Stevenage RIGS site. The pebbly sand filled deep and wide solution pipes that were lined with a thick layer of dark brown Clay-with-flints *sensu stricto* (Plate 28), and at the surface a thin (<1 m) bed of glacial gravel containing quartzite pebbles and other glacial erratics extended over the pipes and intervening areas where the Chalk rose close to the land surface.

It therefore seems that, before the Anglian glaciation, a fairly continuous cover of Plateau Drift derived from silty clays and sands of the Reading Formation covered much of the Upper Chalk outcrop in northeast Hertfordshire, certainly as far east as the Baldock-Stevenage area. This suggests that the Sub-Palaeogene Surface was preserved over this part of the county as well as areas to the south-west. The cover of Plateau Drift was then partly eroded by ice and subglacial meltwater streams during the Anglian glaciation, leaving thin, discontinuous patches of Plateau Drift and beneath them associated remnants of degraded Sub-Palaeogene Surface.

Locally there is evidence for incorporation of Plateau Drift or Clay-with-flints *sensu stricto* into basal layers of the Anglian till (Hopson *et al.*, 1996, pp. 72-75), confirming that these materials existed before the ice advance. It is also possible that some of the patches mapped as 'Clay-with-flints' in parts of northeast Hertfordshire east of Weston and Wallington originated by weathering of a thin layer of till over Chalk and acquired their reddish brown colour by oxidation during one or more post-Anglian interglacials. Reddened soils derived from chalky till have been reported in parts of Essex (Sturdy *et al.*, 1979).

5.4. Later Caenozoic landscape development

The interpretation of the Plateau Drift and Clay-with-flints *sensu stricto* outlined in Section 5.3 has important implications for the history of landscape development of the Chilterns during the later Tertiary and Quaternary. As the originally impermeable Palaeogene sequence was uplifted by crustal movements, it was progressively thinned by subaerial, probably mainly river erosion. No evidence remains of this denudational phase, which could have started in Hertfordshire soon after deposition of the Bagshot Formation. During the later Palaeogene and subsequent periods, it continued until the Palaeogene cover reached the critical thickness when its basal layers (Upnor Formation and lower parts of the Reading Formation) became much more permeable and could no longer support the drainage network causing the erosion. At this stage the surface lowering by subaerial erosion was largely replaced by weathering, including the subsurface dissolution of chalk beneath the permeable cover and the illuviation of clay through the cover. The cessation of surface erosion explains why a fairly continuous veneer of weathered basal Palaeogene sediments has been preserved (as Plateau Drift) across the Chalk dip-slope, even within the Anglian glacial limit. To a degree, the Plateau Drift plays a passive protective role in preserving the Chalk beneath from further subaerial erosion. It also explains why modern streams traversing thicker Palaeogene deposits in southeast Hertfordshire and even some of the larger Palaeogene outliers disappear down swallow-holes into the Chalk near the margin of the Palaeogene outcrop.

The main geomorphological implication of the origin of Plateau Drift is that the land surface on which it lies is the exhumed Sub-Palaeogene Surface somewhat lowered by sub-surface dissolution of Chalk and slumping of the Plateau Drift into pipes and other cavities created by the dissolution. It is equivalent to ancient land surfaces formed by weathering and irregular lowering of bedrock beneath a thick soil mantle in tropical regions, which have been termed

etchplains (Thomas, 1994). The extent of the lowering by sub-surface weathering probably varies depending on a range of factors, including time since the Plateau Drift was created, its particle size distribution and relative permeability. In Hertfordshire, most of the Plateau Drift was derived from the clay-rich and less permeable Upnor Formation and basal layers of the Reading Formation. Where the basal Palaeogene deposits were sandy and more permeable, the Sub-Palaeogene Surface could have been lowered by subsurface dissolution of chalk more than it has beneath the clay-rich Plateau Drift. For example, in the cutting for the Baldock by-pass penetrating Pebbly Clay and Sand, the chalk was dissected by much wider and deeper solution pipes (Plate 29) than normally occur beneath the less permable clay-rich Plateau Drift. However, any effect of this type may have been less than that resulting from differences in the time since lowering began. More importantly for future work, where the exact extent of individual Palaeogene transgressions remains unknown, it is possible that they can be reconstructed by petrographic studies that indicate the source of the Plateau Drift, such as detailed particle size distribution, mineralogy, clast types and micromorphological characteristics in thin section.

Dating the start of weathering and transformation of unaltered Palaeogene deposits into Plateau Drift in any particular area is very difficult. However, several features of the Plateau Drift and its relationship to other deposits allow some time limits to be placed. These include:

1. In east Hertfordshire, Plateau Drift derived from Reading Beds locally underlies Anglian till, which is still calcareous and unweathered in its lower part. In places, rafts are incorporated into the till. This suggests that at least some of the Plateau Drift had been formed before the Anglian glaciation about 450,000 years ago.

2. An important part of the weathering process converting Palaeogene clays into Plateau Drift was the formation of red mottles in the soil matrix, which indicate precipitation of red iron oxides, mainly haematite (γ-Fe$_2$O$_3$), in a warm and seasonally humid (e.g. Mediterranean) climate. Red mottles have not formed in British soils during the Holocene, as they are completely absent from those developed on deposits of the last (Devensian) cold stage of the Quaternary. However, they are characteristic of paleo-argillic soils (Avery, 1980) formed during the last (Ipswichian) and earlier interglacials on some older Quaternary deposits (Section 7.4). The weathering to produce red mottles in the Plateau Drift therefore occurred during or before the Ipswichian Interglacial, which elsewhere is dated to 128,000-115,000 years ago (Section 6.9).

3. Similarly, the amounts of oriented illuvial clay in the Plateau Drift are much greater (often >25% by area of a thin section) than occur in British Holocene soils, which have about 8% at the most. The larger amounts are typical of paleo-argillic soils, again indicating development of the Plateau Drift during the Ipswichian or earlier warm and seasonally humid periods. Very often thin sections of the Plateau Drift also show fragments of the illuvial

Plate 29. General view of deep wide pipes filled with yellow Pebbly Clay and Sand exposed in cutting for Baldock by-pass (TL 251319), Weston Hills, 2004.

clay bodies, which have been separated from the voids in which they formed and then incorporated within the soil matrix, a feature that is thought to result from disruption and disturbance by frost action (cryoturbation) in the Devensian or earlier cold stages. Further, a more complicated climatic history is often suggested by disrupted fragments of illuvial clay bodies that have been impregnated with red iron oxides after incorporation into the soil matrix. These must have originated by clay illuviation in a pre-Ipswichian interglacial, and were then disrupted during a pre-Ipswichian cold stage before being impregnated with haematite in a subsequent interglacial, which could itself have been the Ipswichian or an earlier interglacial.

4. A fourth line of evidence for dating the transformation of Upnor and Reading Formations into Plateau Drift is the presence within the Plateau Drift of funnel-shaped depressions filled with silty sediment (Section 6.8). The silty infills have often been worked for brick-making in the past (Section 10.4). Barrow (1919a, pp. 31-34) referred to them as the 'true brickearth', to distinguish them from the surrounding Plateau Drift, which had previously been shown as Brickearth on the 'Old Series' geological maps. Mineralogical studies suggest that the true brickearth is composed mainly of periglacial windblown dust or loess (Avery *et al.*, 1982). The depressions originated as karstic dolines, that is they were formed by inwashing or collapse of the Plateau Drift into large solution cavities in the chalk beneath (Barrow and Green, 1921a). Consequently, they post-date the transformation of Palaeocene sediments into Plateau Drift. Their silty infills often contain loess that is mineralogically different from, and therefore probably older than, the widespread Late Devensian loess in southeast England (Catt, 1985). A pre-Late Devensian age for the infills is also indicated by the presence of abundant Lower Palaeolithic flint implements at some sites, including Gaddesden Row (TL 038135) and Caddington (TL 0619) (Section 8.2). At present, neither the loess-containing infills nor the flint artefacts can be dated more precisely than pre-Ipswichian, which means the dolines (and therefore the transformation of nearby Palaeogene sediment into Plateau Drift) are yet older.

5. At Rothamsted, the isolated blocks of disturbed Red Crag were incorporated into upper layers of the Plateau Drift (Section 5.2). This suggests that, as at Little Heath, the Red Crag was originally deposited on undisturbed Reading Beds, which at Rothamsted was subsequently transformed into Plateau Drift.

These five lines of indirect dating evidence suggest that most of the Plateau Drift in Hertfordshire was formed during the Quaternary by weathering and disturbance of a veneer of basal Palaeogene sediment overlying the Chalk. This leaves the later Palaeogene and the whole of the Neogene for subaerial erosion of almost the complete sequence of Palaeogene sediments, a total thickness of at least 140 m. It is possible that the highest parts of the Chilterns, above the known limit of the Red Crag transgression, were exhumed before the Quaternary, but at present we have no evidence for this.

5.5. Earlier theories of Caenozoic landscape development

The monumental synthesis of the Caenozoic history of southeast England by Wooldridge and Linton (1955)

incorporated a very different history of Neogene landscape development from that outlined in Sections 5.3 and 5.4. They correlated numerous unfossiliferous sand and gravel deposits occurring at higher levels on the margins of the London Basin with the Lenham Beds of Kent and the Red Crag at Rothamsted, and suggested that they all occur on a marine (wave-cut) erosion surface of Plio-Pleistocene age, which is still extensively preserved on the Chalk dip-slopes of the Chilterns and North Downs. They noticed, as did Topley (1875) and other 19th century geologists, that interfluve remnants of the dip-slope do not show a uniform

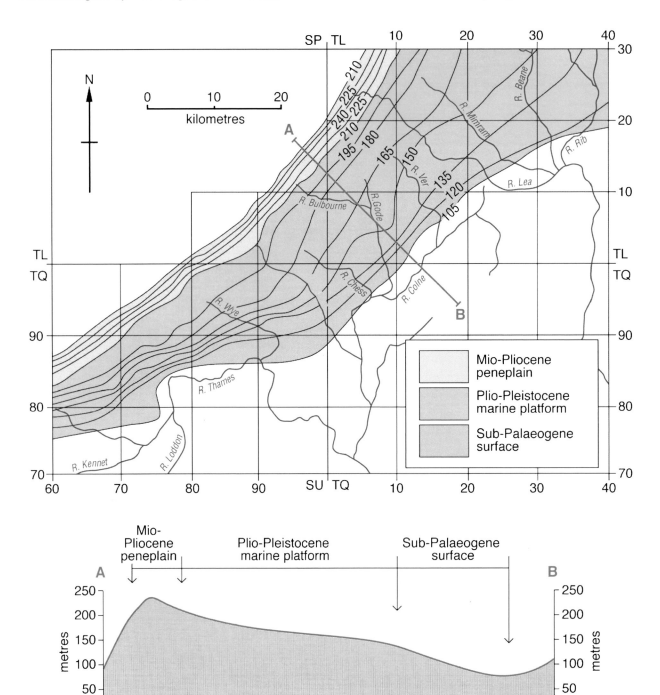

Figure 5.5. Generalized (continuous) contours (m OD) for the land surface of the Chilterns, and distribution of the three facets recognized by Wooldridge and Linton (1955).

gradient down the dip-slope, as one might expect from the major fold patterns of the London Basin and Weald, but can be divided into three fairly distinct parts (Fig. 5.5). The generalized contours shown in Figure 5.5, known as continuous contours, were drawn by joining points of equal height on interfluves and spurs ignoring minor contour indentations, a method originally used elsewhere by Linton (1956). With increasing height on the dip-slope, the three facets recognized by Wooldridge and Linton (1955) are:

1. A gently sloping area extending up from beneath the main outcrop of the Palaeogene formations (i.e. an exhumed part of the Sub-Palaeogene Surface).

2. A more gently inclined area apparently truncating the exhumed Sub-Palaeogene Surface and extending from *c.* 150 m to 200 m OD, where it terminates in a short but slightly steeper slope at 200-210 m OD. As the Lenham Beds and high-level Red Crag outliers at Rothamsted, etc lie on this surface, it was interpreted as a marine erosion surface (wave-cut platform) of Plio-Pleistocene age, and the steeper backslope as a degraded cliffline. The marine platform is widest (15-20 km) in the northern Chilterns, including Hertfordshire, and much narrower (5-10 km) in Buckinghamshire towards the Thames valley (Fig. 5.5).

3. An undulating summit surface above *c.* 210 m OD, interpreted as remnants of an earlier Mio-Pliocene peneplain, produced by long continued fluvial erosion with almost complete elimination of higher interfluves.

If the Sub-Palaeogene Surface (1) is projected with uniform slope to higher levels, it passes over the other two facets, which Wooldridge and Linton (1955) concluded must therefore have been cut into chalk beneath it, the higher facet (3) by subaerial river erosion and the lower (2) by marine erosion following the subaerial phase. They envisaged that only the exhumed Sub-Palaeogene Surface had been folded by Tertiary earth movements, and that the two higher surfaces were unaffected because they originated by erosion after the main (Miocene) phase of tectonic activity, the so-called 'Alpine Storm' (Wooldridge and Linton, 1955, p. 11).

Most of the Palaeogene outliers listed in Section 4.4 and shown in Figure 4.1 occur on the Sub-Palaeogene surface, as would be expected. But a few (e.g. at Lane End, Cowcroft, Great Gaddesden and Harpenden) are on the Plio-Pleistocene marine platform, and the existence of these can only be explained within the Wooldridge and Linton model if parts of the Sub-Palaeogene Surface had been sufficiently down-faulted or down-folded for parts of it to lie well below the level of the Plio-Pleistocene marine planation surface. However, the known structural features of the Chilterns (Section 5.7) offer little support for this explanation. Another problem with their model is that projection of the Plio-Pleistocene marine platform to lower levels within the London Basin implies that Red Crag should here occur over *in situ* Palaeogene formations. But in these situations (e.g. Harrow Weald Common, TQ 147929), Wooldridge and Linton found only unfossiliferous gravels. At Harrow Weald Common and other sites, these have subsequently been

reinterpreted as early Pleistocene river terrace gravels of either the Thames (Moffat and Catt, 1986b) or of south bank tributaries, such as the Mole and Wey (Bridgland, 1994, pp. 101-105).

The distribution of Plateau Drift on the Chilterns (Fig. 5.3) and other parts of the Chalk outcrop in SE England provides further evidence conflicting with the Wooldridge and Linton model. They suggested (1955, p. 55) that, although the soils on the exhumed Sub-Palaeogene Surface are derived mainly from a thin veneer of basal Palaeogene deposits (i.e. Plateau Drift), those on the marine platform were formed instead from Plio-Pleistocene marine sediments and those on the Mio-Pliocene peneplain from what they called 'true residual Clay-with-flints', i.e. the simple insoluble residue of Chalk that accumulated over a protracted period of Neogene and Quaternary weathering. However, the Plateau Drift, formed from basal Palaeogene deposits, extends over all three of their landscape units (Fig. 5.3) and suggests, as explained in Section 5.3, that they are all parts of the Sub-Palaeogene Surface. On their marine platform, Plio-Pleistocene marine deposits are much more restricted in distribution (Section 5.2) than they suggested. In addition, the 'true residual Clay-with-flints', said to occur only on their Mio-Pliocene Peneplain, simply does not exist anywhere in Britain. The acid-insoluble residue of the flinty but otherwise very pure basal Upper Chalk (Lewes and Seaford Chalk Formations) that lies beneath the Chiltern scarp crest contains too little clay, silt and sand in relation to the large number of flint nodules to produce a deposit resembling Plateau Drift. Long continued chemical weathering of the Upper Chalk followed by Quaternary gelifraction (frost shattering) would in fact produce what Reid (1899) vividly described as a 'stony desert of angular flints'. The natural insoluble residue of the Chalk is in fact only a minor component of both Clay-with-flints *sensu stricto* and Plateau Drift, and these materials contain much additional clay, which was derived ultimately from basal Palaeogene formations, though it has been modified and redistributed to varying degrees by the pedogenic processes of acid weathering, illuviation and cryoturbation.

Thus the superficial materials now known to occur on all three of the Chalk dip-slope facets are different from those postulated by Wooldridge and Linton (1955), and do not support the different origins that they attributed to the facets.

5.6. The drainage network of the Chilterns

In support of their model of Neogene-early Pleistocene landscape development, Wooldridge and Linton (1955) also cited the geomorphological evidence of a supposed difference in drainage networks on their Mio-Pliocene peneplain and Plio-Pleistocene marine platform. In southeast England as a whole, the drainage pattern on the marine platform was thought to be discordant to geological structures, the river valleys cutting across minor folds rather than running along outcrops of softer or weaker beds orientated by the structures. They suggested that this

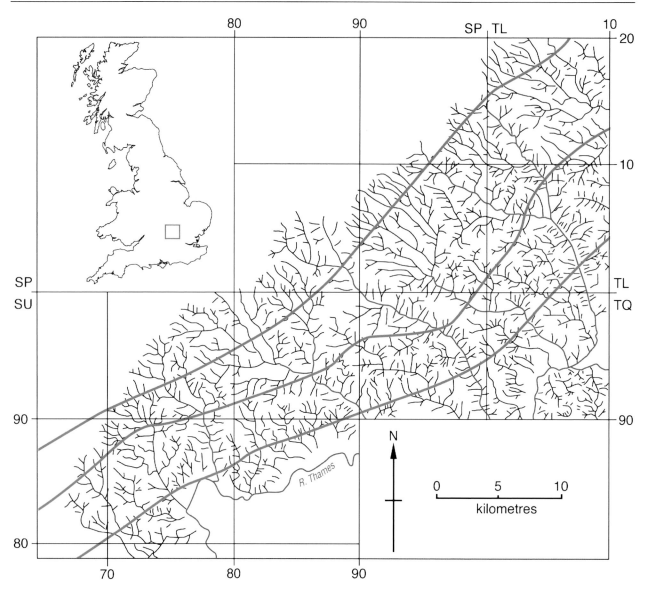

Figure 5.6. Valley network of the Chilterns, redrawn from Moffatt and Catt (1986a). Black lines are dry valleys, blue lines are semi-permanent rivers and red lines the boundaries between the three facets of Wooldridge and Linton (1955).

resulted from superimposition of the rivers onto folded Chalk and Palaeogene beds from an unconformable cover of virtually horizontal Plio-Pleistocene marine sediments, on which the rivers were initiated after regression of the Red Crag sea. In contrast, the drainage on the Mio-Pliocene peneplain was said to be well adjusted to structure, reflecting a presumed long period of development directly onto the folded Chalk.

However, Jones (1974) showed that in Sussex and Wessex the best evidence for drainage discordance is found where the Plio-Pleistocene platform itself is poorly expressed, and that discordance is virtually absent around the London Basin where the platform is well developed. In southeast England as a whole the drainage is generally accordant with the major fold axes but often discordant with smaller folds and faults, a pattern that is best explained in terms of initial development on a land surface influenced by early Tertiary macro-folding, the rivers then later maintaining their courses across slowly developing minor structures (Jones 1999, p. 9).

Since Wooldridge and Linton developed their model of

landscape evolution, it has become possible to measure and compare the characteristics of drainage basins quantitatively and objectively by the method of morphometric analysis (Strahler, 1958). When this was applied to the dry valley network of the Chilterns by Moffat and Catt (1986a), they found no consistent differences between the three facets of Wooldridge and Linton (1955).

For their work, Moffat and Catt defined the valley system of the Chilterns from aerial photographs and Ordnance Survey 1:25,000 maps, the valley axes being extended to the highest contour with a distinct 'v' shape. The valley pattern for the higher (unglaciated) south-western Chilterns is illustrated in Figure 5.6, which also shows the boundaries between the three facets of Wooldridge and Linton (1955). No obvious differences in the valley network between the facets can be seen. On all three facets the network is a mixture of dendritic and trellised patterns, the latter characterized by two sub-parallel sets of valleys, one orientated approximately NW-SE and the other perpendicular to it, i.e. approximately NE-SW. The trellised

94

Variable	Derivation	Group 1	Group 2	Group 3	Group 4	Group 5
Drainage density	$\dfrac{\text{Total length of net}}{\text{Basin area}}$	1.84	2.69	1.90	1.90	1.73
Valley frequency	$\dfrac{\text{Total number of segments}}{\text{Basin area}}$	1.55	5.02	2.12	2.18	2.62
Basin circularity	$\dfrac{6.283\ \sqrt{\text{basin area}}/\pi}{\text{Basin perimeter}}$	0.74	0.82	0.70	0.80	0.80
Basin elongation	$\dfrac{2\sqrt{\text{basin area}}/\pi}{\text{Basin length}}$	0.56	0.68	0.53	0.71	0.80
Width/length ratio	$\dfrac{\text{Basin width}}{\text{Basin length}}$	0.31	0.48	0.29	0.49	0.63
Lemniscate ratio	$\dfrac{\text{Basin length}^2}{4 \times \text{Basin area}}$	1.03	0.69	1.14	0.65	0.52
Relief ratio	$\dfrac{\text{Basin relief}}{\text{Basin length}}$	19.36	33.44	13.45	30.89	20.64
Ruggedness number	$\dfrac{\text{Drainage density} \times \text{Relief}}{528}$	0.47	0.40	0.33	0.45	0.19
Mean link length	$\dfrac{\text{Total length of net}}{\text{Number of links}}$	0.84	0.47	0.62	0.64	0.56
1st:2nd length ratio	$\dfrac{\text{Length of 1st-order segments}}{\text{Length of 2nd-order segments}}$	2.00	2.81	2.45	2.51	2.44
1st:2nd bifurcation ratio	$\dfrac{\text{Number of 1st-order segments}}{\text{Number of 2nd-order segments}}$	3.58	2.63	4.44	3.92	2.84

Table 5.1. Morphometric variables of 3rd-order basins in the SW Chilterns and mean values of the variables for five basin groups.

pattern suggests some measure of control by geological structure, the NW-SE valleys perhaps reflecting the regional dip (i.e. they are consequent valleys), and the NE-SW valleys possibly a regional pattern of joints, faults or minor folds in the Chalk bedrock. Also evident in Figure 5.6 is a slight change in valley orientation between the extreme southwestern Chilterns near the Thames valley and the northeastern Chilterns, for example near Hemel Hempstead. In the former area, the two valley orientations approach NNW-SSE and NNE-SSW, whereas in the latter they are often closer to WNW-ESE and NNE-SSW. This suggests that the direction of regional dip swings gradually from SSE near the Thames to ESE in the northeast Chilterns.

To analyse the valley network in greater detail, valley segments were ordered according to a standard system in which the highest (fingertip) segments were designated 1st-order segments, 2nd-order segments were produced by the confluence of two such 1st-order segments and 3rd-order segments resulted from the uniting of two 2nd-order segments (Fig. 5.7).

The watersheds between 3rd-order drainage basins (i.e. the basins including all valleys down to the confluence of two 3rd-order segments) were then plotted using contours on the 1:25,000 maps. On the Chiltern dip-slope between the present Thames valley and a line drawn between Luton and Welwyn, fifty-five 3rd-order basins were delineated. For each of these, twelve indices of basin form (total valley length, total number of valley segments, number of valley links, basin area, length of basin perimeter, basin length, basin width, basin relief, mean length of 1st-order segments, mean length of 2nd-order segments, number of 1st-order

segments, number of 2nd-order segments) were measured from the map. As many of these are dependent on basin size, a further eleven variables, less dependent on basin size, were then calculated from the original measurements (Table 5.1).

Cluster analysis of the 11 indices of basin form, using the CLUSTAN 1C program of Wishart (1978), showed that the 3rd-order basins could be divided into five groups (Table 5.1), the distributions of which are shown in Figure 5.8. The five groups can be distinguished in the following ways:

1. Medium to large elongate basins with low width/length ratios, high lemniscate ratios, low drainage densities and low valley frequencies. They also have the highest mean

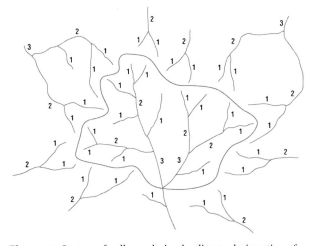

Figure 5.7. System of valley ordering leading to designation of 3rd-order drainage basins.

95

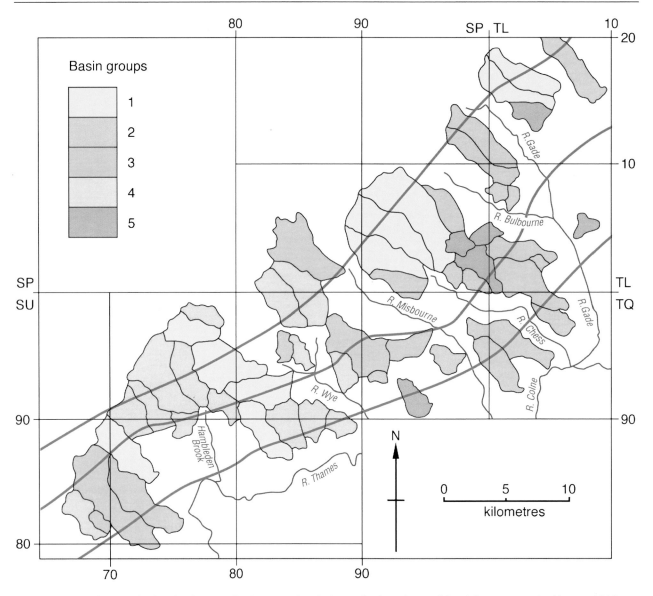

Figure 5.8. Distribution of 3rd-order drainage basin groups in relation to the three facets of the Chilterns recognized by Wooldridge and Linton (1955). See text for description of each group.

link lengths and lowest mean 1st:2nd length ratio. They occur near the top of the Chalk dip-slope and in central parts of the interfluves, though between Stokenchurch and Marlow one extends down to the Thames floodplain.

2. Small basins with very large drainage densities and valley frequencies, low 1st:2nd bifurcation ratios and very high average relief ratio. All except two are situated on sands and gravels, such as Reading Formation sands, the 'Pebbly Clay and Sand' of BGS maps and terrace gravels of the proto-Thames (see Section 6.2).

3. Basins with the largest 1st:2nd bifurcation ratios and lemniscate ratios but the smallest width-length ratios. All except two of this group occur northeast of the R. Wye.

4. Basins with similar drainage densities and valley frequencies to those of Group 3, but with larger width-length and relief ratios and lower lemniscate ratios. These occur at all levels on the dip-slope but only southwest of the Misbourne valley. Groups 3 and 4 together account for almost 60% of the 3rd-order basins identified, and like

Group 1 basins occur mainly on Chalk, though some have 1st-order segments on Plateau Drift.

5. Six small basins with low drainage densities, lemniscate ratios and ruggedness numbers but large width/length ratios and fairly large valley frequencies. They occur mainly on areas of Plateau Drift (e.g. near Chesham), though in their lowest reaches some cut through to Chalk.

The distribution of the five groups of 3rd-order basins does not support Wooldridge and Linton's suggestion that their Plio-Pleistocene marine platform and Mio-Pliocene peneplain have different drainage patterns. Figure 5.8 shows no correlation between any of the five groups and the three facets. Instead the distribution of basins seems to be controlled mainly by the structure of the Chalk and the lithology of overlying superficial materials. The features suggesting structural control include the elongate shapes of many of the basins parallel to the dip of the Chalk and a change in the predominant direction of elongation of some basin groups from NW-SE in the southwest Chilterns to WNW-ESE in the northeast Chilterns, similar to the possibly dip-related change in overall valley orientation noted previously. This change in direction is most evident in the very elongate basins of Groups 1 and 3. The main features indicating lithological control of the drainage pattern are (a) the almost exclusive restriction of the less elongate Groups 2 and 5 basins to sandy deposits and Plateau Drift, respectively, and (b) most of the basins of Groups 1, 3 and 4 have long 2nd- and 3rd-order segments incised into Chalk, though their short 1st-order segments are usually on Plateau Drift. The soft, homogeneous and unstructured nature of the sands and Plateau Drift allows many valley segments to develop and join after short distances to give small 3rd-order basins with small 1st:2nd bifurcation ratios and mean link lengths, but high drainage densities and valley frequencies. The sporadic occurrence of the sandy deposits often causes the Group 2 basins to attain 3rd-order status only on reaching the main through-valleys, thus explaining their large relief ratios. The variation in basin characteristics also invalidates the suggestion of Young (1905) that the entire valley systems of chalkland areas, including the Chilterns, were simply superimposed from an earlier cover of Palaeogene beds.

In the extreme south-western Chilterns, the dry valleys (mainly of Group 4 basins) are more deeply incised than those (mainly in Group 3 basins) northeast of a line between Wendover and Beaconsfield. In the southwest, the valleys are incised deeply enough to expose large expanses of New Pit and Holywell Nodular Chalk formations (Middle Chalk) in the valley bottoms, but these valley floor outcrops narrow progressively north-eastwards and eventually disappear from all but major through-valleys such as that of the Upper Lea. There are five possible reasons for the difference in depth of incision:

1. If minor folds are more pronounced in the northeast than southwest Chilterns, the Chalk there is probably more fissured, and this may locally increase water flow (transmissivity) through the Chalk. In areas between the folds, the greater transmissivity has lowered the water table so that the valleys dried out sooner and incision ceased earlier, thus giving shallower valleys. In contrast, the valleys in areas between the weaker, less fissured folds of the southwest Chilterns would have remained wet for longer, and thus continued to deepen.

2. Remnants of the Lewes and Seaford Chalk formations (basal Upper Chalk) are thicker in the southwest Chilterns and, as the underlying New Pit Chalk Formation is harder and more resistant to fluvial downcutting, it limited the depth of valleys in the northeast Chilterns where it is closer to the surface.

3. Basin relief and depth of incision can be controlled by regional slope (Mather and Doornkamp, 1970), and as this decreases slightly from southwest to northeast (Fig. 5.5), it could account for the decrease in valley incision in the same direction.

4. The interfluves covered by Plateau Drift and Clay-with-flints *sensu stricto* have been lowered by sub-surface dissolution of chalk, whereas those beneath unaltered Palaeogene deposits have not. As Palaeogene outliers are common in the south-western Chilterns, but are largely replaced by Plateau Drift in the northeast, the shallower valleys in the northeast could reflect the greater interfluve lowering there.

At present it is difficult to decide which of these explanations best accounts for the difference in depth of incision; perhaps all contributed in some measure. To judge between them, we need to know more about the hydrology of the Chalk in relation to its structure, the resistance of various lithological units to downcutting, and rates of subsurface dissolution beneath the Plateau Drift.

The influence of the structure of the Chalk and the lithology of overlying deposits on the drainage patterns of the Chilterns suggests that at least some of the valley network must have originated in a temperate climate. Chalk and other deposits invaded by permafrost in a periglacial environment would behave as a more homogeneous surface layer, and any drainage network initiated on it would probably be completely dendritic with fewer differences than those observed between the various types of drainage basin. So, although there is considerable evidence for periglacial modification of the dry valleys during Pleistocene cold stages (Section 6.10), it seems the overall pattern was initiated earlier.

If the drainage network on the Chilterns was initiated in temperate conditions, it can only have been when the water table in the Chalk was considerable higher than it is now. This must have been at a time in the Neogene or Early Quaternary when the Chilterns were much closer to the sea level of the time and/or the climate was much wetter than now. Evidence for the rainfall of southeast England at these times is sparse, but the dominantly Quaternary uplift of the Chilterns indicated by the height of the Red Crag at Rothamsted and deposits of probably similar age at Little Heath etc (Section 5.2) may be sufficient to account for a higher water table as the Chalk would then have been much closer to sea level. The sequence of Thames terraces declining in height through the Quaternary (Section 6.3) provides further evidence for post-Neogene uplift of the Hertfordshire area.

5.7. Structural features affecting the Chalk and later formations

South of Hertfordshire, the Mesozoic succession of southern England is affected by major E-W structures, such as the London Syncline (Ellison *et al.*, 2004), Wealden Anticline (Jones, 1999) and Hampshire and Wessex Synclines (Chadwick, 1993). Boreholes and geophysical evidence show that south of the Variscan Front Thrust (Section 2.6), the Palaeozoic basement sinks steeply to -1600 m to -2000 m OD beneath a rapidly increasing thickness of softer Mesozoic strata. In addition to the major folds, the thicker Mesozoic sequences are also affected by major faults, monoclines and periclines, which are also mainly orientated E-W

(Chadwick and Evans, 2005, Figs. 7 and 9). All these major structures probably originated by northward compression of the thick but soft Mesozoic successions against the rigid London Platform during the Alpine Orogeny. The Wealden Anticline and a similar major fold along the English Channel are closely superimposed on earlier (Variscan) graben-like extensional basins, whereas the London, Hampshire and Wessex synclines are superimposed on underlying compressional horst blocks of Variscan origin. These examples of inversion tectonics (Cooper *et al.*, 1989) often also show reversal of the original (Variscan) displacement along individual faults.

However, in Hertfordshire and neighbouring areas north of the present Thames valley, there are no similar major structures and no clear examples of inversion tectonics. Any folds and faults affecting the Chalk and later deposits are much smaller in scale. This is probably because the soft Cretaceous and Palaeogene deposits north of London are underlain at depths of only -100 to -200 m OD by the hard Palaeozoic rocks of the London Platform (part of the Midlands Microcraton), which was probably rigid enough to resist the strongest effects of Alpine compression, but transmitted some minor forces to the relatively thin Cretaceous-Palaeogene cover.

Known minor structures

Numerous minor structures affecting the Chalk and Palaeogene beds of the Hertfordshire area have been recorded in exposures or inferred from lines of boreholes or from outcrop displacements indicated by detailed BGS or other geological mapping. The main examples of these structures, shown in Fig. 5.9, are:

1. A pair of faults extending NNE-SSW and forming a minor graben at Bennetts End, Hemel Hempstead (TL 073064). When exposed, the eastern fault had a hade of about 50° and brought the Harwich and Reading Formations against Chalk; the western one, almost vertical, brought the Chalk back up against the same Palaeogene sequence. The faults were originally seen in brickpits in 1861 and 1864 (Whitaker, 1889, Vol. 1, pp. 208-209), and were still visible until about 1900 (Hopkinson and Morison, 1891; Anon, 1892b; Green, 1900), but have since been obscured. Gilbert (1923) described extensions of the same structures in the nearby Acorn Brickpit and, according to Sherlock (1922, pp. 26 and 32), they pass northwards into a zone of disturbance south of Cupid Green (TL 070083).

2. A fault extending NNE-SSW across the Chess valley southeast of Chesham, downthrowing to the east. It was exposed in the railway cutting for the Metropolitan Line at Chesham Bois (SP 969000), where it affects a hardground (part of the Chalk Rock succession) near the boundary between the New Pit and Lewes Chalk formations (Sherlock, 1922, p. 28).

3. Two NE-SW faults north of Gerrards Cross (SU 9988), which form a minor graben, letting London Clay Formation down into the Reading Formation.

4. An anticline affecting the Chalk and all Palaeogene formations up to the London Clay Formation, extending ENE from Radlett (TQ 9916) through Ridge (TL 2100) and Newgate Street (TL 3005) towards Broxbourne (TL 3707) and plunging in the same direction (Sherlock and Pocock, 1924, p. 4 and Fig. 2; Lawrence, 1966). This results in small inliers, in which outcrops of Upnor and Reading formations and locally even Chalk are surrounded entirely by London Clay, in Northaw Great Wood (TL 2904), the valley to the south (TL 2801) and the valley of the Cuffley Brook. About 3 km to the north, a parallel syncline extends ENE from Water End (TL 2204) towards Epping Green (TL 2906).

5. A NE-SW anticline along the foot of the Chiltern scarp between Sharpenhoe (TL 0630) and Edlesborough Hill (SP 9819) (Shephard-Thorn *et al.*, 1994, Fig. 32).

6. A gentle anticline with an axis pitching approximately south-eastwards, exposed in the Chalk quarry at Ivinghoe Aston (SP 962176) (Brown, 1969, p. 64). This is probably a south-westward extension of the NE-SW anticline at Edlesborough described by Shephard-Thorn *et al.* (1994).

7. A NE-SW syncline passing into a normal fault with a throw of approximately 5 m, previously exposed in one of the Pitstone chalk quarries (SP 9414) (Brown, 1969, p. 64).

8. An ENE-WSW anticline or monocline along the course of the River Pinn between Pinner (TQ 1189), Eastcote Village (TQ 1088) and extending west of Ruislip (TQ 0787) (Hopkinson 1887c; Wooldridge, 1926), which results in a line of Reading Formation inliers (Bromehead, 1925, p. 7). The uparching of lower parts of the London Clay Formation in the railway tunnel south of Potters Bar (TQ 2699) (Prestwich, 1851, p. 49) could be an ENE continuation of this fold. In the same area, Hester (1942) suggested the presence of a further anticline to the north extending eastwards from Harefield (TQ 0591), three ENE-WSW synclinal axes between and on either side of the two anticlines, and a series of three NNW-SSE asymmetrical anticlines with intervening synclines crossing the ENE-WSW structures almost at right angles.

9. A gentle syncline extending ENE from Willesden (Bromehead, 1925), probably accounting for outliers of the Claygate Member at Willesden Green (TQ 2284) and of the Bagshot Formation at Hampstead (TQ 2686) and Highgate (TQ 2887).

10. An anticline extending NW-SE between Radlett (TQ 1699) and Finchley (TQ 2590) (Bromehead, 1925).

11. A NW-SE anticline in the lower Lea Valley between Lea Bridge (TQ 3586) and Stratford (TQ 3884), and another extending NNW from Edmonton (TQ 3392) (Bromehead, 1925).

12. These NW-SE folds in the lower Lea valley area are crossed by NE-SW or ENE-WSW folds producing dome-shaped inliers of Blackheath Pebble Beds (Harwich Formation) and Woolwich and Reading Formation surrounded by London Clay on the valley floor (Flavin and Joseph, 1983). The NE-SW folds include, from north to south, a syncline through Enfield (TQ 3396)

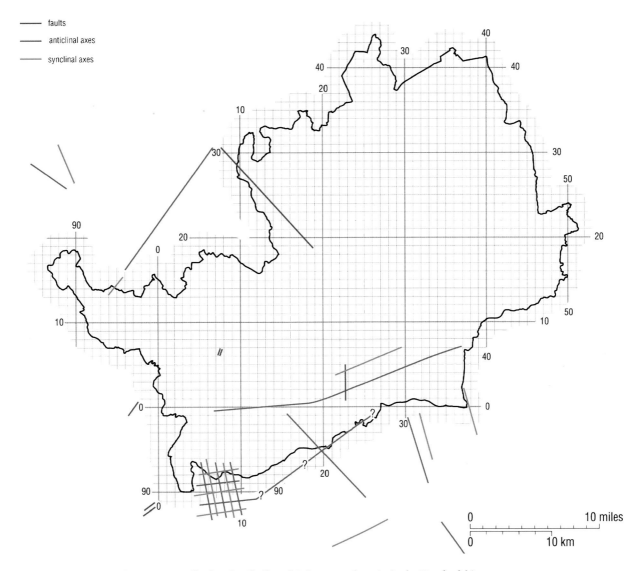

Figure 5.9. Minor tectonic structures affecting the Chalk and Palaeogene deposits in the Hertfordshire area.

and Waltham Abbey (TL 3800) (Sherlock and Pocock, 1924, Fig. 2), an anticline through Brimsdown (TQ 3697) (Hayward, 1955), a syncline extending from Hampstead Heath to Epping Forest, and an anticline with an axis close to Angel Road Station, Edmonton (TQ 339924) (Hayward, 1957).

13. A N-S fault along the valley of the Mimmshall Brook west of Potters Bar (TL 2401) and Brookmans Park (TL 2404) (Nowell, 1994).

14. A NW-SE anticline extending north-westwards from South Mimms towards St Albans, possibly crossed by a weak NE-SW anticline (Wooldridge, 1921).

15. A NW-SE monocline or normal fault with a downthrow of about 10 m to the northeast affecting the Chalk beneath Lilley Bottom from Whitwell (TL 1821) to Barton-le-Clay (TL 0831) in south Bedfordshire (Shephard-Thorn *et al.*, 1994; Hopson *et al.*, 1996).

16. A NW-SE syncline affecting the Oxford Clay and Ampthill Clay along the Ouzel Valley east of Stoke Hammond (SP 8829), and an associated WNW-ESE anticline south of Soulbury (SP 8827), both in east

Buckinghamshire (Shephard-Thorn *et al.*, 1994, Fig. 31).

17. An anticline or dome at Windsor (Whitaker, 1901, Fig. 5), which brings Chalk and the Reading Formation to the surface from beneath a wide outcrop of London Clay Formation on the south bank of the Thames.

Most of the structures listed above fall into two fairly well defined groups, one orientated ENE-WSW or NE-SW, and the other (NNW-SSE or NW-SE) approximately at right angles to the first. Wooldridge (1923) and Wooldridge and Linton (1955, Fig. 9) added other structures to this list, including two NE-SW 'faint synclinal lines' linking various Palaeogene outliers on lower parts of the Chiltern dip-slope between The Swillett (TQ 0295) and Burns Green (TL 3022) and between Colliers End (TL 3720) and Manuden (TL 4926) in Essex. However, these two folds were poorly substantiated; the only evidence given for their existence was that the chains of outliers are approximately parallel to the regional strike of the Chalk.

De Freitas (2009, Fig. 13) noted that, over the London Basin as a whole, the pattern of rivers, including many of the 'lost rivers' of central London (Barton, 1992), is similar to the rectilinear pattern of minor structures. Using this relationship, he postulated the existence of many other faults in the region, along which movement which could be important for groundwater flow and land stability. But further work is needed to justify their existence.

Structures assessed from borehole evidence

To reassess the structures of the Chiltern area more comprehensively and in greater detail, Moffat *et al.* (1986) assembled all available height data from boreholes and known outcrops for three stratigraphic levels, the Sub-Cenomanian, Sub-Senonian and Sub-Palaeogene surfaces. Structure contours for each surface were then drawn by various interpolation programmes, including SYMAP, gradient interpolation and a procedure known as standard regression kriging. None of these three methods gives reliable contours in areas with few data points, but there was considerable agreement between them in the better documented regions. As shown in Figures 5.10-5.13, the best reconstructions of the three surfaces, given the borehole data known at present, indicate that none of the three surfaces is a simple flat plane, as claimed by Wooldridge and

Linton (1955).

The Sub-Cenomanian Surface (i.e. the base of the Chalk) is the least reliable, as it is constructed from only 50 data points. Consequently, the structure contours (Fig. 5.10) show only a fairly uniform slope, which is the general regional form of the surface. However, they also show the following fairly clear features:

1. A change in direction of dip from approximately NW-SE in the southwest Chilterns to WNW-ESE in the northeast Chilterns, accompanied by a decrease in the angle of dip from approximately 0.5° in the southwest to about 0.3° in the northeast. The change occurs along a line extending from near Berkhamsted south-eastwards to Harrow. Generalized contours on the Chiltern dip-slope (Fig. 5.5) show roughly similar changes in the direction and angle of slope.
2. A minor NW-SE syncline beneath the head of the Bulbourne valley near Tring. This has considerable hydrogeological importance (Section 9.7).
3. A maximum height of over 120 m OD beneath the highest part of the Chalk escarpment near Wendover.

The Sub-Senonian Surface (i.e. the boundary between the

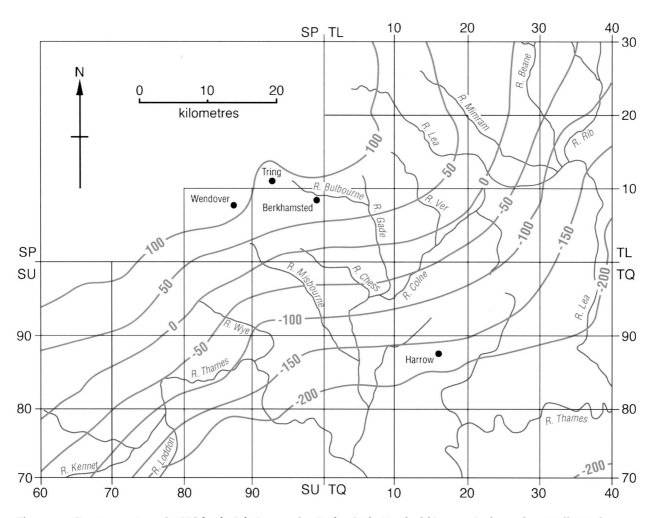

Figure 5.10. Structure contours (m OD) for the Sub-Cenomanian Surface in the Hertfordshire area (redrawn from Moffatt et al., 1986).

Middle and Upper Chalk marked by the Hitch-Wood or other hardgrounds forming the Chalk Rock within the Lewes Chalk Formation), was constructed from 238 fairly evenly distributed data points. Recent re-examination of the data for this surface using the more modern geostatistical method of residual maximum likelihood to calculate empirical best linear unbiased predictions (Lark and Webster, 2006) showed no significant improvement in the construction of contours for this surface. Consequently, the detail that it shows (Fig. 5.11) is more reliable than for the Sub-Cenomanian Surface, and includes the following features:

1. A change in direction and dip along the Berkhamsted-Harrow line similar to that observed on the Sub-Cenomanian Surface.
2. A short monocline (indicated by slight bunching of the 100 m and 50 m structure contours) extending south-westwards from Hemel Hempstead to Coleshill.
3. Further NE-SW monoclines at 150-200 m OD a short distance southeast of the Chiltern scarp crest, especially near Dunstable and Stokenchurch.
4. Minor NW-SE synclines near the heads of the Bulbourne valley near Tring and the Wye valley northeast of Stokenchurch.

The larger number of data points for the Sub-Senonian Surface allowed a further, more detailed assessment of structures. This was done by expressing the general slope as a quadratic trend surface and then calculating deviations (residuals) from that surface by the process of punctual kriging at the nodes of a fine grid. The values of residuals were then contoured to show areas above and below the general slope. The resulting contours (Fig. 5.12) are reliable only in areas of the greatest density of data points, but show the following clear features:

1. The monoclines with axes close to the Chiltern scarp crest are confirmed and shown to be the western margins of basins elongated approximately NE-SW, one extending south-westwards from Dunstable to Tring and the other from Princes Risborough to Russell's Water. It is in these areas that the 'degraded cliff' backing the Plio-Pleistocene marine platform of Wooldridge and Linton (1955) is best developed.
2. Another basin centred close to Hatfield reaches to a depth of at least 40 m below the generalized Sub-Senonian Surface (quadratic trend surface). The north-western side of this basin coincides in part with an area near Wheathampstead where the intersection between the

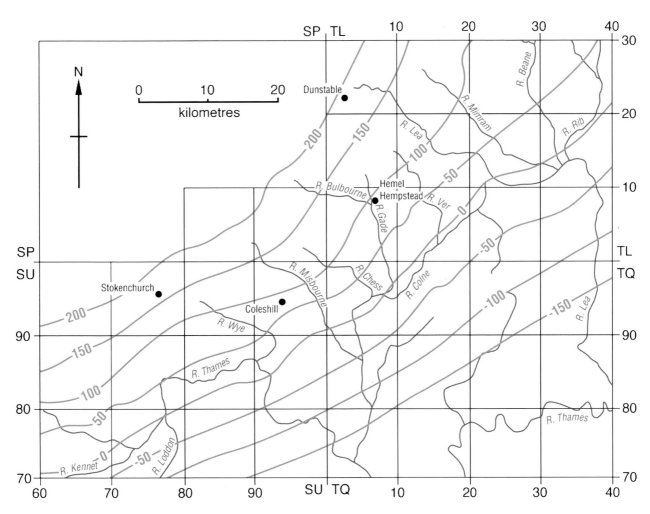

Figure 5.11. Structure contours (m OD) for the Sub-Senonian Surface in the Hertfordshire area (redrawn from Moffatt et al., 1986).

Sub-Palaeogene Surface and Plio-Pleistocene marine platform of Wooldridge and Linton (1955) is most strongly expressed (Fig. 5.5). Also, the difference in height of the present land surface (approximately 30 m) over a distance of 3-5 km between Wheathampstead and Hatfield is similar to the height difference on the north-western side of the basin.

3. As well as the elongated basins aligned NE-SW, the map of contoured residuals (Fig. 5.12) also shows some features aligned NW-SE. The most notable are minor synclines at the heads of the Wye, Misbourne and Bulbourne valleys, the last also evident in the structure contour maps for the Sub-Senonian Surface (Fig. 5.11) and Sub-Cenomanian Surface (Fig. 5.10). Also, whereas the lower course of the River Chess between Rickmansworth and Croxley Green is aligned NW-SE, parallel to other Chiltern rivers, the upper reaches of this river between Chenies and Chesham are aligned WNW-ESE close to the axis of an anticline. These features provide further evidence for structural control of the drainage pattern.

The Sub-Palaeogene Surface is even better defined than the Sub-Senonian Surface, as it is constructed from 495 data points. However, it is poorly defined near the crest of the Chilterns, where there are few reliable data points. Also it is more difficult to interpret in terms of geological structure, because some of its features could have resulted from irregular marine or subaerial erosion of the Chalk before deposition of the basal Palaeogene deposits. Nevertheless, it shows many features in common with the two lower surfaces, including a change in dip direction and a decrease in angle of dip from southwest to northeast along the Chilterns. As with the Sub-Senonian Surface, residuals above and below the general trend surface (in this case a cubic trend surface) were calculated, and then contoured (Fig. 5.13).

Like the map of residuals for the Sub-Senonian Surface (Fig. 5.12), Figure 5.13 shows contours that trend predominantly SW-NE. It also shows the following distinctive features:

1. A monocline trending SW-NE and falling to the southeast between Chenies in the Chess valley and High Wycombe in the Wye valley. This coincides with an area where the intersection between the Plio-Pleistocene marine erosion surface and the Sub-Palaeogene Surface (Fig. 5.5), as defined by Wooldridge and Linton (1955), is most clearly expressed.

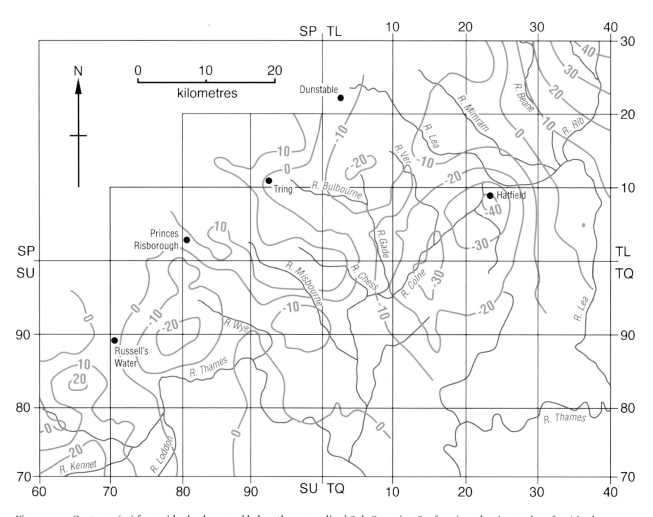

Figure 5.12. Contours (m) for residuals above and below the generalized Sub-Senonian Surface (quadratic trend surface) in the Hertfordshire area (redrawn from Moffatt et al., 1986).

2. Dome-like structures at Windsor, Binfield, South Mimms and Puckeridge. Some of these are elongated SW-NE.

3. A fairly steep-sided NW-SE syncline coinciding with the upper part of the Gade valley.

The main structures affecting the Chiltern dip-slope are therefore two monoclines elongated NE-SW. One lies close to the scarp crest, where it is most strongly expressed in the Sub-Senonian Surface between Dunstable and Tring and between Princes Risborough and Russell's Water. The other occurs at a lower level to the southeast, and is evident mainly in the Sub-Senonian Surface near Wheathampstead and between Hemel Hempstead and Coleshill, though it is also seen in the Sub-Palaeogene Surface between Chenies and High Wycombe. The flexures often form the north-western flanks of basins elongated from NE to SW, and coincide with areas where the breaks in general slope of the present land surface at the upper and lower boundaries of the Plio-Pleistocene marine platform of Wooldridge and Linton (1955) are best developed. Neither the breaks in slope nor the monoclinal flexures extend throughout the Chilterns from the Thames to the eastern boundary of Hertfordshire, but the flexures occur where the breaks in slope are most evident. This strongly suggests that the three 'facets' of the dip-slope recognized by Wooldridge and Linton (1955) reflect folds in the underlying Chalk. The dip-slope in its entirety is therefore best interpreted as the exhumed Sub-Palaeogene Surface, which was folded together with the Chalk by later earth movements, a conclusion agreeing with the evidence given in Section 5.4 that the distribution of Plateau Drift derived from basal Palaeogene deposits defines the exhumed Sub-Palaeogene Surface on the Chiltern dip-slope.

Approximately transverse to the NE-SW monoclines are the NW-SE synclines and anticlines, which coincide with several of the through-valleys of the Chilterns and could have determined their courses. The south-westward decline and change in dip and direction of the Sub-Cenomanian and Sub-Senonian surfaces as the Thames valley is approached could be the north-eastern limb of a parallel, though much larger NW-SE syncline. The alignments of these two sets of fold axes coincide approximately with the two main groups of individual minor structures recognized previously in the region and listed above, but are at approximately 45° to the major reactivated Variscan faults and folds south and west of the London Platform (Chadwick and Evans, 2005). The alignment of chalkland valleys along minor anticlinal and synclinal axes has also been noted in areas south of the Thames (Mortimore, 1993, p. 75).

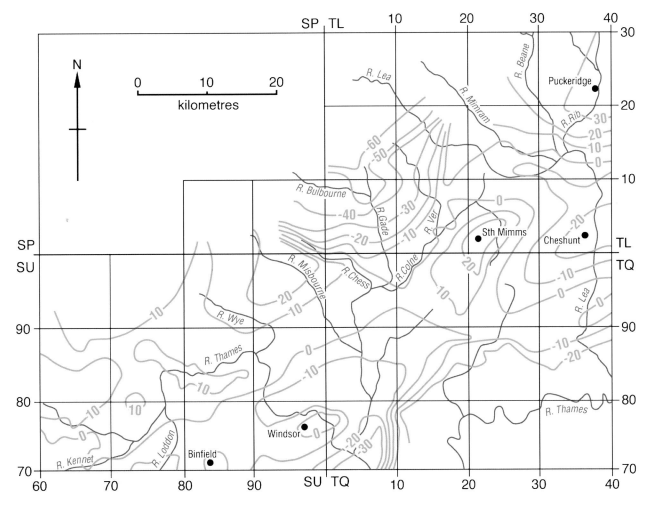

Figure 5.13. Contours (m) for residuals above and below the generalized Sub-Palaeogene Surface (cubic trend surface) in the Hertfordshire area (redrawn from Moffatt et al., 1986).

Ages of tectonic episodes

Most of the structures affecting the Chalk and Palaeogene strata in the Hertfordshire area must have originated in some period or periods after the Late Cretaceous, and many must have formed after deposition of the London Clay Formation, but it is difficult to date them more precisely. Wooldridge (1926) and Wooldridge and Linton (1955) recognized two main periods of Tertiary ('Alpine') earth movements in southeast England as a whole, one resulting in emergence after deposition of the Upper Chalk and initiating major folds such as the Weald and London Basin, and the other in the mid-Tertiary (the 'Alpine Storm'), enlarging the major folds to their present size and producing small scale folds and faults. The later period of tectonic activity was dated to the late Oligocene or early Miocene, because on the Isle of Wight beds as young as Oligocene are affected by a major monoclinal flexure (the Isle of Wight Monocline) and in the Alps there was a major phase of deformation at this time. The remaining parts of the Caenozoic were envisaged as essentially times of tectonic quiescence, though previously Wooldridge (1926) had suggested that sedimentation of various Palaeogene formations was influenced by minor phases of contemporaneous tectonism.

Recent studies integrated within the theory of plate tectonics have shown that, from the later Mesozoic to the present day, Britain has been surrounded by at least four major zones of disturbance: (a) the Alpine compression zone to the south, resulting from continental collision between Africa and Europe, and in which Trümpy (1973) recognized five phases of movement between the Cretaceous and Pliocene, (b) the subsiding North Sea Basin to the east (Ziegler, 1975), which extends southwards into (c) the Rhine, Rhône and Saône grabens, and (d) tension associated with the widening North Atlantic (Ager, 1975; Stoneley, 1982). The last is thought to result from the major Greenland mantle plume, which in turn seems to have spawned satellite hotspots causing pulses of uplift in various parts of the British Isles, including southeast England. All of these factors could have influenced Hertfordshire at any time over this long period. Their relative effects at any particular time are difficult to determine, but there is no reason to restrict the structural features of Hertfordshire or any other part of southeast England to Alpine compression in the two distinct (Early and Mid-Tertiary) phases suggested by Wooldridge and Linton (1955).

A long history of Cretaceous and later tectonism in southeast England is indicated by several pieces of evidence:

1. The detailed lithostratigraphic subdivision of the Chalk in southeast England that has emerged in recent decades (Chapter 3) indicates that the depositional environment of the Late Cretaceous was spatially more variable than was previously thought. Although this partly reflects worldwide eustatic changes in sea-level (Hancock, 1975, 1989), it can also be attributed to penecontemporaneous folding and faulting, often along lines that continued to be active later in the Tertiary (Mortimore, 1986; Robinson, 1986; Mortimore and Pomerol, 1987, 1991,

1997). At least one structure in Hertfordshire, the Lilley Bottom fault/monocline (No.15 in the above list), comes into this category, because it influenced Late Cretaceous sedimentation, the Cambridge Greensand occurring only on its north-eastern side (Section 2.8), and the Lower Chalk thinning rapidly north-eastwards across it from 75 m to 60 m in total thickness.

2. Pulsed tectonic activity, again possibly accompanied by eustatic sea-level fluctuations (Pomerol, 1989), is indicated by the repeated early Palaeogene marine transgressions from the east and intervening regressions (Chapter 4), which created the polygenetic multifacetted Sub-Palaeogene Surface (Curry, 1965).

3. Continuing pulses of deformation in the mid-Tertiary (Oligocene and Miocene) probably led to progressive growth of the Wealden Anticline, formation of the Isle of Wight Monocline and deepening of the London and Hampshire Basins (Jones, 1999); these pulses remain the most likely principal (though not the only) cause of many structures affecting the Chalk and Palaeogene sequence of Hertfordshire.

4. In the late Neogene the eastward tilting following the Red Crag transgression (Section 5.2) provides evidence for continuing crustal deformation in southeast England, associated partly with subsidence of the North Sea Basin but mainly with uplift over a hotspot satellite to the mantle plume beneath western Britain and the north Atlantic. Also the staircase of Thames terraces formed throughout the Pleistocene (Section 6.3) is thought to result primarily from the same tilting (Westaway *et al.*, 2002). From the later part of the terrace sequence in the Upper Thames Valley, Maddy (1997) and Maddy *et al.* (2000) have estimated a land uplift rate of 0.07-0.1 mm yr^{-1} over the last 250,000 years in the Hertfordshire area.

Fission track dating

Further evidence for episodes of regional uplift and erosion during the Tertiary has been provided in recent decades by the study of fission tracks in apatite grains extracted from sediments of various ages in the English Midlands (Green, 1989). The spontaneous fission of the small amounts of ^{238}U atoms present in apatite crystals produces tracks of molecular damage within the grains at a fixed rate over time, so that the length and abundance of the tracks together with a measure of the uranium content can be used to date the time of original crystallization (Hurford and Green, 1982). The tracks intersecting a polished surface of a grain are enlarged for measurement with an optical microscope by etching in dilute nitric acid.

However, radiation damage is repaired or annealed if the grain is subjected to temperatures in excess of about 100°C, for example if detrital apatites in sediments are deeply buried beneath a considerable thickness of younger deposits. Over periods of 10-40 Ma total annealing occurs at *c.* 125°C, depending on the Cl/F ratio of the grain, so that measured track density in a sediment sample depends on the period of time since the sample was cooled below 100°C. This cooling happens after periods of uplift have resulted in erosion, thereby bringing the sample closer to the surface.

From measurements on apatites obtained from surface exposures of Triassic and Carboniferous sediments and crystalline basement rocks and from borehole samples of various ages and known temperatures, Green (1989) showed that, after a phase of elevated temperature (probably deep burial) in the Late Cretaceous (*c.* 80 Ma), there were two episodes of cooling resulting from regional uplift and erosion, one in the early Palaeogene (*c.* 70-55 Ma) and the other in the mid-Tertiary (Oligocene-Miocene). The combined uplift and erosion in the two episodes was probably about 1 km, possibly as much as 3 km in northwest England (Lewis *et al.*, 1992). These results confirm that the two tectonic episodes originally proposed by Wooldridge and Linton (1955) led to the main periods of post-Chalk erosion in eastern England, but they do not exclude the possibility of tectonic activity, perhaps leading to less severe erosion, at other times in the Caenozoic (Jones, 1999).

Reactivation of structures

Wooldridge and Linton (1955) recognized that some of the minor folds in southeast England could have resulted from reactivation of faults that originated in the Palaeozoic basement during the late Carboniferous Variscan Orogeny. This idea was subsequently developed for other parts of southern England by Lake (1975), Stoneley (1982) and Chadwick (1986, 1993), and is now widely accepted, at least for the Weald and Wessex (Jones, 1999). For example, geophysical evidence has shown that the numerous E-W *en echelon* monoclinal folds of the Weald are draped over faults in underlying Mesozoic strata, which in turn pass downwards into steeply inclined Variscan thrusts in the Palaeozoic basement. Some of the minor folds and faults affecting the Chalk and Palaeogene strata in Hertfordshire could have originated by similar reactivation of basement structures. In particular, Lee *et al.* (1991) suggested from geophysical evidence that the NW-SE alignment is common throughout southeast England and probably indicates reactivation of major Variscan structures in the Precambrian and Lower Palaeozoic basement. These in turn were probably aligned along earlier Acadian (late Caledonian) structures on the eastern flank of the Midlands Microcraton (Section 2.6).

The difference in alignments between many of the Hertfordshire structures and those to the south and west suggests that the relatively thin Mesozoic and Palaeogene cover on the London Platform has been influenced since the Cretaceous by a somewhat different combination of tectonic factors than other parts of southern England (Jones, 1980). South of the Variscan Front Thrust, the Alpine structures were aligned essentially E-W by reactivation of structures produced by Variscan compression. But the NW-SE structures known on the eastern side of the Midlands Microcraton, which were in turn determined by reactivation of Acadian (Caledonian) structures, suggest that the SW-NE and NW-SE alignments over the London Platform in Hertfordshire reflect reactivation of basement structures produced by Variscan extension.

5.8. Evidence for recent tectonic activity

Two further pieces of evidence show that Alpine and other tectonic activities similar to those inferred since the Late Cretaceous continue even today.

Evidence from sea-level change

Using radiocarbon dates for a large number of samples that constrain past sea levels, Shennan and Horton (2002) have shown that relative sea level has risen at average rates of 0.4-1.2 mm yr^{-1} during the late Holocene (over the last 4000 years) at numerous points around the coast of southeast England from Yorkshire to Cornwall. In areas closest to Hertfordshire, such as the Thames Estuary and East Anglia, the rates range from 0.6 to 0.9 mm yr^{-1}. This can be attributed mainly to continuing eastward tilting of southern England, because it postdates the worldwide (eustatic) rise in sea level after the last glaciation. Also it excludes any rise attributable to global warming (melting of glaciers and thermal expansion of the ocean) over the last century or so, which is calculated from long-term tide gauge records to be an additional 1 mm yr^{-1} (Woodworth *et al.*, 1999). However, attempts to verify changes in ground level using high performance global positioning systems (Bingley *et al.*, 1999) have so far given conflicting evidence.

The recent history of minor earthquakes

As Britain lies within the Eurasian Tectonic Plate some distance from its western and northern boundaries, it is seismically fairly stable, but not uniformly so (Musson, 2007). Compared with parts of the country further west and north, few earthquakes have been recorded in southeast England, and Lilwall (1976) regarded it as suitable for assessing the country's 'background' level of seismic activity for numerical comparison with land areas at higher earthquake risk, such as south Wales and the Great Glen of Scotland.

Historical records of earthquakes affecting Hertfordshire and surrounding areas from the Mediaeval period onwards have been reviewed by Hopkinson (1908), Davison (1924) and Musson (1994). Most of the earliest records are unfortunately vague with respect to location, merely stating that the tremors were felt widely in England; these included minor events in AD 974, 1060, 1067, 1076, 1081, 1088, 1089, 1099, 1120, 1133, 1158, 1201, 1202, 1228, 1246, 1247, 1275, 1480 and 1580. The earliest definite record, with an account of effects in Hertfordshire, was on 13th December 1250 at approximately 3 am. It was described by Matthew Paris, a monk of the Benedictine Abbey of St Albans, who wrote that it was felt over much of the Chilterns and in St Albans, where there was a sound of dreadful subterranean thunder, causing birds to fly backwards and forwards in confusion. It is consequently often described as the St Albans earthquake, though the epicentre may have been some distance from the city.

On 4 January 1299, an earthquake with an epicentre probably within Hertfordshire or north London, led to partial collapse of St Andrews (now St Marys) Church, Hitchin (Hine, 1927, p.74); the church was rebuilt in 1305. On 25 May, 1551, a tremor felt at Albury and Benington was recorded in 1565 by John Stow (Hopkinson, 1908) and, according to Hine (1929, p.199), another tremor was felt in Hitchin on 8 December 1749. Soon afterwards, on 19 February 1750, a major earthquake felt as far away as Italy and western France was reported in Hertford, St Albans, Stanmore, Finchley and central London, as well as many parts of Essex, Kent and the Thames Valley. This was followed a month later (19 March 1750) by 3-4 shocks causing minor damage in Lambeth and also felt in many Hertfordshire towns and villages, including Hertford, Ware, Cheshunt, Copthall, Gobions, Northaw, Hertingfordbury, Hatfield, Hitchin and Panshanger. Musson (1994) suggested that the 1750 quakes resulted from movement on a fault beneath London. A few years later, on 1 November 1755, the Great Lisbon Earthquake, which was felt throughout Europe, including most of England and southern Scotland, caused the water of ponds at Patmore Hall near Little Hadham, and Wickham Hall near Bishop's Stortford to move backwards and forwards from south to north (Hopkinson, 1908), suggesting that the earthquake wave was propagated in this direction. On 6 October 1863, a tremor felt throughout England, Wales and Ireland was recorded at Hitchin, Hemel Hempstead and Berkhamsted, and on 28 January 1878 another was felt across northern France and southern England, with 3-4 vibrations recorded in St Albans.

The great Colchester earthquake of 22 April 1884 was felt throughout Hertfordshire about 9:20 am (Meldola, 1888). In the epicentral area south of Colchester, it caused damage to over 1000 buildings and its intensity, based on contemporary accounts, has recently been estimated at 4.7 (Weston, 2006). On 17 December 1896, an earthquake with an epicentre near Hertford was felt in many parts of England, Wales and Ireland, and its effects throughout Hertfordshire and adjacent counties were recorded in detail by Fordham (1898). It occurred about 5:30 am, and many people reported their beds shake, twist or heave, often to the accompaniment of rumbling noises and the rattling of windows and crockery, though little structural damage was reported. The wave seems to have been propagated from west to east or WSW to ENE, as beds orientated north-south or NNW-SSE rocked from side to side.

In the earlier part of the 20th century, very few earthquakes were recorded in southeast England. Musson (1994) mentions only three that could have affected Hertfordshire because they were felt over much of the country; these were on 14 January 1916, 7 June 1931 (with an intensity of 6.1, the largest ever recorded in Britain, though the epicentre was over the Dogger Bank) and 11 June 1938. In 1967 the British Geological Survey (then Institute of Geological Sciences) began seismographic recording at a growing network of sites throughout Britain, and since 1980 they have published annual catalogues of tremors recorded instrumentally, with magnitudes according to the Richter scale. Most of the epicentres for these have been located in the north Midlands, Wales and west of Scotland, or on the floors of the North Sea and English Channel, and

there have been very few in southeast England. Those with epicentres nearest to Hertfordshire were near Buckingham on 18 November 1985 (Turbitt, 1987) and 26 January 1990 (Turbitt, 1992), near Witney (Oxfordshire) on 8 March 1988 (Turbitt, 1990), near Wallingford on 8 January 1994 (Walker, 1995), near Maidenhead (Berkshire) on 8 December 1996 (Walker, 1997) and near Carterton (Oxfordshire) on 24 March 1999 (Walker, 2000), but all of these were of very low magnitude. The two earthquakes of greater magnitude that have occurred in the 21st century, with epicentres near Folkestone (Kent) on 28 April 2007 and at Market Rasen (Lincolnshire) on 27 February 2008, were scarcely felt in Hertfordshire and caused no recorded damage.

This historical review indicates that, although earthquakes have been rare and usually of low intensity in the Hertfordshire area, even compared with other parts of Britain, they have occurred at irregular intervals, suggesting that some minor tectonic activity lingers on even today. Indeed, the area has probably never been completely stable since at least the Cretaceous and possibly much earlier (Muir Wood, 1989). Although there are several possible causes of seismic activity in Britain, including upwelling plumes of anomalously hot, low-density material in the earth's mantle (Bott and Bott, 2004; Arrowsmith *et al.*, 2005), none explains adequately the distribution of recorded earthquakes (Musson, 2007). As to the future, it is currently very difficult to predict earthquakes, even in areas close to tectonic plate boundaries that have suffered frequent large tremors in the past. In Hertfordshire, the risk is small, and the threat to life and property even less, though the records of occasional damage over limited areas show that it cannot be ignored completely. Particularly at risk are older buildings with shallow foundations on soft unconsolidated sediments, such as alluvium.

5.9. Revised history of Caenozoic development of the Chiltern landscape

It is now clear that the model of Caenozoic landscape development proposed by Wooldridge and Linton (1955) is unsatisfactory. The main reasons for this are:

1. Marine Plio-Pleistocene deposits are much less common on their Plio-Pleistocene marine platform than they believed. Where they do occur (Rothamsted and Little Heath in Hertfordshire), they either lie on thin unmodified Palaeogene formations or are incorporated as disturbed remnants into the Plateau Drift, and do not rest directly on Chalk.
2. Soil surveys of the Chilterns have failed to confirm the differences in soil type that they predicted between the three dip-slope facets.
3. The distribution of Plateau Drift, formed by modification of basal Palaeogene deposits, suggests that all three facets are parts of the exhumed Sub-Palaeogene Surface.
4. Although all three facets do exist locally on the Chilterns as areas of slightly different general slope, they can be

explained in terms of monoclinal flexuring of the Sub-Palaeogene Surface before it was exhumed.

5. The differences in drainage patterns that Wooldridge and Linton postulated between the two upper facets do not exist. Structural control of the dry valley patterns is no less marked on the Plio-Pleistocene platform than on the Mio-Pliocene Peneplain, and there is little evidence for a discordant superimposed pattern on any part of the Chilterns.

6. The single period of Mid-Tertiary earth movements (the 'Miocene Storm') required to explain the discordance is an over-simplification of the tectonic history of southeast England, as there is now evidence for numerous pulses of activity from the Late Cretaceous to the present day.

If the Chiltern plateau surface between dry valleys is simply the warped Sub-Palaeogene Surface, the Plio-Pleistocene marine transgression/s accomplished much less erosion of the Chalk than Wooldridge and Linton envisaged, and possibly none at all. The sea probably invaded a landscape of Palaeogene beds and, although it may have cut a widespread platform in them, thus hastening the exhumation of the Sub-Palaeogene Surface, it never cut extensively into the Chalk. Final stripping of the Palaeogene cover by later subaerial erosion explains the preservation of numerous Palaeogene

outliers better than does marine erosion. Also, resumption of subaerial erosion after the Plio-Pleistocene transgression/s explains why so few genuine remnants of Plio-Pleistocene marine beds have been preserved.

The widespread preservation of Plateau Drift is also explained by final subaerial exhumation of the Sub-Palaeogene Surface. Once the Palaeogene cover had been reduced to a certain thickness (*c.*15 m) over the Chalk, it became more permeable and streams on its surface disappeared into the Chalk. Erosion then virtually ceased, so that most of the basal Palaeogene veneer was preserved as a layer of Plateau Drift. However, continuing irregular weathering of Chalk beneath the Plateau Drift and lateral redistribution of surface layers of the Plateau Drift by periglacial mass movement during cold stages of the Quaternary has transformed the Sub-Palaeogene Surface into the British equivalent of a tropical etchplain (Jones, 1999).

Formation of Plateau Drift by pedogenic modification of basal Palaeogene beds seems to have occurred at Rothamsted after the Red Crag transgression, but this need not be true throughout the Chilterns. It could have started earlier near the Chiltern summits and then progressed slowly south-eastwards. However, it must have reached its present extent, delimited by the edge of the main Palaeogene

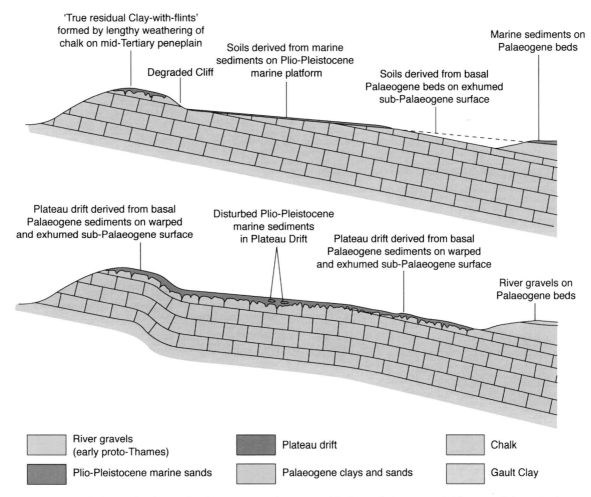

Fig. 5.14. Summary of Chiltern landscape development according to Wooldridge and Linton (1955) (above) and the revised account given in this chapter (below).

outcrop between Harefield, Bushey, Radlett, North Mimms, Essendon and Hertford, before the Anglian glaciation about 450,000 years ago, because the glacier invaded a landscape rather similar to that of present-day Hertfordshire (Section 6.6). The edge of the main Palaeogene outcrop has therefore retreated at least 10 km south-eastwards from Rothamsted to its pre sent position in about 2.2 million years.

The main features of the Chiltern landscape, i.e. the steep scarp-slope and gently but irregularly inclined dip-slope, therefore reflect late Neogene and early Pleistocene subaerial erosion, which exhumed the gently folded Sub-Palaeogene Surface. But there is no evidence for stages in the history of this erosion, such as the Mio-Pliocene peneplain proposed by Wooldridge and Linton (1955). Hepworth (1998) suggested that the Plio-Pleistocene marine platform originated as a pediment downslope from Wooldridge and Linton's degraded cliff, but there is no sedimentological evidence for this (Catt, 2000). Lesser landscape features of the Chilterns, such as the terraces of the main rivers and the modification of the dry valley network in periglacial conditions, are attributable to Quaternary processes, which are discussed in the next chapter. Figure 5.14 compares the two main interpretations of Chiltern landscape development, the earlier (mainly erosional) model of Wooldridge and Linton (1955) and that outlined in this chapter, which explains the main landscape features in terms of exhumation of a gently folded Sub-Palaeogene Surface.

5.10. The origins of puddingstone and sarsenstone

As both types of silcrete (puddingstone and sarsenstone) have been recorded as rafts and lenticular masses at various levels within the Palaeogene sequence of southern England (Potter, 1998, Table 1; see also Section 4.5) and northern France (Summerfield and Goudie, 1980, Table IV), subsequent erosion and disruption of this sequence can explain the much more common silcrete blocks found in younger deposits and on the present land surface. However, it has also been suggested, for example by Cholley (1943), Kerr (1955), Clark *et al.* (1967), Dury (1971) and Small (1980), that the silcrete blocks represent the remnants of siliceous duricrusts formed on temporarily stable later Tertiary land surfaces during the progressive subaerial erosion of the Palaeogene deposits. Duricrusts are hard layers in soil profiles composed of various minerals (commonly silica forming silcrete, iron oxides forming ferricrete, calcium carbonate forming calcrete, dolomite forming dolocrete and calcium sulphate forming gypcrete), which have been precipitated from water either percolating downwards through the profile (in a humid climate) or moving upwards by capillary action under the influence of rapid evaporation from the surface (in an arid climate).

Most types of duricrust are impersistent in that they can redissolve when the climate or soil environment (e.g. pH, Eh) changes. However, the greater hardness and chemical resistance of silcretes ensures that, once formed, they persist not only through most climatic or pedogenetic changes but also as clasts in younger deposits following their disruption

and erosion. Consequently their occurrence as clasts in many of the Neogene and Quaternary deposits of the Hertfordshire area does little to clarify their mode of formation or ultimate source. Those found on the present land surface have probably accumulated either by frost-heaving from deposits below or by erosion of the surrounding fine soil on slopes under arable agriculture. Many sarsenstones and puddingstones have also been moved unknown distances by man, so their present distribution cannot be used to indicate at all clearly the previous occurrence of either Palaeogene formations or possible later duricrusts.

Pedogenic and diagenetic silcretes

The largest known silcrete blocks or rafts of *in situ* puddingstone are no more than about 10 m across and 2 m thick, and most are much smaller than this, so it is likely that they originated as separate siliceous concretions rather than parts of a once continuous surface duricrust (Hepworth, 1998). Root impressions in some sarsenstones have been used as evidence for a near-surface pedogenetic (duricrust) origin, but could equally well have been inherited from Palaeogene plants buried in the original sediment before it was silicified. Examples from Hertfordshire (Hemel Hempstead, Watford and St Albans) were recorded by Anon. (1892) and Salter (1912). Another feature often seen

Plate 30. Sarsenstone with mammillated surface, Hatfield Road Museum, St Albans (with thanks to St Albans Museum Service).

in sarsenstones, a hummocky, reniform or mammillated surface (Plate 30), is also thought to indicate a pedogenetic origin, the hummocks forming on the upper surface of the duricrust close to the soil surface. Hepworth (1998) described them as 'growth structures', probably implying progressive deposition of silica within a porous medium such as soil or sandy sediment. The most likely mode of growth is progressive enlargement and eventual coalescence of several adjacent subspherical concretions, which could have occurred either within a soil horizon or at greater depth within sandy sediment.

Summerfield and Goudie (1980) reviewed the known occurrence and properties of puddingstone and sarsen in southern England and compared them with silcretes in other parts of the world. They divided those found in parts of South Africa, including the Kalahari and Cape coastal zone, into weathering profile silcretes and non-weathering profile silcretes. The former (pedogenetic silcretes) were thought to contain more titanium (>1.5% TiO_2) and to show in thin section a 'floating' fabric (F-fabric), in which sand and coarse silt grains (>30 µm) 'float' in a finer clay-rich matrix and do not form a self-supporting framework. In contrast, the non-weathering profile (diagenetic) silcretes were said to be Ti-poor and to show in thin section a simpler, grain-supported fabric (GS-fabric), in which particles >30 µm in size form a self-supporting framework and the intergranular spaces are largely filled with authigenic opal, cryptocrystalline silica, chalcedony or optically-continuous overgrowths of crystalline quartz on the detrital quartz grains. The relatively high concentrations of Ti in weathering profile silcretes were thought to result from deposition of microcrystalline anatase (TiO_2) coincident with the pedogenetic silicification (Summerfield, 1983b, 1984). Summerfield and Goudie (1980) described the microfabric of puddingstones as conglomeratic (C-fabric), that is consisting of flint pebbles set in a sandy matrix with a GS-fabric and with sharp contacts between pebbles and matrix.

Four of the five sarsenstones from southern England studied by Summerfield and Goudie (1980) had the characteristics of non-weathering profile silcretes. The fifth, a sarsen from the Newbury area, had an F-fabric and 2.08% TiO_2. So, although many sarsens and puddingstones with GS- or C-fabrics seemed to have originated by diagenetic precipitation of silica, it is possible that some sarsens originated in soil profiles on old land surfaces during, between or after deposition of the various Palaeogene formations. However, with respect to Hertfordshire, it is impossible to generalize from such a limited number, especially as none of those studied by Summerfield and Goudie (1980) were obtained from within the county.

Research on silcretes over the last 20 years has cast some doubt on the simple micromorphological and chemical criteria used to distinguish weathering profile and non-weathering profile types. For example, in the Kalahari region, Nash *et al.* (1994) identified silcretes with non-weathering profile characteristics in situations with good evidence for deep weathering, and also found Ti-rich silcretes unrelated to weathering profiles, particularly where the original host sediments were Ti-rich. Nevertheless,

pedogenetic silcretes are usually richer in Ti than diagenetic silcretes, though there is probably some overlap between the two (Thiry and Milnes, 1991). From work on silcretes in South Australia and the Paris Basin, Milnes and Thiry (1992) refined the micromorphological criteria for differentiating pedogenetic from groundwater (diagenetic) silcretes, and identified fairly consistent vertical variations in macromorphology, micromorphology and silica mineralogy through the profile of pedogenic silcretes. These variations and many of the more complex micromorphological features, which they reported in pedogenetic silcretes as resulting from redeposition of illuvial clay or precipitation of microcrystalline TiO_2 from percolating water, are absent from diagenetic silcretes. They also showed that some silcretes may be multiphase, with a later pedogenic profile superimposed on an earlier and micromorphologically simpler diagenetic silcrete.

A few puddingstone blocks, such as the one near Standon church (TL 396221), are coarsely bedded with layers distinguished by flint pebbles of different sizes (Plate 31) or different total pebble contents. These are unlikely to have been silicified within a soil profile, because disturbance by root growth, animal burrowing and other soil mixing processes would have destroyed the stratification.

An extreme form of stratification in local silcretes is the type in which puddingstone and sarsenstone pass vertically

Plate 31. Puddingstone block showing undisturbed layers with different sizes of pebbles, Standon (TL 396222).

Plate 32. Blocks showing Hertfordshire Puddingstone and sarsenstone layers, Castle Hill (SP 993085), Berkhamsted (photo E. H. Brown).

or even laterally into one other. Hepworth (1998) mentioned examples of these combined forms in Windsor Great Park (SU 968726) and another at Castle Hill, Berkhamsted, is a designated Hertfordshire RIGS (Plate 32). These clearly indicate a non-pedogenetic origin for the silcretes concerned. However, a few silcrete blocks in Hertfordshire show numerous flint pebbles scattered throughout a sandy (sarsenstone) matrix, and these may be pedogenetic.

Source of the silica in silcretes

The silica dissolved in natural waters is usually derived from the weathering of silicate minerals, including clay minerals, in acidic soils (Rayot *et al.*, 1992). Other possible sources include quartz, opaline diatoms (Siever, 1959) and the opal phytoliths that grasses and some trees secrete for strengthening their stems and roots, which accumulate in soils on death of the plants (Wilding and Drees, 1971). Because it is an amorphous form of silica, opal is more soluble than crystalline forms such as quartz (Krauskopf, 1959). Also, as originally suggested by Waugh (1970) for silica cementation of the Permian Penrith Sandstone of northwest England, another possible source of soluble silica in arid desert environments is the very fine quartz dust formed by aeolian abrasion of sand grains, as the fine particles are probably more soluble than coarser quartz grains. Nevertheless, there is no evidence for a desert environment in southern England at any time during the Caenozoic. As described in Sections 4.5 and 4.7, the sedimentological, palaeopedological and palaeontological evidence from parts of the Palaeogene sequence suggests only humid climatic conditions, with mean annual temperatures considerably greater than at present, especially around the Palaeocene/Eocene Thermal Maximum (55.8 Ma). This type of climate would certainly have favoured weathering of clay and other silicate minerals, dissolution of opal and downward leaching of silica-rich waters.

Precipitation of silica

The silica dissolved in acidic soils under a warm humid climate may be transported downwards through permeable layers and then reprecipitated either in lower soil horizons to form pedogenetic silcrete or may be carried to much deeper layers to form non-weathering profile or diagenetic silcrete (Stephens, 1966). As a thick layer of impermeable London Clay would have prevented downward movement of such waters, it is unlikely that the soils from which silica was removed to produce puddingstone and sarsenstone in the Upnor and Reading formations were developed on land surfaces younger than the London Clay. In Hertfordshire, the source of the silica was almost certainly soils formed either (a) after regression of the sea in which the Upnor Formation was deposited or (b) during or immediately after deposition of the Reading Formation but before the transgression/s leading to deposition of the Harwich and London Clay formations.

Dissolved silica may also move laterally across the landscape either in surface streams or in shallow groundwater that later emerges to feed rivers and lakes. In suitable circumstances, including rapid evaporation in an arid environment and a coarse porous sediment matrix favouring redeposition, silica transported in this way is reprecipitated to form what Ullyott *et al.* (1998) have called drainage-line silcretes. For example, in the Lake Eyre Basin of central Australia and the Gibson Desert of Western Australia, extensive silcretes seem to have been deposited in sandy alluvial sediments from silica-rich surface waters flowing across areas of low relief in a hot arid environment (Stephens, 1971). Similar drainage-line silcretes also occur in the Okavango Delta of the Middle Kalahari desert in Botswana (Nash *et al.*, 1998). The alluvial environment of deposition of the Reading Formation proposed in Section 4.5 could well have favoured formation of puddingstones and sarsenstones in this way.

In natural surface and ground waters, silica occurs in solution mainly as monosilicic acid (H_4SiO_4), which is almost completely undissociated at pH <9, but forms $H_3SiO_4^-$ ions in more alkaline conditions. A change in pH from >9 to <9 would therefore favour precipitation of silica, and this could occur when silica-rich alkaline water mixes with less alkaline surface or ground water (Summerfield, 1979). Soil pH values as high as 9 mainly occur in hot arid (desert) environments, where sodium ions become concentrated in the soil because of capillary rise of mildly saline water and rapid surface evaporation. Rapid evaporation can also lead to slow precipitation of silica as a near-surface duricrust, and Twidale and Hutton (1986) suggested that seasonally alternating warm humid and arid conditions could explain the almost simultaneous release of silica by weathering and its redeposition in the soil. However, there is no evidence for this type of seasonal climatic variation in Britain during the Caenozoic.

Precipitation of silica can also occur locally where the temperature of hot silica-rich water decreases suddenly, as around hot springs of volcanic regions, but again there is no evidence for this activity in southeast England at any stage in the Caenozoic. Deposition is also known to occur in the micro-environment around the decomposing roots of trees, such as the palmyra palm (*Borassus fabellifer*), which grow in tropical coastal regions (Hendry, 1987). The opal deposited during life as phytoliths in the root cells of these trees probably acts as a template for deposition of further amorphous silica from solution as the dead roots decompose. This is a likely environment during the Palaeogene in southeast England, and the mechanism could well explain the occasional sarsens, possibly pedogenetic silcretes, in which root remains are preserved. However, phytoliths have never been observed in thin sections of English silcretes.

The silica precipitated in the laboratory or from modern surface waters, such as hot springs, initially forms amorphous hydrated silica gel, but later dehydrates to form opaline silica and may eventually crystallize as low-temperature microcrystalline quartz or cristobalite-tridymite (Krauskopf, 1959). This sequence of changes may have occurred during formation of some silcretes. However, very slow crystallization of quartz can also occur directly from groundwater (Krauskopf, 1959), because in warm natural waters (other than seawater, which contains very little silica in solution) the silica concentrations at pH <9 are usually slightly above the equilibrium for quartz (4-11 ppm at 25°C), but well below that for amorphous silica (100-120 ppm at 25°C). This mechanism of precipitation could have been involved in formation of diagenetic or drainage-line silcretes, including perhaps some puddingstones and sarsenstones.

From a study of thin sections of numerous silcretes on the eastern South Downs, Sussex, Ullyott and Nash (2006) reported that most of the silica cement occurs as optically continuous quartz overgrowths on detrital quartz grains. Finer (microcrystalline and cryptocrystalline) silica cement occupies some pore spaces between the detrital grains, and often shows interlocking or gradational contacts with the overgrowths. Where the finer material is less abundant the silcretes are less well indurated, a type they described as saccharoid silcrete. Thin sections of silcretes from the Chiltern area show mainly microcrystalline and cryptocrystalline cements, but the saccharoid type is unknown, suggesting that there are different cementation histories in the two regions. So, further studies, including scanning electron microscopy of the silica cements, are required to clarify exactly how cementation occurred in Hertfordshire silcretes.

Joints in silcretes

Many puddingstone blocks and some sarsenstones show large planar fractures (joints), some of which are stained with iron compounds precipitated from percolating groundwater. An iron-stained example is visible in the exposure of *in situ* Hertfordshire Puddingstone exposed at Wood Hall Stud Estate (Plate 17) (see chapter 4 header photo). Occasionally two joints intersect at almost 90° (Plate 33). The natural joints always cut uniformly across pebbles and matrix, indicating that these two components are similar in composition and hardness. It is possible that

Plate 33. Block of Hertfordshire Puddingstone showing two joints intersecting at almost 90° and cutting uniformly across matrix and flint pebbles; puddingstone cairn at Merry Hill (TQ 131940), Bushey (photo J. D. Fearnside).

they originated by exposure to rapid temperature changes (e.g. expansion by heating in daytime sunshine followed by contraction with sharp night-time frosts) during cold stages of the Pleistocene. But this is considered unlikely because, where puddingstone surfaces are exposed to present-day physical weathering, they show only loosening of the pebbles and angular fragmentation of the matrix by a network of small multidirectional cracks. It is more likely that the large, often conjugate, joints resulted from tectonic stresses (folding or faulting) deep within the earth's crust during the Alpine Orogeny beneath a considerable thickness of younger deposits, including the London Clay and Bagshot Beds. Consequently they are compatible either with silicification in Palaeogene soils before deposition of the London Clay or with later precipitation of silica from groundwaters, but not with formation as a duricrust close to a late Tertiary erosion surface that was never subsequently buried.

In conclusion, we can say that in Hertfordshire most of the puddingstone and sarsen blocks found in Plateau Drift and Quaternary deposits (mainly glacial and river gravels) and on the present land surface were derived by disruption of non-weathering profile (diagenetic or drainage-line) silcretes formed in the pebble beds and sands of the Reading and Upnor formations before deposition of the Harwich and London Clay formations. This is indicated by the little that is known about their microfabric and chemical composition and by the presence of old iron-stained joints. Although the silica cement was ultimately derived from chemical weathering in soils under the warm humid climate of the late Palaeocene and early Eocene, few silcretes seem to have had a strictly pedogenetic origin, i.e. with dissolution and redeposition of silica both occurring within the same soil profile (Ullyott et al., 1998, 2000). But more micromorphological and perhaps chemical analyses of silcrete blocks in the county are needed to confirm this conclusion.

In other parts of southern England and in northern France, sarsens were also formed in both older and younger Palaeogene sands (Summerfield and Goudie, 1980; Potter, 1998; Ullyott and Nash, 2006, Fig. 1), probably as both diagenetic and pedogenetic silcretes. Isaac (1983) described silcretes in the Sidmouth area, east Devon, which seem to have formed in association with residual kaolinitic clays in thick subtropical weathering profiles during the Palaeogene. But at present there is no evidence in Hertfordshire or other parts of southeast England for deep Palaeogene weathering profiles of this type. Nor is there any geomorphological evidence for erosion surfaces cutting across Palaeogene formations on which subtropical Caenozoic weathering profiles might have developed. The additional silcretes at other stratigraphic levels ranging from the late Palaeocene (Thanet Sands Formation) to at least the Oligocene (Fontainebleau Sandstone in the Paris Basin) indicate that silicification was not restricted to a single short Palaeogene episode with a unique palaeoclimate.

Colours and textures of Hertfordshire Puddingstone

Although many of the flint pebbles in puddingstone are black-coated, similar to those in the various Palaeogene formations, some forms of the rock have yellow, brown, red, white, grey or green pebbles, and when broken the pebbles show red, yellow, brown or grey colours internally (Plates 3 and 33). Sometimes the siliceous matrix between the pebbles is similarly variable in colour, and often shows attractive colour-banding. In the variety that Davies and Baines (1953) termed 'Bradenham Puddingstone', after the village of Bradenham near High Wycombe, the flint pebbles are usually white-coated, subrounded or even angular flint fragments of various sizes up to 20 cm long set in a coarse pale grey matrix. Small angular or even crescentic fragments of grey or black flint, usually less than 1 cm across, are common also in other types of puddingstone. Like the rounded pebbles, they usually 'float' in the matrix of silicified quartzose sand, though some puddingstones with less matrix are clearly clast-supported rather than matrix-supported. The angular fragments probably originated by collisions between flint pebbles during transportation by waves on marine beaches of the Upnor Formation or by rivers during deposition of the Reading Formation.

The range of colours commonly seen in the pebbles and matrix of puddingstone has never been investigated mineralogically, though analyses by X-ray diffraction and electron microscopy could well shed valuable light on the geological history of the rock. The rare green coatings may be glauconitic, and probably indicate incorporation of glauconite-coated pebbles originating in the marine Thanet and Upnor formations. The red colours are almost certainly attributable to haematite and the browns and yellows to hydrated iron oxides/hydroxides. Black and dark grey are probably the natural colours of unweathered flint, though the black frequently seen on pebble surfaces

Plates 34-41. Uses of Hertfordshire Puddingstone. Top left to bottom right: 34: Roman quern composed of Hertfordshire Puddingstone from excavations at Gorhambury Roman Villa (with thanks to St Albans Museum Service); 35: Puddingstone archway, Batlers Green (TQ 155984) near Aldenham; 36: Chest tomb of brick and puddingstone, Aldenham churchyard; 37: Puddingstone war memorial, Latimer (TQ 003989); 38: Puddingstone and sarsenstone blocks framing entrance to ice-house, Ashridge (SP 992121); 39: Puddingstone marking Hertfordshire-Bedfordshire boundary, Ashridge College; 40: Puddingstone foundation for buttress, Great Gaddesden Church; 41: Puddingstone protruding from west wall of St Stephens Church, St Albans.

suggests shallow impregnation with black iron or manganese oxides. The pale grey and white coatings may result from surface weathering and loss of the opaline silica component of flint by dissolution in water. The silica lost in this way could have been redeposited as part of the silica matrix, but occasionally there is evidence of redeposition of silica as quartz crystals within small cavities (vughs) inside flint pebbles. This range of features suggests a very complex history of iron and silica mobilization and redeposition under changing environmental conditions either during the original deposition of the pebbly sand or during subsequent pedogenesis and diagenesis. However, despite the obviously close depositional association between puddingstone and sarsenstone, their pedogenetic and diagenetic histories were very different, because sarsenstones show almost none of the colour variation so common in puddingstones.

5.11. Uses of puddingstone and sarsenstone

Ask anyone to name a rock for which Hertfordshire is famous, and more will probably reply puddingstone than any other. For geologists, it is a fine example of a conglomerate; among lapidarists, it is known worldwide for its range of beautiful colours and ability to retain a high polish; archaeologists know it as an occasional alternative to flint for making stone tools; local historians emphasize its importance for marking boundaries and routes; among farmers it is notorious for the damage it can cause to ploughs and other machinery; and builders now recognize it as an unreliable foundation material, though it has long been used as a building stone, especially in churches. Together with the extreme hardness of puddingstone, which ensures that surfaces preserve a high polish, the attractive range of colour and composition explains why lapidarists from all over the world value Hertfordshire Puddingstone above almost all other rock types. The numerous ornamental uses of polished specimens include brooches, pendants and handles for high quality cutlery.

The hardness of puddingstone also led to its use in various archaeological periods for production of tools, including Palaeolithic handaxes, Neolithic axeheads and early Roman querns (small hand milling machines for production of flour). Wymer (1985, p. 251) figured a rolled puddingstone handaxe, now in Colchester Museum, which was found at Notley Road (TL 760220) in Essex. The British Museum collection contains two possible puddingstone flakes from Caddington (TL 0619) and a more convincing thick puddingstone flake with secondary edge flaking found at Markyate (TL 0616) by W. G. Smith. Luton Museum also has several Palaeolithic puddingstone artefacts from Caddington and Gaddesden Row, a handaxe from Harpenden and a polished Neolithic puddingstone axehead from Wauluds Bank.

Querns. The Roman puddingstone querns are typically bun- or beehive-shaped, with a conical hopper in the centre of the upper stone (Plate 34), to allow grain to be fed to the flat grinding surface against the lower stone, which has a flattened hemisphere shape. Some have short horizontal holes for a wooden handle to assist rotation, and others are grooved around the circumference so that they could be gripped by an iron or leather band. Shaping querns from a block of hard puddingstone must have involved considerable time and effort, and was probably achieved by repeated hammering with a small piece of puddingstone or sarsenstone, though the narrow vertical and horizontal perforations would have required some form of special tool. In total, well over 250 puddingstone querns are known (Robinson, 1994), possibly as many as 700. The large collections in the museums at Ashwell, Aylesbury, St Albans, Bedford, Colchester, Hertford, Letchworth, London, Luton, Saffron Walden, Colchester, Ipswich and other towns (Curwen, 1941; King, 1986) are from sites spread over a wide region extending from north Kent to Buckinghamshire, Essex, Suffolk, Norfolk and Lincolnshire, and many of these could have been manufactured outside Hertfordshire. However, Curwen (1941) suggested that their uniform beehive shape suggests a single factory in Hertfordshire, with distribution possibly via the network of Roman roads in southeast England. According to Lovell and Tubb (2006), there was a quarry and possible factory for the production of puddingstone querns near Puckeridge.

Buildings and marker-stones. As a building stone, puddingstone has been used in numerous ways. At Batlers Green (TQ 155985) it has been used to face the lower walls of the newly rebuilt Home Farm and to line an archway in a nearby farm building (Plate 35). On the western side of Radlett, for example in Gills Hill (TQ 159996), there are numerous garden walls built of multicoloured puddingstone, and in Aldenham churchyard (TQ 140985) there is a 20th century chest tomb built mainly of puddingstone (Plate 36). Latimer (TQ 003989) and Brent Pelham (TL 433308) have puddingstone war memorials (Plate 37). Large blocks were widely used to assist horse-mounting, and at Water End (TL 036106) and elsewhere in the county they have been used as wheel-guards at the corners of old houses to prevent damage by passing traffic. At Ashridge College near Little Gaddesden the entrance to a subterranean icehouse (SP 993119) is built of puddingstone (Plate 38), some pieces of which grade into pebble-free sarsenstone. The garden at Ashridge College also has a fine puddingstone grotto and rock garden. A few blocks are located on county or parish boundaries; they could have been moved to form boundary markers, though it is also possible that some boundaries were drawn through existing stones. For example, in the garden of Ashridge College there is a large block marking the boundary between Hertfordshire and Bedfordshire (Plate 39).

Perhaps the most common use as a building stone in Hertfordshire and adjacent counties is in church walls dating from the Saxon, Mediaeval and Norman periods up to about the mid-14th century. Potter (1998) recorded 103 churches in the region with at least one piece of puddingstone in their fabric. In Hertfordshire, it is most extensively used in older parts of the churches at Abbots Langley (TL 095023), Aldenham (TQ 140985), Great Gaddesden (TL 029113), Hatfield (TL 235084) and Sarratt (TQ 038984) but few, if any, Hertfordshire churches built partly or completely in these periods have none at all. The largest blocks, usually 80-150 cm across and up to 40 cm thick, were often used undressed as foundation stones for buttresses. Examples of this type of use can be seen at Great Gaddesden (Plate 40) and at Chesham (SP 986015) in Buckinghamshire. The name Chesham is probably derived from the Anglo-Saxon *Ceastelesham* (= enclosure or settlement by a castle or heap of stones), which may refer to a Neolithic puddingstone circle that could have provided the foundation stones of the church. Smaller pieces (<50 cm across) were either incorporated into church walls completely undressed or crudely fractured so that the broken surfaces form part of the outer facing of a wall. In some churches (e.g. St Stephens in St Albans) undressed blocks have been laid so as to protrude slightly from the external wall surface (Plate 41), possibly to emphasize their presence.

False puddingstone. In many parts of south Hertfordshire, blocks of a fairly hard conglomerate composed of brown iron oxides or of calcium carbonate cementing mainly rounded flint pebbles, but also containing some subangular flints, quartzite pebbles and other far-travelled rocks, are often found on the floors and lower side slopes of valleys cut through Anglian glacial deposits (Section 6.6) or the Pebble Gravels (Section 6.4) into the London Clay. Harder blocks of this rock, known locally as false puddingstone, have been used, like true Hertfordshire Puddingstone, in mediaeval church towers and walls; for example, the ferruginous form has been used at St Mary North Mymms (TL 222045) (Plate 42). Although the two are superficially similar in appearance, false puddingstone can readily be distinguished from true Hertfordshire Puddingstone by the lack of silica cement and the subangular flints and far-travelled rocks, which never occur in true puddingstone. These constituents suggest formation in Anglian glaciofluvial gravels or in Devensian or Holocene gravels incorporating clasts from the glacial deposits or the Pebble Gravels. The iron forming the ferruginous cement was probably precipitated from water that had flowed through and over the oxidized upper layers of London Clay. In these layers finely disseminated pyrite (FeS_2), originating in the strongly reducing conditions on the sea floor during deposition of the London Clay, is oxidized to iron oxides and hydrated oxides. In the presence of organic matter, the oxides and hydrated oxides can subsequently dissolve in water passing through soils that have become anaerobic because of perennial or seasonal waterlogging. When this iron-rich water reaches more oxygen-rich conditions in streams depositing the gravel, the iron is redeposited as a cement between the pebbles.

Sarsenstones. These have sometimes been used in similar ways to puddingstone. According to Evans (1902), a Palaeolithic implement made of sarsenstone was found near Bedmond in 1885, though the most famous examples of the prehistoric use of sarsens in England are at Stonehenge and Avebury, Wiltshire (Green, 1997). The name 'sarsen' is thought to be a corruption of 'saracen', because Stonehenge and other megalithic sites were previously associated

with pagan people, which included the Moslems of Arabia (Saracens), who fought Christians in the Crusades.

Sarsens from Chiltern sources were also used at various times in the building of Windsor Castle (Hepworth, 1998). Within Hertfordshire they have been incorporated into Pre-Reformation church buildings in much the same way as puddingstone, though probably less frequently. Potter (1998) listed only three churches in Hertfordshire containing sarsens, Sarratt (TQ 039984), Sawbridgeworth (TL 485148) and the ruined Minsden Chapel (TL 198246), though the list should also include St Marys at Hemel Hempstead (TL 054078), which has a large sarsen beneath the northwest buttress (Hepworth, 1998), St Marys at North Mymms (TL 222045), St Michaels and St Stephens in St Albans (TL 142061), Christ Church Chorleywood, St Andrew and St Mary Watton-at-Stone, St Catherine Sacombe, St Lawrence Bovingdon and St Margaret of Antioch Bygrave.

A very common use of sarsenstone was for paving setts and kerbstones. Numerous examples can be seen in the older

Plate 42. Ferruginous 'false puddingstone', south wall of tower of St Marys Church, North Mymms (TL 221045).

Plate 43. Sarsenstone setts, Church Lane, Berkhamsted.

streets of St Albans, Hemel Hempstead, Berkhamsted (Plate 43) and other Hertfordshire towns. These probably also came from Chiltern sites, such as Walter's Ash (SU 8398), where sarsens were previously quarried from the Plateau Drift and dressed on site by hammer and chisel (Spicer, 1905; Woodward and Herries, 1905). A few sarsenstones have also been used as marker-stones in Hertfordshire. For example, one in the corner of St Stephens churchyard, St Albans (TL 141061) probably marks the junction of the Roman Watling Street and the Hatfield-Reading toll road.

5.12. Puddingstone in myth, legend and poetry

The widespread presence of puddingstone in older church buildings has been attributed to the directive of Pope Gregory the Great to Abbot Mellitus in AD 601 (as recorded by the Venerable Bede) that whenever possible pagan temples and venerated stones should be incorporated into the structure of English Christian churches (Davies and Baines, 1953).

Other names. Whether puddingstone really was a subject of pagan veneration before the early Christian period is unclear, but it has certainly had mythical and religious associations for a long period. For example, until quite recently it was widely known among rural populations in the Hertfordshire area as growingstone, motherstone or breedingstone, names which reflect the myth that it grows in the soil. Puddingstones were thought to be either male or female and able to produce small stones, which subsequently grow, and where several pieces were found in the same part of a field, the largest was sometimes called the motherstone. These misapprehensions probably arose because stones can appear suddenly in the topsoil when they are lifted by ploughing or frost-heaving, and may then be further exposed if surface runoff from heavy rain washes away the surrounding fine soil. To prevent damage to farm machinery, stones thus exposed would have been removed to field margins or used for building or other purposes. Gardner (1967) reported that, in some fields east of St Albans, rafts of puddingstone close to the soil surface were so abundant that they had to be broken up and the lumps removed before satisfactory crops could be grown.

Another pagan name, woestone, may also have originated through the sudden appearance of puddingtones by erosion during heavy rainstorms, as these could in turn have led to misfortunes such as flooding and loss of crops. The superstition that puddingstone can ward off evil may account for other names, such as witchstone or hagstone. Many Hertfordshire countryfolk still have a special regard for puddingstone, keeping pieces in their pockets for good luck or on their doorsteps to discourage the entry of evil spirits. Connections with the church may also explain another local name, angelstone.

Marker-stones. A controversial theory involving puddingstone arose from the suggestion of Rudge and Rudge (1952a, 1952b) that pieces were used to mark an ancient (Mesolithic) trackway leading from Grimes Graves, Norfolk, to Stonehenge, via Cheshunt and St Albans. They claimed that over 200 puddingstones marked the 193 miles of this trackway. Some were thought to be sighting stones on hilltops and others were used to indicate where streams might be forded. A detailed summary of the route and full list of the puddingstones involved were published posthumously by Rudge (1994), though some of the stones listed are sarsenstones or even large glacial erratics rather than true puddingstones, and others are now known to have been moved from their original positions. For example, the list included the large sarsenstone (Plate 30) in front of the Museum of St Albans in Hatfield Road (TL 151075), which was originally sited at the junction of Dagnall Street and Market Place in the city centre (Salter, 1912). In east Hertfordshire the route was based mainly on the list of large surface boulders, including glacial erratics, given previously by Salter (1912). However, there is no other archaeological or historical evidence for the trackway, and Warren (1954) suggested that it could be a chance or random alignment, as sighting of stones over distances of 200 m or more would have been difficult in the densely wooded landscape of the early Holocene. Throughout most of its course in Hertfordshire, puddingstones are so abundant on the surface that the Rudges must have made an unconsciously biased selection to produce a clearly defined trackway. Also, the purpose of the track is less certain than the Rudges suggested, because both Grimes Graves and Stonehenge originated in the Neolithic, and neither actually existed in the Mesolithic period. Consequently the theory never enjoyed much support.

Ley lines. A related but even stranger idea concerning puddingstone involves the suggestion that, together with many prehistoric sites, older (pre-Reformation) churches, wells, springs, ponds and even isolated pine trees, puddingstones, sarsenstones and other large blocks occur on straight 'ley lines', which were the source of a mysterious hidden power used in the Neolithic period for moral as well as physical guidance. The concept of ley lines originated with the theories of Watkins (1925), who believed that Neolithic trackways followed exactly straight lines between hilltop sighting points, many of which were subsequently developed for use as burial mounds, stone circles, hilltop forts, churches or moated homesteads. Between the sighting points, the trackways were thought to be indicated by a range of 'mark points', including marker-stones such as sarsenstones, puddingstones or glacial erratics, many of which are found at or near old road (ley line) intersections.

In the 1930s 'ley hunting' became a popular pursuit of ramblers and amateur archaeologists, many of whom hankered after a Neolithic 'golden age' when man was in closer communion with nature's hidden powers. Later the subject was expanded by a lunatic fringe who postulated, *inter alia*, a lost race of Neolithic giants responsible for design of the ley network, and utilization of the lines by unidentified flying objects (UFOs) for navigational purposes. In view of such developments, it is hardly surprising that exhaustive, rational assessments of the theory, even by sympathetic professional archaeologists such as Williamson and Bellamy (1983), have found little or no scientific support for ley lines. Also statistical analyses have shown that the number of non-random alignments of mark points throughout the country is far fewer than the total ley lines identified, even by serious ley hunters.

Many dowsers, such as Underwood (1968) and Graves (1980), have claimed the ability to trace ley lines using dowsing rods, which they believe can react to the hidden power ('earth currents') transmitted along the lines. In the 1970s Frank Stoakes, a dowser who lived in St Albans, traced Hertfordshire ley lines by this method and believed that many of the mark points in the area are puddingstone 'mark stones'. On October 14th 1979 he demonstrated this ability to the Hertfordshire Geological Society, and several sceptical members of the society who held his rods undoubtedly experienced them moving uncontrollably over a piece of puddingstone almost completely buried beneath the turf on the cricket field at Nomansland (TL 175125). Frank also suggested that the St Albans street called Stonecross (TL 152079) obtained its name from the intersection of ley lines over the large raft of buried puddingstone exposed in the excavation for the Seventh Day Adventist Church (Catt and Moffat, 1980), which is close to one end of Stonecross. Through its effectiveness in locating groundwater, minerals and even archaeological features such as buried walls and ditches, dowsing has achieved some scientific credibility. But the claim that it can trace less real features such as ley lines stretches this credibility close to breaking point.

The large blocks of puddingstone (probably silicified Bagshot pebble beds) found on the land surface in parts of Wessex, such as Black Down west of Dorchester (Arkell, 1947), were used to make prehistoric monuments, such as the hilltop stone circle at Kingston Russell (ST 578878) and the Nine Stones of Winterbourne Abbas (ST 613903). In this area similar myths and legends have developed to those of Hertfordshire. Few rock types have featured in poetry, but the poet Oliver Wendell Holmes (1809-1894) helped to make puddingstone famous by offering his own amusing myth about the origin of the Wessex specimens in his poem *The Dorchester Giant*:

They flung it over the Roxbury Hills,
They flung it over the plain,
And all over Milton and Dorchester too
Great lumps of pudding the giants threw;
They tumbled as thick as rain.

Giant and mammoth have passed away,
For ages have floated by;
The suet is hard as a marrow bone,
And every plum is as hard as stone,
But there the puddings lie.

And if, some pleasant afternoon,
You'll ask me out to ride,
The whole of the story I will tell,
And you shall see where the puddings fell,
And pay for the punch beside.

Chapter 6.

Quaternary deposits and later landscape development

John Catt and Allan Cheshire

6.1. Introduction

The Quaternary is the final part (variously described as Sub-Era, Period or Epoch) of geological time, leading to the present day. It began with a further significant deterioration in the earth's climate around 2.58 Ma, which was followed by numerous large and rapid glacial-interglacial climate cycles in mid latitude regions, including Britain. At approximately 0.45 Ma (450,000 years ago), these eventually led to the appearance of a glacier in Hertfordshire. However, glaciations affected areas to the north both before and after this date. For the earth as a whole, the popular name 'Ice Age' is therefore a gross over-simplification, as there were approximately 50 of the glacial-interglacial cycles during the Quaternary. Confusingly, the term 'glacial' is commonly used even in areas where cold periods did not result in glaciation. For example, Hertfordshire was probably glaciated only once, but other Quaternary cold periods (glacials) also brought arctic conditions to the county, so that its landscape was repeatedly modified by processes of periglacial erosion and deposition (French and Williams, 2007), which were dependent on sub-zero air temperatures persisting for many months throughout every winter and perennial ground-ice extending to depths of 10 metres or more below the land surface.

After the Plio-Pleistocene (Red Crag) marine episode, the county was never again invaded by the sea, even in the interglacials, when worldwide sea levels were within a few metres of the present. As a result, all the Quaternary deposits in the county are terrestrial in origin rather than marine. Most are variable in thickness, have restricted outcrops and change rapidly in composition both laterally and vertically. Consequently, correlation of deposits from site to site is often difficult. In addition, there is little palaeontological evidence to assist correlation. Indeed, indigenous fossils are often absent, so that conditions of deposition must usually be inferred from sediment characteristics only.

The contrast between Quaternary terrestrial deposits and most pre-Quaternary marine sediments, which are less variable in composition and thickness, show a more regular stratigraphic order and are usually fossiliferous, led over 150 years ago to the distinction between Quaternary 'drift' deposits and pre-Quaternary 'solid' formations.

These two terms were preserved until quite recently in the legends of BGS maps, though since 2004 they have been replaced by 'superficial deposits' and 'bedrock', respectively (Section 1.2). 'Drift' originated in the concept of deposition by waters of the biblical flood or by icebergs drifting in those waters. The same idea led to use of the term 'diluvium' for many drifts. However, both implied an extremely unlikely submergence of even the very high mountains in Scotland and Wales, which have a patchy cover of these deposits.

For drift or diluvial deposits containing far-travelled rocks (erratics) and fossils, the problem of origin was resolved by Louis Agassiz and other Swiss geologists of the mid-19th century, who proposed that land-based glaciers similar to those still occurring in Norway and many Alpine valleys were previously much more extensive, even covering parts of East Anglia and the Midlands as well as northern England, Scotland and Wales. However, some drift deposits are clearly not glacial in origin, and it was only through the 20th century exploration and study of modern periglacial (e.g. arctic) environments that geologists became aware of the full range of other possible terrestrial origins for Quaternary deposits.

In the early 19th century, it was recognized that river valleys often contain an important type of drift known as 'alluvium', much of which must have been deposited during recent river floods. The distinction between diluvium and alluvium led to the simple, though grossly unequal, subdivision of Quaternary time into the Pleistocene and Holocene, the latter commencing with the rapid climatic amelioration at the end of the last major cold period, now dated by the radiocarbon method to 10,000 years BP (BP = before present). Many interglacials were not significantly different in length from the Holocene, and in Britain interglacial climates were either similar to or a little warmer (< 4°C warmer) than that of the Holocene. Consequently, the Holocene is now regarded as the latest in a long succession of interglacials and, unless global warming resulting from pollution of the atmosphere halts the expected natural cooling cycle, it will be followed sometime in the future by a new glacial period (Gibbard *et al.*, 2006).

During glacials, the intensely cold polar regions expanded, leading to steepening of the temperature gradient between the poles and equator, and thus to compression of the major climatic zones towards the equator. During interglacials,

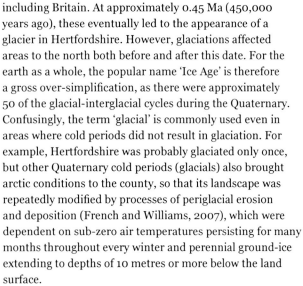

the reverse happened and the climatic zones returned approximately to their present positions. As a result, mid-latitude regions such as Britain experienced strong climatic oscillations throughout the Quaternary, and these resulted in repeated changes in plant and animal life and in processes of erosion and deposition. One might expect this to result in clear glacial-interglacial stratigraphic sequences in areas such as Hertfordshire, but in practice such sequences have proved very difficult to establish throughout Britain. This is partly because extensive glacial and periglacial erosion during cold periods has removed much of the evidence. But in addition, the lack of indigenous fossils in deposits of cold periods and the lithological variability of most Quaternary deposits makes them difficult to correlate from site to site. The interglacial deposits of rivers, lakes and mires are more fossiliferous, but they had limited lateral continuity even before any later episodes of erosion. Also, they are difficult to date because there were few evolutionary changes in most plant and animal groups over the relatively short timespan of the Quaternary. In fact, most variations in Quaternary fossil assemblages resulted from climate change and local differences in depositional environments. As these environmental changes were repeated in successive interglacials, the fossil assemblages can lead to miscorrelations and conflation of two or more interglacials. Perhaps the most rapidly evolving animal group useful for dating Quaternary sediments are the mammals, but their remains (bones and teeth) are only rarely preserved in abundance, and individual specimens, such as those commonly found in river alluvium, are sometimes derived from earlier sediments.

Methods for dating Quaternary deposits

A range of isotopic and other numerical dating methods have been developed specifically for use with Quaternary

Epochs	Stages	Dating (years before present)
Holocene	Holocene (warm)	11,700-present
Late Pleistocene	Devensian (cold)	117,000-11,700
Late Pleistocene	Ipswichian (warm)	128,000-117,000
Mid Pleistocene	Wolstonian (cold)	360,000-128,000
Mid Pleistocene	Hoxnian (warm)	425,000-360,000
Mid Pleistocene	Anglian (cold)	480,000-425,000
Mid Pleistocene	Cromerian (warm)	790,000-480,000
Early Pleistocene	Beestonian (cold)	1,750,000-790,000
Early Pleistocene	Pastonian (warm)	1,840,000-1,750,000
Early Pleistocene	Baventian (cold)	1,920,000-1,840,000
Early Pleistocene	Antian/Bramertonian (warm)	1,960,000-1,920,000
Early Pleistocene	Thurnian (cold)	2,050,000-1,960,000
Early Pleistocene	Ludhamian (warm)	2,100,000-2,050,000
Early Pleistocene	Pre-Ludhamian (cold)	2,580,000-2,100,000

Table 6.1. British Quaternary stages (after Mitchell et al.*, 1973) and approximate dating.*

deposits (Walker, 2005). However, some (e.g. radiocarbon and uranium-series dating) can only be applied to limited parts of Quaternary time, and others (e.g. amino-acid racemization and thermoluminescence dating) can be used only with very specific materials with known depositional histories. Palaeomagnetic dating, using the known sequence of almost instantaneous polarity reversals in the earth's magnetic field (Fig. 6.1), is suitable where there is a continuous sequence of deposits with no major time gaps, but these are rare in Britain.

The radiocarbon method presents an additional problem in that the concentration of the radioactive isotope (^{14}C) in the atmosphere varied in the past. As a result, dates on organic materials based upon the known ^{14}C decay rate have to be corrected to calendar years. This is done using a calibration curve based on dates for materials whose exact age is known from other sources (e.g. tree rings, annually laminated lake sediments or corals dated by the uranium-series method). For example, in terms of calendar years, the Pleistocene-Holocene boundary (10,000 ^{14}C years BP) was actually close to 11,700 calendar years ago.

Quaternary stages

Despite the numerous difficulties of dating and correlating deposits, a sequence of 14 separate climatic stages (7 glacials and 7 interglacials) was proposed for the British Pleistocene by Mitchell *et al.* (1973), and is still used today with a few possible additions (Bowen, 1999). Although this system of stage names (Table 6.1) is used in this and other chapters, it should be emphasized that it has severe weaknesses. First, it is now known that there are long time gaps in the sequence, notably one lasting about 1 Ma in the later part of the Early Pleistocene of East Anglia (Zagwijn, 1975), an area where all the Early Pleistocene stages were defined. Second, the interglacials and some of the earlier glacials are distinguished by relatively minor differences in pollen assemblages, which may not provide a sound basis for long distance correlation. Within a limited area, such as Hertfordshire, the overall similarity in interglacial pollen assemblage sequences can lead to the strong possibility of incorrectly equating the deposits of different interglacials.

A third problem is that the stages are based on climatic changes, so that boundaries between them, drawn mainly from palaeobotanical evidence, are diachronous. Plants migrate very slowly in response to climate change, so the pollen or other botanical evidence for any given change appears significantly earlier at one end of the country than at the other. For example, the warming at the start of an interglacial, though possibly quite rapid in terms of air temperatures across the country, is recorded much earlier in the plant assemblages of southern England than in those of northern Scotland, simply because it takes several centuries for any new warm-loving genera entering the country to migrate that distance. Being more mobile, animals, especially Coleoptera or beetles (Coope, 1977), provide more immediate evidence for climatic changes with much less diachronism, but it is rare for them to be as abundant throughout a depositional sequence as pollen grains.

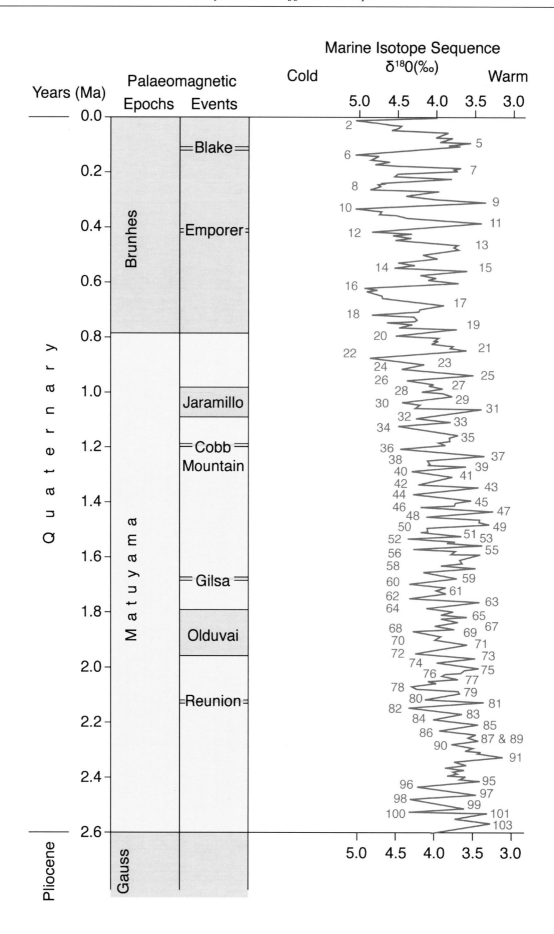

Fig. 6.1. Subdivision of the Quaternary based on palaeomagnetic events and the marine isotope sequence, redrawn from Funnell (1995).

Glacial deposits

The glacial deposits by which many glacial stages are recognized are also diachronous, because the glaciers advanced very slowly from the mountainous ice accumulation areas in northern Britain to lowland depositional regions such as Hertfordshire. Glacial deposits therefore represent small, usually later, parts of the cold stages, though they are often thicker and more extensive than other (periglacial) deposits of cold stages. The main type of deposit left after glaciers melt is the massive, usually unstratified and poorly sorted sediment termed till (previously boulder clay), though this is often associated with stratified gravels, sands and sometimes finer deposits laid down in meltwater lakes and channels formed within, beneath, on top of or in front of the ice sheet. The coarse stratified deposits laid down mainly in proglacial meltwater channels are termed glaciofluvial or outwash sediments.

Studies of modern glaciers have shown that tills may be deposited by several different processes. Lodgement till accumulates beneath ice that is actively moving. The sediment particles are released and 'plastered' on the subglacial surface as the basal ice melts because of increased pressure against irregular bedrock surfaces, where the ice traverses permeable substrata or where geothermal heat rises from beneath. Ablation till accumulates above the ice where it is released by surface melting. As this type is less compacted and initially saturated with water, it is inclined to flow downslope *en masse*, for example into hollows in the glacier surface or down the steep snout of the glacier; this leads to a third type known as flow till. Debris released into shallow meltwater channels within the glacier but not dispersed to create stratified glaciofluvial deposits forms meltout till. This is often crudely stratified, with upper layers draped over stones deposited on lower layers. Meltout till can also be released at the base of ice that is no longer moving (stagnant or dead ice) or from ice at the glacier surface where this is buried beneath ablation till.

Other records of Quaternary climatic change

More complete records of Quaternary climate change than that established in Britain have been obtained over the last few decades from various other parts of the world. These include (a) pollen assemblage sequences from the sediments of long-established lakes in Andean and Mediterranean areas, and (b) the loess (periglacial windblown silt) deposits with numerous interglacial palaeosols (buried soils) in those parts of China and central Asia that were too dry or too far from mountains to experience glacial advances in cold stages. In addition, a complete sequence of cold-warm cycles covering not only the Quaternary since 2.6 Ma but also the Neogene and much of the later Palaeogene (Lourens *et al.*, 2005) has been provided by micropalaeontological and oxygen isotope studies (Section 1.2) of sediments from the floors of major oceanic basins, such as the Atlantic and Pacific. It is these oceanic sequences that provide the best evidence for the 50 or more separate major cold stages (glacials) over the last 2.58 Ma (Fig. 6.1).

The glacial-interglacial cycles are now known to be driven by perturbations in the earth's orbit around the sun, often called Milankovitch cycles (see Bell and Walker, 2005, pp. 77-80 for further details), which have influenced the amount of solar radiation reaching the earth as a whole or at different latitudes (Huybers, 2006).

Based on oxygen isotope stratigraphy, the oceanic record is divided into marine isotope stages (MISs) numbering backwards in time from the Holocene (MIS 1). Glacials consequently have even numbers and interglacials odd numbers, with the exception of MIS 3, which is a slightly milder middle part of the last major cold stage (MISs 2-4), equivalent to the Devensian of Mitchell *et al.* (1973). The MIS boundaries in oceanic sediments are drawn conventionally half way between the temperature maxima and minima indicated by oxygen isotopes in foraminifera, and seem to be globally isochronous. However, they are not exactly equivalent in time to the boundaries between terrestrial stages, such as those of Mitchell *et al.* (1973), which even where they are well dated are based on various other criteria. Where the oceanic sediments are thick because they accumulated rapidly, it is possible to detect climatic oscillations at higher resolution than the major glacial-interglacial cycles. This has allowed some interglacial MISs to be divided into substages. For example, the last or Ipswichian Interglacial (MIS 5) is divided into five substages (MISubstages 5e-5a), the earliest of which (5e) was warmer than 5c or 5a, whereas the intervening 5d and 5b substages were almost as cold as glacial stages. The penultimate interglacial (MIS 7) is similarly subdivided into MIS 7e–7a, with 7e and 7c both slightly warmer than 7a, and all three much warmer than 7d and 7b. In addition, at least three substages (an arctic 11b separating temperate 11a and 11c substages) have been recognized in MIS 11 (Tzedakis *et al.*, 2001), which is equivalent to the Hoxnian Interglacial of the British sequence. The cold stages were also climatically quite variable, with numerous milder intervals (interstadials) separating the coldest periods (stadials).

Causes of climate change

Studies of the isotope records from deep sea sediments have shown that the Pleistocene glacial-interglacial cycles were not of regular length or intensity. In particular, towards the end of the Early Pleistocene (*c*. 900 ka BP), the climate gradually changed from one dominated by cycles lasting approximately 40 ka to another with cycles about 100 ka long. This Mid Pleistocene Transition (Head and Gibbard, 2005) resulted from a change in the dominant control of earth's long-term climate from that of the medium length 40 ka Milankovitch solar cycle (the obliquity of the ecliptic cycle) to that of the longest cycle (the 100 ka orbital eccentricity cycle). The Mid Pleistocene Transition was followed in the late Cromerian around MIS 13 (*c*. 500 ka BP) by a large increase in the amplitude of the glacial-interglacial cycles, such that the subsequent interglacials (MIS 11, 9. 7, 5 and 1) became slightly warmer than those before, and the glacials (MIS 12, 10, 8, 6, 4 and 2) colder as well as longer, resulting in more extensive ice sheets in northern and southern polar regions. The first such glaciation (the Anglian in MIS 12) resulted in the only occasion when Hertfordshire was invaded by a glacier.

A puzzling aspect of the 100 ka eccentricity cycle is that it has a very weak influence on insolation (the amount of solar radiation reaching the earth), so that although it may have dictated the timing of the later Quaternary glacial-interglacial cycles, its effect must have been amplified by other factors. One possibility is that amplification occurred through albedo (reflectance) changes resulting from expansion and decay of ice, snow and vegetation covers. With the slight cooling resulting from the small initial decrease in insolation, there would have been an increase in snow and later in icesheet cover plus a partial loss of dark-coloured, energy absorbing vegetation; together these effects would have amplified the cooling by reflecting more solar radiation back into space. The greater length of the 100 ka cycles thus resulted in more extensive glaciations than those produced by the preceding 40 ka cycles. Other suggested amplification mechanisms involve changes in ocean circulation (Khodri *et al.*, 2001) and in atmospheric 'greenhouse gases', particularly carbon dioxide, methane and water vapour (Raynaud *et al.*, 2000).

A third Milankovitch cycle, resulting from the precession of the equinoxes, has a periodicity ranging from 19 ka to 23 ka. Superimposed on the obliquity and eccentricity cycles, this probably accounts for some other fairly long-term climatic changes detected in the deep ocean sediments and also some terrestrial sequences, such as the substages within MISs 7 and 5.

Although the Milankovitch astronomical cycles amplified in various ways seem to explain the major long-term (glacial-interglacial) climatic cycles, there were other shorter climatic fluctuations during the Quaternary, which are not readily explained by the Milankovitch cycles. These may have been superimposed on the Milankovitch cycles throughout the Pleistocene and even earlier periods, but they are known in detail only for about the last 50,000 years (the later Devensian and Holocene Stages). They have been attributed to a range of factors, including short-term variations in solar output, volcanic activity and changes in patterns of ocean water circulation.

Fluctuations in the solar constant (amount of radiant heat emitted by the sun) are indicated mainly by changes in sunspot activity and the frequency of solar flares. The sunspot/solar flare cycles mainly follow an 11-year periodicity, which has now been correlated with numerous environmental phenomena, including meteorological records of air temperature, rainfall and thunderstorms, and with sea-surface temperatures. They have also been related to the variable production of cosmogenic isotopes (e.g. ^{14}C, ^{10}Be), which are formed by interactions between atmospheric gases and cosmic rays, as recorded in annual tree-rings (Stuiver and Brazunias, 1993) and cores through the Greenland and Antarctic ice caps (Yiou *et al.*, 1997). Multiples of the 11-year (Schwabe) sunspot cycle have also been detected, including the 22-year (Hale), 88-year (Geissberg) and 211-year (Suess) cycle. Notable increases in atmospheric ^{14}C and ^{10}Be have been linked to a sharp climatic

deterioration around 2600 BP, which has been recognized in tree-rings, ice cores and deep-sea cores. Increased production of the cosmogenic isotopes has also been related to sunspot minima in the Mediaeval period, notably the Spörer Minimum (1416-1534 AD) and Maunder Minimum (1645-1715 AD), which coincided with pulses of climatic deterioration known collectively as the Little Ice Age.

Volcanic eruptions affect climate in the short-term mainly by injecting large volumes of volatile sulphur compounds into the atmosphere. These are disseminated globally and converted into sulphuric acid, which cools the atmosphere by back-scattering incoming solar radiation. Recent major eruptions, such as those of Tambora (1815), Krakatoa (1883), Santa Maria (1902), Mt Agung (1963) and Mt Pinatubo (1991), were each associated with near-global temperature decreases of 0.2-0.8°C lasting several years (Zielinski, 2000), and Crowley (2000) has suggested that volcanic activity contributed strongly to cooling during the Little Age Ice.

Following closure of the Panama Straits by collision of North and South America in the Late Pliocene, there was a change in the circulation of Atlantic water, so that warm, strongly saline and therefore denser surface water from tropical areas (the Gulf Stream) now drifts northeastwards from the Caribbean into the Nordic Seas north of Scotland. Here the warm water sinks to lower levels, forming North Atlantic Deep Water (NADW), and in the process releases heat to adjacent land masses, such as Britain, Iceland and western Scandinavia (Broecker and Denton, 1990). The cooled, overturned NADW then returns at depth to the southern oceans. The increased evaporation of water from the warm north Atlantic probably led to increased precipitation on surrounding land areas; when this occurred as snow, it could have resulted in rapid expansion of glaciers in cold stages.

The present style of Atlantic circulation, with warm surface water reaching to at least 60° N, was typical of interglacial climates, including much of the Holocene. However, during glacials polar surface water extended further south, so that the Gulf Stream could reach no further north than the latitude of Portugal (40° N). Also at times the circulation assisted by formation of NADW ceased completely because of large influxes of less dense freshwater into the north Atlantic. These influxes resulted either from seaward drainage of large proglacial lakes or from sudden increases in the production and melting of icebergs when parts of the Laurentide (north American) and Fennoscandian ice sheets surged into the ocean. A shutdown of oceanic circulation leading to sudden cooling of Britain and other land masses previously warmed by the Gulf Stream was the likely cause of a short (~1000 year) cold period (the Loch Lomond Stadial) at the end of the Devensian immediately before the start of the Holocene (Lehman and Keigwin, 1992). Partial shutdowns caused by freshwater influxes from large north American glacial lakes into the north Atlantic may also account for short, less severe cold spells early in the Holocene at approximately 11.2 ka and 8.2 ka calendar years BP (Fisher *et al.*, 2002).

During the Devensian, periodic instability and collapse

of the Laurentide and Fennoscandian ice sheets resulted in other discharges of fresh meltwater often laden with icebergs into the north Atlantic. These Heinrich Events, which are recognized in the ocean floor sediments by layers of coarse ice-rafted debris (Heinrich layers), also led to cooling of north Atlantic surface water by partial shutdown of circulation and thus to chilling of surrounding land areas, including Britain. This resulted in the colder (stadial) episodes of the Devensian and possibly earlier glacials. Intervening periods of ice sheet stability with better ocean circulation and less cooling were probably responsible for the slightly warmer interstadials of the Devensian Stage.

Subdivision of Quaternary time

The base of the Quaternary (2.58 Ma) is drawn at an important reversal of the earth's magnetic field between the Gauss period of normal geomagnetic polarity and the Matuyama period of reversed polarity. In the oceanic sequence it probably lies early in the warm MIS 103 (Shackleton *et al.*, 1990). The numerous reasons for choosing this boundary were summarized in Section 5.1, and have been argued in detail by Gibbard *et al.* (2005, 2010). Despite other proposals, it was agreed by the International Union of Geological Sciences in June 2009. Westaway *et al.* (2002) suggested that the Red Crag in East Anglia and the equivalent deposits in Hertfordshire at Rothamsted and Little Heath (Section 5.2) approximate in age to MISs 98-95 but, as discussed in Section 5.2, they could be slightly older (i.e. Late Pliocene rather than Early Pleistocene).

Between 2.58 Ma and the beginning of the Holocene, Pleistocene time is divided into three parts – Early, Mid and Late (Fig. 6.1). By international agreement, the end of the Early Pleistocene is drawn at another palaeomagnetic polarity reversal, between the Matuyama reversed and Brunhes normal periods. This occurred within MIS 19, about 780,000 years ago. The boundary between the Mid and Late Pleistocene is drawn at the beginning of the last interglacial (MIS 5e), known as the Ipswichian in Britain (Mitchell *et al.*, 1973) or the Eemian elsewhere in Europe. It has been dated to approximately 126,000 BP in sediments off the Portuguese coast, but is slightly earlier (128,000 BP, the MIS 6-5e boundary) in the deep ocean isotope record (Gibbard, 2003).

Periglacial deposits

In cold stages, there were several important processes of deposition other than those resulting directly from glaciation. The absence of a dense vegetation cover stabilizing the soil surface led to frequent erosion by the wind. Fine sand particles in the 60-200 μm size range were carried short distances and then redeposited as the sandy periglacial deposit known as coversand. Slightly finer (coarse silt, 20-60 μm) particles could be transported greater distances (up to several hundred km), and where they were redeposited form the characteristic silty periglacial aeolian sediment known as loess (Fig. 6.2).

Short cool summers and long winters with temperatures

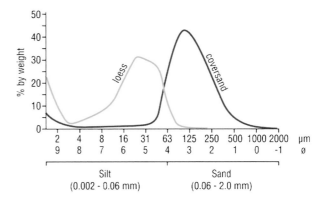

Fig. 6.2. Typical particle size distributions of loess and coversands.

well below 0°C led to layers of permanently frozen sediments (permafrost) many tens of metres thick and often containing lenses, laminae and vertical wedges of ground ice. The upper 1-2 m of permafrost melted in summer to form an active layer, which was often saturated with water because the ice-rich sediment or rock beneath was impermeable. On even quite gentle slopes (<2°), the active layer was likely to flow under gravity, a process termed gelifluction. The ill-sorted sediments (gelifluction deposits) that accumulated on footslopes or valley floors by this process are shown on BGS Drift Geology maps as head.

Subdivision of interglacials by pollen sequences

Where fairly complete vegetation sequences through individual interglacials are known, usually from lake deposits, it is possible to use the changes in pollen assemblages over time to divide interglacials in northwest Europe into four broad climatic periods (Turner and West, 1968) (Fig. 6.3). These have now been recognized in British interglacials that are most frequently represented by pollen-rich deposits, including the Cromerian, Hoxnian and Ipswichian Interglacial Stages (Table 6.1). At the beginning of each interglacial, a Pre-temperate period (I) is characterized by a rapid increase in the pollen of the two cold tolerant trees pine (*Pinus*) and birch (*Betula*) at the expense of grass and herb pollen. In the succeeding Early temperate period (II), increasing warmth encouraged partial replacement of birch and pine by oak (*Quercus*), elm (*Ulmus*), lime (*Tilia*), hazel (*Corylus*) and (in poorly drained soils) alder (*Alnus*). These genera together constitute what is often termed mixed oak forest. In the succeeding Late-temperate period (III), the mixed oak forest include genera that migrated more slowly from warmer regions, such as hornbeam (*Carpinus*) or silver fir (*Abies*). Finally, as the interglacial approached its end, the Post-temperate period (IV) witnessed a return of birch and pine with increasing amounts of grassland pollen, as cooling progressively eliminated the warm-loving mixed oak genera. For any given interglacial, the four periods are indicated by abbreviations, such as HoI, HoII, HoIII and HoIV for the Hoxnian; IpI, etc for the Ipswichian; CrI, etc for the Cromerian.

Within any of the four parts of an interglacial, minor

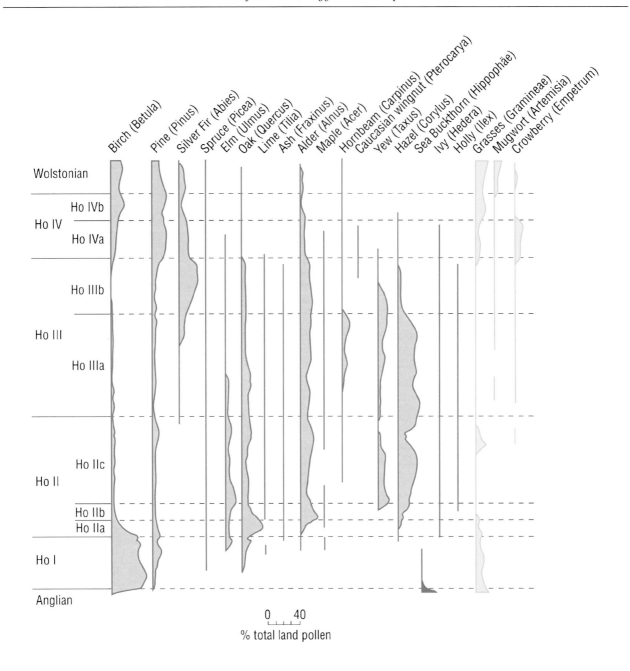

Birch (Betula)
Pine (Pinus)
Silver Fir (Abies)
Spruce (Picea)
Elm (Ulmus)
Oak (Quercus)
Lime (Tilia)
Ash (Fraxinus)
Alder (Alnus)
Maple (Acer)
Hornbeam (Carpinus)
Caucasian wingnut (Pterocarya)
Yew (Taxus)
Hazel (Corylus)
Sea Buckthorn (Hippophäe)
Ivy (Hedera)
Holly (Ilex)
Grasses (Gramineae)
Mugwort (Artemisia)
Crowberry (Empetrum)

Wolstonian

Ho IVb
Ho IV
Ho IVa

Ho IIIb
Ho III
Ho IIIa

Ho IIc
Ho II
Ho IIb
Ho IIa

Ho I

Anglian

0   40

% total land pollen

Fig. 6.3. Climatic periods within the Hoxnian Interglacial (MIS 11) based on vegetation changes at Marks Tey, Essex, redrawn from Turner (1970).

changes in vegetation at individual sites allow local pollen assemblage biozones to be recognized, which are usually named after the two or more most abundant genera found in a particular layer or layers of sediment. Assemblage biozones can also be defined for animal groups, such as molluscs, mammals, beetles, ostracods, etc. Each assemblage biozone should show a limited variation in composition, and fairly distinct boundaries with other biozones above and below. Where the same sequence of assemblage biozones is recognized over a fairly large area, each is termed a regional assemblage biozone, and may be used for correlation of deposits within that region. Also, if it can be dated at one site by any method, then the dating may be extended to other sites within the region.

Palaeontological distinctions between interglacials

Some of the Quaternary interglacials in northwest Europe have been distinguished by small, but what are thought to be significant, differences in pollen assemblages. For example, different tree genera, such as silver fir (*Abies*), maple (*Acer*) and beech (*Fagus*) seem to have appeared at the climatic optimum (period III) of different interglacials, and there are characteristic curves over time through different interglacials for the relative abundance of hazel (*Corylus*) and spruce (*Picea*) pollen (West, 1980). In addition, some of the earlier interglacials can probably be distinguished by the occasional return of different tree genera that were previously present in the warm climate of the Neogene, such as swamp cypress (*Taxodium*), sweetgum (*Liquidambar*), hemlock (*Tsuga*) and Caucasian wingnut (*Pterocarya*).

Within limited areas, some fossil animal groups, including mammals, molluscs, beetles and ostracods, can be used to distinguish different interglacials. This evidence is discussed below in relation to particular deposits.

6.2. History of the Thames

The Hertfordshire area is fortunate in having what is probably the most complete Quaternary sequence in Britain, the fluvial deposits of the Thames (Fig. 6.4). These represent most of the Quaternary after the Red Crag marine transgression, including much of the 1 Ma hiatus in the East Anglian sequence. Westaway *et al.* (2002) have tentatively correlated the Thames sequence with the MIS sequence using a range of dating evidence. Other Quaternary deposits in the county provide mere snapshots of a few imprecisely dated and poorly correlated Quaternary events. The southern North Sea basin, which subsided throughout the Quaternary, has another fairly complete sequence (Cameron *et al.*, 1992), probably the thickest (>1 km) in the northwest European region, but correlation with the terrestrial deposits of Hertfordshire and East Anglia is possible at certain levels only.

Before it was diverted by the Anglian glaciation of MIS 12 (Section 6.6), the Thames flowed north-eastwards from Marlow close to Beaconsfield, Rickmansworth, Watford, St Albans, Hatfield, Hertford and Bishop's Stortford, to enter the North Sea off the East Anglian coast (Hey, 1965, 1980; Bridgland, 1994). East of the M1 near Bricket Wood, this early proto-Thames valley is cut in Chalk and filled by fluvial sediments and an increasing thickness of glacial deposits, but it can still be traced at least as far east as Ware in the broad shallow valley (Vale of St Albans) lying between the foot of the Chiltern dip-slope (the Sub-Palaeogene Surface) near Abbots Langley, St Albans and Lemsford and the small Palaeogene escarpment extending from Radlett to North Mymms, Essendon and Little Berkhamsted (Plate 44). Further east, a continuation of the buried valley beneath Bishops Stortford, Chelmsford and Colchester, was identified by Wooldridge and Henderson (1955) as their 'Mid Essex Depression'.

The deposits left by the Thames, often termed terrace aggradations, are coarse gravels composed mainly of angular to subrounded flint fragments, with smaller but variable amounts of rounded pebbles of flint (probably derived from Palaeogene deposits), pebbles of quartz, quartzite, sandstone and chert, and also occasional subangular blocks of volcanic rocks from north Wales. The last five components are grouped as 'exotics', because they are derived from outside the present catchment of the river. Their presence led to the previous description of the deposits as 'Glacial Sand and Gravel' or 'Glacial Gravel with Bunter Pebbles', for example on early BGS maps of Hertfordshire. The gravels usually rest on an eroded surface of Chalk, and in their lower parts are often slightly chalky and pale coloured, but upper layers close to the ground surface are decalcified and often reddish

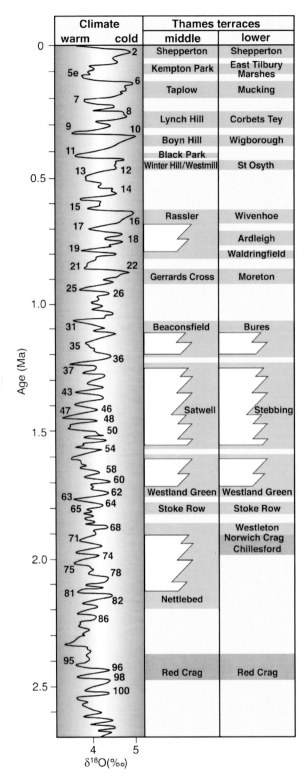

Fig. 6.4. Sequence of terraces of the middle and lower Thames and tentative correlation with Marine Isotope Stages, redrawn from Westaway et al. *(2002).*

brown in colour because of weathering in the Holocene and earlier interglacials (Plate 45). The lower (calcareous) layers are weakly stratified, often with cross-bedded units, but the weathered layers are much less well bedded, because they were disturbed by collapse when the chalk fragments were dissolved by temperate weathering. Many of the gravels have also collapsed into solution cavities in the chalk beneath or

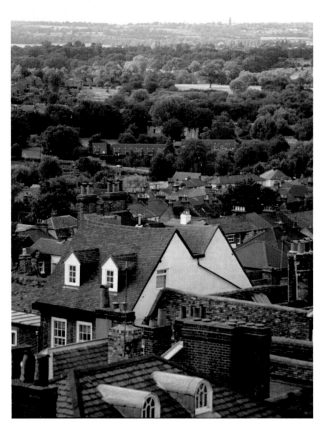

Plate 44. *View of Vale of St Albans looking southwards from summit of the mediaeval clock tower (TL 147072), St Albans.*

Plate 45. *Gerrards Cross Gravel with weathered reddish brown upper layer, Westwood Pit (TQ 0798) near Watford.*

have slumped downslope during later cold stages (McGregor and Green, 1983a; Whiteman, 1992).

Origin of the terraces

Structures such as cross-bedding within the sands and gravels usually suggest deposition by a multichannel braided river. Unlike the present rivers of lowland Britain, such as the modern Thames, which have large single channels, braided rivers have numerous small anastomosing channels, and occur where the flow of water is low or strongly seasonal, the supply of coarse sediment is large, and the valley sides are unstable and subject to erosion. During the Quaternary in lowland Britain, these conditions were typical of cold stages, when large amounts of sediment were transported to the valley floor by gelifluction on the thinly vegetated valley sides, and the flow of the river was usually unable to remove it efficiently. Thin layers of reddish brown flinty clay interbedded with the gravels near the original valley sides probably represent gelifluction deposits that accumulated in these conditions (Gibbard, 1983a). River flow sufficiently rapid to wash away the gelifluction deposits (nival floods) probably occurred only during short periods of summer thaw.

Based on evidence from some of the later aggradations, Maddy *et al.* (2001, Fig. 3) have suggested cycles of changing

fluvial activity related to the glacial-interglacial climatic cycles, in which each gravel was mainly aggraded during a cold stage on a valley floor inherited from uplift-driven incision during the previous cold stage (Fig. 6.5). Each cycle of gravel aggradation produced an almost flat-topped depositional surface or terrace, sloping gently downhill in the direction of water flow. Terrace formation included three main phases, beginning with (a) incision and some gravel aggradation in the later part of one cold stage, followed by (b) deposition of fine organic channel and floodplain sediments during the succeeding interglacial, and concluding with (c) further aggradation of gravel to create the terrace surface in the early part of the next cold stage. Because of valley floor scouring early in the third phase of each cycle, the interglacial sediments were almost completely removed, but are sometimes preserved at valley-side locations as lens-shaped masses where the deeper channels containing them were quickly buried by gravel of phase (c). Through the Quaternary, the river cut progressively deeper into its bedrock floor, mainly as a result of the tectonic uplift of southern England (Westaway *et al.*, 2002) and subsidence of the North Sea basin (Section 5.2). As a result the terraces decrease in age with decreasing height above present river level.

Between the Chalk escarpment near Goring and the North Sea, the maximum height of the pre-Anglian Thames terrace

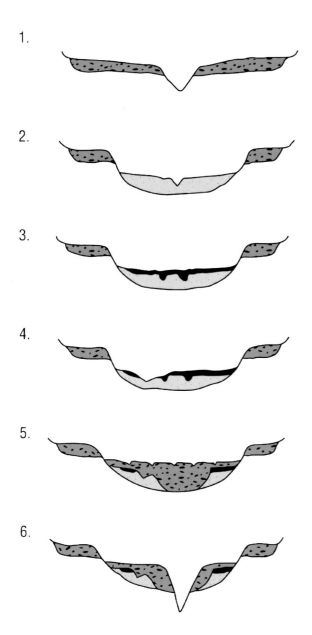

1. Glacio-isostatic uplift and melting of snow and ground ice leads to incision by single-thread river into earlier terrace gravels at the end of glacial period.

2. Increased flow early in interglacial widens valley and earlier terrace gravel is redeposited on the new valley floor, with a coarser lag upstream and a finer sandy gravels downstream.

3. Early interglacial gravels are overlain later in interglacial by finer channel sands and overbank silts with organic (peaty) deposits in ephemeral ponds.

4. Cooling at the transition from interglacial to glacial leads to increased flood frequency and erosion with localized downcutting.

5. Decreased vegetation cover and increased sediment supply from valley sides by gelifluction leads to rapid deposition of gravels in glacial period by nival multi-thread river. Some downcutting by early floods. Later floods mainly redistribute existing sediment.

6. Renewed uplift and increased discharge at end of glacial period leads to rapid incision by single-thread river and repetition of cycle.

Fig. 6.5. Changes in fluvial erosion and deposition over a glacial-interglacial cycle leading to formation of Thames terraces, redrawn from Maddy et al. (2001).

surfaces ranges from about 200 m OD immediately east of Goring to 20 m OD in the Colchester and Clacton areas. At levels below about 115 m OD, they form fairly continuous benches extending along the valley sides approximately parallel to the direction of river flow and sloping gently to the east. However, at higher levels they are much less continuous because of later dissection, and the isolated patches of gravel are weathered throughout and more disturbed, aspects which reflect the greater age of the higher terraces.

Before about 1960, most work on the Thames sequence was based on geomorphological studies in the Middle Thames valley between Oxford and Hertford (for the pre-Anglian proto-Thames) or Oxford and London (for the modern, post-diversion course). This led to the recognition of the following sequence of terrace features in order of descending height and decreasing age: the Harefield, Rassler, Winter Hill, Black Park, Boyn Hill, Lynch Hill, Taplow, Upper Floodplain and Lower Floodplain Terraces (Hare, 1947; Sealy and Sealy, 1956), the first seven named after sites where they were observed to be well developed. However, in the last 3-4 decades, research has concentrated more on the gravelly deposits themselves rather than on the terrace surfaces as geomorphological features. In particular, the proportions of flint and other clast types have been used to distinguish different gravel aggradations and correlate them downstream from site to site (Hey, 1965; McGregor and Green, 1978, 1983b; Gibbard, 1985; Green and McGregor, 1999). The different aggradations are named after sites where they have been clearly exposed. As a result, two parallel sets of names have developed,

Morphostratigraphic Units	Lithostratigraphic units	Tentative dating (MIS)
Lower Floodplain Terrace	Shepperton Gravel	4-2
Upper Floodplain Terrace	Kempton Park Gravel	6-4
Taplow Terrace	Taplow Gravel	8-6
Lynch Hill Terrace	Lynch Hill Gravel	10-8
Boyn Hill Terrace	Boyn Hill Gravel	12-10
Black Park Terrace	Black Park Gravel	Late 12
Upper and Lower Winter Hill Terraces	Winter Hill and Westmill Gravels	Early 12
Rassler Terrace	Rassler Gravel	20-16?
Lower Gravel Train (= Harefield Terrace)	Gerrards Cross Gravel	22
Higher Gravel Train	Beaconsfield Gravel	36-31
-	Satwell Gravel	54-37
-	Westland Green Gravel	62-55
-	Stoke Row Gravel	64
-	Nettlebed Gravel	82-68

Table 6.2. Names of terrace gravels and equivalent surfaces in the Middle Thames (based on Bridgland, 1994; Westaway et al., 2002).

a morphostratigraphic set for the terrace surfaces as geomorphological features, and a lithostratigraphic set for the gravel aggradations of which the terraces are composed (Table 6.2).

Distinguishing and dating the terraces

The pre-diversionary (pre-Anglian glaciation) lower Thames in East Anglia deposited a sequence of ten aggradations, which together form the Kesgrave Sands and Gravels (Rose et al., 1976; Rose and Allen, 1977). In southern parts of East Anglia, the successive aggradations (lithostratigraphic members) of this formation form a series of SW-NE terrace

surfaces largely buried beneath Anglian glacial deposits (Whiteman, 1992, Fig. 4) (Fig. 6.6). Here the terrace surfaces occur at successively lower levels south-eastwards, indicating a progressive south-eastward migration (uniclinal shifting) of the proto-Thames, culminating in a course in the early Anglian along the Mid-Essex Depression through Chelmsford and Colchester. The uniclinal shifting probably resulted from the progressive tilting of southern England through the Quaternary that resulted from subsidence in the southern North Sea basin and uplift over the mantle 'hotspot' affecting western Britain and the Midlands (Bott and Bott, 2004).

Using clast lithology and allowing for a gentle longitudinal

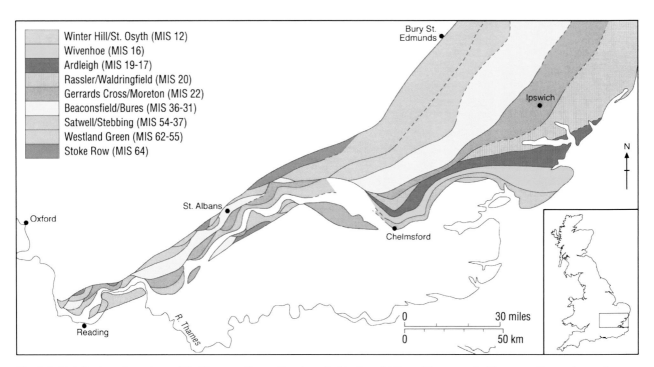

Fig. 6.6. Distribution of members of the Kesgrave Formation deposited in the middle and lower proto-Thames valley, redrawn from Whiteman and Rose (1992), and tentative correlation with marine isotope stages (from Westaway et al., 2002).

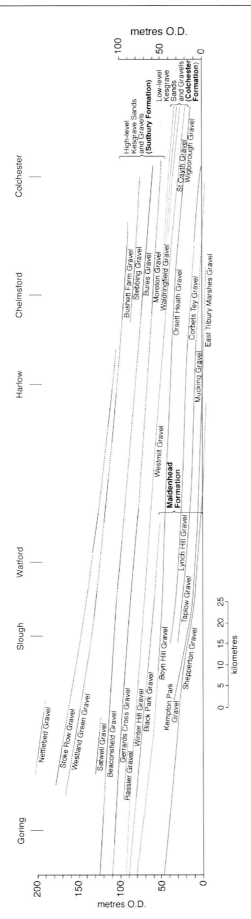

gradient of about 0.5 m km⁻¹, the terrace aggradations can be traced upstream from Essex and Suffolk through the Vale of St Albans (Fig. 6.7) at least as far as the Goring Gap (Whiteman and Rose, 1992). In the Maidenhead-Goring area, they were grouped as the Middle Thames Valley Gravel Formation (Gibbard, 1985) or Middle Thames Formation (Gibbard, 1999). Here they occur mainly on lower parts of the Chilterns dip-slope (Fig. 6.8), at levels lower than the isolated remnants of the marine Red Crag. However, their distribution here suggests much less southward migration of the river than east of St Albans. Between successive aggradations there was downcutting but little lateral channel migration, as some of the aggradations can be recognized as 'paired terraces' on either side of the valley.

From later work, principally on counts of pebble types, Whiteman and Rose (1992) divided successive aggradations of the pre-Anglian Kesgrave Sands and Gravels and their upstream equivalents into an earlier Sudbury Formation and a later Colchester Formation. Gravels of the Sudbury Formation contain more pebbles from outside the present Thames catchment (West Midlands, Welsh borderland, south-western Pennines and north Wales) than those of the Colchester Formation. The two are also distinguished by differences in terrace surface gradients, degree of soil development on the terrace surfaces (Kemp, 1987a, 1987b) and pollen assemblages from the occasional lenses of interglacial organic sediment within the gravels.

As the gravels are thought to have been deposited in very cold conditions, it is likely that the Pleistocene cold stage during which a particular terrace aggradation was completed (i.e. phase c of the cycle proposed by Maddy *et al.*, 2001) was equivalent to one of the main cold marine isotope stages (MISs). Therefore, once one terrace aggradation can be firmly dated (e.g. by any organic sediments it contains) and thereby linked to the MIS sequence, others can be related to major MIS stages simply by counting backwards or forwards in time (i.e. up or down the altitudinal terrace sequence, respectively). After he retired to live in Hertfordshire, this approach to dating the Thames terraces was pioneered by Percy Evans (1971), using an early reconstruction of Pleistocene climatic change based on micropalaeontological and oxygen isotope evidence from Caribbean marine cores. Unfortunately, Percy incorrectly related cycles of Thames aggradations to successive interglacial sea levels, which were then thought to have declined progressively since the Pliocene, thus accounting for the gradual decline in terrace levels over time. The later realization that the terrace aggradations in fact represent cold rather than warm stages has led to a much firmer correlation with the MIS sequence. The latest version, using a range of linking dates based on biostratigraphic and palaeomagnetic evidence from southeast England, The Netherlands and the southern North Sea, is by Westaway *et al.* (2002) (Fig. 6.4).

Fig. 6.7. Long profiles of the Thames terraces from Essex through the Vale of St Albans to the Goring Gap (redrawn from Whiteman and Rose, 1992).

6.3. The Thames terrace sequence

The Nettlebed Gravel

The highest and therefore oldest known Thames gravel aggradation is the Nettlebed Gravel, which occurs mainly in the Nettlebed area, Oxfordshire, on Priest's Hill (SU 700872) and the nearby Windmill Hill (SU 702872). A small patch of gravel at Kimble Farm (SU 749888) may be a downstream equivalent (Turner, 1983). At Nettlebed, the deposits overlie the London Clay and Reading formations at 200-210 m OD. They were originally regarded as marine (Prestwich, 1890; Monckton and Herries, 1891), and Wooldridge (1927) correlated them with the high-level Plio-Pleistocene marine deposits at Lane End, Little Heath and Lenham. However, Salter (1896), Horton (1977, 1983), Turner (1983), Gibbard (1985), Bridgland (1994) and Rose *et al.* (1999) have all suggested that they are fluvial in origin, because they occupy channels approximately parallel to the orientation of the Thames through the Goring Gap (NW-SE), and the sand grains that they contain show evidence in scanning electron micrographs for fluvial modification of earlier (Palaeogene?) marine surface features. In addition, a channel at Priest's Hill contains humic silts and clay, which have yielded a typical assemblage of Early Pleistocene pollen and other remains of terrestrial plants (Turner, 1983). Unfortunately, the exact relationship of the interglacial deposits to the Nettlebed Gravel is unclear; a temporary excavation in 1975 showed that they are overlain by clayey gravel, but this could be a gelifluction deposit derived from Nettlebed Gravel and Palaeogene clays outcropping upslope rather than Nettlebed Gravel *in situ*.

The Nettlebed Gravel contains 81-96% flint (most of which is from the Chalk, and rather less than half is well rounded Palaeogene pebbles), 1-15% quartz pebbles and small amounts of quartzite (0.3-4.1%) and Carboniferous chert (0.1-1.8%) pebbles. The quartz and quartzite (including sarsen pebbles) could be derived from the local Reading Formation (White, 1906; Moffat, 1986) but, together with the Carboniferous chert, indicate a Midlands source for a small proportion of the gravel (Turner, 1983; Gibbard, 1985). Later Thames terrace gravels, principally members of the Sudbury Formation, contain much larger amounts of clasts from Midland sources, so it is quite likely that at the Nettlebed stage the Thames had a relatively small or low energy catchment west of the Goring Gap, probably extending no further than the Cotswolds (Maddy *et al.*, 2001, Fig. 1A). Also, from the few sites where it has been identified, the Nettlebed Gravel seems to form a more steeply sloping surface (1-1.4 m km⁻¹) than the younger terraces (Whiteman and Rose, 1992), again suggesting that Nettlebed was relatively close to the limit of the Thames catchment at the time.

The pollen assemblage from the organic deposits at Priest's Hill provides no clear evidence for age. However, Westaway *et al.* (2002) suggested that the Nettlebed Gravel was deposited some time between MIS 82 (2.14 Ma) and MIS 68 (1.87 Ma).

This was based upon a tentative correlation of the earliest Thames terraces and their likely equivalents in East Anglia with the better dated Early Pleistocene sequence of The Netherlands (Gibbard *et al.*, 1991), and on the idea that in the Early Pleistocene the coldest episodes indicated by terrestrial fossil evidence in northwest Europe are equivalent to times when the oceanic oxygen isotope record indicates the greatest build-up of glaciers worldwide.

Gibbard (1983a, 1985, 1989) and most other workers have correlated the Nettlebed Gravel with part of a much more extensive Early Pleistocene flint-rich gravel known as the Pebble Gravel. This occurs over large areas of south Hertfordshire and north Middlesex mainly on the southern side of the proto-Thames valley, and is described in detail in Section 6.4. Because of this likely correlation and the more local source of its clasts, Gibbard later (1989) separated the Nettlebed Gravel as a formation (the Nettlebed Formation) distinct from his Middle Thames Formation.

The Stoke Row Gravel

This terrace gravel is the highest and oldest member of the Sudbury Formation of Whiteman and Rose (1992). It is more extensive than the Nettlebed Gravel, but still occurs only as disconnected remnants, at least three of which (at Bedmond, Sherrardspark Wood and Furneux Pelham) are within Hertfordshire (Fig. 6.8). Hey (1965) correlated the remnant at Stoke Row (SU 686834) with his Westland Green Gravels, but it occurs at 174 m OD, about 6 m higher than the long profile for the Westland Green Gravel projected from sites further east, so Gibbard (1983a, 1985) separated it as a slightly earlier aggradation.

The Stoke Row Gravel contains less total flint (36-75%) but much more quartz (14-50%) and quartzite (4-13%) than the Nettlebed Gravel. The amounts of Palaeogene flint pebbles and Carboniferous chert are more variable, but are sometimes considerably greater than in the Nettlebed Gravel. The quartz and quartzite seem to be derived from various Triassic, Carboniferous and Devonian sources in the West Midlands and south-western Pennines (Whiteman and Rose, 1992). By this time, the Thames had therefore considerably expanded its catchment into much of the Midlands (Maddy *et al.*, 2001, Fig. 1B). From the Vale of St Albans, its downstream course is thought to have been north-eastwards, eventually reaching the North Sea through Norfolk and Suffolk. Whiteman and Rose (1992) originally suggested that the Stoke Row Gravel was deposited in MIS 68, but Funnell (1995) and Rose *et al.* (1999) later presented arguments in favour of correlation with MIS 64, which is dated to 1.78 Ma, and this was accepted by Westaway *et al.* (2002).

Gravels at Bedmond (TL 104037) and Sherrardspark Wood (TL 225138) were attributed to the Stoke Row Gravel by Moffat and Catt (1986b), because they are approximately 10 m higher than the local level of the Westland Green Gravels, and their quartz/quartzite + sandstone ratios are greater than those of the Westland Green Gravels. The site (Hillcollins Pit) at Furneux Pelham (TL 442267) lies at 107 m OD, and exposes 3-4 m of bedded sandy gravel.

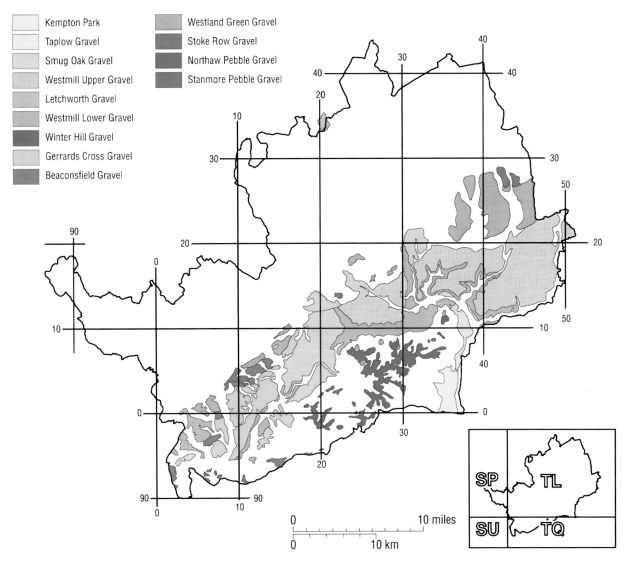

Legend:
- Kempton Park
- Taplow Gravel
- Smug Oak Gravel
- Westmill Upper Gravel
- Letchworth Gravel
- Westmill Lower Gravel
- Winter Hill Gravel
- Gerrards Cross Gravel
- Beaconsfield Gravel
- Westland Green Gravel
- Stoke Row Gravel
- Northaw Pebble Gravel
- Stanmore Pebble Gravel

0   10 miles
0   10 km

Fig. 6.8. Distribution of proto-Thames gravels and Pebble Gravels in Hertfordshire (redrawn from Bridgland, 1994).

Hey (1983) originally grouped it with his Westland Green Gravels, but Bridgland (1994) suggested that it is a few metres too high and closer to the profile of the Stoke Row Gravel as projected from other Hertfordshire sites to the west. Like some of the younger Thames gravels in Hertfordshire, the gravel at Furneux Pelham also contains traces (<1%) of chert from the Lower Greensand of the Weald (Cheshire, 1986a). These were probably introduced by one or more south-bank tributaries of the proto-Thames, such as early equivalents of the rivers Mole, Wey or Wandle.

The Westland Green Gravel

This aggradation is also discontinuous and often strongly disturbed, but has been identified at many more sites than the earlier gravels. It was originally recognized at numerous sites between Goring and Bishop's Stortford by Hey (1965), who designated a type-site at Westland Green (TL 422215) in east Hertfordshire. It contains similar amounts of quartz (7-46%), total flint (33-88%) and Palaeogene flint pebbles (13-53%) to the Stoke Row Gravel, but is slightly richer in quartzite (5-19%). There are also traces of Carboniferous

chert, Lower Greensand chert and Welsh volcanic rocks at some localities (Hey, 1965; Gibbard, 1985). The Welsh rocks suggest that an early upland glaciation of Wales somehow fed sediment into the upper Thames catchment at this time (Hey and Brenchley, 1977). Apart from Westland Green, exposures of the gravel have also been reported at Coldharbour (SU 635800), Cray's Pond (SU 637505), Bowsey Hill (SU 807802), Ashley Hill (SU 8381), Hodgemoor Wood (SU 977944) near Chalfont St Giles, Chorleywood (TQ 023953), Hatfield Park (TL 2407), Bell Bar (TL 253059), Essendon (TL 2708), Bramfield Wood (TL 285167), Little Berkhamsted (TL 2907), Hertford Heath (TL 353115), Colliers End (TL 369204), Albury (TL 429263) and Bishop's Stortford (TL 477219). Figure 6.8 shows the full distribution of this terrace throughout the county. Gravels at Mardley Heath (TL 247185) may also have originally been part of the Westland Green Gravel, but Moffat and Catt (1986b) suggested that they have been mixed with angular flint from the Chalk. Hey (1965) also included the gravels at Furneux Pelham and Stoke Row, but these are now attributed to earlier aggradations, as outlined above.

The quartzite pebbles are variable in colour (white,

131

yellow, brown, red and purple) and size, and many show quartz veins. Hey (1965) suggested that, although many are from the Triassic Bunter Pebble Beds (now Kidderminster Conglomerate) of the West Midlands, the white ones are from Cambrian rocks of the Welsh borderland and those with quartz veins (together with the quartz pebbles) from areas of intense quartz veining, such as parts of Wales. The Carboniferous chert fragments are mainly subangular and often contain crinoid ossicles and/or sponge spicules. Together with many of the sandstones, they are probably from the southern Pennines.

Following his initial work in the proto-Thames valley, Hey (1980, 1982) extended his Westland Green Gravel into East Anglia, where he correlated it on the basis of clast lithology with part of the Kesgrave Sand and Gravel Formation and with a marine gravel resting on chalk at Beeston Regis (TG 260402) on the north Norfolk coast. The latter had previously been related to the cold Pre-Pastonian *a* or Baventian Stage (West, 1980; Zalasiewicz *et al.*, 1991). However, subsequent work (Whiteman and Rose, 1992) suggested that this correlation is incorrect, and that the Westland Green Gravel is older than Pre-Pastonian *a*. In East Anglia, its equivalent is probably the highest and oldest member of the Kesgrave Sand and Gravel Formation, the Bushett Farm Gravel (Whiteman, 1992). Westaway *et al.* (2002) consequently equated it with the MIS 62-54 period (1.74-1.57 Ma).

In further work, Hey (1986) extended the Westland Green Gravel into the Evenlode valley northwest of Oxford, where he found a lithological and altitudinal equivalent in the Waterman's Lodge Member of what has long been known as the Northern Drift of the Cotwolds (Hull, 1855). The Evenlode valley therefore provided a route for transportation of the exotic components of the Westland Green, and perhaps other Thames gravels, from Wales and the south Midlands into the present Thames valley near Oxford. Whiteman (1992) showed that the valley's long profile cleared the summit of the Cotswolds, so that the river could have had access to the south Midlands.

The Satwell Gravel

This terrace aggradation has been recognized over only a short section of the Thames valley between Goring and Marlow. It was defined by Gibbard (1983a) from sites outside Hertfordshire at Kingswood Common (SU 694825), Bromsden Farm (SU 716847), Bix (SU 729846) and Hulton's Farm, Hambleden (SU 794870), with a type-site at Satwell (SU 706839). The height of the terrace surface in this area ranges from 131 to 128 m OD, giving a gradient of 0.6 m km⁻¹. Projecting this slope downstream suggests that it correlates with the Stebbing Gravel member of the Kesgrave Sand and Gravel Formation in Essex (Whiteman, 1992). In the single sample analysed by Gibbard (1985), the Satwell Gravel is again rich in quartz (43%) and quartzite (11%), but with smaller amounts of Chalk-derived flint (26%) and Palaeogene flint pebbles (6%) than in any older terrace gravels.

Westaway *et al.* (2002) suggested that the Satwell Gravel

was deposited in one or more cold stages between MIS 54 (1.57 Ma) and MIS 36 (1.2 Ma).

The Beaconsfield Gravel

This name was first used by Gibbard (1978a) for a weathered, disturbed and dissected, but fairly continuous terrace aggradation recognizable between Goring and the M1 near St Albans. Previously it had been identified by Wooldridge (1938) and Hare (1947) in the Beaconsfield area as the 'Higher Gravel Train'. Here it contains more Chalk-derived flint (38-76%), but fewer Palaeogene flint pebbles (10-11%) than most of the higher aggradations (Gibbard 1985). Quartz (8-43%) and quartzite (5-17%) are as common as in the Satwell, Westland Green and Stoke Row Gravels, and locally there are also traces of Carboniferous chert.

The type-site proposed by Gibbard (1978a) was at Beaconsfield (SU 945911). He also identified sites further west at Heath Holtspur, Flackwell, Warren Wood, Benham's, Withy Copse, Valentine Wood and Goring Heath, and further east at Seer Green and Chalfont St Giles, Chalfont Common and Millhouse Farm (TL 114037). McGregor and Green (1983b) extended its distribution north-eastwards to the M1 near Hemel Hempstead (Fig. 6.8), and Green *et al.* (1982) and Whiteman (1992) have suggested that it correlates with a lithologically similar aggradation (the Bures Gravel) in the Sudbury Formation of Essex. The evidence that the Thames continued to flow through the Vale of St Albans when the Beaconsfield Gravel was deposited conflicts with the earlier suggestion by Wooldridge (1938, 1960) and Hare (1947) that it was diverted southwards into the 'Middlesex Depression' (Finchley Valley), where it was joined by a south bank tributary (a combined early Mole/ Wey river). However, Gibbard (1979) concluded that the Finchley Valley in North London was instead occupied only by the Mole/Wey tributary, which was confluent with the Thames near Ware.

According to Westaway *et al.* (2002), the Beaconsfield Gravel was deposited between MIS 36 (1.2 Ma) and MIS 32 (1.08 Ma).

The Gerrards Cross Gravel

This is the lowest and youngest member of the Sudbury Formation of Whiteman and Rose (1992). Because of its degraded nature and occurrence approximately 20 m lower than the Beaconsfield Gravel (Higher Gravel Train), Wooldridge (1938) originally described it as the 'Lower Gravel Train'. However, in the Harefield-Rickmansworth area, Hare (1947) was able to map a convincing terrace surface at this level, which he named the Harefield Terrace. Both Wooldridge and Hare thought that at this stage the Thames continued through the 'Middlesex Depression', but Gibbard (1977), Green and McGregor (1978a) and McGregor and Green (1983b) traced the gravel into the Vale of St Albans (Fig. 6.8). Gibbard (1977) originally designated a type site in a temporary exposure at Leavesden Green (TL 105004), but later (1983) redefined a large exposure at Wapsey's Wood near Gerrards Cross (SU 969887) as the type site. He also recorded 5 m of the gravel over chalk in sections cut for the M1 motorway and 9 m at Sopwell (TL 144053) near St Albans. There have also been extensive exposures at Westwood Quarry (TQ 071993) beside the M25 near Watford (Green and McGregor, 1978b; McGregor and Green 1983b; Gibbard, 1985) (Plate 45).

The twin tunnels for the London-Birmingham railway line (TQ 099987–TQ 089999) between Watford and Leavesden Green beneath the Earl of Essex's estate were dug through Chalk overlain by the Gerrards Cross Gravel. During construction of the first tunnel in 1837, the looseness of the dry gravelly terrace deposits and the irregular junction with the chalk beneath contributed to an unfortunate accident. Ten workmen excavating a vertical shaft from the tunnel to the ground surface penetrated the base of a large solution pipe filled with loose sand and gravel and were buried alive when the sediment collapsed into the tunnel (Osborne and Osborne, 1839, pp. 11-112). Exposures of similar solution pipes seen in 1872 when the cutting north of Watford Junction station was widened and the second tunnel dug were described by Whitaker and Hopkinson (1872).

The Gerrards Cross Gravel is again composed mainly of flint (38-67%), of which 13-19% is rounded Palaeogene pebbles. However, it is richer in exotic clasts than any other terrace aggradation. These include quartz (18-34%), quartzite (7-34%), Lower Greensand chert (1.4-3.4%), Carboniferous chert (0.7-1.0%) and various metamorphic and igneous rocks (0.2-0.5%). They suggest either that the river's catchment was considerably enlarged at this time, or that glaciers were feeding sediment into parts of the catchment west of the Goring Gap. The igneous rocks are mainly greenish grey rhyolitic lavas and tuffs, which reach their maximum abundance in the Gerrards Cross Gravel, and are sometimes of considerable size (up to 30 cm across). They are lithologically similar to Ordovician volcanic rocks in the Snowdonia area (Hey and Brenchley, 1977), from where they must have been transported at least part of the way by a glacier. McGregor and Green (1983c) noted that the volcanic clasts are locally concentrated in areas that could have been sites where large blocks of glacier ice melted out on or within the gravel.

Extrapolating the surface of the Harefield Terrace downstream to Essex suggests that the Gerrards Cross Gravel equates with the Moreton Gravel, the youngest and lowest member of the Sudbury Formation (Whiteman, 1992). Following earlier proposals by Rose *et al.* (1999) and Maddy *et al.* (2000), Westaway *et al.* (2002) concluded that the Gerrards Cross Gravel was deposited in MIS 22 at approximately 870,000 BP. The distribution of the Moreton Gravel suggests that by this time the mouth of the proto-Thames had migrated southwards into southern Suffolk (Maddy *et al.*, 2001, Fig. 1C). However, the presence of Lower Greensand chert and Hertfordshire Puddingstone pebbles in deposits of the Hill House Formation at Happisburgh, northeast Norfolk (Parfitt *et al.*, 2010), which date from about MIS 25-21 (936,000-814,000 BP), suggests that not long before this the proto-Thames had entered the North Sea through northeast Norfolk.

The Rassler Gravel

In the Reading area, Sealy and Sealy (1956) mapped fragments of a terrace surface lying at a level intermediate between their Harefield and Winter Hill Terraces. The main fragment is at Rassler Wood (SU 822854), but Gibbard (1983a) suggested that the deposits here accumulated by downslope mass movement, probably from the Gerrards Cross Gravel. Other fragments between Goring and Reading, at Hodmore Farm (SU 683783), Kidmore End (SU 698793) and Cowfields Farm (SU 734820), were attributed to the Winter Hill Terrace (Gibbard, 1985). However, Whiteman (1992) correlated them on altitudinal evidence with the Waldringfield Gravel (the oldest member of the Colchester Formation), which forms a well defined buried terrace in Essex and Suffolk. Bridgland (1994, pp. 119-120) agreed with this interpretation, but also grouped the slightly lower Ardleigh and Wivenhoe Gravels in Essex with the Waldringfield Gravels as equivalents of the Rassler Gravel. As a result, Westaway *et al.* (2002) dated the Rassler and all three of these Essex gravels to the period between MIS 20 (790,000 BP) and MIS 16 (640,000 BP).

The Winter Hill Gravel

The name Winter Hill Terrace was first used as a geomorphological term by Ross (1932) for a clearly defined terrace surface south of Bourne End. Hare (1947) later divided it into two, the Winter Hill Terrace *sensu stricto* above and the Black Park Terrace below, and suggested that at Bourne End the former can be further divided into two. Both Hare (1947) and Wooldridge (1938, 1960) believed that the Thames continued to flow through the 'Middlesex Depression' at the Winter Hill stage, but Gibbard (1977) showed that it occupied the Vale of St Albans, where he correlated the Winter Hill Gravel with the Westmill Gravel, which underlies the Anglian glacial deposits. East of Burnham, Gibbard (1983a) confirmed Hare's suggestion that the Winter Hill Terrace *sensu stricto* should be divided into two subunits with different gradients: (a) a Lower Winter Hill Terrace, which continues eastwards with a gradient of 0.5 m km⁻¹ as far as Fulmer and then turns north-eastwards to Denham and Rickmansworth, where its gravel passes laterally into the Westmill Gravel; and (b) an Upper Winter Hill Terrace, which remains almost horizontal at 80-82 m OD between Burnham and Denham (e.g. at Denham Aerodrome, TQ 0288), because it was created as a delta where the river entered a lake dammed by ice in the Vale of St Albans. A deltaic origin is supported by large-scale cross bedding shown by the Winter Hill Gravel beneath the upper terrace at Stoke Common (SU 983852), so the 80-82 m level indicates the approximate height of the lake surface at this time. The Lower Winter Hill Gravels are exposed in a small pit at Burnham Beeches (Eyres, 2007, Fig. 6.4). Because of their clear association with the Anglian glaciation, the Winter Hill and Westmill Gravels are dated to MIS 12 (474,000-427,000 BP). In Essex, their equivalent is probably the St Osyth Gravel, the youngest member of the Colchester Formation (Bridgland, 1994).

In terms of gravel lithology, the Winter Hill Gravel contains 73-83% flint, of which 6-8% consists of rounded Palaeogene pebbles. Quartz pebbles form 10-17% and quartzite 2-8%. Chert brought by south-bank tributaries from the Lower Greensand of the Weald is usually more abundant (1-7%) than in earlier Thames gravels, and there are also traces of Carboniferous chert and Welsh igneous rocks, suggesting that a glacier existed again close to the north-western limits of the Thames catchment. However, the decline in total exotic components compared with the Gerrards Cross Gravel suggests a decrease in the size of the river's catchment beyond the Chalk outcrop. The decrease may have resulted from capture of the Thames headwaters by a Midlands river (the proto-Soar), which flowed north-eastwards towards Leicester and then into the North Sea through the northern part of East Anglia where, as the Bytham River, it deposited the Ingham Sands and Gravels.

The Black Park Gravel

Following Hare's recognition (1947) of the Black Park Terrace, Sealy and Sealy (1956) extended it upstream to Henley, where Clarke and Dixon (1981) showed that it passes into the Caversham Channel, an abandoned channel of the Thames between Caversham and Henley north of the modern valley near Reading. Eastwards, Gibbard (1979) traced it through Uxbridge and Richmond to Wimbledon Common. Further east it is difficult to recognize in the Lower Thames valley, but Gibbard correlated it with gravels on Dartford Heath in northwest Kent, showing that it was the first deposit of the Thames after the river had been diverted out of the Vale of St Albans into approximately its present course through London. Later Bridgland (1980, 1988) extended it into southeast Essex, where the Thames joined the northward flowing River Medway, but suggested that the Dartford Heath Gravels should be correlated with the later Boyn Hill Gravels.

Lithologically, the Black Park Gravel is distinguished from the Winter Hill Gravel and most other members of the Colchester and Sudbury formations in containing less quartz (6-9%), quartzite (4-6%), Carboniferous chert (<0.5%), igneous rocks (<0.2%) and Palaeogene flint pebbles (5-9%), but more angular flint. Because of this and the new post-diversion course of the river, Gibbard (1985) grouped the Black Park Gravel with all younger Thames terrace gravels as the Maidenhead Formation. The smaller amounts of exotic clasts suggest that the Thames catchment in the south Midlands had become more restricted, possibly because of glacial deposition and river diversion in this area during the Anglian Stage. However, much of the angular flint was probably introduced by a new south bank tributary, the River Kennet, as the Black Park Gravel has been equated with the earliest (Silchester) gravel terrace of the Kennet (White, 1907; Gibbard, 1982).

The Black Park Gravel is dated as late Anglian (MIS 12), deposited during retreat of ice from the Vale of St Albans, because at Uxbridge (TL 006832) the Thames was joined at the Black Park stage by an outwash stream from the ice sheet in the Vale of St Albans. The outwash stream initiated the

River Colne and deposited a lithologically different gravel, the Smug Oak Gravel of Gibbard (1977, 1979) (Section 6.6).

At Highlands Farm Pit (SU 744813) in the abandoned Caversham Channel and at Hillingdon (TQ 072824) in Middlesex, the Black Park Gravel has yielded large numbers of Lower Palaeolithic flint artefacts (Arkell and Oakley, 1948; Wymer, 1956, 1968). They have also been found in the Silchester Gravel of the Kennet (Wymer, 1968).

Post-Anglian deposits of the Thames

As the post-Anglian Thames sequence is related entirely to the river's present course through London, it is absent from Hertfordshire. Therefore it will be described briefly; further details are given by Gibbard (1985) and Bridgland (1994), and Ellison *et al.* (2004, Fig. 29) show the different courses of the river through the London area at various Anglian and later periods.

Deposits post-dating the river's diversion form a sequence of gravel terraces, which are much more extensive and continuous in the Middle and Lower Thames than those of the pre-Anglian period. Originally three were identified by Whitaker (1889, Vol. 1) in the Maidenhead district, and were later named the Boyn Hill, Taplow and Floodplain Terraces in descending order (Pocock, 1903; Sherlock and Noble, 1922). Dewey and Bromehead (1921) divided the last into two, which they named Upper and Lower Floodplain terraces, and in the Slough-Beaconsfield area Hare (1947) recognized an additional terrace, the Lynch Hill Terrace, between the Boyn Hill and Taplow terraces. Later additions to the sequence, including division of the Taplow Terrace into two (Sealy and Sealy, 1956) and the suggestion that a Stoke Park Terrace occurs between the Boyn Hill and Lynch Hill terraces of the Yiewsley area (Allen, 1978), were subsequently rejected by Gibbard (1985). As with the pre-Anglian terraces, a sequence of equivalent lithostratigraphic terms for gravels underlying each of the terrace surfaces has been established. The Boyn Hill Gravel and Taplow Gravel (Bromehead, 1912) form the terraces with the same two names, and Gibbard (1985) introduced the names Lynch Hill Gravel, Kempton Park Gravel and Shepperton Gravel for the deposits forming the Lynch Hill, Upper Floodplain and Lower Floodplain terraces, respectively (Table 6.2, Figs 6.4 and 6.7).

The Taplow, Lynch Hill and Kempton Park gravels are overlain by 1-3 m of much less stony, yellowish brown loamy sediments, which have usually been shown as 'brickearth' on BGS maps. They have been renamed as the Langley Silt Complex (Gibbard, 1985) or Langley Member (Gibbard, 1999), and Gibbard *et al.* (1987) reported thermoluminescence dates ranging from 2300 BP (late Holocene) to 19,000 BP (Late Devensian). Their distribution in central and west London is indicated by Ellison *et al.* (2004, Fig. 37). Petrographic analyses of the Langley Silt at various sites (Gibbard *et al.*, 1987; Harding *et al.*, 1991; Rose *et al.*, 2000) have suggested that it is a heterogeneous alluvial, aeolian and colluvial (slopewash) deposit derived from various fine local sediments, including Palaeogene formations on the valley sides and windblown loess of Late

Devensian (MIS 2) age. Locally it contains Neolithic and other Holocene artefacts, and is probably composed of soil material eroded from nearby slopes following soil cultivation for early arable agriculture. But where it rests on extensive spreads of the Taplow Gravel, as at Prospect Park near Heathrow Airport (Rose *et al.*, 2000), its lower layers are probably loess *in situ*. Its patchy distribution can often be attributed to widespread removal for brickmaking since the Roman period.

In terms of clast lithology, the post-Anglian terrace gravels continue the progressive decline over time in content of exotic components (quartz, quartzite, Carboniferous chert, Lower Greensand chert and igneous rocks) begun with the Gerrards Cross Gravel (Gibbard, 1985). As a result the youngest (Shepperton) gravel contains 91-92% angular flint and only 3.5% exotic components in total; the remaining 4-6% is Palaeogene flint pebbles. Many of the gravels have also yielded Palaeolithic flint artefacts, most of which have been mildly to heavily abraded by fluvial transportation following derivation from sites up-river. Most notable is the rich assemblage from the Lynch Hill Gravel in the Furze Platt area on the northern side of Maidenhead (Harding *et al.*, 1991; Harding and Bridgland, 1999), where a total of over 1600 handaxes have been found (Roe, 1968a), including one 32 cm long, the largest ever found in Britain (MacRae, 1987).

At two sites in Buckinghamshire, Taplow Station Pit (SU 912811) and Fern House Gravel Pit (SU 883885), the Taplow Gravel has yielded mammalian remains, including straight-tusked elephant (*Palaeoloxodon antiquus*), mammoth (*Mammuthus primigenius*), woolly rhinoceros (*Coelodonta antiquitatus*) and musk ox (*Ovibos moschatus*). Most of these indicate a cold climate, but the elephant suggests warm interglacial conditions. The mixture can be explained either by derivation of some remains from earlier deposits upstream or by formation of the Taplow Terrace according to the three-phase model of Maddy *et al.* (2001).

The best evidence for the three-phase model of terrace aggradation comes from the succeeding Kempton Park Gravels (Upper Floodplain Terrace). In central London, Gibbard (1985) showed that aggradation of the Taplow Gravel was followed by incision late in MIS 6, before aggradation of the Kempton Park Gravel. The lowest part of the Kempton Park Gravel, the Spring Gardens Gravel of Gibbard (1985), is overlain by organic interglacial deposits, previously exposed at Rwanda/Uganda House, Trafalgar Square (TQ 301804), which have been dated by the amino acid method (Bowen *et al.*, 1989) and on biostratigraphic evidence (Gibbard, 1994) to the Ipswichian Interglacial (= MIS 5e). The interglacial deposits are in turn overlain by the main part of the Kempton Park Gravel, which has a well-established Early (MIS 4) and Mid Devensian (MIS 3) age (Gibbard, 1985; Coope *et al.*, 1997).

Using the terrace aggradation model of Maddy *et al.* (2001) and various lines of dating evidence, Westaway *et al.* (2002) suggested that the Boyn Hill Gravel was deposited in late MIS 12, MIS 11 and early MIS 10 (420,000-350,000 BP), the Lynch Hill Gravel in MISs 10-8 (340,000-250,000 BP) and the Taplow Gravel in MISs 8-6 (250,000-140,000

BP). By the same model, the Shepperton Gravel (Lower Floodplain Terrace) was deposited in the Late Devensian (MIS 2, 26,000-10,000 BP) on an erosion surface cut shortly after the climatic deterioration from MIS 3 to MIS 2. The modern alluvium of the Thames is thus equivalent to the interglacial phase (b) of the Maddy *et al.* (2001) model, though much modified by human activities in the Late Holocene, particularly the greatly increased inputs of fine inorganic sediment from agriculturally induced soil erosion.

A late MIS 12 (or later) date for the Boyn Hill Gravel is indicated by the fact that it overlies Anglian till (the Hornchurch Till = Ware Till) in a cutting at Hornchurch (TQ 547874) for the railway between Romford and Upminster (Bridgland, 1994, pp. 176-185; Whiteman and Bridgland, 1995). The till at this site is up to 5 m thick, including a thin weathered upper layer, and occupies a depression in the London Clay Formation, which originated either as a minor tributary valley to the pre-Anglian Medway-Darent valley, previously termed the 'Romford River' by Holmes (1896), or as a lake basin (Warren, 1912).

Interglacial faunas of the post-Anglian Thames Terraces

In addition to the Ipswichian deposits discovered at Trafalgar Square, all the post-Anglian terraces from central London downstream contain isolated fragments of fossiliferous interglacial deposits. These have yielded rich assemblages of mammal remains (bones and teeth), molluscs and ostracods, all of which have proved very useful for dating the gravel aggradations and terrace surfaces, and thus relating them to marine isotope stages.

The Hoxnian Stage (MIS 11) is represented by deposits at Swanscombe, Kent (TQ 598745) within the Orsett Heath Gravel, which is the downstream equivalent of the Boyn Hill Gravel (Gibbard, 1994). This site is probably most famous for the discovery of an occipital and two parietal bones of a female human skull (Ovey, 1964), but numerous pointed handaxes have also been found in the upper part of the gravel, and molluscs and mammal remains (Schreve, 2001) are common. A chronologically important member of the mammal assemblage is cave bear (*Ursus spelaeus*), which in Britain is known only from the Hoxnian Interglacial; in later interglacials it was replaced by brown bear (*Ursus arctos*). The assemblage also contains a large form of fallow deer (*Dama dama clactoniana*), two species of rhinoceros (*Stephanorhinus kirchbergensis* and *Stephanorhinus hemitoechus*), mole (*Talpa minor*), rabbit (*Oryctolagus cuniculus*), giant beaver (*Trogontherium cuvieri*) and European pine vole (*Microtus subterraneus*), all of which have been found at other Hoxnian sites in Britain but not in later interglacials. Significant also is the absence of spotted hyaena (*Crocuta crocuta*), which occurs in later interglacials, but is unknown from the Hoxnian. The abundant molluscs from Swanscombe are also chronologically important, in that they include a 'Rhenish suite' (Kennard, 1938) characteristic of the Rhine and Thames basins, consisting of *Corbicula fluminalis*, *Belgrandia marginata*, *Valvata naticina*, *Unio crassus*, *Viviparus diluvianus* and *Theodoxus serratiliniformis*, the last two of which are known only from the Hoxnian.

MIS 9 is represented by fragmentary interglacial deposits at Purfleet (TQ 568789), Little Thurrock (TQ 625783) and other sites in Essex within the Corbets Tey Gravel, the downstream equivalent of the Lynch Hill Gravel. The mammal fauna at these sites differs from those of MIS 11 in containing brown bear and spotted hyaena, and in lacking cave bear, the large fallow deer, mole, rabbit, giant beaver and European pine vole. Macaque monkey (*Macaca sylvanus*) occurs in both MIS 11 and MIS 9 faunas, but not in those of later interglacials. The Rhenish molluscs present include *Corbicula fluminalis*, *Valvata antiqua* and *Belgrandia marginata* but not *Theodoxus serratiliniformis* or *Viviparus diluvianus*.

Interglacial deposits of MIS 7 occur at Aveley (TQ 551808), Uphall Pit, Ilford (TQ 446865), West Thurrock (TQ 598783), Crayford (TQ 517758) and other sites within the Mucking Gravel, which is equivalent to the Taplow Gravel. They have yielded a more diverse mammalian fauna than MIS 9, including straight-tusked elephant (*Palaeoloxodon antiquus*), woolly mammoth (*Mammuthus primigenius*), small-toothed mammoth (*Mammuthus trogontherii*), horse (*Equus ferus*), narrow-nosed rhinoceros (*Stephanorhinus hemitoechus*), woolly rhinoceros (*Coelodonta antiquitatus*), musk ox (*Ovibos moschatus*), jungle cat (*Felis chaus*), leopard (*Panthera pardus*), verticornis deer (*Premegaceros verticornis*), clawless otter (*Cyrnaonyx antiqua*), ground squirrel (*Citellus citellus*), common mole (*Talpa europaea*), white-toothed shrew (*Crocidura russula*), Norway lemming (*Lemmus lemmus*) and collared lemming (*Dicrostonyx torquatus*), most of which are unknown from other post-Anglian interglacials. The cold indicators in this assemblage seem to be truly associated with the interglacial (phase b) rather than the preceding and succeeding cold stages (phases a and c), and have been explained by Schreve (2004) in terms of climatic variation within MIS 7 which, like MIS 5, can be divided into five substages (7e-7a) in the oceanic record. The evidence for this comes mainly from Aveley, where the oldest interglacial deposits contain a mammal assemblage (the Ponds Farm Mammal Assemblage Biozone) dominated by warm-loving temperate woodland species, and are overlain by deposits with cooler temperate grassland species (the Sandy Lane Mammal Assemblage Biozone). Among the molluscs from the MIS 7 deposits, the main member of the Rhenish fauna is *Corbicula fluminalis*.

Because they have only been distinguished in the last few years, the deposits now known to date from MISs 10-6, i.e. between the Hoxnian and Ipswichian interglacials, would have been included in the Wolstonian Stage as defined by Mitchell *et al.* (1973). At present they remain undefined within the sequence of British terrestrial stages, and the Wolstonian is now regarded as a complex of three major cold stages and two interglacials. Previously Gibbard (1994) regarded the deposits of the two interglacials (MISs 9 and 7) as Ipswichian (MIS 5e) in age, because their pollen assemblages are similar to those of Ipswichian sites in East Anglia. However, now that all three can be distinguished by their mammalian and mollusc faunas, it is clear that pollen assemblages are unreliable for dating in this part of

the Mid and Late Pleistocene and can lead to conflation of interglacials.

An important member of the interglacial (MIS 5e) mammal fauna from Trafalgar Square, namely hippopotamus (*Hippopotamus amphibius*), has also been recorded from numerous dated Ipswichian sites as far north as Yorkshire, but is unknown from any other post-Anglian interglacials in Britain, so it seems to be a reliable biostratigraphic indicator of the Ipswichian. Other mammals common in British Ipswichian deposits but rare or absent in earlier post-Anglian interglacials (MISs 11, 9 and 7), though they reappeared in the Holocene, include wild boar (*Sus scrofa*), badger (*Meles meles*) and hare (*Lepus timidus*). From evidence at Trafalgar Square and other British sites, the Ipswichian mammal fauna also included straight-tusked elephant (*Palaeoloxodon antiquus*), narrow nosed rhinoceros (*Stephanorhinus hemitoechus*), lion (*Panthera leo*), wild cat (*Felis sylvestris*), aurochs (*Bos primigenius*), bison (*Bison priscus*), red deer (*Cervus elaphus*), a fallow deer (*Dama dama*) smaller than that in the Hoxnian, giant deer (*Megaloceros giganteus*), brown bear (*Ursus arctos*), wolf (*Canis lupus*), red fox (*Vulpes vulpes*), spotted hyaena (*Crocuta crocuta*), European beaver (*Castor fiber*), water vole (*Arvicola terrestris cantiana*), field vole (*Microtus agrestis*), bank vole (*Clethrionomys glareolus*), wood mouse (*Apodemus sylvaticus*) and Eurasian common shrew (*Sorex araneus*). Among the ostracods from Trafalgar Square, *Cyprideis torosa* is a clear indicator of Ipswichian age, and also suggests a brackish water environment.

Notable for their absence in the Ipswichian are the Rhenish mollusc *Corbicula fluminalis*, horse (*Equus* spp.) and man (*Homo* spp.), which were present in all the earlier post-Anglian interglacials. Apart from the cranial fragments at Swanscombe, the presence of *Homo* in the earlier interglacials of the Thames valley is indicated entirely from flint artefacts of various cultural types. To explain their absence from Ipswichian sites throughout Britain, it has been suggested that late in the Wolstonian (MIS 6) *Homo* was driven southwards across the Channel (then dry because of the eustatic fall in sea level) by increasingly cold conditions, and was prevented from returning when an abrupt transgression early in MIS 5e rapidly separated Britain from the remainder of Europe. However, numerous other thermophilous land animals did make the crossing, so the suggestion is unconvincing.

6.4. The Pebble Gravels

These extensive Early-Mid Pleistocene deposits occur as thin (2-5 m) dissected patches of unfossiliferous sandy gravel overlying the London Clay Formation in southern parts of the county near Bushey Heath, Borehamwood, Shenley, Ridge, Potters Bar, Northaw, Brookmans Park, Hatfield Park, Essendon, Little Berkhamsted, Bayford, Newgate Street, Broxbourne and Hertford Heath (Fig. 6.8). Eastwards from Potters Bar and Hatfield Park they are often overlain by Anglian glacial deposits. In adjacent parts of the former county of Middlesex, they form similar patches north of

Stanmore and near Arkley and Monken Hadley. In most of these areas they are exposed only in shallow overgrown pits where the gravel was previously worked mainly for road metal.

Like the Early Pleistocene Nettlebed Gravel, to which they are probably equivalent (Gibbard, 1983a, 1985), the Pebble Gravels are composed essentially of flint (62-99%), which mainly occurs (50-80%) as small (<32 mm), well rounded and polished black pebbles derived from Palaeogene formations. The surfaces of slightly larger grey flint pebbles often show numerous 'chatter-marks', which are crescent-shaped scars produced by repeated collisons with other large pebbles. The rarer angular flints derived from the chalk are usually even larger, occasionally up to 150 mm across, and quite strongly weathered with a thick white patina. There are also small but variable amounts of white vein-quartz pebbles (0.3-29%) and brown quartzites (0.3-7%), mainly in the 4-16 mm range. Traces of chert from the Carboniferous Limestone and from the Lower Greensand of the Weald ('pinhole chert') also occur locally, mainly in the 4-8 mm range, but sometimes extending to 32 mm across. These exotic components distinguish the Pebble Gravels from the Bagshot and other Palaeogene pebble beds, which contain only flint pebbles (Whitaker, 1889, p. 291). The pebbles in the Pebbly Clay and Sand of BGS maps are also entirely of flint (Sherlock and Pocock, 1924, p. 30).

Origin of the Pebble Gravels

In early accounts (Hughes, 1868; Whitaker, 1889, p. 293), the Pebble Gravels were interpreted as marine beach deposits, possibly equivalent to the gravels at Little Heath near Berkhamsted (Barrow, 1919a). Salter (1896) originally suggested they were glacial in origin, but divided them into four types based on clast lithology, and noticed that their elevation declined gently from west to east, which later (1898) led him to suggest that they originated as river gravels. Wooldridge (1927) initially agreed with this, but later (Wooldridge and Linton 1955; Wooldridge, 1960) changed his mind in favour of a marine origin. On the basis of height, Barrow (1919a, p. 43) divided the various patches into two: (a) a coarser ('large-pebble gravel') occurring on a gently sloping plateau at approximately 500 ft (155 m) OD in north London (Middlesex) and southwest Hertfordshire; and (b) a finer ('small-pebble gravel') on a similarly sloping surface at approximately 400 ft (120 m) OD in central Hertfordshire. These are now described under the names Stanmore Pebble Gravel and Northaw Pebble Gravel (Fig. 6.8), respectively (Bridgland, 1994, p. 94), though Barrow's small-pebble gravel also included deposits later separated by Hey (1965) as the Westland Green Gravel.

In their re-examination of the sedimentary evidence for the Plio-Pleistocene marine transgression of Wooldridge and Linton (1955), Moffat and Catt (1986b) showed that the gravel at Harrow Weald Common (TQ 147929), one of the few remaining exposures of the Stanmore Pebble Gravel (Bridgland, 1994, pp. 101-105), is more likely to be an early Thames deposit than a marine gravel. However, most of the patches of Stanmore and Northaw Pebble Gravels in

north London and south Hertfordshire are located several kilometres south of the proto-Thames course through the Vale of St Albans, and the surfaces on which they lie have a slightly steeper gradient than any of the Thames terraces. Consequently Bridgland (1994) suggested that they were deposited by south-bank tributaries of the Thames (early Mole, Wey and Wandle rivers) rather than by the Thames itself, and this could account for the localized occurrence of Lower Greensand chert from the Weald. However, Bridgland (1994) disagreed with Gibbard's (1985) suggestion that they are equivalent to the Nettlebed Gravel, and instead regarded the Stanmore and Northaw Pebble Gravels as tributary equivalents of the Stoke Row and Westland Green Gravels, respectively.

More recently, Ellison *et al.* (2004, p. 52) have supported Wooldridge's later view (1960) that the Pebble Gravels are marine. The reasons given were: (a) the gently sloping surface on which Harrow Weald Common and other patches of Stanmore Gravel lie coincides approximately with the inclined base of the Red Crag on the Chilterns (Moffat and Catt, 1986b) and in Essex and Suffolk (Mathers and Zalasiewicz, 1988), and (b) the surface textures of sand grains observed by scanning electron microscope (Hey *et al.*, 1971) indicate deposition in a low energy beach environment. However, at 145 m OD, Harrow Weald Common lies at least 15 m below the sub-Red Crag surface projected eastwards from Lane End through Little Heath (Bridgland, 1994, Fig. 3.6), and the surface features indicating a marine origin for sand grains could have been inherited (like the well rounded flint pebbles) from Palaeogene marine deposits.

Nowell (1991) suggested that, downstream from its confluence with the Wealden rivers, the proto-Thames at both Pebble Gravel stages flowed northwards into East Anglia through the gap in the Chalk cuesta between Stevenage and Hitchin. By removing the effect of the later Quaternary tectonic tilting, he showed that an eastward or north-eastward course from the Vale of St Albans, like that of the later Kesgrave Sand and Gravel Formation, would have been blocked by higher ground in Essex and south Suffolk. The northerly course explains the absence of any deposit equivalent to the Pebble Gravel beneath the Kesgrave Formation in southern parts of East Anglia. But no equivalent deposits are known along the Stevenage-Hitchin route either. The oldest Quaternary deposits in the Stevenage-Hitchin Gap are the Letchworth Gravels (Section 6.6), which seem to have been deposited much later, in the early Anglian, by a southward-flowing Letchworth River or by glacial outwash, though the gap itself could have originated much earlier.

In Hertfordshire, the Lower Greensand chert component is most abundant east of a SSW-NNE line drawn through Totteridge, Barnet, Potters Bar, Little Berkhamsted and Epping Green (Barrow, 1919a; Sherlock and Pocock, 1924, pp. 26-27; Lawrence, 1966; Bridgland, 1999), and Wooldridge (1927) used this to divide the lower (400-ft) Pebble Gravel into western and eastern types. At sites close to the eastern side of the line, such as Epping Green (TL 297063), Well Wood near Northaw (TL 271032) and Northaw Great Wood (TL 281040), Lower Greensand chert forms only 0.3-0.7% of the 16-32 mm fraction (Hey, 1965; Cheshire, 1986a, p. 22). Further east, the gravel extends to elevations much less than 400 ft (120 m) OD along minor spurs overlooking the lower Lea valley (Salter, 1905a; Sherlock and Pocock, 1924), and in this area contains much more Lower Greensand chert. For example, in overgrown pits at 70-73 m at Nursery Grove (TL 353077) near Hoddesdon, the 8-32 mm fraction contains 10% Lower Greensand chert (Cheshire, 1983), and in gravel beneath Anglian till at 76 m OD at Goffs Lane, Goffs Oak (TL 331027) the same size fraction contains 18% (Cheshire, 1986a, p. 272). Although shown as Pebble Gravel on the BGS map (Sheet 239), it is likely that the gravels occurring at these lower levels were deposited later than the 400 ft (Northaw) Pebble Gravel after a period of downcutting by a south-bank tributary, probably the proto-Mole/Wey, that carried a greater concentration of gravel derived from the Weald.

Wooldridge (1927) dismissed the deposits at elevations below the 400 ft (120 m) plateau as resulting from later downslope washing from the plateau. But at present there are no known sources of chert-rich gravels on the eastern side of the 120 m plateau. Further gravel samples from eight sites mapped as Pebble Gravel by BGS near Wormley West End (TL 337060) at heights ranging from 75 to 94 m OD have been analysed for pebble lithology, and were found to be broadly similar in composition to those from Nursery Grove and Goffs Lane, though the percentage of Lower Greensand chert in the 8-32 mm fraction increased with decreasing height, from 2% at 94 m OD to 13% at 76-80 m OD. This suggests that inputs from the south bank Mole/Wey tributary increased over time as it incised its bed, probably grading to a proto-Thames flowing at progressively lower levels. If the Pebble Gravels at 120 m and higher levels are equivalent to the Nettlebed Gravel (Section 6.3), which is dated to between MIS 82 and MIS 68 (Westaway *et al.*, 2002), then the chert-rich proto-Mole/Wey gravels at levels down to 70 m OD are probably equivalent to one or more of the Middle Thames terrace gravels younger than the Nettlebed Gravel, such as the Westland Green, Beaconsfield or Gerrards Cross Gravels. At even lower levels in the lower Lea valley, yet younger gravels, also deposited by the proto-Mole/Wey and rich in Lower Greensand chert, have been equated by Cheshire (1983) with the St George's-Dollis Hill Gravel of Gibbard (1979), now the St George's Hill Member of the Mole-Wey Formation (Gibbard, 1999). As this is Anglian in age (Section 6.6), the chert-rich parts of the Pebble Gravel lying at 70-120 m OD must be older than Anglian, and so are unlikely to be equivalent to Thames gravels as young as the Winter Hill Gravel.

East of the lower Lea valley, gravels rich in Lower Greensand Chert form another north-south belt in eastern Essex south of the Blackwater estuary, where they have been attributed to an early northward continuation of the River Medway (Bridgland, 1988, 1994, 1999). These form a series of terraces declining in height eastwards. The chert is most abundant in the higher (older) terrace fragments (the High-level East Essex Gravels), but in the Southend area the lower terrace gravels (or Low-level East Essex Gravels) contain small amounts of quartz, quartzite, Carboniferous chert and

Rhaxella chert (from the Jurassic of northeast Yorkshire) in addition to the Lower Greensand chert. These exotic western and northern components were probably brought by the post-diversionary Thames during or soon after the Anglian glaciation, and suggest that the Thames was then confluent with the Medway that was heading northwards from Rochester into Essex. Immediately upstream of this confluence, the newly diverted Thames probably occupied a valley cut by another south-bank tributary, the River Darent, which had been captured by the Medway well before the Anglian Stage (Bridgland, 1999).

6.5. A possible pre-Anglian glaciation

Invasion of the proto-Thames valley and parts of the Chiltern Hills by an early (pre-Anglian) glacier has been suggested by various geologists studying the Hertfordshire area. The evidence cited in support of this idea has included the presence of till-like deposits, often containing far-travelled clasts, diversion of the Thames into a course through Middlesex and disturbance of the Plateau Drift at certain localities. However, all of these are now interpreted as resulting from non-glacial processes.

Materials resembling weathered till (boulder clay) in containing far-travelled clasts set in a stiff clay-rich matrix are widespread along the former course of the Thames through Hertfordshire, but are now interpreted as clay-enriched interglacial soils formed on fluvial gravels containing exotic (but not glacially deposited) pebbles. For example, beneath the cover of Anglian till in southeast Hertfordshire, the upper parts of the Pebble Gravel have been considerably modified at sites such as Ashendene Farm, Epping Green (TL 304067) by pre-Anglian interglacial soil development (Moffat and Catt, 1982). The main interglacial soil-forming processes were enrichment in clay by illuviation (redeposition of clay carried down from overlying soil horizons by water percolating through cracks and root channels), and the production of prominent red (5YR 4/8 – 2.5YR 3/6) mottles by local mobilization of iron in solution and its redeposition as haematite during seasonal changes in groundwater level.

The 'Pebbly Clay Drift'

The amounts of illuvial clay incorporated into the Pebble Gravel to form this soil material are so great that the loose sandy gravel has been converted into a stiff cohesive sandy clay with dispersed pebbles. This led Thomasson (1961) to interpret it as a weathered till, which he named the Pebbly Clay Drift. However, in thin section, the illuvial clay differs from the non-illuvial clay in tills by occurring almost entirely as characteristic strongly birefringent bodies (argillans) composed of well orientated clay particles coating the walls of voids. In contrast, the clayey matrix of tills contains many sand and silt particles, and the clay is more weakly orientated and therefore much less birefringent. Strongly birefringent illuvial clay bodies occur in the clay-enriched paleo-argillic Bt horizons of soils that have persisted on the present land surface since at least the last (Ipswichian) interglacial (Section 7.6). They also occur in Holocene surface soils formed on Devensian deposits, but in much smaller amounts, and in the Holocene soils they are not accompanied by the bright red mottles, which probably indicate warmer and drier summers similar to those of the present Mediterranean climate.

Using particle size, mineralogical and clast lithological analyses, Moffat and Catt (1982) showed that, apart from its greatly increased clay content and red mottling, the interglacial soil buried by Anglian till at Epping Green is similar in composition to the Pebble Gravel beneath, and contains no new components, as would be expected if it were glacial in origin. Near the southeast corner of Northaw Great Wood (TL 291035), Thomasson (1961) did identify far-travelled clasts and sand minerals in a layer of red-mottled Pebbly Clay Drift 3.3 m thick. However, Avery and Catt (1983) later showed that what Thomasson had mapped as Pebbly Clay Drift (TL 279039) in this area originated as a thick post-Anglian paleo-argillic soil developed on the Anglian till, and this explained the far-travelled components identified by Thomasson. Taken together, the evidence from Northaw Great Wood and Epping Green therefore indicated that materials corresponding to Thomasson's Pebbly Clay Drift originated by soil development in two different interglacials, one before the Anglian glaciation (soil on Pebble Gravel) and one after it (soil on Anglian till).

In one of their drill cores through the buried soil at Ashendene Farm, Moffat and Catt (1982) penetrated a near-vertical wedge-shaped fissure filled with well-sorted sand, which had a detailed particle size distribution similar to that of coversand (Fig. 6.2), and was therefore windblown. The sand was probably Anglian in age because its heavy mineral suite resembled that of Anglian glacial deposits. Many aspects of the sequence at Ashendene Farm, including the illuvial clay enrichment, the red mottling and the presence of a fissure (probably an ice-wedge cast) filled with Anglian coversand, are similar to those of the buried Valley Farm Soil described by Rose *et al.* (1978), which was formed on proto-Thames terraces of the Kesgrave Sand and Gravel Formation in interglacials preceding the Anglian glaciation in Essex and Suffolk. Developed on the somewhat older Pebble Gravel, the buried soil at Epping Green may represent a longer period of time (from approximately 1.87 Ma to 0.5 Ma) than the Valley Farm Soil, but in other respects the two are indistinguishable.

The 'Chiltern Drift' and 'Northern Drift'

The reinterpretation of the Pebbly Clay Drift casts serious doubt on the concept of a pre-Anglian glaciation of the proto-Thames valley in southeast Hertfordshire. Nevertheless, a pre-Anglian glaciation had also been proposed for higher parts of the valley in southwest Hertfordshire, based on the presence of a weathered, red-mottled sandy clay containing exotic clasts (quartz, etc) in the areas around Chorleywood and Chalfont St Giles. Originally described by Barrow (1918, 1919a, p. 17) as a boulder clay or till composed partly of reworked clay from

the Reading Formation, this material was later termed the 'Chiltern Drift' by Wooldridge (1938) and Wooldridge and Linton (1955). They attributed it to an early glaciation, with ice entering the Thames valley through the Goring Gap and diverting the river into the 'Middlesex Depression' (or 'Finchley Depression') between the 'Higher Gravel Train' (Beaconsfield Gravel) and Winter Hill stages. Catt (1981) tentatively related this glaciation to the cold Beestonian Stage of Mitchell *et al.* (1973).

McGregor and Green (1983a) pointed out that the height range of the area occupied by the Chiltern Drift, as delimited by Wooldridge and Linton (1955), coincides with those of the higher (500 ft) or Stanmore Pebble Gravel and Westland Green Gravel, and all of the gravels they analysed from this area were similar in composition to one or other of these Thames gravels. At Mardley Heath (TL 241181), a site originally described by Wooldridge and Cornwall (1964) as an outlier of Chiltern Drift, studies of clast lithology by Moffat and Catt (1986b) later showed that the deposit was also composed mainly of Westland Green Gravel. So it is very likely that, like the Pebbly Clay Drift, the Chiltern Drift originated by interglacial pedogenic clay enrichment of early Thames terrace gravels. This would explain its two till-like characteristics, namely a moderate clay content and the presence of exotic clasts. Also, by showing that the river was never diverted into the Middlesex Depression, Gibbard (1977, 1979) removed the geomorphological need for a pre-Anglian glaciation in the Thames Valley. From lithological studies of gravels at Dollis Hill (TQ 235863) and other sites in northwest London, which are now defined as the St George's Hill Member of the Mole–Wey Formation (Gibbard, 1999, p. 54), he showed (1979) that the Middlesex Depression, now occupied by the modern River Brent and Dollis Brook, originated as the valley of a south bank tributary of the Thames, the Mole-Wey River.

Further west, patches of similar red-mottled sandy clay with far-travelled clasts occurring along the Evenlode Valley in north Oxfordshire, the 'Northern Drift' of Hull (1855), were again attributed to an early glaciation by Tomlinson (1929), Richardson *et al.* (1946, pp. 108-113) and others. But after careful reinvestigation of these patches, Hey (1986) concluded that they also originated by prolonged pedogenetic modification of river gravels, because they lie on a series of gently sloping surfaces resembling river terraces. One of the terrace gravels, the Waterman's Lodge Member, was regarded as the source of exotic clasts entering the Upper Thames catchment at the Westland Green stage.

Glacial origin of the Plateau Drift

Yet another area in which an early glaciation has been suggested is the higher part of the Chilterns in Buckinghamshire above the level of the highest known Thames terrace gravel. Here Sherlock and Noble (1912) proposed a glacial origin for the Plateau Drift (Clay-with-flints in their terminology) on account of the way the Reading Formation has been churned up and mixed with flint nodules from the underlying Chalk. Later, Sherlock (1930) asserted that the 'Pebbly Clay and Sand' of BGS maps was also glacial in origin. But, as described in Section 5.3, the disturbance of the Reading Formation to produce Plateau Drift (including the Pebbly Clay and Sand) can be explained by collapse into solution cavities in the chalk beneath and by deep-reaching cryoturbation during Pleistocene cold stages. Barrow (1915, 1919a, pp. 26-31) agreed with the suggestion of Sherlock and Noble and, in sections exposed at Cowcroft near Chesham, described how the Plateau Drift (his Clay-with-Reading-pebbles) had been thrust over Chalk and disturbed clay of the Reading Formation along a series of steeply inclined 'slides'or 'thrust-planes'. Photographs illustrating these structures are included in Barrow (1915, 1917). He interpreted the thrusting as glacial in origin, but the absence of erratics here and elsewhere on the higher Chiltern plateau makes the glacial hypothesis difficult to sustain (Avery and Thomasson, 1956). Also, it is now known that similar structures can originate in a periglacial environment, for example by mass movement (gelifluction) of seasonally thawed sediment into steep-sided depressions created by localised melting of ground ice (alases) or by dissolution of underlying chalk (dolines). Consequently, this evidence for a Chiltern glaciation is also now regarded as invalid.

An early glaciation of Salisbury Plain and other parts of southern England was invoked by Kellaway (1971) to explain how blocks of dolerite (the 'bluestones'), rhyolite and Palaeozoic sandstone were transported from areas in south Wales (mainly the eastern Preseli Hills of Pembrokeshire) to Stonehenge. Later Kellaway et al. (1975) also suggested that the Clay-with-flints (Plateau Drift) throughout southern England and northern France is a weathered till. However, Green (1997) has strongly refuted these ideas, mainly on the basis of the complete absence of naturally occurring erratic clasts in the Plateau Drift and other superficial deposits of the chalklands. In addition, despite the obvious difficulties of transporting blocks weighing several tons to Stonehenge from such distant sources, it is now widely accepted that the technical abilities of late Neolithic and early Bronze Age peoples were sufficient to achieve this.

In summary, all the evidence cited in the past for a pre-Anglian glaciation of the Hertfordshire area can now be readily explained in other ways, based in particular on the better understanding now available of Quaternary processes such as periglacial disturbance and interglacial pedogenesis. As a result, there is now general agreement that the first (and probably the only) glaciation of the area occurred in the Anglian Stage (MIS 12).

6.6. The Anglian cold Stage

In the deep oceanic sequence, the equivalent of the Anglian (MIS 12) started with a climatic deterioration about 474 ka and ended around 427 ka (Bassinot *et al.*, 1994) when warming led to MIS 11 (= the Hoxnian Interglacial in Britain). The Anglian Stage is named after East Anglia, where two main cold periods or stadials have been recognized within it. The earlier of these (the Gunton Stadial) produced glaciation in north-eastern parts of East Anglia, but ice did not reach as far south as Hertfordshire. However, in the later Lowestoft Stadial, ice did reach Hertfordshire and western Essex, its margin fluctuating to cause at least four minor advances into this area (Allen *et al.*, 1991).

In Hertfordshire the deposits of the Anglian Stage consist mainly of (a) river gravels of the proto-Thames and its tributaries laid down immediately before the Lowestoft glaciation, (b) tills, glaciolacustrine sediments and glaciofluvial gravels resulting directly from the glaciation and (c) river gravels deposited soon after the glaciation. In addition, early Anglian (pre-glacial) aeolian periglacial deposits were probably deposited over much of the county, but have been identified at only a few localities, such as Ashendene Farm, Epping Green (Section 6.5).

Some Hertfordshire place names probably originated from being sited on patches of the various Anglian fluvial and glaciofluvial gravels (Gover *et al.*, 1938). These include Sandon (= sandy hill), Standon (stony hill) and Stanstead (stony place), as in Stanstead St Margarets and Stanstead Abbots.

During the Anglian Stage, the landscape and drainage of the area were changed more dramatically and permanently than at any other time in the Quaternary. The most significant event in this context was the diversion of the proto-Thames from its course through the Vale of St Albans and Mid-Essex Depression into its present valley through London, and this provides a convenient basis for subdividing the account of the Anglian in Hertfordshire.

The landscape of Hertfordshire at the beginning of the Anglian

Contours representing the topography of Hertfordshire immediately prior to the Lowestoft Stadial ice advance can be drawn from the heights of points at the base of Anglian sediments preserved in various parts of the county, though in areas where post-Anglian erosion has removed the basal sediments the contours are conjectural. Using height data from wells, boreholes and other exposures of basal Anglian sediments, this method has been used to reconstruct the sub-Anglian surface by Wooldridge and Henderson (1955), Brown (1959), Gibbard (1977, Fig. 13), Baker and Jones (1980, Fig. 4), Cheshire (1986a, Figs 1.12 and 1.13) and Hopson *et al.* (1996, Fig. 24).

Early Anglian river valleys. When combined (Fig. 6.9), these reconstructions show the broad proto-Thames valley (0.5-1.0 km across) extending from the Watford area through the Vale of St Albans into the Mid-Essex Depression between Harlow and Sawbridgeworth. The left-bank valleys from the Chiltern 'through-gaps' (see Section 6.10) can also be identified. The floor of the proto-Thames valley declines from approximately +60 m OD under central Watford to +38 m OD between Harlow and Sawbridgeworth, a gradient of about 0.5 m km^{-1}. Over this distance the valley included several bends. Between Watford and Roestock (TL 2005), the course was approximately SW-NE. It then turned northwards towards Stanborough (TL 2211), but then swung

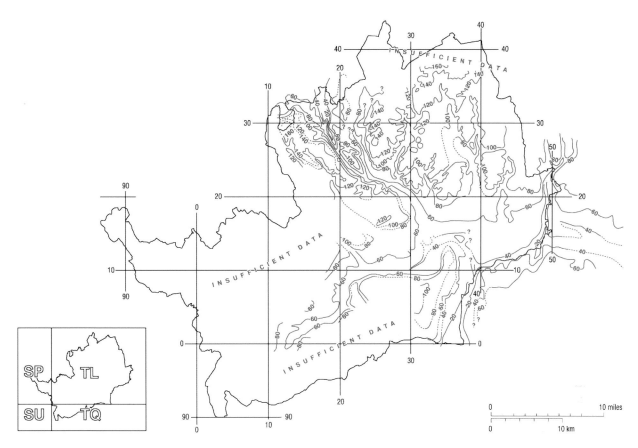

Fig. 6.9. The Sub-Anglian Surface in Hertfordshire with contours at 20 m intervals. Solid lines are shown where the surface is well defined from boreholes, wells and intersections with the present land surface, pecked lines where the elevation is less certain. Based on Hopson et al. (1996) for the area covered by BGS 1:50,000 sheet 221 (Hitchin), British Geological Survey (1990) for the area covered by BGS 1:50,000 sheet 222 (Great Dunmow), Gibbard (1977) for part of southwest Hertfordshire and Cheshire (1986a) elsewhere. Contours from the first three sources are omitted where Anglian deposits are sparse or absent, and in parts of northeast Hertfordshire the contours shown are for the Sub-Quaternary rather than the Sub-Anglian Surface.

eastwards to Brickendonbury (TL 330104). Here the valley curved northwards again towards Bengeo (TL 3213) around a pronounced buried river bluff about 35 m high cut in Upper Chalk and Palaeogene formations up to the London Clay. At Bengeo it turned eastwards again to Mardocks Farm (TL 394145), then south-east to Eastwick (TL 4311) and finally eastwards into the Mid-Essex Depression.

Apart from the proto-Thames valley, other valleys were in existence before ice arrived in the Anglian glaciation, including those approximately coincident with the present upper Lea, Mimram, Beane, upper Rib, upper Ash, and upper Stort, all left-bank tributaries of the proto-Thames. In addition, two almost parallel buried valleys (the Hitchin and Stevenage Channels) extend northwards from the Stevenage area to beyond Hitchin. They lie beneath the Hitchin-Stevenage Gap, which is a broader feature than any of the other tributary valleys and contains a thicker sequence of Anglian sediments, second only in Hertfordshire to that of the proto-Thames valley. Almost certainly one or both of these channels formed at least a shallow col in the Chalk escarpment before the Anglian, though no undisputed pre-Anglian fluvial sediments have been identified within them, or indeed within any of the other left-bank tributaries of the proto-Thames.

Unlike the other 'through gaps' in the Chilterns of Hertfordshire, such as the Tring Gap (now partly occupied by the Bulbourne), the Dagnall Gap (drained partly by the Gade), the Dunstable Gap (drained partly by the Ver), the Luton Gap (drained by the upper Lea) and the Lilley Gap (drained partly by the Mimram), which have no surface or buried continuations northwest of the present Chalk scarp, the Hitchin-Stevenage Gap seems to suggest that before the Anglian the proto-Thames catchment extended beyond the Chilterns. This is because the Hitchin Channel probably continues northwards as various drift-filled depressions, including those beneath the Ivel and Ouse valleys (Hopson *et al.*, 1996). However, these rivers are now part of the drainage leading into The Wash, and the drift-filled depressions in south Bedfordshire could also have been part of a pre-Anglian Wash drainage basin, with headwaters in the Hitchin Channel, which later was greatly deepened by subglacial erosion in the Anglian (Brownsell, 2008). In contrast, the Stevenage Channel does not seem to have continued northwest of the Chiltern scarp, and may represent the head of a left-bank proto-Thames tributary.

Glacial erosion. Parts of the mapped sub-Anglian surface are lower than the landscape at the beginning of the Anglian

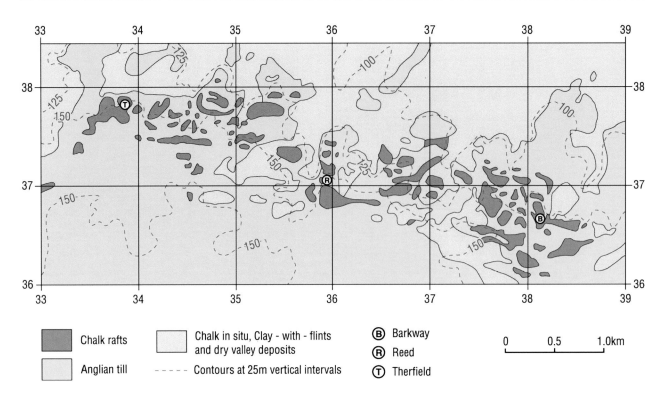

Fig. 6.10. *Distribution of glacially displaced chalk rafts in the Therfield-Reed-Barkway area (redrawn from Hopson* et al., *1996)*

Stage, because they were eroded during the advance of the Lowestoft Stadial glacier but before deposition of the basal glacial sediments. This occurred by three mechanisms – erosion by the glacier itself, erosion by subglacial meltwater under pressure and erosion by meltwater flowing over the land surface beyond the margin of the glacier.

There is considerable evidence that much of the Chalk outcrop in north Hertfordshire was extensively eroded by the glacier itself. Clayton (2000) suggested that this erosion set the Chalk scarp east of Hitchin back to the SSE by 10-26 km and moved the base of the Chalk 5-8 km in the same direction. However, the patches of Plateau Drift (shown as Clay-with-flints on BGS 1:50,000 Sheet 221) preserved beneath the Anglian till east of Hitchin and Stevenage suggest that at least some of the Chalk dip-slope here still approximates to the Sub-Palaeogene Surface (Section 5.3), though some of the patches could be rafts within the till. It was probably the old scarp crest that bore the brunt of the erosion. It was lowered by at least 10 m, and this may help explain why scarp-slope coombes are much more weakly expressed east of Hitchin (Section 6.10), where the crest has been glacially lowered, than in areas further west where the scarp crest was not glaciated. Glacial erosion of the scarp may also explain the extensive Lower Chalk bench that projects northwards from the foot of the main (Middle Chalk) scarp near Hitchin, Luton and Dunstable (Wooldridge and Smetham, 1931) and possibly in areas even further southwest.

In the area between Therfield (TL 3337) and Barkway (TL 3836), subglacial erosion of the scarp resulted in southward (uphill) displacement by several hundred metres of large

chalk rafts up to 15 m thick and 600 m wide (Woodward, 1903a, 1903b; Jones, 1938; Bromley, 1967b; Hopson, 1995; Hopson *et al.*, 1996, pp. 85-88). Two of the rafts are clearly exposed in small chalk pits (Section 3.5), which are HMWT reserves and are also designated as RIGS (Hertfordshire RIGS Group, 2003). At the Barkway Pit RIGS (TL 381366), a thin layer of till lies between displaced slices of Chalk Rock dipping northwards at about 60°, i.e. contrary to the regional dip (Plate 6), and the Reed Pit RIGS (TL 359370) is cut entirely in a raft about 15 m thick (Plate 8), which is inclined northwards at up to 45° and currently exposes a sequence from just above the Reed Marl through the Chalk Rock to several metres above the brown-stained Top Rock.

Bromley (1967) described a third raft of Chalk Rock overlying a thrust plane in the Park Farm pit (TL 338378), Therfield. Using aerial photographs, Hopson (1995) identified many other rafts composed mainly of Chalk Rock in a zone about 7 km × 1 km extending along the degraded scarp (Fig. 6.10). The mode of raft emplacement proposed by Hopson (1995) and Hopson *et al.* (1996, Fig. 22) involved ice impinging on a scarp-foot bench of Chalk Rock, disturbance and incorporation of detached rafts into a subglacial deformable wedge, lodgement of rafts and till against the steep Upper Chalk scarp, and finally downslope slumping and normal faulting during melting of the glacier. To explain the similar chalk rafts incorporated into Anglian glacial deposits exposed near Cromer on the north Norfolk coast, Banham (1975) proposed that water held in front of and beneath the glacier as it advanced upslope weakened the chalk and reduced its shear strength by locally increasing its porewater pressure. Displacement caused by the lateral push of the glacier then occurred mainly along a low-angled thrust (plane of décollement) developed in an original planar weakness in the chalk, such as a marl band.

Buried valleys. Subglacial meltwater under pressure also caused considerable erosion of bedrock in Hertfordshire. Deep, steep-sided valleys filled with gravel and till have long been known in the area from boreholes sunk for water supply (Woodland, 1945, 1970). In East Anglia, a radiating pattern of infilled buried valleys cut in the Chalk bedrock are thought to have been formed by subglacial meltwater streams under the hydrostatic pressure resulting from confinement beneath the thick, heavy Anglian ice sheet. Because of their similarity to buried valleys (*Rinnentaler*) close to the Elsterian (= Anglian) ice margin in north Germany, Denmark and north Poland, Woodland (1970) described them as subglacial tunnel valleys, and similar, though often larger, boat-shaped ('scaphiform') valleys filled with Anglian glacial deposits overlain by interglacial marine clays have been described from the intervening floor of the North Sea (Wingfield, 1990).

Hopson *et al.* (1996, p. 88) divided buried glacial channels in the Hitchin area into six types (Fig. 6.11), of which three (Types 1-3) were probably eroded by subglacial meltwater. The Type 1 buried channels are arranged radially to the Anglian ice sheet margin and suffered moderate erosion. They probably followed pre-Anglian valleys and are today occupied by four modern rivers, the Quin, upper Rib, Beane and Old Bourne (a tributary of the Beane). Type 1 also includes the Stevenage Channel, which lies within the Hitchin-Stevenage Gap but is represented by a weaker modern valley than the others. The Type 2 buried channels are also arranged radially to the ice sheet, but have little or no present surface expression. Rather than occupying pre-Anglian valleys, they were probably eroded by water in englacial channels, which were superimposed on the bedrock surface by basal melting of the glacier. Only two such channels are known, both in the upper Beane catchment. The Type 3 buried channels are also aligned radially to the ice sheet, but they are much larger than Types 1 and 2. With widths up to 2 km and depths sometimes exceeding 100 m below the adjacent pre-Anglian surface, they are equivalent in size to the tunnel valleys or *Rinnentaler* of areas further east. The Hitchin Channel, extending northwards for 23 km from Junction 7 of the A1(M) near Langley (TL 235225) to Broom (TL 171428) near Biggleswade, is one such valley. The Stort-Cam Channel, which can be traced northwards for 41 km from Harlow through east Hertfordshire and western Essex (Hopson, 1981) to Whittlesford, Cambridgeshire, is another. Both are scaphiform valleys with 'trough and sill' long profiles extending to below present sea level, -50 m OD in the Hitchin Channel and -4 m OD in the Stort-Cam Channel. At its southern end, the Hitchin channel has a sill or threshold near Langley. The 'uphill sections' of their long profiles suggest erosion by water under hydrostatic pressure beneath the glacier. The Ash-Brook Channel, between the Hitchin and Stevenage Channels, also resembles Type 3 but is only 3 km long.

In the lower Lea valley, several deep narrow, probably scaphiform, channels conforming to Type 1 of Hopson *et al.* (1996) were also probably eroded subglacially (Cheshire, 1981). Boreholes, including those sunk in 1972 for the Stanstead Abbotts by-pass, showed the southern end of a channel oriented approximately N-S and cut into a chalk surface at *c.* 21 m OD, with its greatest depth of -3 m OD near St Margarets Farm (TL 382114). The numerous boreholes for the Rye Meads Sewage Works (TL 3910) (Hayward, 1956) and Rye House Power Station (TL 3809) further south penetrated the chalk surface at *c.* 20 m OD but showed no trace of the channel, which therefore has no outlet to the south and must have a S-N downhill gradient. As the flow direction was probably N-S, this gradient is indicative of a subglacially-eroded Type 1 channel. At the A10/M25 interchange near Waltham Cross, numerous boreholes penetrated a gravel-filled channel oriented approximately NE-SW and cut into the western side of the modern lower Lea Valley (Cheshire, 1981). The channel cuts through 7-13 m of London Clay Formation and the entire thickness of the Palaeocene formations (21 m) into Chalk. The deepest point detected was -12.9 m OD, suggesting a scaphiform long profile. Boreholes at Edmonton (TQ 326928) recorded by Hayward (1957) showed that the general London Clay surface here is at 15 m OD but is locally eroded by a channel cutting down to at least 2.5 m OD. The lowest 3.8 m of sediment penetrated in this channel were described as grey or greyish brown firm sandy clay with pebbles and fragments of chalk; this was probably till, again suggesting that the channel was cut subglacially.

Hopson *et al.* (1996) identified one of each of their Types 4, 5 and 6 on the BGS Hitchin 1:50,000 sheet (Fig. 6.11). The Type 4 channel, described briefly as a tangential ice marginal channel, extends from near Pirton (TL 1429) to near Offley Grange (TL 1628). The Type 5 channel occurs close to the limit of glaciation in the Mimram valley, where two sections of the proto-Mimram valley near King's Walden (TL 1623) and Codicote (TL 2118) were buried by ice, which deposited till and glaciofluvial gravels in the channels and displaced the river several hundred metres to the southwest. The Codicote channel was previously described by Sherlock (1919, 1937) and Wooldridge (1953). It contains over 20 m of glacial deposits, mainly glaciofluvial sands and gravels containing fractured flints, quartz and quartzite pebbles, sandstone blocks, Palaeogene flint pebbles and rare igneous fragments; Sherlock (1919) included photos of the gravels exposed in a pit on Codicote Heath or High Heath (TL 2018). The only Type 6 channel identified by Hopson *et al.* (1996) is in the upper Lea valley, which was west of the limit of glaciation but carried meltwater depositing glaciofluvial sediment. Several of the channels identified further south by Wooldridge (1953) may also be of this type.

Evidence for minor erosion by subglacial meltwater is provided by small channels cut in bedrock but preserved beneath glacial deposits. For example, at Little Hadham Chalk Pit (TL 440229), a channel approximately 3 m wide and 1 m deep is cut in chalk and filled with current-bedded sand overlying a coarse gravel composed of strongly abraded iron-stained flints, the whole sequence being covered by a layer of chalky till.

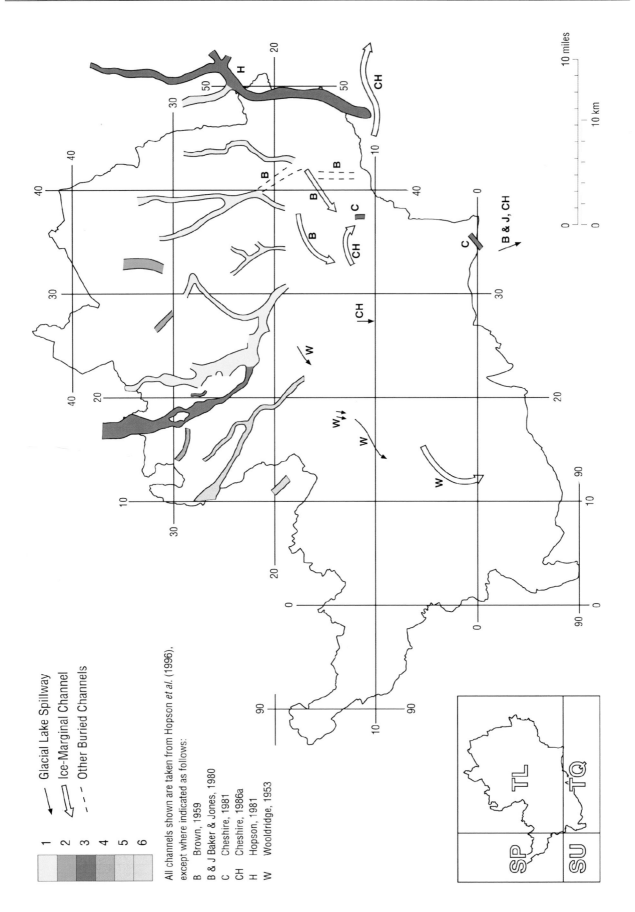

Fig. 6.11. *Location of buried subglacial valleys, ice-marginal channels and glacial lake spillways in Hertfordshire. Buried valley types 1-6 redrawn from Hopson* et al. *(1996); other features from: (B) Brown (1959); (B and J) Baker and Jones (1980); (C) Cheshire (1981); (CH) Cheshire (1986a); (H) Hopson (1981); and (W) Wooldridge (1953).*

Spillways. Other parts of the sub-Anglian surface were also eroded by glacial meltwater flowing in subaerial channels beyond the glacier margin (Fig. 6.11). Where the ice sheet dammed an earlier river, it produced a proglacial lake, and when this became deep enough to overflow into an adjacent valley, erosion occurred in the spillway or valley cut by the overflow. The most important examples of this in the Hertfordshire area were associated with (a) blockage of the proto-Thames valley and diversion of its water from the Mid-Essex Depression into the Lower Lea valley (Cheshire, 1986a; Bridgland and Cheshire, 1994), (b) diversion of the proto-Thames from the Vale of St Albans into the present Middle Thames valley (Gibbard, 1977; Baker and Jones, 1980; Cheshire, 1986a; Bridgland, 1994), (c) diversion of the proto-Mimram into the modern Mimram valley near Codicote and Kings Walden (Wooldridge, 1953; Brown, 1959; Hopson *et al.*, 1996, p. 101) and (d) temporary diversions of the proto-Lea and proto-Ver south-westwards around the ice lobe occupying the Vale of St Albans (Wooldridge, 1953). The now dry Harpenden valley between Nomansland Common (TL 1712) and Sandridge (TL 1710) and also the dry Beech Bottom valley between Sandridge and the Ver Valley near Verulamium (TL 1307) may also have originated as ice-marginal spillways carrying water from ice-dammed lakes in the Lea and Harpenden valleys (Wooldridge, 1953).

The nature of the land surface at the beginning of the Anglian did much to shape the subsequent pattern of ice movement in the region. Observations of the thickness and surface gradient of modern ice sheets and computer generated reconstructions of former ice masses (Lowe and Walker, 1997, Figs 2.12-2.17) indicate that glacier surfaces are convex near their margin, with surface gradients in the range 4.5-20 m km^{-1} (mean 11 m km^{-1}), decreasing up-glacier to where the ice is about 500 m thick. Projecting even the least of the surface gradients (4.5 m km^{-1}) 50-60 km back from the known margin of the Anglian glacier at Bricket Wood (TL 1200) and Finchley (TQ 2489) gives an ice thickness of 225-270 m north of the Chalk scarp in Bedfordshire and Cambridgeshire. This thickness was sufficient to allow the glacier to move southwards or south-westwards over the highest parts of the Chalk scarp east of Hitchin, though initially it would have invaded lower areas, especially the 'through-valleys'. However, the absence of glacial deposits south and west of Luton shows that the ice sheet was here unable to surmount the Chalk scarp, and consequently divided into two lobes, one following the Vale of Aylesbury north of the scarp and the other entering the Vale of St Albans to the south. As it was closer to its distal margin, the glacier was probably a little thinner in this region, but it is also possible that the pre-Anglian Chalk scarp was higher than in northeast Hertfordshire.

In summary, it is possible to indicate various ways in which the pre- and early-Anglian landscape of Hertfordshire differed from the present topography. First, the Chalk scarp in northeast Hertfordshire would probably have been several kilometres further north and up to 10 m higher, continuing the trend of the present scarp between Tring and Hitchin and its overall relief in terms of crest height and depth of

valley incision. Although the glacial erosion of interfluves near the Chalk scarp initially made the valleys of northeast Hertfordshire shallower, some were later deepened by subglacial meltwater under pressure. However, they were then almost completely infilled with glacial deposits, so that they are now weakly expressed in the present topography. Second, the early Anglian proto-Thames valley, in which up to 20 m of Anglian fluvial, glacial and glaciofluvial deposits accumulated at its north-eastern end, was a shallower feature than the modern Vale of St Albans. The modern successors of the proto-Thames, the Lea and Colne, have eroded to greater depths since the Anglian. In central Watford, the modern floor of the Colne is about 10 m lower than the floor of the proto-Thames, and in the Ware area the modern floor of the lower Lea is approximately 17 m lower. Third, at the start of the Anglian, the relief of the London Clay outcrop in southeast Hertfordshire was relatively subdued, despite the major right-bank tributary of the proto-Thames, the proto-Mole/Wey, crossing its eastern flank. At Bullscross Farm (TL 343004), the floor of the proto-Mole/Wey valley was at about 57 m OD compared with the neighbouring floor of the modern Lea at 19 m OD, whereas the interfluve to the west would have been little higher than the present elevation of the Northaw Pebble Gravel at about 120 m OD. This gives a local pre-Anglian relief of 60-65 m compared with more than 100 m today, so the extent of incision of the south Hertfordshire plateau has increased considerably since the Anglian. As suggested in Section 4.7, an increased rate of incision could have resulted partly from glacio-isostatic rebound after melting of the Anglian glacier. But in addition, downcutting may have been accelerated by the local lowering of base level that resulted from glacial diversion of drainage from a long proto-Thames course into the North Sea through the Mid-Essex Depression to a much shorter course via the lower Lea.

Anglian deposits in Hertfordshire

Many sites in east Hertfordshire, west Essex and south Bedfordshire expose two or more lithologically different chalky tills, often separated by glaciofluvial gravels. In Hertfordshire, many early workers recognized the presence locally of a lower dark-coloured till as well as a more widespread upper till: Hughes (1868) described '20 feet of dark blue clay' at Bayfordbury (TL 415104); Hopkinson and Salter (1899) recognized a thin lower boulder clay in the railway cutting and adjacent gravel pit west of Woodhall Farm (TL 235106) near Hatfield Hyde; Monckton and Hopkinson (1906) described a similar sequence in a gravel pit near the same farm; Pocock (1914b) and Williams (1918, 1921) described two boulder clays at Tyttenhanger (TL 179059), the lower being 'dark red-brown' in colour; Evans (1954) recorded two thin tills separated by gravels near Sleapshyde (TL 204067); and in the area covered by BGS Sheet 239 (Hertford), Sherlock and Pocock (1924) identified at least eight sites exposing a lower, darker boulder clay or till. Green (1918) and Sherlock (1924) mentioned three boulder clays in the Ware and Hertford-Amwell areas. Some of these were among the numerous sites investigated by

West and Donner (1956), Clayton (1957), Clayton and Brown (1958) and Gibbard (1977). Most adopted a subdivision into two tills, though Clayton and Brown (1958) also identified a middle till complex.

Later detailed work on the particle size distribution, carbonate content (of the 63 µm-8 mm fraction) and non-calcareous small clasts (8-16 mm) of numerous till samples from sites in Hertfordshire and adjacent areas enabled Cheshire (1986a, 1986b) to distinguish a total of four different Anglian tills, and this sequence was followed by Allen *et al.* (1991) and Bridgland and Cheshire (1994). They were named (in ascending order) the Ware, Stortford, Ugley and Westmill Tills, later the Ware, Stortford, Ugley and Wadesmill Members of the Lowestoft Formation (Lewis, 1999, p. 26). No temperate climate deposits or soils have been recorded between these, so they probably represent minor fluctuations of the margin of a single ice sheet, which further north in East Anglia and the southeast Midlands deposited a single undifferentiated unit known as the Lowestoft Till. The four tills can be used to subdivide the Anglian succession in central Hertfordshire (Table 6.3), and reconstruct a sequence of local events during the Anglian.

The Westmill Lower Gravel

Originally recognized by Gibbard (1977), this is the youngest fluvial deposit of the proto-Thames, probably dating from the final (early Anglian) phase of the river before it was diverted out of the Vale of St Albans by the Anglian glacier. Gibbard (1983a) concluded that it was deposited in a cold climate, as indicated by the presence of small ice-wedge casts at Moor Mill Quarry (TL 143025) and Hertingfordbury (TL 302121), and the presence of cold-tolerant ostracods in channel silts at Westmill Quarry (TL 342162) (Robinson, 1978). The ostracod assemblage included *Paralimnocythere compressa*, which is typical of Middle Pleistocene fluvial environments in a cold steppe or tundra environment.

Although Gibbard (1983a) originally concluded that this gravel was deposited during the Anglian Stage, and should be correlated with that forming the lower unit of the Winter Hill Terrace further west, he later renamed it as the Westmill Member and regarded it as the last unit of the pre-Anglian Middle Thames Formation (Gibbard, 1999). Lewis (1999) also regarded it as older than Anglian but, as it was clearly deposited in a cold climate and all the known deposits overlying it are glacial or glaciofluvial in origin, there seems no good reason for assigning it to any date other than early Anglian.

Like other proto-Thames gravels, the Westmill Lower Gravel (Plate 46) consists of trough and planar cross-bedded units indicating flow from SW to NE (Gibbard, 1977, Fig. 6) in a braided multichannel river. This mode of deposition also suggests a cold climate. In addition, it contains lenticular masses of sand and silt. The fluctuations in discharge indicated by the rapid changes in particle size suggest seasonal snowmelt in a cold, poorly vegetated catchment. The gravel was deposited on the floor of the proto-Thames valley on a gradient of approximately 0.6 m km^{-1} between Watford and the Mid-Essex Depression (Fig. 6.9). The valley floor was 0.5-1.0 km wide, but the braid plain created by aggradation of the gravel was eventually about 5 km wide in western Essex. The maximum recorded thicknesses of the gravel are 8.8 m at Westmill Quarry (TL 3415), 8 m at Watton Road Quarry (TL 3014) and 6.5 m at Moor Mill Quarry (TL 1503), suggesting a gradual eastward thickening. However, it is thinner at the easternmost known exposure in Hertfordshire, Eastwick Lodge Farm (TL 441118) near Harlow, where 3-5 m lies between the London Clay and Anglian till.

The 8-16 mm fraction of the Westmill Lower Gravel (28 samples averaging about 1400 clasts each from 8 sites in the Vale of St Albans and Mid-Essex Depression) contains mainly angular flint (mean 60.4%), with 14.3% Palaeogene flint pebbles (total flint 74.7%), 7.6% quartz and 5.3%

Colne Basin	Lea Basin		
Hoxnian lake deposits at Hatfield, Stevenage, etc (see Section 6.7)			
Smug Oak Gravel	Westmill Till (Wadesmill Member)		
	Westmill Upper Gravel (Hertford Member)	Ugley Gravel (Ugley Green Member)	
		Ugley Till (Ugley Member)	
		Hoddesdon Gravel (Hoddesdon Member)	
		Stortford Till (Stortford Member)	
		Thorley Gravel (Cock Lane Member)	
	Ware Till		
Moor Mill Laminated Clay	Ware Till (Ware Member)		
	Holwell Sand and Bullscross Farm Gravel	Ware Till	
	Ware Till		
		Watton Road Laminated Silt	Ware Till
	Westmill Lower Gravel (Westmill Member)		

Table 6.3. Schematic representation of the lithostratigraphic units recognized in the Anglian sequence of the Vale of St Albans. Names in parentheses are equivalents proposed by Lewis (1999).

Plate 46. *Westmill Lower Gravel of proto-Thames overlain by chalky outwash gravel deposited during advance of the Ware Till ice, Westmill Pit (TL 3415). Note the different directions of current bedding foresets, indicating a change in the direction of water flow from SW-NE to N-S approximately.*

quartzite. Southern tributaries of the proto-Thames carried more Palaeogene flint pebbles, but those from the north contributed almost none. In addition, there is 1.4% chert from the Lower Greensand, originating from southern tributaries, and 6.1% chalk. Jurassic limestones (0.5%) and *Rhaxella* chert from the Hambleton Hills of north Yorkshire (0.4%) suggest a minor exotic input from the north, probably brought by the approaching ice sheet. They provide another reason for dating the Westmill Lower Gravel as Anglian. A northern tributary (the proto-Beane), following approximately the present course of the Beane, carried more chalk (14-44%) and Jurassic limestones (1.2%) than the proto-Thames.

The surface of the Westmill Lower Gravel slopes gently southwards across the Vale of St Albans. For example, between Westmill Quarry (TL 3415) and Foxholes Quarry (TL 338124) the slope is 1.36 m km⁻¹. This can be explained in two ways. First, it could result from the deposition of an alluvial fan with a N-S gradient at the confluence of the proto-Beane and proto-Thames. Second, it could result from glacioisostatic depression (northward tilting of the land surface) as the Anglian ice sheet approached from the northeast or north. If the Westmill Lower Gravel was

deposited during the period of northward tilting, it would have formed an approximately horizontal surface, which was later tilted to the south when glacioisostatic rebound preferentially uplifted areas to the north.

In the area west of Hertford, Gibbard (1977, 1983a) did not divide his Westmill Gravel into Upper and Lower subunits, because he believed that the Ware Till, which lies between the two subunits in the Ware area, does not extend up the Vale of St Albans beyond Hertford. However, as will be seen later, the Ware Till can in fact be recognized westwards up the Vale of St Albans as far as Bricket Wood Common (TL 1200) near Watford, so the gravel beneath it can now be identified as the Westmill Lower Gravel throughout the Vale. To the southwest of Bricket Wood Common, it passes laterally into the lower subunit of the Winter Hill Terrace (Section 6.3).

The Letchworth Gravel

During the latest BGS survey of the Hitchin area (Sheet 221), patches of reddish brown gravel rich in quartzite and quartz pebbles were identified at Fairfield Hospital (TL 204353), Standalone Farm (TL 208338), Lower Wilbury Farm (TL 203337) and on either side of the Pix Brook (TL 211345 and TL 210341) approximately 1 km northwest of Letchworth (Fig. 6.8). The gravels, named the Letchworth Gravels by Hopson *et al.* (1996, pp. 76-78) and Smith and Rose (1997), are 3-4 m thick and rest on a planar surface cut in Lower Chalk at 66-68 m OD. Together with a particle size distribution typical of fluvial sediment, this suggests that they were deposited either by a river (the Letchworth River) flowing southwards through the Hitchin Gap from the south Midlands to join the proto-Thames near Ware, or by glacial meltwater.

The height and stratigraphic position of the Letchworth Gravels immediately beneath the Anglian till suggest correlation with the Westmill Lower Gravel of the proto-Thames. Smith and Rose (1997) decided that their lithological composition indicates a source similar to gravels of the Middle Pleistocene Bytham River, which drained the southwest Midlands between Stratford-on-Avon and Leicester for a long period before it was overridden by the Anglian glacier. Initially the Bytham was confluent with the proto-Thames near Happisburgh in northeast Norfolk (Parfitt *et al.*, 2010). Later the confluence was probably near Bury St Edmunds in south Suffolk, but subsequently it had its own course to the North Sea through north Suffolk when the proto-Thames had slipped southwards to flow through north Essex (Rose, 1994).

Despite the broad lithological similarity of the Letchworth Gravel to those of the Bytham, a direct connection between the two immediately before the Anglian is unlikely, because no other deposits of similar composition are known between them, and the elevation of the lowest (immediately pre-glaciation) Bytham Gravels, 90 m OD at Stratford-upon-Avon and 65 m OD near Leicester, is too low to permit flow over the intervening 70-90 km. In addition, the most likely sources of the coloured quartzite pebbles in the Triassic rocks of the southwest Midlands are now separated

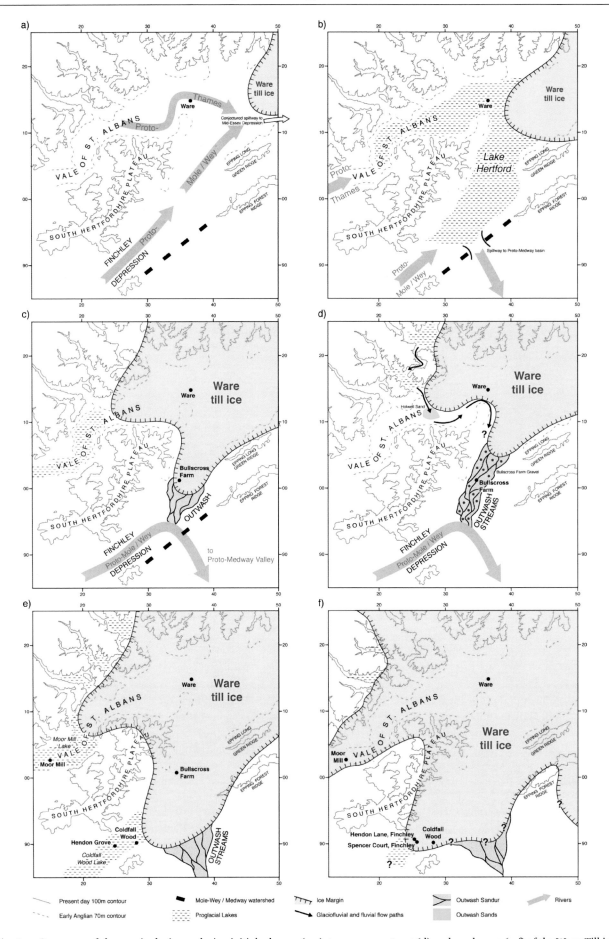

Fig. 6.12. Sequences of changes in drainage during initial advance (a-c), temporary retreat (d) and readvance (e-f) of the Ware Till ice sheet in Hertfordshire.

from Letchworth by the Jurassic scarps of the Cotswolds and Northamptonshire. Smith and Rose (1997) therefore suggested that the Letchworth Gravel was reworked in the early Anglian from much older (Early Pleistocene) gravels deposited when a fluvial connection was possible, presumably at a much higher level, between the southwest and southeast Midlands.

Alternatively, the gravel could have been deposited as outwash from a glacier that invaded the area, either early in the Anglian before deposition of the chalky Ware Till (Boreham and Langford, 2006) or during the ice advance that deposited the Ware Till. The three samples analysed by Smith and Rose (1997) were taken from the exposed upper surface of the deposit in ploughed fields near TL 205354, where any chalk and other limestone components originally in the gravels could have been removed by subsequent weathering. More recently, eight other samples obtained from greater depths (beyond the reach of decalcification) at Lower Wilbury Farm and Fairfield Hospital, have shown that in unweathered form the gravel contains around 7.1% chalk and 13.4% Jurassic limestones in the 8-16 mm fraction. This reduces the similarity to the gravels of the Bytham River and makes a glaciofluvial origin more likely. Some of the recently found clasts of Jurassic oolitic limestone are large angular to subangular boulders; one weighing 15.5 kg has been identified as from the Ketton area of Rutland. Smaller clasts of dolerite, granite and porphyry from more distant sources have also been found. Together with the angular Jurassic limestone boulders, which are probably too large to have been carried from Rutland by a river, these exotic components suggest that a glaciofluvial origin for the Letchworth Gravel is more likely than deposition by a Midlands river.

The Ware Till

During later phases of deposition of the Westmill Lower Gravel, the Anglian Lowestoft ice sheet was approaching from the NNE. It overtopped the Chalk cuesta in Suffolk and west Essex, but on entering the proto-Thames valley in west Essex it was deflected to flow NE-SW up the valley (Fig. 6.12a). Ice approaching the Hitchin area from the NNE also invaded the Hitchin-Stevenage Gap and further west spread southwards into the Lilley Bottom valley east of Luton. These two ice streams were then probably confluent with ice moving up the proto-Thames valley. The till deposited by the initial advance into south Hertfordshire was the Ware Till, though chalky gravel was deposited over the Lower Westmill Gravel by outwash streams flowing approximately N-S (Plate 46). Southwest of Luton the ice was unable to override the Chalk scarp, and was probably deflected southwestwards along the scarp to invade the Vale of Aylesbury, though here there is conflicting evidence for the age of the ice advance (Section 6.8).

Lake Hertford. When it reached a position just east of Ware in the proto-Thames valley, the Ware Till glacier dammed the river to form an ice-marginal lake near Hertford (Fig. 6.12b). This was named Lake Hertford by Clayton and Brown (1958), who suggested that it extended southwards along the earlier proto-Mole/Wey valley (now the lower Lea valley) into the Finchley Depression. Finely laminated silts and clays (Table 6.3), termed the Watton Road Laminated Silt (Gibbard, 1977) after a type site at Watton Road Quarry (TL 341149), accumulated in Lake Hertford. Lake Hertford probably existed for several centuries, as Gibbard (1977) recorded 485 varve-like silt-clay couplets in the deposits at Watton Road Quarry. As the couplets were fairly uniform in thickness throughout the sequence, he concluded that during sedimentation the ice margin slowed or halted. Unless the lake drained through or under the ice, it probably existed long enough for overflow channels or spillways to be eroded across the lowest cols on its margin. Initially there was probably a spillway along the southern margin of the ice sheet eastwards from Harlow (Cheshire, 1986a) but later, as the ice dam rose higher up the southern side of the proto-Thames valley, another spillway developed across a col on the eastern flank of the proto-Mole/Wey valley southwest of the present Epping Forest ridge (Baker and Jones, 1980) (Fig. 6.12b). At this stage the water ultimately discharged into the proto-Medway (Bridgland and Cheshire, 1994) along a course approximating to the modern lower Lea and lower Thames valleys.

Evidence for the diversion down what is now the lower Lea valley is seen at Bullscross Farm (TL 340006) (Fig. 6.12c), where gravels of the northward-flowing proto-Mole/Wey were deposited in a channel eroded down to at least 50.5 m OD and are overlain by gravel deposited by streams from the north (Cheshire, 1986a). The upper gravel (the Bullcross Farm Gravel) is 4 m thick and very chalk-rich, and contains cross-bedded units indicating NNE-SSW flow. It lies between two layers of Ware Till, the lower one less than 80 cm thick, the whole sequence suggesting two successive ice advances with a minor episode of retreat during which the Bullscross Farm Gravel was deposited (Fig. 6.12d). The reversal of flow implies drainage of at least the southern part of Lake Hertford through the spillway created across the interfluve from the flooded proto-Mole/Wey valley into the proto-Medway valley. This diversion of proto-Thames water, augmented by meltwater from the Ware Till ice sheet, was the first of two during the Anglian, but was short-lived, perhaps lasting only a few hundred years, because the continuing ice advance up the Vale of St Albans soon blocked the northern end of the lower Lea valley.

Following drainage of the southern arm of Lake Hertford, the proto-Mole/Wey continued to follow its course through the Finchley Depression. However, the second and more extensive advance of the Ware Till ice, after deposition of the Bullscross Farm Gravel, dammed the proto-Mole/Wey to form a lake in which the Coldfall Wood Laminated Beds (Gibbard, 1979) were deposited at Coldfall Wood (TQ 276901) and Hendon Grove (TQ 243895) (Fig. 6.12e). The ice subsequently advanced over the lake deposits to its maximal position at Finchley (Fig. 6.12f).

The Holwell Sand. In the Vale of St Albans, the ice that deposited the Ware Till continued its advance south-westwards up the proto-Thames valley, and in doing so

Plate 47. Westmill Lower Gravel overlain by Moor Mill Laminated Lake Clays and Ware Till, Moor Mill Pit (TL 138022) near Bricket Wood.

overrode the Watton Road Laminated Silts. However, in the Welwyn Garden City area a retreat of the ice margin is suggested by the Holwell Sand, which was previously seen within the Ware Till in three former quarries at Holwell Court (TL 277104), Holwell Hyde (TL 263116) and Waterhall Farm (TL 296106). Deposition of the Holwell Sand may have occurred at the same time as the minor retreat leading to deposition of the Bullscross Farm Gravel (Fig. 6.12d), especially as measurements of the direction of cross-bedding in the Holwell Sand show that it was deposited by water flowing southwards towards the southern side of the Vale of St Albans near the lower Lea valley. The cross-bedded units are large, indicating rapid water flow, but as there is no gravel component there must have been traps for coarser sediment upstream, such as ice marginal lakes in the lower Mimram and Beane valleys. A temporary retreat of the Ware Till ice margin is also indicated at other sites where glaciofluvial gravels divide the till, such as Cold Christmas (TL 362168), Standon (TL 402225), Cooper's Green (TL 190091) and Ongar (TL 566023).

The Moor Mill lake. Following the minor retreat stage, the Ware Till ice continued its advance up the proto-Thames valley and impounded another lake south of St Albans (Fig. 6.12e). Gibbard (1977, 1978a) named this the Moor Mill Lake, and in its deposits, the Moor Mill Laminated Clay, he counted at least 342 varve-like couplets at the type site of

Moor Mill Quarry (TL 145027). He believed that the lake was dammed by an ice advance later than that of the Ware Till, one that deposited a till which he named the Eastend Green Till. However, Cheshire (1986a) showed that the till overlying the Moor Mill Laminated Clay is petrographically similar to the Ware Till further east, and that no younger till extends further west than north Hatfield. From the known distribution of the laminated clays, the Moor Mill Lake extended eastwards only as far as London Colney, though this was probably a temporary limit determined by the constantly moving glacier margin. The level of the lake surface is probably indicated by the upper surface of the deltaic deposits of the Winter Hill Upper Gravel at 80-82 m OD between Burnham and Denham (Section 6.3).

The Moor Mill Laminated Clay becomes coarser upwards and is overlain by Ware Till (Plate 47). The upward coarsening probably indicates deposition of coarse sediment from melting icebergs that broke away from the glacier as it advanced into the lake. After overriding the lake deposits (Fig. 6.12f), the glacier finally extended to Bricket Wood Common (TL 1200), which is the south-western limit of any ice margin in Hertfordshire. The Moor Mill Lake overflowed southwards through a col near Uxbridge, forming a spillway that became the first part of a new course for the Thames through London (Gibbard, 1977). Thus the permanent diversion of the Thames out of the Vale of St Albans was accomplished by the first and most extensive (Ware Till) ice advance into Hertfordshire (Cheshire, 1986a; Allen *et al.*, 1991; Bridgland, 1994).

The Finchley ice limit. During its later advance, the Ware Till ice also formed an important lobe extending southwards into the valleys of the lower Lea and the former Mole-Wey as far as Finchley (Fig. 6.12f). In this area, 5 m of grey chalky till and up to 9 m of brown sandy clay with Jurassic fossils were exposed over London Clay when the railway cutting (TQ 252907) at Finchley Central station was dug (Walker, 1871), and similar successions were recorded near Whetstone (Woodward, 1889) and in other parts of Finchley (Hopkinson, 1910). Samples obtained from more recent exposures in this area at Hendon Lane (TQ 249904) and Spencer Court (TQ 250903) were petrographically similar to the Ware Till, and what is probably the same till overlies the Coldfall Wood Laminated Beds 2.5 km away at Coldfall Wood (Gibbard, 1977). In Essex, the Ware Till ice extended into the Roding valley and, in the Ingrebourne valley, reached the southernmost limit of any Anglian till at Hornchurch (TQ 547874), where it is overlain by the Boyn Hill Gravel deposited in MIS 12 (Bridgland, 1994, Fig. 4.5).

In the area between Finchley and Barnet, Lawrence (1964) identified possible ice marginal lakes and associated overflow channels. He suggested that the lakes occupied valleys cut in London Clay, such as Folly Vale and the Dollis Valley, now containing the minor misfit streams of the Folly Brook and Dollis Brook. Overflow channels at the western ends of these lakes were identified at Holecombe Dale (TQ 222933) and Moat Mount (TQ 210945), respectively, and lake strand lines were suggested north of Totteridge (TQ 228942-TQ 244946) and west of Totteridge Church

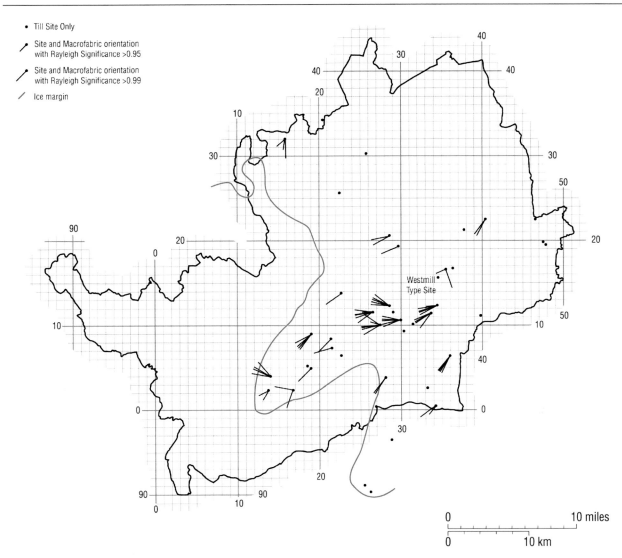

Fig. 6.13. Location of sites exposing the Anglian Ware Till in Hertfordshire, with macrofabric orientations indicating directions of ice movement.

(TQ 243941), but no lacustrine or strand deposits were recognized. Further north, he also proposed further ice-marginal lakes near Potters Bar, with possible overflow channels at Fenny Slade (TL 268001), Barvin Hill (TL 295009) and Plumridge Hill (TQ 277997), and a glacial lake in Nyn Park (TL 278028).

Ice flow directions. To assess directions of ice movement, Cheshire (1986a and later unpublished work) measured the orientation of at least 50 elongate stones in 83 samples of Ware Till at 23 sites in Hertfordshire and west Essex. During their movement in ice that is not subject to strong compression, elongate stones are thought to become gradually orientated with their longest face or edge parallel to the direction of movement. Thus, in common with Rose (1974), Baker (1976) and Gibbard (1977), Cheshire measured the orientation of the a-axis of each stone, which runs parallel to the longest faces or edges (Andrews, 1971). As such, it is not necessarily the longest axis of the stone; for example, in a brick-shaped stone the longest axis is the slightly longer line joining diagonally opposite corners, which gives a false indication of ice movement. However,

in ovoid stones, the a-axis is equivalent to the longest axis. The stones thought to orientate best are those in which the ratio between the a-axis and the next longest (b-) axis perpendicular to the a-axis is at least 1.2:1. However, stones with an a:b ratio greater than 3:1 were rejected, because they tend to roll within or beneath the ice, so that their a-axis lies at 90° to the direction of ice movement. The preferred orientation of stones measured in this way is often referred to as the till's macrofabric.

Of the 83 sets of macrofabric measurements made on the Ware Till, 53 from 23 sites gave statistically significant (non-random) preferred orientations of a-axes (Fig. 6.13), all suggesting deposition by lodgement, a process involving direct release from the slowly melting base of the ice sheet as it moved over bedrock, earlier Quaternary sediments or till already deposited. In the Vale of St Albans, the clast orientations show that the initial ice movement was strongly controlled by the winding topography of the valley, but as the ice lobe thickened it spread laterally, engulfing the valley sides and moving in a more uniform south-westward direction.

Wooldridge (1953) and others noted the local occurrence

of two tills in the western part of the Vale of St Albans, but where they have been studied it seems that both can be attributed to the single (Ware Till) ice advance. For example, at the former Hatfield Polytechnic pit (TL 212069), Rose (1974) studied the macrofabric and other sedimentary properties of a lenticular mass of till which, during subsequent excavations for the A1(M), was shown to lie above the main Ware Till. He concluded that, instead of being deposited by lodgement beneath the glacier, the till lens had slumped or flowed into its present position from material that had accumulated on a glacier surface during melting. Its petrographic properties are similar to those of the Ware Till (Cheshire, 1986a), so it is reasonable to conclude that the glacier on which it accumulated was the one that deposited the Ware Till. This mode of deposition may explain other patches of a second till in the western Vale of St Albans, though it is also possible that some resulted from minor readvances after stillstand or retreat phases similar to that associated with the Holwell Sand.

The bulk mineralogical composition of the Ware Till at Holwell Hyde and Westmill was reported by Little and Atkinson (1988): quartz forms 18-26%, calcite 4-15%, and the main clay minerals (in order of abundance) are illite, montmorillonite and kaolinite. Geotechnical properties of the till at Garston and the above two sites were described by Marsland (1977) and Little and Atkinson (1988), respectively.

The Smug Oak Gravel

As the ice that deposited the Ware Till stagnated and waned, meltwater flowed away from it in two directions: south-westwards along the Vale of St Albans and southwards down the lower Lea, both valleys by then abandoned by the proto-Thames. The two discharges were approximately contemporaneous and deposited the Smug Oak Gravel in what is now the Colne basin and the Westmill Upper Gravel in the Lea basin (Table 6.3). Both gravels contain local and glacial components, but there is less non-durable glacial material, such as chalk, in the Smug Oak Gravel than generally occurs in the Westmill Upper Gravel. Measurements of palaeocurrent directions by Gibbard (1977, Fig. 12) and Cheshire (1986a, Fig. 7.9) showed that gravels deposited by the south-westward (Smug Oak) meltwater flow extend about 5 km east of the present Colne/Lea interfluve, so the initial catchment of the Smug Oak river was more extensive than that of the modern Colne. The upper Lea was then a tributary of the early Colne, but after the Anglian Stage it was captured by the middle Lea, and now contributes to the modern Lea basin.

The type-site for the Smug Oak Gravel designated by Gibbard (1977) was at Moor Mill Quarry (TL 1402), but because of back-filling the gravel is now visible here only in a preserved but overgrown section at TL 143030. The Geological Conservation Review and Regionally Important Geological Site at TL 145027 (Bridgland, 1994, pp. 129-134; Hertfordshire RIGS Group, 2003) is no longer exposed. The average composition of the gravel at Moor Mill is 66.3% angular flint, 24.1% Palaeogene flint pebbles (total flint

90.4%), 3.4% quartz, 4.8% quartzite and 0.2% chalk. In earlier exposures at Hatfield (Gibbard, 1974) and Radlett Airfield Quarry (TL 1503), the gravel had similarly small chalk contents. Many of the chalk and other soft, non-durable clasts derived from the ice sheet were perhaps removed by abrasion in the fast-flowing glacial meltwater streams. Alternatively, their proportion was decreased by large contributions of local angular flint and Palaeogene pebbles brought in by runoff of local (non-glacial) origin, i.e. from rain or melting snow.

The Westmill Upper Gravel (Hertford Member)

Although the Westmill Upper Gravel was contemporaneous, at least in part, with the Smug Oak Gravel, events during its deposition were complicated by two readvances of the Anglian ice sheet into eastern Hertfordshire (Cheshire, 1986a; Bridgland and Cheshire, 1994). These may partly explain its greater non-durable glacial clast content compared with the Smug Oak Gravel. It has also been termed the Hertford Member of the Lowestoft Formation (Lewis, 1999), but this additional name seems unnecessary. In the eastern part of the Vale of St Albans, it is the first glaciofluvial deposit after the diversion of the Thames. Its type-site is at Westmill Quarry (TL 346154), where it is usually separated from the Westmill Lower Gravel by the Ware Till though, where this till has been removed by glaciofluvial erosion, the Westmill Upper Gravel rests directly on the Westmill Lower Gravel. Because two readvances of ice depositing separate tills interrupted deposition of the Westmill Upper Gravel in east Hertfordshire, the sequence shown in Table 6.3 can be recognized in this area.

The Thorley Gravel. This is 1.7 m thick at Westmill Quarry (TL 346154), where it lies between the Ware Till and Stortford Till. Its type site is in a borehole at Bishop's Stortford (TL 479195), where it is rich in non-durable clasts; the 8-16 mm fraction here contains 60.5% chalk, 12.7% other limestones, 12.3% angular flint, 3.0% fossil shells and shell fragments, 1.9% phosphatic nodules (from the Upper Greensand and Gault Clay north of the Chalk outcrop), 1.4% quartzite, 1.3% vein quartz and 1.1% Palaeogene flint pebbles. It is also visible at Cock Lane Quarry (TL 354077), Hoddesdon, which was used as the type site by Lewis (1999). However, chalk and other non-durable clasts are less abundant here, either because of attrition in the outwash flow or by dilution with non-glacial material brought by the Lea. Also, the gravel's relationships to the Ware and Stortford Tills cannot be demonstrated at Cock Lane Quarry, so this is not really suitable as a type site.

The Stortford Till. The readvance of ice to deposit this till (Cheshire, 1986a) made little progress into the Vale of St Albans, the lower Lea and Roding valleys (Fig. 6.14). The designated type site is the borehole at Bishop's Stortford (TL 479195) where it is 12 m thick. The ice was confined to areas of low relief in east Hertfordshire and west Essex. In terms of the three petrographic properties by which the various

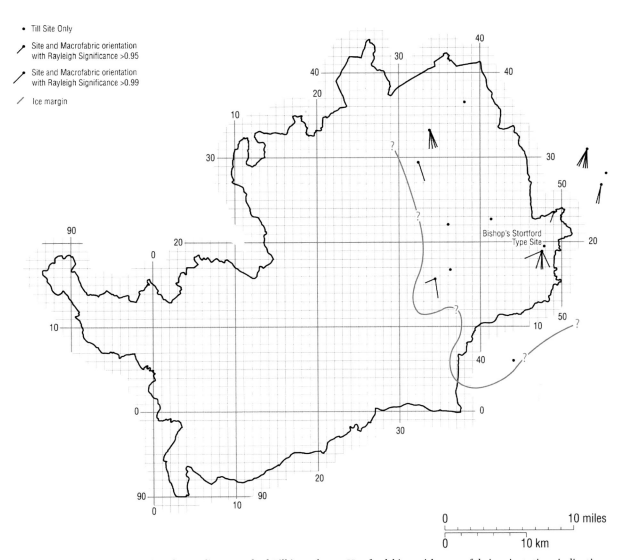

- Till Site Only

Site and Macrofabric orientation
with Rayleigh Significance >0.95

Site and Macrofabric orientation
with Rayleigh Significance >0.99

Ice margin

Fig. 6.14. Location of sites exposing the Anglian Stortford Till in and near Hertfordshire, with macrofabric orientations indicating directions of ice movement.

Anglian tills can be distinguished (particle size distribution, carbonate content of the 63 μm-8 mm size fraction and lithology of small clasts), the basal layers of the Stortford Till at Bishop's Stortford are similar to the underlying Ware Till, but at higher levels there are progressive changes. In particular, a strong particle size peak in the medium sand (125-500 μm) fraction typical of the Ware Till decreases upwards and eventually disappears. As with the Ware Till, the pattern of ice movement indicated by stone (a-axis) orientation measurements in the Stortford Till reflects the influence of topography upon glacier flow. This produced a convergent pattern, with ice approaching from the NNE at Widdington (TL 530310) (Baker, 1976) and Elsenham Sand Quarry (TL 551267), both on the interfluve between the Rivers Stort and Cam, but from the NNW at Hyde Hall Farm (TL 339332) and Cottered (TL 325295) further west on the Beane-Rib interfluve. In the Hitchin-Stevenage area, Hopson *et al.* (1996, Table 12) recognized six tills, which they related to four separate ice advances, but until these tills can be related petrographically to those distinguished further south by Cheshire (1986a), it is not clear which, if

any, of them equates to the Stortford Till.

The Hoddesdon Gravel. As the Stortford Till ice margin retreated northwards, meltwater flow was re-established to deposit the Hoddesdon Gravel sub-unit of the Westmill Upper Gravel. The cross-bedding structures in the Hoddesdon Gravel suggest that the flow followed the general alignment of the Beane and Stort valleys southwards into the lower Lea valley. The average composition of the Hoddesdon Gravel, based upon analyses of the 8-16 mm fraction of 23 samples is: 51.5% angular flint, 10.6% chalk, 5.8% other limestones and calcareous fossils, 5.0% vein quartz, 3.9% Palaeogene flint pebbles, 4.8% quartzites and 4.3% phosphatic nodules. However, the non-durable components (chalk and other limestones) decrease in abundance from locations close to the ice margin, such as Westmill Quarry (TL 346154), Frogmore Quarry (TL 284206) and Whitehall Pit (TL 290211), to zero at more distal sites in the lower Lea valley, such as Foxholes South Pit (TL 340123) and Hoddesdon Pit (TL 354077). Much of the decrease can be attributed to abrasion during transportation in the fast-

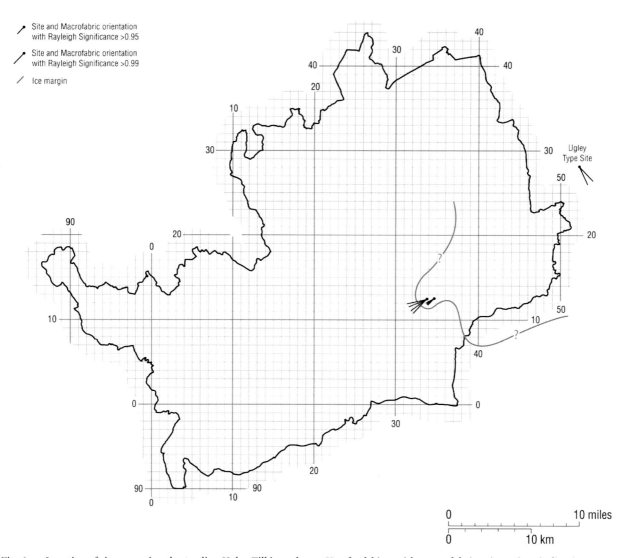

- ↗ Site and Macrofabric orientation with Rayleigh Significance >0.95
- ↗ Site and Macrofabric orientation with Rayleigh Significance >0.99
- ╱ Ice margin

Fig. 6.15. Location of sites exposing the Anglian Ugley Till in and near Hertfordshire, with macrofabric orientations indicating directions of ice movement.

flowing meltwater streams, but carbonate has also been removed from much of the gravel in the lower Lea valley by post-depositional weathering.

The Ugley Till. Ice then advanced again to deposit the Ugley Till. This was the least extensive of the four ice advances during the Anglian Stage (Fig. 6.15), and did not interrupt drainage from the Beane basin into the lower Lea valley. The till is known from three sites only. The type-site is Ugley Quarry SSSI (TL 520280) in Essex, where it consists of up to 7 m of dark grey lodgement till. The other sites where it has been recorded are the former Foxholes South (TL 340123) and Foxholes East (TL 345127) Quarries, where the till occurred as lenticular masses occupying at least ten channels up to 20 m wide and 2 m deep. Measurements of stone a-axis orientation show that the ice moved NW-SE at Ugley and NE-SW at the two Foxholes sites (Fig. 6.15), thus following a strongly curving path. The till is strongly calcareous and has a small medium sand (125-500 μm) content. It is petrographically indistinguishable from the later Westmill Till, so it is only when clearly separated from

the Westmill Till by intervening gravels, as at Ugley and the two Foxholes sites, that it can be identified with certainty. Also it is possible that, because of their similarity, till designated as Westmill Till in some surface exposures may in reality have been Ugley Till. However, as the Westmill Till was deposited by the final and more extensive Anglian ice advance, it is likely that any till on the surface in central and east Hertfordshire is the Westmill Till.

The Ugley Gravel. The next gravel, the Ugley Gravel, occurs between the Ugley and Westmill Tills and is distinguished from the Hoddesdon Gravel by its greater contents of chalk and other limestones, which persist even at distal sites down the lower Lea valley. In the 8-16 mm fraction, its mean composition is: 48.2% angular flint, 21.5% chalk, 7.9% other limestones and calcareous fossils, 3.6% Palaeogene flint pebbles, 1.1% phosphatic nodules, 3.8% quartz and 2.7% quartzites. The chalk content decreases irregularly from north to south: 37.4% at Ugley Quarry (TL 520280), 20.2% at Westmill Quarry (TL 346154), 23.1% at Foxholes South Quarry (TL 340123) and 10.6% at Hoddesdon Pit (TL

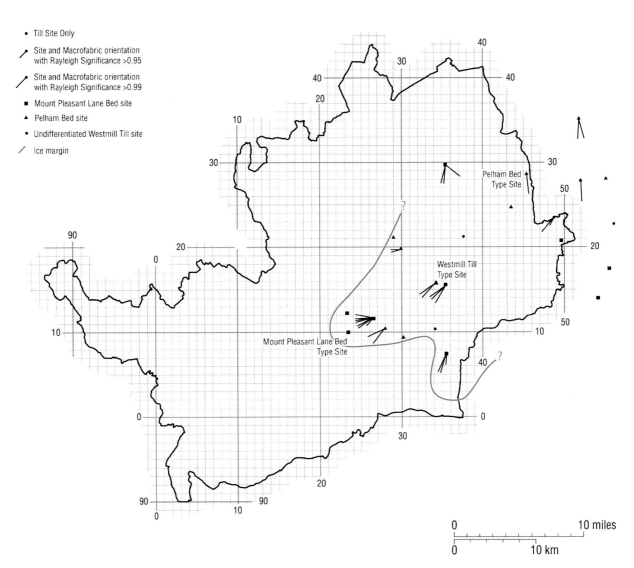

● Till Site Only

↗ Site and Macrofabric orientation
  with Rayleigh Significance >0.95

↗ Site and Macrofabric orientation
  with Rayleigh Significance >0.99

■ Mount Pleasant Lane Bed site

▲ Pelham Bed site

● Undifferentiated Westmill Till site

╱ Ice margin

Pelham Bed
Type Site

Westmill Till
Type Site

Mount Pleasant Lane Bed
Type Site

0   10 miles

0   10 km

Fig. 6.16. Location of sites exposing the Westmill Till in and near Hertfordshire, with macrofabric orientations indicating directions of ice movement.

354077). It is the only gravel in the Lea valley that remains chalky south of Ware, but it is not known how far south the chalk content survives. Trough and planar bedding and occasional silt beds indicate a seasonally variable flow regime characteristic of outwash deposits, and the cross-bedded units at Hoddesdon Pit indicate SSW flow. It is not known whether the ice sheet retreated completely from the Stort-Lea basin during deposition of the Ugley Gravel, but its thickness (9.5 m at Ugley Quarry) suggests a longer period of deposition than either the Thorley or Hoddesdon Gravels.

The Westmill Till

Deposition of the Ugley Gravel ceased with a further final readvance of ice from the north to deposit the Westmill Till (Fig. 6.16). This is the uppermost member of the Lowestoft Formation in Hertfordshire, and generally forms the surface of interfluves in eastern parts of the county. It is up to 8 m thick, and in unweathered form is dark grey and very calcareous but, where it is less than 2 m thick, weathering has altered it to a carbonate-free, light yellowish brown

or yellowish brown clay. Clast orientation measurements suggest that the ice approached from the north in northeast Hertfordshire and northwest Essex, then veered south-westwards in the area between Bishop's Stortford, Hertford and Hoddesdon. In exposures seen when the Watton at Stone by-pass was constructed (TL 299200), the ice movement was E-W across the Beane valley. Lobes of ice penetrated the Vale of St Albans as far west as north Hatfield and the Lower Lea valley as far south as Hoddesdon (TL 354077), but the glacier did not encroach upon the south Hertfordshire Plateau southwest of Hertford Heath (TL 3511).

As with the Stortford Till, some properties of the Westmill Till are not uniform throughout its thickness. However, the Westmill Till shows a sharp break in properties, whereas the Stortford Till shows gradual changes from bottom to top. No change is discernible in the field, but some of the petrographic variates determined by laboratory analyses clearly show that the Westmill Till comprises two distinct beds (Fig. 6.16). The lower is termed the Pelham Bed, with a type site at Pelham Grid Station (TL 456286). This achieves a maximum known thickness of 7.3 m in a borehole

Plate 48. Ice-pushed folds in till and glaciofluvial gravels, previously exposed at Sundon Pit (TL 0327) (Photo Hugh Prudden).

at Henham (TL 556282) in Essex, and occurs widely in northeast Hertfordshire and northwest Essex. The upper part, the Mount Pleasant Lane Bed, with a typesite at Mount Pleasant Lane, Hatfield (TL 233099), reaches a maximum observed thickness of 4 m in the former Holwell Hyde Quarry (TL 263116), where it rests unconformably on the Ware Till. It also occurs widely in northeast Hertfordshire and northwest Essex, but its southern and south-western limit is at least 5 km beyond that of the Pelham Bed. The main properties distinguishing the two till beds relate to the mineralogical composition of parts of the sand fraction: in the 0.5-1.4 mm range, quartz and flint are both more abundant in the Mount Pleasant Lane than the Pelham Bed and, in the 0.355-4 mm range, *Rhaxella* Chert from the Corallian of northeast Yorkshire is more abundant in the Pelham than the Mount Pleasant Lane Bed. These and other distinguishing properties become less distinct north-eastwards, and the two beds merge in north Essex. As there are no deposits of gravel, sand or bedded silt between the two, there was probably no retreat of ice during deposition of the Westmill Till.

In broad terms, both parts of the Westmill Till are petrographically similar to the Ugley Till. All three contain little medium sand (125-500 μm), but show small peaks in the fine sand at 90 μm and coarse silt at 45 μm, and have carbonate contents exceeding 63%. The small amounts of medium sand probably indicate that up-glacier sources of sand, such as the Woburn Sands, were not exposed, possibly because they were buried under an earlier till. The large carbonate contents show that erosion of the Chalk escarpment in southern East Anglia was still active.

Each of the previous tills in Hertfordshire rests conformably on beds below with little evidence of disturbance structures. However, deposits beneath the Westmill Till are often strongly disturbed: at Holwell Court (TL 277104), the till was previously seen to lie unconformably across three earlier units now folded by the ice advance, and at Eastend Green (TL 296106) and Bunkers Hill (TL 301095), previous exposures showed gentle folding along NW-SE axes in the underlying sediments. There are also structures within the till itself, such as (a) shear planes inclined upwards towards the southwest in quarries at Holwell Hyde (TL 263116) and Westmill (TL 346154) and in hand-dug pits at Baas Hill (TL 359064) near Broxbourne (Cheshire, 1978), and (b) slickensides oriented to the southwest observed during construction of the Watton at Stone bypass (TL 299200). These structures within and below the Westmill Till suggest that the ice moved more actively than during deposition of the earlier tills, possibly because of increased subglacial porewater pressures. However, it did not reach as far as the ice that deposited the Ware Till, so its advance may have been curtailed by rapid warming at the end of the Anglian Stage.

The Hitchin Gap till sequence

Hopson *et al.* (1996, Table 12) tentatively equated lodgement tills encountered in boreholes penetrating deposits filling the buried Hitchin and Stevenage Channels, i.e. the Priory (= Stevenage) Till below and the Maydencroft Till above, with the Ware and Eastend Green tills, respectively, of Gibbard (1977). But as the Eastend Green Till is no longer recognized, these correlations are no longer tenable. Subsequently, Brownsell (2008) reinvestigated the sequence of deposits in the Hitchin and Stevenage Channels and parts of south Bedfordshire, using more recent borehole evidence and lithological analyses similar to those Cheshire (1986a) used to differentiate and correlate tills in parts of Hertfordshire to the south and east. Her results indicate a more complex history of glaciation in this area than that proposed by Hopson *et al.* (1996). She found till similar to the Ware Till on the interfluve between the Hitchin and Stevenage Channels and also on either side of the Hitchin Gap, thus confirming that the Ware Till was deposited by an extensive advance from the NNE across north Hertfordshire. However, within the Hitchin Gap the till lithologically most similar to the Ware Till proved to be the Charlton Till, which lies between the Priory and Maydencroft Tills and is separated from the Priory Till beneath by gravels that were probably deposited during a glacial retreat phase. This implies that the Priory and Stevenage tills were deposited by a small ice lobe that temporarily occupied the Hitchin Gap before the more extensive advance that deposited the Charlton and Ware Tills.

In the Hitchin Channel, the deposits overlying the Maydencroft Till include yet another till, the Vicarsgrove Till, which Brownsell (2008) correlated with the Graveley Till occurring in higher parts of the sequence filling the Stevenage Channel. She suggested that both of these are local waterlain or flow tills deposited in meltwater lakes formed in the channels during final decay of the Anglian glacier.

Correlation of the Maydencroft Till with the Westmill Till of south and east Hertfordshire is perhaps supported by the presence of 'ice-push' fold structures in gravels beneath the Maydencroft Till previously exposed at the former Primrose Hill Quarry (TL 165324) near Holwell, north of Hitchin. Some of these folds were isoclinal, overturned towards the south, and were among the most severe glacitectonic deformations recently exposed in the Hertfordshire area. This pit was designated as a RIGS (Hertfordshire RIGS Group, 2003), but is currently being infilled. The chalk rafts on the eroded Chalk escarpment south of Royston (Hopson, 1995) may provide further evidence of glacitectonic disturbance by the ice that deposited the Maydencroft Till (Brownsell, 2008). Also, at the now infilled Sundon Pit (TL 0327) on the northern side of the Chalk escarpment north of Luton, exposures in the 1950s and 1960s showed spectacular evidence for disturbance of till and gravels by an ice advance from the north, which created isoclinal folds (Plate 48), reverse faults and thrusts, followed by collapse structures (diapirs and accommodation faults) during glacial retreat.

Large erratic boulders

In addition to the abundant local and far-travelled clasts found in the various Anglian tills and gravels of Hertfordshire, there are numerous large, far-travelled boulders scattered across the glaciated eastern parts of the county. These must have been brought originally by the Anglian ice sheet, though many have almost certainly been

Plate 49. Erratic block of Millstone Grit from Yorkshire or Derbyshire, Royston town centre (TL 356407).

relocated by human activities. Perhaps the most famous is the large boulder of Millstone Grit from the Carboniferous of Derbyshire or West Yorkshire, which has been erected in Royston (Plate 49) at the junction of Ermine Street and the Icknield Way. It is likely that the town's name is taken from this erratic, as in the 11th century a Lady Roysia, Rohesia or Roisia erected a cross (now lost) incorporating the stone at the road junction.

Other large erratic boulders in east Hertfordshire were listed by Crosskey (1882, 1884), Fordham (1886), Salter (1905b, 1912) and Harmer (1928). They indicate that the Anglian ice sheet originated mainly in Scotland and northern England, as they include numerous pieces of Millstone Grit, other sandstones from Lincolnshire and Yorkshire, Carboniferous Limestone, basalts and dolerites from Northumberland and southern Scotland, porphyry from the Cheviots, syenite from Charnwood Forest (Leicestershire), granites from Scotland and the Lake District, oolitic limestone, septarian nodules from the Oxford or Kimmeridge Clays, diorite, schist and gneiss. Elsden (1886) described thin sections of many of the igneous boulders found by Fordham (1886) in the Ashwell area. Beside the B1037 at Cottered (TL 317292) there is an erratic of Carboniferous Limestone measuring *c.* 0.7 m × 0.6 m and another of Millstone Grit measuring *c.* 1.2 m × 1.0 m. In Romeland Gardens, St Albans (TL 144071), there is a similarly sized block of Carboniferous Limestone, and a block of pink porphyritic granite measuring *c.* 1.5 m × 1.4 m occurs beside the A10 at Buckland (TL 355337). Near Letchworth, Hill (1911b) recorded a block of Lower Cretaceous Spilsby Sandstone from Lincolnshire, which was over 5 m long. Other localities from Lincolnshire southwards to Highgate, north London, where this rock has been found as erratics, were mapped by Kelly and Rawson (1983, Fig. 4).

Inputs of Scandinavian ice that had crossed the North Sea are indicated by a large boulder of larvikite from the Oslofjord area found near Bury Field (TL 352143), Ware (Barrow, 1910; Sherlock, 1915; Green, 1918), which is now

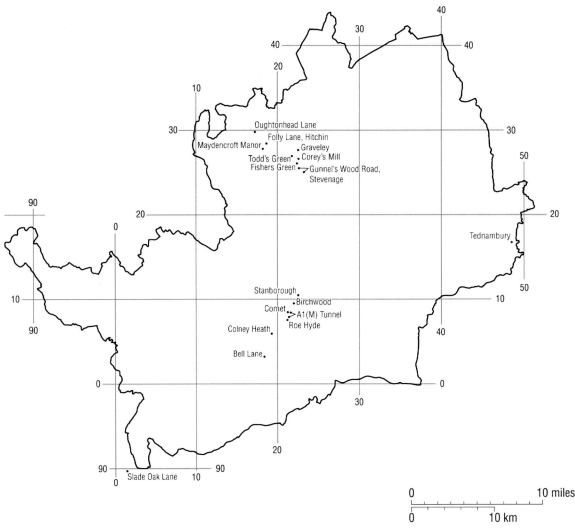

Fig. 6.17. Location of known Hoxnian Interglacial sites in Hertfordshire.

displayed in the grounds of Hertford Castle (TL 325126), and by small pieces of Permian rhomb porphyry, from the same part of Norway, found at Offley (TL 1426) near Hitchin and Fortis Green (TQ 2789) near Finchley (Salter, 1912). Larvikite was also reported from glaciofluvial gravel exposed at Vicar's Grove (TL 193257) near Hitchin (Bloom and Wooldridge, 1930). Numerous erratics from southern Norway have been recorded in East Anglia, especially in northeast Norfolk, and are common in northeast England. Those in Hertfordshire may have been brought across the North Sea to areas further north early in the Anglian glaciation, and then secondarily transported later in the Anglian by the southward moving glacier. Similarly, erratics from the Midlands and southern Pennines could have been glacially derived from the deposits of early rivers, such as the Bytham and Ancaster (Rose, 1994), which flowed eastwards into East Anglia and south Lincolnshire, respectively.

6.7. The Hoxnian Interglacial

The widespread Anglian glacial deposits in the Vale of St Albans and areas to the northeast are overlain at numerous sites (Fig. 6.17) by lacustrine deposits containing pollen assemblages and other fossils indicating increasingly warm climatic conditions. These have been attributed to the late Anglian and early Hoxnian Interglacial on account of their similarities in pollen sequences to lake deposits overlying the Lowestoft Till at Hoxne (TM 176769), Suffolk (West 1956), and Mark's Tey (TL 912242), Essex (Turner, 1970), both of which have been yielded uranium-series dates close to 400 ka, i.e. within MIS 11 (Rowe *et al.*, 1999; Grün and Schwarcz, 2000). Hoxnian deposits are much more common in Hertfordshire than those of other Pleistocene interglacials. They are also more common than in other English counties. This probably reflects the major landscape change in Hertfordshire that resulted from the Anglian glaciation, and the greater abundance of kettle holes that are likely to form where the ice sheet is breaking up near its limit.

Sites near the A1 between Hatfield and Stevenage

In the 1960s, an important sequence of interglacial lake deposits (Fig. 6.18) attributed to the Hoxnian (Sparks *et al.*, 1969) was exposed in a gravel pit at Roe Hyde (TL 212075) near Hatfield Polytechnic, now the Hatfield campus of the University of Hertfordshire. The exposure was later lost during construction of the A1(M). Sparks *et al.* (1969) also described similar deposits found in trial borings and an exploratory excavation (TL 227103) for construction of the A1 at Jack Olding's Roundabout near Stanborough. Later Gibbard (1977, Fig. 10) noted similar lake deposits in excavations for the A1 at the Comet Roundabout (TL 213083), Birchwood Roundabout (TL 220093) and other sites near Hatfield. He also described further sites at Colney Heath (TL 192059) and Bell Lane (TL 183031) (Gibbard, 1977, pp. 461-463) and at Fishers Green, Stevenage (TL 224260) (Gibbard and Aalto, 1977). Other interglacial lake deposits exposed in the 1985 excavations for the cut-and-cover tunnel of the A1(M) northeast of the Comet Roundabout at Hatfield (TL 2108) were described by Foster (2004). Yet others have been encountered during the construction of the Little Wymondley by-pass at Todds Green (TL 219269), in a temporary excavation on a construction site near the A1(M) at Corey's Mill (TL 226265), in boreholes near Gunnel's Wood Road in Stevenage (TL 227256 and TL 232250) and by augering near Graveley (TL 227287), all of which were briefly described by Hopson *et al.* (1996, p. 107). Unfortunately none of these interglacial sites is exposed today, but others are very likely to be found in the future.

Most of the lake deposits probably accumulated in kettle holes, i.e. enclosed hollows which originated by melting and collapse of large blocks of glacier ice buried within the Anglian glacial sediments, i.e. till at Roe Hyde and Fishers Green and glaciofluvial gravels elsewhere. Some blocks were perhaps covered by Smug Oak Gravels deposited by minor meltwater streams. As a result the lowest post-glacial sediments in some of the lake basins are gravels that have been disturbed, contorted and sometimes faulted by collapse when the buried ice melted. The melting would have

occurred quite rapidly when the climate began to improve towards the close of the Anglian Stage but before the full warmth of the Hoxnian Interglacial was established.

The oldest lacustrine deposits, for example at Roe Hyde (Fig. 6.18), are light grey silty clays containing very little organic matter and with sparse plant macro-remains and pollen assemblages. The macro-remains are mainly of aquatic plants, such as common bulrush (*Scirpus lacustris*) and fennel-like pondweed (*Potamogeton pectinatus*), but the pollen assemblages indicate a cold-tolerant, mainly open ground vegetation surrounding the lake, with patches of sea buckthorn (*Hippophaë rhamnoides*) scrub and woodland consisting of willow (*Salix* spp.) and birch (*Betula* spp.), the latter probably including the dwarf arctic species *B. nana*. Juniper (*Juniperus communis*) was also present locally. The herbaceous plants present around the lake at this time included flax (*Linum austriacum*), white flax (*Linum catharticum*), sea plantain (*Plantago maritima*), sheep's sorrel (*Rumex acetosella*), mugwort (*Artemisia* spp.), thistles (*Cirsium* spp.), valerian (*Valeriana officinalis*) and various members of the Compositae, Rubiaceae, Ranunculaceae and Umbelliferae families. At some sites these late Anglian deposits resemble the annually laminated *varved sediments* of seasonally frozen lakes, and locally they contain worn foraminifera washed out of the underlying glacial deposits. At Roe Hyde, their upper layers consist of white or pale grey calcareous marls (Fig. 6.18) composed almost entirely of encrusted stem fragments and gametangia (oogonia) of the carbonate accreting stonewort *Chara*. Stoneworts such as *Chara* are green algae, which are an important component of the pioneer vegetation in shallow, newly formed lakes with clear stagnant water rich in bicarbonate (Wood, 1950; Moore, 2005).

At the Roe Hyde, Bell Lane and Fishers Green sites, the late Anglian lake deposits are overlain by *Chara* marls and darker grey (more organic) silts containing less pollen of sea buckthorn and herbaceous genera but more of birch and juniper. This *Betula-Juniperus*-herb pollen assemblage biozone indicates expansion of the birch woodland to the exclusion of the shade-intolerant sea buckthorn, probably because of increasing temperatures at the beginning of

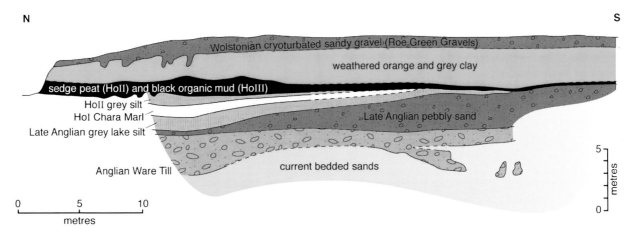

Fig. 6.18. North-south section in late Anglian, Hoxnian and early Wolstonian deposits previously exposed at Roe Hyde Pit, Hatfield, redrawn from Sparks et al. *(1969).*

Plate 50. Hoxnian marls, peat and organic mud of HoIII, overlain by silty clays and sandy gravels (Roe Green Gravels) previously exposed at Roe Hyde Pit (TL 212075), Hatfield.

the Hoxnian interglacial. It is therefore attributed to the Pre-temperate HoI. Towards the top of these early Hoxnian silts, there is a decrease in birch pollen and increases in grass, juniper and herb pollen, which Gibbard (1977) and Gibbard and Aalto (1977) interpreted as indicating a fall in the regional water table level, possibly because of decreased rainfall. This caused the lakes at these sites to dry up so that sedimentation ceased. As a result there is no further record of the interglacial vegetation sequence at Bell Lane.

However, at Roe Hyde and Fishers Green, sedimentation resumed after a break, with deposition of HoII or early HoIII marls and organic silts that rest unconformably on the HoI silts. They contain macroscopic remains of aquatic plants, such as white water lily (*Nymphaea alba*), bogbean (*Menyanthes trifoliata*), whorled water milfoil (*Myriophyllum verticillatum*), mare's tail (*Hippurus vulgaris*), common bulrush (*Scirpus lacustris*), fen pondweed (*Potomogeton coloratus*), fennel-like pondweed (*Potomogeton pectinatus*), marsh cinquefoil (*Potentilla palustris*), branched bur-reed (*Sparganium erectum*), scorpidium moss (*Scorpidium scorpioides*) and sedges (*Carex* spp.), and pollen of pine (*Pinus*), oak (*Quercus*), elm (*Ulmus*), lime (*Tilia*), hazel (*Corylus*), alder (*Alnus*) and ferns (*Polypodium*). These taxa indicate a renewed rise in the water table and development around the lake of mixed oak forest and fen woodland in full interglacial conditions (Sparks *et al.*, 1969; Gibbard, 1983b). The rise in the water table probably resulted from increased precipitation.

At Roe Hyde, this layer was in turn overlain by 20 cm of

sedge peat containing abundant macro remains of aquatic and fen plants, suggesting that sedge communities spread over the lake, and fen woodland rich in birch invaded its shallower parts. The fenland macro-remains included mainly tree birch (*Betula* sp.), great pond sedge (*Carex riparia*), celery leaved crowfoot (*Ranunculus scleratus*), narrow-leaved water parsnip (*Berula erecta*), water mint (*Mentha aquatica*) and fen sedge (*Cladium mariscus*). A black organic mud 1.35 m thick (Plate 50) then accumulated in HoIII, the upper layers of which contain increasing amounts of grass (Graminae), heather (Ericales) and conifer pollen, especially silver fir (*Abies* sp.), but smaller quantities of pollen from the thermophilous mixed oak forest taxa. This assemblage suggests a temperature decline towards the end of the Hoxnian and decreased oceanicity, possibly because of a eustatic decline in sea level. Finally, less organic silty clay and sandy gravels were deposited, indicating erosion of surrounding land surfaces on which the vegetation cover was much sparser because of the continuing climatic deterioration. Similar sandy gravels are widespread in the Vale of St Albans, and were named the Roe Green Gravels by Gibbard (1977), who attributed them to gelifluction under periglacial conditions in the succeeding cold stage (MIS 10).

At Fishers Green, the pollen of thermophilous mixed oak woodland genera found in black muds of early HoIII were partly replaced in the grey silty clays of late HoIII by silver fir, spruce (*Picea*), pine, yew (*Taxus*) and Ericales. These suggest that soils on land surfaces surrounding the lake were becoming acidic after a long period of weathering in the earlier parts of the interglacial. A parallel decline in alder pollen indicates thinning of fen woodland around the lake, and a rapid increase in grasses in the uppermost interglacial sediments heralds the end of the interglacial. Cool conditions at this time are also indicated by fruits of the flexible naiad (*Naias flexilis*). The interglacial sediments at Fishers Green are overlain by cryoturbated brown sands, flinty gravels and grey silty sands with flint pebbles, which were probably deposited by a stream in the early Wolstonian (MIS 10). Current bedding in the lowest sands indicate that this flowed from SE to NW, i.e. towards the Hitchin-Stevenage gap.

Beales (1977) found 19 species of water fleas (Cladocera) in the early interglacial (HoI) deposits at Fishers Green, the assemblage indicating stagnant and moderately alkaline (hard) water. Mollusc fragments were also found at this level, but both molluscs and Cladocera were absent from the later interglacial deposits, possibly because of increasing water acidity. Sparks *et al.* (1969) recorded numerous freshwater molluscs from the late Anglian and earlier Hoxnian deposits of HoI and HoII below the sedge peat at Roe Hyde. The most abundant species were *Valvata cristata*, *Valvata piscinalis*, *Bythinia inflata*, *Lymnaea peregra*, *Lymnaea glutinosa*, *Planorbis laevis*, *Planorbis crista*, *Planorbis contortus*, *Segmentina complanata*, *Sphaerium corneum*, *Pisidium milium* and *Pisidium nitidum*. The absence of molluscs from the peat (late HoII) and black organic mud (HoIII) was attributed to the water becoming too acidic, possibly by microbiological liberation of sulphate ions, because crystals of gypsum, produced by the action of sulphuric acid on calcium carbonate, were present in the peat. The molluscs confirm that the sediments accumulated in a small lake, but provide no precise indication of age. As at Hoxne, the late Anglian deposits have a sparse fauna consisting mainly of *Planorbis crista*, with subordinate *Planorbis laevis*, *Valvata piscinalis* and *Lymnaea peregra*, but similar assemblages occur in the late glacial deposits of other cold stages. The same four species persist into the overlying interglacial deposits, where they are accompanied by an increasing list of other species, reaching 20 in total in the full interglacial (HoII) silts and marls containing mixed oak forest and fenland pollen. This progressive diversification reflects the climatic improvement early in the Hoxnian Interglacial.

Foster (2004) recorded molluscs from two sites in the 1985 excavations for the A1(M) at Hatfield, one (Site B) approximately 700 m south of the southern exit of the tunnel (TL 213076), and the other (site C) approximately 300 m north of the southern exit (TL 216085). These probably represented two different pools rather than a single large lake. The overall assemblage was similar to that recorded from Roe Hyde by Sparks *et al.* (1969), indicating an initially shallow, stagnant, lacustrine environment, but giving way later in the interglacial to a wider range of marsh and slow-moving stream environments as the lake was infilled. The peat that terminated the interglacial sequence at site C also yielded four species of poorly preserved gastropods: *Armiger crista*, *Valvata cristata*, *Bythinia tentaculata* and *Sphaerium corneum*. *Valvata piscinalis* and several species

of the bivalve *Pisidium* found in silty clay beneath the peat suggested a more dynamic water flow after deposition of the thick *Chara* marls that formed most of the sequence.

Foster (2004) also identified 18 species of ostracods from deposits at the same two sites. They were found throughout the interglacial sequence, including the peat at site C, though the assemblage was most diverse (up to 13 species) in the silts just below the peat. Some, such as *Herpetocypris reptans*, *Cypridopsis vidua*, *Pseudocandona rostrata*, *Cyclocypris laevis* and *Cyclocypris ovum*, occurred throughout the interglacial sequence, whereas others, including *Ilyocypris monstrifica*, *Ilyocypis quinculminata* and *Ilyocypris gibba*, were more common in later parts of the interglacial. *I. monstrifica* and *I. quinculminata* are good indicator species for the Hoxnian. Like the molluscs, the overall assemblage indicates a shallow lacustrine environment persisting throughout the interglacial, with water depth increasing during accumulation of the *Chara* marl above a basal grey silty clay, but decreasing later with deposition of the upper silty clay in gently moving water. Changes in the abundance of certain trace elements in the ostracod carapaces suggested that the climate was warmest during deposition of the *Chara* marls.

The Slade Oak Lane site

A Hoxnian sequence in a slightly different environmental setting was described by Gibbard *et al.* (1986) from Slade Oak Lane (TQ 016897) close to the M25 near Denham, Buckinghamshire. The interglacial sediments at this site occur in a steep sided funnel-shaped depression nearly 40 m deep, which penetrates the Gerrards Cross Gravel and silty clays of the Reading Formation to the Chalk. They are mainly dark grey organic muds, which are underlain and overlain by much less organic deposits, including sands, clayey gravels and silty clays containing flint pebbles. As the site is 14 km outside the Anglian ice limit in the Vale of St Albans, the depression cannot have originated as a kettle hole, and is more likely to be an infilled doline formed by subsidence following localized dissolution of the Chalk bedrock beneath. Dolines of similar size and shape and filled with silt-rich 'brickearth', a mixture of loess (windblown silt) and fine sand and clay washed in from the surrounding Plateau Drift, are fairly common on the Chilterns (Avery *et al.*, 1982) (Section 5.4). Many of the sediments from above and below the organic muds at Slade Oak Lane had a similar particle size distribution to the Chiltern 'brickearths', but mineralogical analyses showed that they were derived almost entirely from weathered Reading Beds or Plateau Drift, and contained little or no far-travelled loess. Nevertheless, they probably accumulated in periglacial conditions by slumping of the doline walls or by gelifluction of sediment eroded from surrounding land surfaces with little or no vegetation cover.

Pollen and macroscopic plant remains from the organic muds at Slade Oak Lane indicated that sedimentation began fairly late in the interglacial, probably in an early part of HoIII. As at the other sites, silver fir (*Abies*) became abundant slightly later, and then the thermophilous tree genera were abruptly replaced by pine, heathers, grasses and

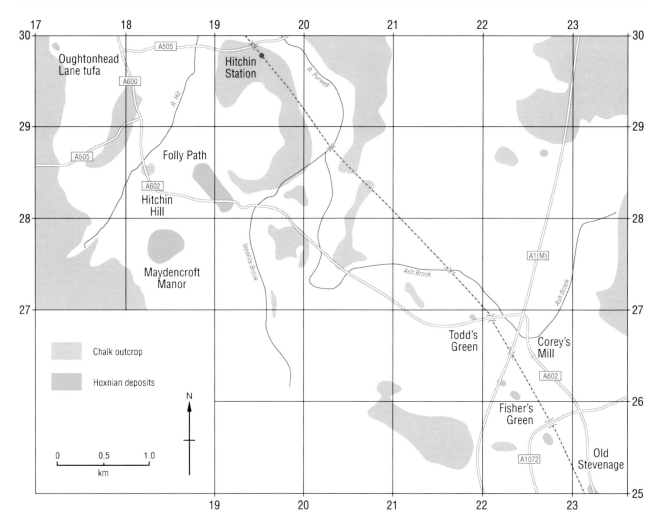

Fig. 6.19. Distribution of Hoxnian Interglacial deposits in the Hitchin area, redrawn from Hopson et al. (1996).

other herb taxa of open ground conditions, indicating the rapid cooling in HoIV at the end of the interglacial. A strong similarity of the curves for abundance of different pollen types to those at Hoxne and Marks Tey leaves little doubt that the Slade Oak Lane sequence dates from the Hoxnian. However, as at the other Hoxnian sites in Hertfordshire mentioned previously, no mammalian remains were found to afford a comparison with the well established faunas of different Middle Pleistocene interglacials in the terraces of the Lower Thames.

Hitchin sites

Further Hertfordshire lake deposits thought to date from the Hoxnian Interglacial (MIS 11) have been known from the Hitchin area (Fig. 6.19) for over a century, and these have yielded mammalian remains among many other fossils. In the late 19th century, they were exposed in workings for 'brickearth' in two areas on either side of Hitchin Hill southwest of Hitchin town centre, one beside Folly Path between the cemetery (TL 189285) and Black Horse Lane (TL 190280), and the other between Maydencroft Manor (TL 182273) and Brick Kiln Lane (TL 183280). The sequence of deposits is broadly similar in the two areas, the lake

deposits lying in a basin or basins between Anglian till and glaciofluvial deposits beneath and the slightly stony 'brickearth' (yellowish brown sandy or silty clay) above. However, it is unclear whether they accumulated in a single large lake more than 1 km across or separate lakes within the N-S depression of the Hitchin-Stevenage Gap. A single lake of this size would probably have been too large to occupy either a doline or a kettle hole, but could have formed between moraines or hummocks on the surface of the Anglian glacial deposits (Hopson *et al.*, 1996, p. 104). The lake deposits were originally described by Hill (1891), and a section exposed near Folly Path was photographed c. 1885 by the local photographer T. B. Latchmore. Two of Latchmore's photographs were reproduced by Bloom (1934, facing p. 38), Boreham and Gibbard (1995, p. 263) and Hopson *et al.* (1996, Plate 10). Following Hill's work, the deposits were investigated in more detail in 1896 with the aid of a grant from the Royal Society of London (Reid, 1897, reprinted 1901). The extent of the deposits, based on evidence from shallow boreholes reported by Hill (1891), Reid (1897, 1903), Gibbard (1974) and Hopson *et al.* (1996), is shown by Hopson *et al.* (1996, Fig. 28) and also in Figure 6.19.

The interglacial deposits at Hitchin can be divided into (a) grey or greyish brown organic silty clays with peaty layers and (b) an overlying discontinuous, well bedded brown calcareous silt, with clayey and sandy layers and beds of white or pale grey *Chara* marl. The maximum combined thickness is about 10 m. Both contain abundant fossils, including plant remains, freshwater molluscs, ostracods, vertebrate bones, fish teeth and insects (beetles). In places shallow decalcification of the lower layer occurred before or during deposition of the upper layer, and this led Boreham and Gibbard (1995) to suggest that the upper layer accumulated in a series of small ponds distinct from and younger than the lake or lakes in which the lower layer was deposited. This could also explain why the upper layer in places rests directly on the glacial deposits (Hill and Monckton, 1896). In addition, decalcification of the upper layer probably occurred before emplacement of the 'brickearth' (Hill, 1891; Hopson *et al.*, 1996, p. 104). Over much of the surrounding area, probably outside the lake and pond margins, the 'brickearth' directly overlies the glacial deposits and reaches a maximum recorded thickness of about 12 m. However, some erosion of the interglacial sediments could have occurred before deposition of the 'brickearth'.

Fossils from the Hitchin interglacial deposits. Most of the faunal and plant macro-remains from the interglacial deposits were from the *Chara* marl. In addition to the oogonia and stems of *Chara*, Reid (1897, 1901, 1903) and Boreham and Gibbard (1995) listed seeds and fruits of aquatic plants, and others representing nearby marsh and, unexpectedly, an open grassland community. In addition, leaves of oak (*Quercus*) indicated temperate forest nearby. The seeds and fruits included bugle (*Ajuga reptans*), water plantain (*Alisma plantago-aquatica*), alder (*Alnus glutinosa*), great burdock (*Arctium lappa*), nodding thistle (*Carduus nutans*), sedge (*Carex* sp.), hornwort (*Ceratophyllum demersum*), thistle (*Cnicus = Cirsium* sp.), dogwood (*Cornus sanguinea*), floating mud-rush (*Eleogiton fluitans*), hemp agrimony (*Eupatorium cannabinum*), ash (*Fraxinus excelsior*), hogweed (*Heraclium sphondylium*), mare's tail (*Hippuris vulgaris*), nipple-wort (*Lapsana communis*), hawkbit (*Leontodon taraxacoides*), gipsy-wort (*Lycopus europaeus*), water mint (*Mentha aquatica*), bogbean (*Menyanthes trifoliata*), water blinks (*Montia fontana*), water milfoil (*Myriophyllum* sp.), greater naiad (*Naias marina*), white water-lily (*Nymphaea alba*), great burnet (*Poterium officinale*), curled pondweed (*Potomogeton crispus*), self-heal (*Prunella vulgaris*), blackthorn (*Prunus spinosa*), wild service tree (*Pyrus torminalis*), pedunculate oak (*Quercus robur*), water crowfoot (*Ranunculus aquatilis*), celery-leaved crowfoot (*Ranunculus scleratus*), creeping buttercup (*Ranunculus repens*), elder (*Sambucus nigra*), common bulrush (*Scirpus lacustris*), woody nightshade (*Solanum dulcamara*), corn sowthistle (*Sonchus arvensis*), bur-reed (*Sparganium* sp.), marsh woundwort (*Stachys palustris*), wood woundwort (*Stachys sylvatica*), chickweed (*Stellaria media*) and horned pondweed (*Zannichellia palustris*). Reid (1897) also recorded the remains of several temperate woodland

mosses, including *Antitrichia curtipendula*, *Homalothecium sericeum*, *Hyocomium brevirostre* (?), *Isothecium* sp., *Neckera complanata*, *Stereodon cupressiformis* and *Zygodon* sp.

Vertebrate remains collected from the *Chara* marl at various times are stored in Hitchin Museum, and were recently re-examined by Dr. A. J. Stuart (Boreham and Gibbard, 1995, p. 268). They include straight tusked elephant (*Palaeoloxodon antiquus*), an indeterminate bear (*Ursus* sp.), an indeterminate rhinoceros (*Stephanorhinus* sp.), an indeterminate vole (*Microtus* sp.), fallow deer (*Dama dama*), red deer (*Cervus elaphus*), roe deer (*Capreolus capreolus*), giant deer (*Megaloceros giganteus*) and either aurochs (*Bos* sp.) or bison (*Bison* sp.), which together indicate a typical temperate interglacial climate. Grazing by the larger mammals could explain why open grassy areas occurred nearby at a time in the middle of the interglacial when only dense mixed oak forest would be expected.

Also from the *Chara* marl, Chapman (1903) recorded 15 species of ostracods: *Candona candida*, *Candona candida* var. *tumida*, *Candona candida* var. *claviformis*, *Candona lactea*, *Candona pubescens*, *Cyclocypris globosa*, *Cyclocypris laevis*, *Cypris virens*, *Darwinula stevensoni*, *Erpetocypris reptans*, *Ilyocypris bradii*, *Ilyocypris gibba*, *Limnocythere inopinata*, *Plonocypris* (= *Cypridopsis*) *vidua* and *Scottia browniana*. In addition, Kennard (1947) reported 12 species of molluscs: *Ancylus lacustris*, *Anodonta* sp., *Bythinia tentaculata*, *Cecilioides acicula*, *Lymnaea lagotis*, *Lymnaea peregra*, *Planorbis carinatus*, *Planorbis leucostoma*, *Planorbis planorbis*, *Sphaerium corneum*, *Valvata antiqua* and *Valvata cristata*. Together with the ostracods, these suggest a freshwater lake or pond with either still or slowly moving water. In the silty clays beneath the *Chara* marl, Kennard (1947) found 9 molluscs: *Ancylus lacustris*, *Bythinia tentaculata*, *Bythinia leachii*, *Lymnaea peregra*, *Lymnaea stagnalis*, *Planorbis planorbis*, *Segmentina complanata*, *Valvata cristata* and *Valvata piscinalis*, which suggest a fairly deep, sluggish stream.

Apart from the ostracod *Scottia browniana*, which strongly suggests a Hoxnian age, none of these fossil assemblages indicates a specific age for the deposits. The vertebrate assemblage is similar to those from other sites thought to date from the Hoxnian in southeast England (Stuart, 1974; Schreve, 2001), but was also present in other interglacials.

Boreham and Gibbard (1995) described pollen assemblages from two boreholes through the Hitchin interglacial deposits at Charlton Lane and Maydencroft Manor. Like all the other Hoxnian sequences in Hertfordshire, neither provided a complete sequence through a typical interglacial. At Charlton Lane, grey silty clays (part of the lower interglacial deposit) yielded mainly pollen of grasses, sedges, herbs and aquatic plants, with small amounts of birch, willow and sea buckthorn in a lower layer, and an assemblage dominated by birch with smaller amounts of pine, willow, oak, elm, alder, hazel, herbs and aquatic plants above. Samples from the Maydencroft Manor borehole, which was probably sited near the lake margin,

Plate 51. Iron-stained Lower Palaeolithic handaxe from Hoxnian Interglacial deposits, Folly Pit (= Jeeves Pit), Hitchin (with thanks to St Albans Museum Service).

contained similar assemblages at lower levels but one with larger amounts of temperate tree taxa above. By comparison with assemblages from other Hertfordshire and East Anglian Hoxnian sites, these confirm that the lower lacustrine deposits date from the late Anglian and earliest part of the Hoxnian (HoI). A single sample of *Chara* marl, collected in 1954 by R. G. West from one of the previously exposed 'brickearth' sections (Jeeves' Pit, TL 192281), yielded a pollen assemblage dominated by temperate tree taxa (mainly hazel and alder) with only a little grass and herb pollen (Boreham and Gibbard, 1995, p. 266). This probably dates from slightly later in the interglacial (HoII?) than the borehole samples, but HoIII and HoIV seem to be missing.

Artefacts. The Hitchin site is also famous for an assemblage of Lower Palaeolithic flint artefacts obtained in the late 19th century, mainly from the basal part of the 'brickearth' previously exposed in Jeeves' Pit (TL 191281) and Ransom's Brickyard (TL 189283), but also from the underlying *Chara* marl (Evans, 1896; Reid, 1897; Oakley, 1947: Hopson *et al.*, 1996, pp. 110-111). They are mostly handaxes in a fine sharp condition (Plate 51), suggesting production at or near the site. The handaxes are similar in technology and dimensions to those from Hoxnian sites such as Hoxne (Wymer, 1985) and Swanscombe (Roe, 1968b, 1981), but artefact technology is not now regarded as a reliable indicator of age in earlier Palaeolithic (pre-Devensian) periods. Evans (1896, Plates XI and XII) figured handaxes from various sites in the Hitchin area, including the 'brickfield', Folly Pit (= Jeeves'

Pit), Highbury, Bearton Green and Ickleford. However, their stratigraphic contexts were not clearly specified, and some could have come from later river gravels or even the present land surface.

The Hitchin 'brickearth'. The exact origin of the 'brickearth' overlying the interglacial deposits at Hitchin is unclear. Reid (1897) suggested it is a mixture of rainwash and wind-transported material equivalent to Palaeolithic loess deposits in central Europe. Boreham and Gibbard (1995) thought that it represents 'colluvial, aeolian and fluvial activity during an early part of the subsequent Wolstonian cold stage', i.e. in MIS 10. In this way it is analogous to the deposit overlying the Hoxnian deposits at Slade Oak Lane and infilling Chiltern dolines (Avery *et al.*, 1982). Hopson *et al.* (1996, p. 107) suggested it resulted from 'a combination of wind action and solifluction', the latter process perhaps accounting for its preferential accumulation in topographic depressions and its variable thickness (up to almost 12 m in places). The absence of organic remains supports deposition in a cold, periglacial environment, such as would have occurred in the Wolstonian.

Oughtonhead Lane tufa. Another deposit at Hitchin thought to date from the Hoxnian Interglacial was originally exposed in 1943 in a trench dug to lay a water pipe along Oughtonhead Lane (TL 172299) on the western side of the town (Fig. 6.17). Originally described by Wiggs (1943, 1944), the trench exposed a tufa or travertine containing a temperate assemblage of non-marine (land and freshwater) molluscs, which were identified in part by Kennard (1947), with a complete list published by Wiggs (1945). The site was later re-excavated by Kerney (1959), who showed that the tufa, and an associated calcareous sandy clay with a similar but more restricted mollusc fauna, overlie unfossiliferous glacial gravels of presumed Anglian age, and are in turn overlain by flinty gravel and sand containing detached masses of the underlying tufa. Erratics, such as vein quartz, red chalk from Lincolnshire, ironstone from the Lower Greensand and Jurassic belemnites and molluscs, were also present in the upper gravel, and Kerney (1959) believed that it represented a second (post-Hoxnian) glaciation. However, Hopson *et al.* (1996, p. 106) suggested that it is a Devensian head (gelifluction) deposit, which could have incorporated erratics derived from Anglian glaciofluvial deposits upslope. The disturbance and gentle folding of the tufa and crushing of the larger molluscs, as recorded by Kerney (1959), might have resulted from an over-riding glacier, but can also be explained by cryoturbation and downslope movement (gelifluction) in periglacial conditions.

The tufa was formed by precipitation of calcium carbonate in one or more marshy pools fed by calcareous springs rising from the Chalk. Calcareous springs are visible in the area today. The most abundant molluscs among the 42 species recorded from the tufa by Kerney (1959) were *Acicula (Platyla) polita, Carychium trodentatum, Planorbis leucostoma, Azeca goodalli menkeana, Discus rotundatus* and *Oxychilus cellarius*. Among the land molluscs present, *Acicula polita, Azeca goodalli menkeana* and some of the less frequent species suggest a temperate woodland environment. The assemblage as a whole indicates a climate at least as warm as southern England at the present day, and the closest modern equivalents of some species are found only in southern Europe. However, little can be concluded regarding the age of the deposit, because there are very few other dated interglacial tufa deposits in Britain, or even elsewhere in Europe, for comparison.

The tufa has also yielded a small assemblage of mammalian teeth, including those of badger (*Meles meles*), bank vole (*Clethrionomys glareolus*), an extinct pine vole (*Pitymys* cf. *arvaloides*), an extinct water vole (*Arvicola cantiana*) and wood mouse (*Apodemus* sp.) (Kerney, 1959; Holyoak *et al.*, 1983). The presence of *Arvicola cantiana* indicates a date between the later part of the Cromerian and the Devensian, but *Pitymys* is unknown after the Hoxnian (Sutcliffe and Kowalski, 1976), so the assemblage agrees with a Hoxnian age. It could also be late Cromerian, but this date is ruled out by the presence of Anglian glacial gravels beneath the tufa. Holyoak *et al.* (1983) attempted to date the tufa by the uranium series disequilibrium method, but it was unsuccessful because the sample had probably lost uranium by post-depositional leaching.

Evidence from beetles at other Hoxnian sites. At certain Hoxnian sites outside Hertfordshire, where the sequence of deposits from later parts of the interglacial is more complete than at any of the sites described above within the county, the assemblages of Coleoptera (beetles) provide evidence for a brief but intensely cold (arctic) episode in the middle of the interglacial, sometime in the early part of HoIII. This sudden climatic deterioration, probably equivalent to MIS 11b, has been described from Hoxne in Suffolk (Coope, 1993; Ashton *et al.*, 2008) and is especially well represented at Quinton in the West Midlands (Coope and Kenward, 2007). At this time, the beetles suggest maximum summer temperatures of only 9-11°C, and minimum winter temperatures as low as -10°C to -27°C. The earlier Hoxnian climate (MIS 11c) was probably similar to that of the Holocene, i.e. a little cooler than other interglacials of the later Mid Pleistocene, and during substage 11a the winters were distinctly colder, though not as severe as in substage 11b. The sequence at Hoxne suggests that most of the temperate deposits there date from the earlier MIS 11c, and the same is probably true of most Hoxnian deposits in Hertfordshire. However, the archaeological assemblages at Hoxne are entirely from the later deposits of the cooler MIS 11a. If humans inhabited the Hertfordshire/Suffolk area only in the later MIS 11a, it may explain why no artefacts have been found at most of the Hoxnian sites in the county. Thus the artefact-containing deposits in the Hitchin area may date from substage 11a rather than 11c.

The Tednambury site

Organic deposits originally noted during BGS mapping for the Epping Sheet (Millward *et al.*, 1987, pp. 56-64) at School Field, Tednambury (TL 484168), in the Stort Valley south of Bishop's Stortford, were later investigated by Betts and

Boreham (2004) and related to the Hoxnian Interglacial. Boreholes showed that organic silts and clays up to about 3 m thick infill a depression resembling a kettle hole approximately 50 m across in the surface of the Anglian till. The oldest lake deposits, directly overlying the till, contained a pollen assemblage dominated by birch (*Betula*) and grass (Poaceae), with small amounts of pine (*Pinus*), willow (*Salix*), sedge (Cyperaceae) and sea buckthorn (*Hippophaë rhamnoides*), an assemblage resembling that of the late Anglian at other sites. In the overlying interglacial deposits, these taxa were replaced by oak (*Quercus*), alder (*Alnus*) and hazel (*Corylus*), with small amounts of lime (*Tilia*), ash (*Fraxinus*) and ivy (*Hedera*). Hornbeam (*Carpinus*) pollen in the highest deposits suggested correlation with a later part of HoII, though the decrease in arboreal pollen seen in late HoII at other sites was not found. Freshwater molluscs, including *Bythinia tentaculata*, *Valvata piscinalis*, *Valvata cristata*, *Lymnaea peregra* and *Gyraulis crista*, were abundant, and at one horizon numerous fish teeth, mainly of rudd (*Scardinius erythrophalmus*), were found.

6.8. The Wolstonian Complex

Although Mitchell *et al.* (1973) used the name Wolstonian for what they thought was a single cold stage between the Hoxnian and Ipswichian Interglacials (Table 6.1), dating of these two interglacials has subsequently shown that the Wolstonian spans a long period (about 230,000 years) of complex climatic change. In the oceanic sequence, it covers three cold stages (MISs 10, 8 and 6) and two warm stages (MISs 9 and 7). MISs 9 and 7 are represented in southeast England by deposits with distinct mammalian assemblages in the lower Thames valley (Section 6.3), but almost no deposits with these assemblages are known in Hertfordshire. Consequently, although the various periglacial deposits (Roe Green Gravels at Hatfield, 'brickearth' at Slade Oak Lane and Hitchin, 'head' at Oughtonhead Lane and river gravels at Fisher's Green) overlying the Hoxnian sediments described in Section 6.7 are likely to date mainly from MIS 10, they could in theory have been deposited in a later cold stage, and may even be Devensian in part. Devensian periglacial deposits are certainly widespread throughout the county, so detailed descriptions of the various post-Hoxnian periglacial deposits are given in Section 6.10. Because of uncertain dating, possible Wolstonian fluvial gravels forming minor terraces in the lower Lea and Colne valleys are also described in Section 6.10.

The main effect of gelifluction and aeolian deposition in periglacial conditions was to smooth out previous irregularities in the landscape by infilling depressions, such as kettle holes and dolines, and eroding minor upstanding areas, such as moraines. Repetition of these processes in what must have been at least four long cold stages (MISs 10, 8, 6 and 4-2) after the Hoxnian Interglacial led to the gently undulating modern topography characteristic of interfluves in the Vale of St Albans (Gibbard, 1977) and many other parts of the county. However, a few features of the original Anglian glacial topography persist locally, especially in areas of glaciofluvial deposits, such as the hummocky kame-like morphology of parts of Codicote Heath (TL 2018) (Wooldridge, 1953).

As the rivers initiated in the Anglian would have continued to flow, at least seasonally, throughout most of each subsequent cold stage, sediment transported into their valleys by gelifluction or the wind did not accumulate there to any extent; most of it was probably evacuated downvalley and deposited ultimately on the floor of the North Sea. Consequently, even the valleys of Hertfordshire preserve only a weak and partial record of events since the Hoxnian. Widespread erosion of soil by gelifluction on interfluves in the glaciated areas of east Hertfordshire may also account for the almost complete absence there of soils showing interglacial pedogenic features (Sections 7.6 and 7.7).

Cryoturbation

Long periods of ground freezing (permafrost) during or after deposition of the deposits overlying the Hoxnian interglacial sediments are often indicated by cryoturbation (frost disturbance) structures. These have disturbed the original bedding in, for example, the fluvial flinty gravel and grey silty sand at Fishers Green and the Roe Green Gravel at Hatfield. As a result, originally horizontal lines of stones now hang in curves (festoons) between high points, and the long axes of many stones, originally lying horizontal, have been realigned close to vertical. Tighter folds, often resembling round- or flat-bottomed flasks (termed involutions), are also common. Comparison of similar structures seen in Anglian sediments in Essex and Suffolk with involutions formed recently in arctic Canada (Murton *et al.*, 1995) suggests that the cryoturbation structures developed by irregular loading during a period of thawing, which resulted from regional climatic warming after the permafrost episode. Consequently they may provide some evidence for climatic fluctuations during the Wolstonian, especially those indicated by the sequence of marine isotope stages.

Loess

The silty brickearth deposits at Hitchin and infilling dolines, such as those at Slade Oak Lane (Gibbard *et al.*, 1986) and various Chiltern sites (Caddington, Gaddesden Row, etc) described by Avery *et al.* (1982), often resemble loess in particle size distribution, but are mineralogically different from the Late Devensian loess (Section 6.10). They often show red mottles suggesting interglacial soil development, so the loess they contain was probably deposited originally during one or more of the Wolstonian cold stages (MIS 10, 8 or 6), and the brickearths were then subjected to subsequent interglacial pedogenesis during MIS 9, 7 or 5. The loess would originally have been deposited on surrounding land surfaces in a periglacial environment, but was then transported into the dolines by gelifluction or by stream activity during either periods of seasonal thaw or in an interglacial. Avery and Thomasson (1956) suggested that numerous large blocks of sarsenstone in a similar brickearth at Prestwood (SP 862014) in Buckinghamshire

were incorporated from the surrounding Plateau Drift by gelifluction. The red mottling probably occurred after doline infilling, as it is most common in the uppermost layers of brickearth.

More precise dating of these brickearths is difficult because the deposits are almost completely unfossiliferous, and their original mineralogical composition has been modified by weathering and incorporation of sediment derived from Palaeogene formations or Plateau Drift. However, at Caddington there is some palaeontological and archaeological evidence for doline infilling during MIS 7; as Caddington, Gaddesden Row and other sites became famous for large numbers of Palaeolithic flint artefacts found mainly in the brickearth, they are described in more detail in Section 8.2. In future, recently developed methods in thermoluminescence dating could usefully be applied to these brickearths when new sites are exposed.

The Marsworth site

One site that does provide some evidence of events during at least the later part of the Wolstonian 'Complex' in the Hertfordshire area is the extensive chalk pits at Pitstone or College Farm (SP 9314), which lies north of the mouth of the Tring Gap and 1-2 km east of Marsworth, Buckinghamshire. Deeper parts of the original pit (now flooded as part of BBOWT's College Lake Wildlife Centre) previously exposed Gault Clay and Lower Chalk, which were excavated for production of cement by Pitstone Tunnel Cement Ltd and later Castle Cement Ltd.

In this area the Lower Chalk forms an extensive bench at the foot of the Chiltern scarp-slope, with Quaternary deposits forming a thin cover over much of the bench. Most of these are chalky gelifluction deposits, often termed Coombe Deposits, which could date from any cold period during the Mid or Late Pleistocene. However, at Marsworth the Coombe Deposits lie between two fluvial channel sediments containing interglacial fossil assemblages (Green *et al.*, 1984; Murton *et al.*, 2001). When exposed by the quarrying, the lower channel, trending WNW-ESE was up to 35 m wide and incised 4-5 m into the Lower Chalk. Its infill consisted of gravelly calcareous sand locally overlain by organic mud. These deposits were overlain by up to 4 m of crudely bedded chalky muds and fine gravels, which extended beyond the channel margins and were interpreted as colluvial deposits washed into the river valley by soil movement in temperate climatic conditions. The colluvium was in turn covered by the Coombe Deposits, which were 2-3 m thick and extended over the whole site. Representing a cold periglacial episode, their upper part was extensively disturbed by involutions and locally by ice-wedge casts (Plate 52), both containing sand (possibly windblown) with a few chalk and flint pebbles. The upper channel, 8 m wide and trending N-S, truncated the involutions and contained finely stratified sandy gravels and calcareous marls, which were overlain by up to 0.6 m of a second colluvium, in which the modern (late Holocene) soil was developed.

The lower channel fill of MIS 7. These deposits contained

numerous transported fragments of tufa up to 1m across, which were presumably derived from nearby scarp-foot springs that were the source of water flowing in the channel. Attempts to date the tufa by both Green *et al.* (1984) and Murton *et al.* (2001) using the uranium series method, based on 230Th/234U ratios determined by α-spectrometry, resulted in a wide range of ages from 149 ka to 321 ka. Rather than indicating the actual age range of the tufa samples, these probably reflect diagenetic changes in the calcite crystals of the tufa or variable contamination with chalk debris or clay derived from contemporary soils. More recently, Candy and Schreve (2007) have obtained further uranium series dates from the tufa using the more precise analytical method known as multi-collector inductively coupled mass spectrometry (MC-ICP-MS). Their results for 13 tufa samples ranged from 208 ka to 254 ka, all but one of which lie within MIS 7 (189-244 ka). However, the dates obtained formed two separate groups, one corresponding to MISubstage 7c and the other to the earlier MISubstage 7e.

An MIS 7 age for the lower channel is also indicated by the abundant mammalian remains in it, which show a strong similarity to assemblages from MIS 7 sites in the Lower Thames Valley, such as Ilford, Aveley and Crayford (Section 6.3), and elsewhere in southern England, including Stanton Harcourt, Oxfordshire (Scott and Buckingham, 1997). The main species present were horse (*Equus ferus*), mammoth (*Mammuthus primigenius*) and northern vole (*Microtus oeconomus*), with less frequent straight-tusked elephant (*Palaeoloxodon antiquus*), narrow-nosed rhinoceros (*Stephanorhinus hemitoechus*), aurochs (*Bos primigenius*),

brown bear (*Ursus arctos*), fox (*Vulpes vulpes*), wolf (*Canis lupus*), water vole (*Arvicola terrestris cantiana*) and water shrew (*Neomys fodiens*). The assemblage closely matches that from the later (cooler) part of the MIS 7 interglacial sequence at Aveley (Section 6.3), i.e. the Sandy Lane Mammal Assemblage Biozone, so the sediments of the lower channel were probably deposited in the final temperate substage of MIS 7 (7a) and the dated tufa fragments beneath were derived from tufa originally precipitated in the earlier warm substages 7c and 7e (Candy and Schreve, 2007).

Coleoptera from the lower channel also indicated an MIS 7 rather than an MIS 5e age. Especially significant in this respect is the abundance of the staphylinid beetle *Oxytelus* (= *Anotylus*) *gibbulus*, which is also common at Stanton Harcourt (Briggs *et al.*, 1985), and today occurs only in the Caucasus Mountains (Hammond *et al.*, 1979). Pollen and plant macrofossils from the lower channel were derived partly from alkaline aquatic vegetation and wetlands surrounding the channel, but mainly indicated herb-rich calcareous grassland similar to that of the present Chiltern landscape, with little evidence for nearby trees or tall shrubs. Despite the absence of woodland, which could have resulted from grazing by the large mammals, the plant assemblage is definitely interglacial, indicating a climate similar to that of central England today. It is also similar to the herb-rich assemblages at Stanton Harcourt (Buckingham *et al.*, 1996) and other MIS 7 sites in southern England. The molluscan assemblages again indicate temperate conditions, with aquatic and marsh species giving way over time to scrub and grassland types. Bone fragments of a brown frog (*Rana* sp.)

Plate 52. Wolstonian Coombe Deposit with sand-filled involutions and ice-wedge cast, Marsworth (SP 936141).

Plate 53. Upper (Ipswichian) channel infill at Marsworth (SP 931145).

were reported from the lower channel deposits by Gleed-Owen (1998).

The upper channel of MIS 5e. The lower part of the sediment infill of the upper channel (Plate 53) contains a very different mammal fauna, which is typical of the Ipswichian Interglacial (MIS 5e) in England. It consists of hippopotamus (*Hippopotamus amphibius*), red deer (*Cervus elaphus*), fallow deer (*Dama dama*), giant deer (*Megaloceros giganteus*), bison (*Bison priscus*), narrow-nosed rhinoceros (*Stephanorhinus hemitoechus*), straight-tusked elephant (*Palaeoloxodon antiquus*) and water vole (*Arvicola terrestris cantiana*). Unfortunately, no other animal or plant fossils were found in the upper channel, and all evidence for it was destroyed during the later episodes of quarrying.

The dating of the two channels to MIS 7 and 5e indicates that the intervening coombe deposit accumulated in MIS 6 (Worsley, 1987). As the involutions in its upper part were truncated by the upper channel, they also formed in MIS 6. The only mammal remains found in the coombe deposit are bones of a small horse (*Equus ferus*), the reduced body size of which probably reflects the cold climate and poor food quality of the vegetation in MIS 6.

Evidence for glaciation. Between College Farm Pit and the cement works at Pitstone (SP 9315), a cutting for a conveyor belt exposed at one point (SP 931147) several layers, each less than 1 m thick, of dark reddish brown sandy clay

separated by thin impersistent layers of angular flint gravel containing a few quartzite and vein quartz pebbles. They were overlain and underlain by grey calcareous silty clays. Beds of flint gravel, also containing quartzite and quartz pebbles, separated the lower silty clay from frost-disturbed Lower Chalk bedrock beneath and also overlay the upper silty clay. Based on evidence for shearing, over-folding and other disturbance of the sequence, Whiteman (1998) interpreted the reddish-brown sandy clay layers as chalky till weathered during an interglacial, and the gravels as glacial outwash deposits. However, many of the structural features could have resulted from slope movement in a periglacial environment (i.e. gelifluction), and the far-travelled quartzose pebbles could have been river-transported from glacial deposits to the north and west. Unfortunately the relationship of this sequence to the two channels and the intervening Coombe Deposit could not be established, as they were separated by a ridge of Lower Chalk bedrock.

Marsworth lies a short distance south of the Anglian ice limit in the Vale of Aylesbury, as drawn by Horton *et al.* (1995, Fig. 24). But this limit may not be accurate. Avery (1964, p. 18) had earlier recorded thin patches of 'brown clay containing scattered sub-angular flints and quartzose pebbles, resembling weathered Chalky Boulder Clay' at SP 928148 (i.e. about 300 m northwest of the conveyor belt section) near the northern margin of the gently sloping platform that fans out north-westwards from Tring Station and terminates in bluffs overlooking the Vale of Aylesbury. Also the upper part of the Chalk scarp in Tring Park (SP

9210) on the southern side of Tring has been eroded back by about 500 m, to form a gently sloping bench cut in the middle part of the Middle Chalk. As there is no hard layer in this part of the Middle Chalk, the Tring Park bench probably originated by glacial erosion, as did the more extensive bench cut in the Lower Chalk northwest of Tring station and the similar Lower Chalk benches in areas northwest of Dunstable, Luton and Hitchin (Wooldridge and Smetham, 1931).

So it is likely that a glacier approached the mouth of the Tring Gap and covered at least the northern part of the Marsworth site. Almost certainly this would have occurred before formation of the lower channel in MIS 7, but there is some confusion over the exact timing of glaciation in the Vale of Aylesbury. Shephard-Thorn *et al.* (1994), Horton *et al.* (1995) and others have correlated it with the Anglian (MIS 12) glaciation of east Hertfordshire and the Vale of St Albans. But Sumbler (1995) assigned chalky till and glaciofluvial gravels near Aylesbury to MIS 10, because they are at the same height as the Blackditch Terrace of the River Thame, which correlates with the Wolvercote Terrace of the Upper Thames, and downstream extrapolation of the Wolvercote Terrace suggests correlation with the Lynch Hill Terrace deposited in MISs 10-8 (Westaway *et al.*, 2002, see Section 6.3). In addition, Keen (1999) has pointed out that the chalky Oadby Till of the east Midlands is nowhere overlain by Hoxnian (MIS 11) deposits. The oldest deposits demonstrably younger than the chalky till of the Midlands, at Biddenham in the Great Ouse valley west of Bedford (Harding *et al.*, 1992) and at Frog Hall, Stretton, Warwickshire (Keen *et al.*, 1997), seem to be MIS 9 in age.

Consequently, Clark *et al.* (2004) have suggested that, despite its lithological similarity to the chalky MIS 12 tills in the Vale of St Albans, east Hertfordshire and most of East Anglia, the chalky till in Buckinghamshire and areas further north in the east Midlands was deposited in MIS 10. In the west Midlands, two glacial deposits separated by Hoxnian deposits have been identified at Quinton (Horton, 1989) in the Birmingham area. Also, at Moreton-in-Marsh Sumbler (2001) has distinguished two glacial events dated to MIS 12 and 10, the latter depositing the chalky Oadby Till. Further work currently in progress on deposits exposed in the conveyor belt cutting at Marsworth should clarify whether there are glacial deposits here and also the timing of the glaciation in the Vale of Aylesbury.

6.9. The Ipswichian Interglacial

The beginning of the Ipswichian Interglacial Stage marks the lower limit of the Upper Pleistocene and is equivalent to the boundary between MIS 6 and MIS 5 in the oceanic sequence, which is dated to *c.* 128 ka BP. The end of the interglacial is dated to *c.* 117 ka BP, equivalent to the end of the warmest part of MIS 5 (i.e. MI Substage 5e).

Waterhall Farm. Apart from the upper channel at Marsworth, which lies a short distance outside Hertfordshire, deposits of the Ipswichian Interglacial have

been recorded at only one site within the county, a gravel pit at Waterhall Farm (TL 299099) in the Lea Valley a few kilometres upstream from Hertford. The valley is here incised into Upper Chalk through two Anglian deposits, about 11 m of till overlying 7-8 m of Westmill Lower Gravel (Gibbard, 1978b). The pit was used by Gibbard (1977) as the type site for his Anglian II ice advance, depositing the Eastend Green Till, but later analyses by Cheshire (1986a; see also Allen *et al.*, 1991) showed that the till here is in fact equivalent to the Ware Till. The sequence of interglacial deposits, previously exposed in a pit cut into a low terrace of the Lea included (in ascending order) a basal current-bedded gravel, a marl containing a few amphibian and rodent bones (Sutcliffe and Kowalski, 1976), a middle reddish-brown fluvial gravel with a rich fauna of large mammals (Gibbard, 1977) and a less fossiliferous bed of buff, horizontally bedded gravels. The reddish brown middle gravel yielded several hundred bones and teeth of hippopotamus (*Hippopotamus amphibius*), giant deer (*Megaloceras giganteus*), straight-tusked elephant (*Palaeoloxodon antiquus*), lion (*Panthera leo*), aurochs and/or bison (*Bos* sp. and/or *Bison* sp.) and spotted hyaena (*Crocuta crocuta*), an assemblage characteristic of the Ipswichian. The upper horizontally-bedded gravel contained a different assemblage of cold-tolerant mammals, including woolly mammoth (*Mammuthus primigenius*), woolly rhinoceros (*Coelodonta antiquitatus*) and horse (*Equus* sp.), and was probably deposited early in the subsequent Devensian cold stage. The rodent remains from the marl included three species, field vole (*Microtus agrestis*), northern vole (*Microtus oeconomus*) and snow vole (*Microtus nivalis*), suggesting treeless ground and a cold climate, so the deposit was probably late Wolstonian in age. Because of extensive quarrying and subsequent infill, the succession is no longer visible.

Other Ipswichian features. As elsewhere in Britain, vegetation dominated by a mixed oak forest would have developed in Hertfordshire during the Ipswichian, though there are no sites where pollen sequences can be used to establish a vegetation succession anywhere in the county. Beneath the forest cover, soils with characteristic interglacial features (reddish matrix colours or mottles and large accumulations of illuvial clay in subsoil horizons) would have developed on whatever pre-Ipswichian deposits occurred on the land surface. These paleo-argillic soils (Sections 7.5-7.7) remain widespread on the present land surface of the Chiltern plateau, the proto-Thames terraces and some Anglian gravels, though it is likely that some of their features are inherited from development in earlier (Mid Pleistocene) interglacials. In other parts of the county, notably in the Chiltern valleys, on the boulder clay plateau of east Hertfordshire and on the London Clay in southern parts of the county, the interglacial paleo-argillic soils are virtually absent, and must have been removed by periglacial erosion in the Devensian and possibly earlier cold stages.

Plate 54. Exposure of Spring Wood Silt (redeposited Devensian loess) at Bunker's Hill Pit (TL 2909) near Waterhall Farm in the Lea Valley near Hertford.

6.10. The Devensian Stage

The Devensian Stage, as defined by Mitchell *et al.* (1973), includes four of the five substages of MIS 5 (i.e. 5d-5a) and the three subsequent MISs (4-2). It is divided into three parts, the Early Devensian (MIS 5d-4, 115-60 ka BP), the Mid Devensian (MIS 3, 60-26 ka BP) and the Late Devensian (MIS 2, 26-11.7 ka BP). Almost all the extensive Devensian deposits in Britain resulted from a major glaciation and associated periglacial activity in the earlier part of MIS 2, which is known as the Dimlington Stadial (Rose, 1985). This episode coincided approximately with glaciation in many other parts of the world, and is consequently known worldwide as the Last Glacial Maximum or LGM. However, the British Dimlington Stadial glacier reached no further south than north Norfolk, the west Midlands and south Wales, so the LGM deposits in Hertfordshire are entirely periglacial in origin. The most extensive are aeolian silt (loess) and gelifluction (head) deposits, though some periglacial windblown sand (coversand) occurs in northeast Hertfordshire, and narrow strips of Late Devensian to early Holocene fluvial deposits occur in association with loess and head along the floors of most river valleys.

After the Dimlington Stadial, the climate was considerably warmer for 2500-3000 years between about 13,500 and 11,000 radiocarbon years BP (16,000-13,000 calendar years ago), after which there was a final very cold period of approximately 1500 years between 11,000 and 10,000 radiocarbon years BP (13,000-11,500 calendar years ago).

The warm period is known in Britain as the Lateglacial or Windermere Interstadial, as it was first defined in sediments from the floor of Lake Windermere. The succeeding cold period is termed the Loch Lomond Stadial, as it resulted in the development of an ice cap near Loch Lomond in western Scotland and small cirque glaciers in the mountains of Wales, the Lake District and the Pennines.

Loess

At Waterhall Farm the Devensian gravel containing remains of mammoth, woolly rhinoceros and horse was overlain by a silty deposit, which Gibbard (1977) named the Spring Wood Silt (Plate 54). He reported similar silty deposits in other river valleys within the Vale of St Albans and, because they often contain thin layers of sand and gravel, suggested that they consist mainly of loess (periglacial windblown silt) redeposited by the rivers. Their association with the Ipswichian gravels as part of the valley-fill sequence at Waterhall Farm led to the suggestion that they accumulated in the Early Devensian (Gibbard, 1977, p. 475), but there is no direct evidence for age. The Lea and other Hertfordshire rivers probably continued to flow, albeit intermittently, throughout most of the Devensian Stage and into the Holocene, and subsequent thermoluminescence dating of the somewhat similar Langley Silt Complex of the Thames Valley (Gibbard *et al.*, 1987, see Section 6.3) indicates that a Late Devensian or even early Holocene age is perhaps more likely for the Spring Wood Silt.

A few loess deposits in southern England have been dated by thermoluminescence methods to the Early and Mid Devensian (Parks and Rendell, 1992), but they are the exception. At almost all sites where loess forming the present land surface has been dated, it accumulated in the Dimlington Stadial (Wintle, 1981; Parks and Rendell, 1992). In eastern England this age is supported by its mineralogical similarity to the coarse silt fraction of Devensian till in east Yorkshire and Lincolnshire (Catt *et al.*, 1974), which has been radiocarbon dated to the later part of the Dimlington Stadial (Penny *et al.*, 1969). The mineralogical similarity also suggests that the loess was derived by wind erosion of the glaciofluvial (outwash) deposits that were probably spread extensively on the exposed floor of the southern North Sea basin when sea level was lowered eustatically during the LGM.

The distribution of Late Devensian loess throughout England and Wales was shown by Catt (1985, Fig. 10.1), based on the 1:250,000 soil maps published by Soil Survey and England and Wales (1983). It covers about 13% of England and Wales, but over 12.7% of the country it is less than 1 m thick. It occurs almost continuously on outcrops of the Chalk and other limestones, on Plateau Drift, river terrace and glaciofluvial gravels, granites, ultrabasic rocks and some pre-Devensian tills, and forms less continuous patches on outcrops of Mesozoic and Caenozoic clay formations. Loess deposits more than 1 m thick cover only 0.4% of the country, occurring mainly in north Kent, the Thames Valley (the Langley Silt Complex) and the coastal plain of west Sussex and southeast Hampshire. In Hertfordshire the thicker deposits, up to 6 m thick according to Sherlock and Pocock (1924, pp. 50-51), are extensive only in the lower Lea valley, where they are shown as 'brickearth' on the BGS Hertford Sheet (239). Here they overlie glaciofluvial gravels or fluvial gravels of the River Lea, which form terraces equivalent to the Taplow and Flood Plain Terraces of the Thames. Smaller patches of thick loess, not usually mapped by BGS, also occur in higher parts of the Lea valley between Wheathampstead and Hertford, in the Gade and Ver valleys, in the Vale of St Albans between Bricket Wood, St Albans, London Colney, Hatfield and Wheathampstead, and over Plateau Drift on higher parts of the Chiltern dip-slope. Figure 6.20 shows the distribution of these and also of thinner loess deposits in Hertfordshire.

As it was deposited by the wind, loess would almost certainly have formed an original layer of much more uniform thickness over Hertfordshire and most of southeast England. Locally thick accumulations could have arisen by original aeolian deposition in situations, such as valleys or the leeside of hills, where the wind speed slackened. But the absence of the deposit over some large areas, notably the outcrops of the London Clay Formation in south Hertfordshire and the Anglian tills in east Hertfordshire, suggests that it has been extensively reworked (eroded and redeposited) during or since the Late Devensian. Reworking could have occurred by mass movement on slopes (gelifluction) in periglacial conditions or by runoff at times when there was little or no vegetation to stabilize the soil surface. Some gelifluction of loess is certainly indicated by streaks and lenticular masses within many of the gelifluction deposits, as described below. However, erosion by runoff was also important in both the Holocene and Late Devensian, and this probably accounts for its absence or very localized distribution on clay formations, which would have had a greater drainage density than more permeable substrates.

Loess is very susceptible to water erosion, as it has a porous structure in which the silt particles are propped apart by narrow clay bridges that are easily broken down when the deposit is saturated; also, the silt particles, once dispersed, can be transported even by very gentle overland flow. Thick accumulations of redeposited loess on lower valley slopes often resulted from water erosion in the mid-Holocene, when the soil surface was exposed by cultivation for primitive farming in the Neolithic, Bronze and Iron Ages. Known as colluvium, hillwash or ploughwash, these accumulations are distinguished from other forms of reworked loess by the presence of charcoal fragments (resulting from land clearance by burning), by an irregular vertical distribution of finely divided organic matter derived from soils upslope, and by the occasional occurrence of human artefacts, such as worked flints or fragments of crude pottery. But during the Late Devensian also, a sparse cover of natural vegetation could have led to water erosion of loess when the climate was slightly warmer than usual, for example in periods of summer thaw or during the Late Devensian Windermere Interstadial. The torrential flow of nival streams charged with large volumes of water from melting snow and shallow ground ice would probably have carried most of the loess reworked in the Late Devensian to areas outside the county, possibly even into the North Sea basin. But during the Holocene, when stream discharge was much less, any eroded loess reaching the valley floors (because it was not redeposited as footslope colluvium) was incorporated into alluvial deposits (Section 6.11).

When unweathered, loess is pale yellowish brown in colour and contains up to about 15% finely divided calcium carbonate, which is probably derived either from limestone fragments crushed during glacial transportation or from frost-shattering and wind erosion of exposed limestone surfaces. In England, the finely divided carbonate is probably derived mainly from chalk, which is both susceptible to frost shattering and easily crushed by a glacier. However, this carbonate component is subject to considerable reorganization by dissolution and localized redeposition, to create a range of hard carbonate concretions. Some of these are oblate, flattened horizontally, and up to 5 cm across. Occasionally several of this type are joined at their edges to create a multiple concretion faintly resembling a human body, and consequently known as a 'loess-doll'. A second type, more common in the loess of Hertfordshire, consists of short cylindrical concretions a few millimetres across, which lie subvertically and often divide downwards like plant roots. Known as rhizoliths, they are thought to have formed around the decomposing roots of grasses and perhaps other plants, which were growing in the loess and became buried as it accumulated. Calcareous loess also contains the shells of land molluscs, notably the small gastropod *Pupilla muscorum*, which were able to survive in the cold and often dry climate of the Dimlington Stadial.

The main effect of Holocene soil development in loess forming the present land surface was to remove the various forms of carbonate by dissolution in percolating water containing dissolved carbon dioxide and other acids created in the soil. In well-drained situations, there has also been some oxidative weathering of iron-containing minerals, which has resulted in a darker brown colour. Consequently, the loess deposits thinner than 70-100 cm are usually brown and carbonate-free throughout. There is also widespread evidence for mixing with subjacent deposits, such as Plateau Drift, either by cryoturbation in the Late Devensian or by deep soil disturbance processes (e.g. earthworm activity or tree-fall) in the Holocene. Cryoturbation may also account for the widespread presence of angular (frost-shattered?) flint fragments and other stones in the thinner loess deposits.

Coversand

During the Late Devensian, and possibly also in the Mid and Early Devensian, the wind eroded sand from earlier sandy deposits and redeposited it as the sediment known as coversand. As sand particles are bigger and heavier than silt, they are transported much shorter distances, usually by the process known as saltation, i.e. in repeated jumps of a few metres or tens of metres at a time. This contrasts with loess, the silt particles of which are carried in semi-permanent suspension for distances of tens or even hundreds of kilometres.

The main evidence for coversand in Hertfordshire is in the soils on the Chalk in north-eastern parts of the county (Fig. 6.20), which are richer in sand than the essentially silty (loess-containing) chalkland soils further southwest. The coversand here averages less than 1 m in thickness, and derivation from the Lower Greensand a few kilometres to the north or from nearby glaciofluvial and river terrace deposits

is likely. Its exact age is unknown, though its widespread occurrence at various levels on the present land surface, association with frost-shattered chalk and disturbance by characteristic frost structures together suggest that it is Late Devensian. Also, in parts of East Anglia, notably the Breckland, there are similar though thicker coversands, which have been dated at Grimes Graves (Norfolk) by thermoluminescence methods to 14.6-13.4 ka (Bateman, 1995). The soils derived from coversand over chalk in northeast Hertfordshire are described in detail in Section 7.7.

The frost structures affecting the coversand are of three main types. The first are involutions and irregular cryoturbations similar to those affecting the MIS 6 Coombe Deposit at Marsworth (Section 6.8) and Wolstonian deposits elsewhere. The second, known as ice-wedge polygons, occur on flat or very gently sloping land surfaces. They consist of a repeating polygonal pattern of wedge-shaped cracks, which penetrate a thin superficial layer of frost-shattered chalk (Coombe Deposit) overlying less disturbed chalk bedrock, and are usually filled with sand. The wedges are 1-2 m deep and 1-3 m wide at the surface, and the polygons are usually 10-20 m across. The polygons originated during periods of severe frost as contraction cracks in the chalk, which were gradually widened by repeated freezing and thawing of water entering them, then filled with windblown sand. The third type consists of alternating stripes of sand and chalk, each several metres wide, which extend down the sides of valleys incised into the flatter surfaces that carry the polygons. The stripes probably originated from polygons that were stretched by mass movement (gelifluction) down the valley sides. As they give rise to soils with very different chemical and physical characteristics, the polygons and stripes often stand out in aerial photographs as crop or semi-natural vegetation patterns (Plate 55). Crop patterns originating in this way are most clearly seen during periods of summer drought, when growth is restricted by shortage of water in the sand-filled polygons and less restricted where chalk is within rooting depth.

Gelifluction or head deposits

In periglacial regions, such as Hertfordshire during the Late Devensian, very low mean annual temperatures for prolonged periods led to freezing of the ground to depths of many metres. However, in warm summer seasons, the air temperature was often high enough to thaw the surface to depths of approximately 1 m. Because it was underlain by still frozen subsurface material or permafrost, in which most of the pores and fissures were filled with ground ice, making it impermeable, the thawed layer became saturated with liquid water and was consequently likely to flow down even very gentle slopes. In present-day periglacial regions,

Plate 55. Aerial view of crop patterns in sugar beet resulting from irregular growth over sand-filled polygons and stripes over Chalk, Brooms Barn Farm, Suffolk.

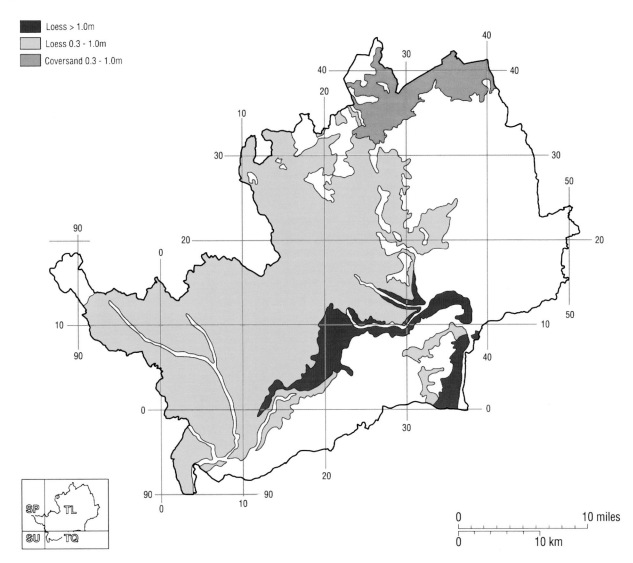

- ■ Loess > 1.0m
- ▢ Loess 0.3 - 1.0m
- ▨ Coversand 0.3 - 1.0m

0   10 miles

0   10 km

Fig. 6.20. Distribution of loess and coversand in Hertfordshire.

such as Siberia and northern Canada, this mobile layer is termed the active layer. Downslope movement of the active layer *en masse* over permanently frozen subsurface layers, a process termed gelifluction, led to accumulation of unsorted, unstratified or crudely stratified, gelifluction or head deposits on footslopes and valley floors. These deposits are very variable in composition, as they were derived from whatever bedrock, unconsolidated sediment or soil material existed upslope.

Coombe Deposits. The commonest gelifluction deposits in Hertfordshire are those characteristic of the Chiltern chalkland valleys and scarp footslope sites, which are now known as Coombe Deposits or Coombe Rock (Plate 52). On early BGS maps they were often shown as Valley Gravel, though this would have included the Late Devensian fluvial gravels discussed below. They are composed principally of frost-shattered chalk fragments. Chalk is very susceptible to frost-shattering (gelifraction), because the small matrix pores retain large amounts of water against gravity, so that when the rock freezes ice crystals form in the pores, expand and thus break the rather soft rock into small

fragments. Because of the abundance of chalk fragments, Coombe Deposits are usually pale coloured, sometimes almost white, but may also contain flint fragments and streaks and lenticular masses of more strongly coloured sediment and soil material. Loess is a common constituent, either dispersed among the frost-shattered chalk or as discrete layers, which are often contorted by the downslope movement and must have been derived from primary loess accumulations upslope. Near the heads of many of the dry Chiltern valleys, the chalky Coombe Deposits pass laterally into coarse brown flinty gravels with a variable clay content and little or no carbonate, which are probably derived mainly from Plateau Drift and Clay-with-flints *sensu stricto*. The Coombe Deposits vary greatly in thickness, and may include pre-Ipswichian deposits (as at Marsworth) as well as Devensian. Avery (1964, p. 21) recorded at least 5 m of flinty gravels in the Harpenden Valley near Kinsbourne Green (TL 1116), and similar values are commonly given as the maximum thickness in other areas (Sherlock, 1922, p. 52; Hopson *et al.*, 1996, p. 109). Evans and Oakley (1952) recorded Coombe Rock at Folly Farm (SP 941141) with an overlying layer of brown chalky clay penetrating festoons in its upper surface. In many valleys, there has been minor stream incision since the deposition of Coombe Rock, so that it often forms low rudimentary terraces up to 2 m above the lowest parts of the valley floor. The upper layers of Coombe Deposits have also been decalcified, leaving a surface residue of brown, clayey or silty flint gravel with an irregular, sometimes deeply piped, lower boundary with unaltered chalky material beneath.

Near the foot of the Chiltern scarp near Tring, thin Coombe Deposits resting on the West Melbury Marly Chalk Formation are progressively replaced at lower levels on outcrops of the Upper Greensand and Gault Clay Formations by fans of crudely stratified gravel composed of angular flint fragments and subrounded waterworn chalk pebbles in a variable sandy or clayey matrix. At a site near Gubblecote (SP 9015), Oakley (1936) attributed the gravel to the combined agencies of late glacial gelifluction and melting snow, and Avery (1964, p. 21) suggested that the sand component is aeolian in origin (i.e. coversand similar to that associated with the Coombe Deposits of northeast Hertfordshire). Spreads of similar deposits occur between Totternhoe and Eaton Bray in Bedfordshire (Shephard-Thorn *et al*, 1994, p. 90), and Hopson *et al.* (1966, pp. 109-110) noted a similar relationship between Coombe Deposits and alluvial fan deposits up to 4 m thick below the Chalk escarpment near Baldock and Letchworth. In the latter area both deposits contain quartz and quartzite pebbles and occasionally also other erratics derived from till or glaciofluvial gravels upslope. On older BGS maps of Cambridgeshire and Bedfordshire, extensive accumulations of similar deposits were shown as 'tjaele gravels' (White and Edmunds, 1932), though Edmonds and Dinham (1965) suggested that various glaciofluvial and river terrace deposits were also included in this term, and its use has been discontinued by BGS.

Clayey gelifluction deposits. Other gelifluction (head) deposits within the county originated as clay-rich mudflows, because they are derived mainly from clay formations. They are usually 2-5 m thick and occur in three main areas. First, on the Gault Clay outcrop between Long Marston (SP 8915) and Puttenham (SP 8814), thin superficial patches of grey clay containing occasional flint and chalk fragments may represent a westward extension of the gravelly head seen between Gubblecote and the Chiltern scarp. Similar grey flinty clays are also extensive on the Gault Clay outcrop east of Toddington, around Hockliffe and southwest of Linslade. Second, in east Hertfordshire, clayey gelifluction deposits derived mainly from Anglian till overlie Chalk of the Lewes and Seaford Formations, which crop out on the lower slopes of the Rib, Quin, Ash, Stort and upper Beane valleys. Millward *et al.* (1987, p. 57) described a section at Olives Farm (TL 405126) between Stanstead Abbotts and Hunsdon exposing 2.6 m of clayey and gravelly head derived from till. Sandy and gravelly head derived from glaciofluvial deposits also occurs locally in eastern parts of the county. Third, on the lower slopes of valleys cut into the London Clay Formation in southwest Hertfordshire, there are slightly sandy and pebbly but otherwise clay-rich head deposits, which are thought to be derived mainly from the London Clay but with minor additions from patches of Pebble Gravel on the interfluves. Where pebbles and other coarse material are absent, this type of clay-rich head is difficult to distinguish from weathered *in situ* London Clay, though in excavations a slip plane between the two can sometimes be identified by downslope striations on the London Clay surface or water seeping from the junction between the two deposits.

Buried soils

Most of the Devensian deposits in Hertfordshire provide no evidence for climatic change over this fairly long period, though elsewhere in Britain there is sedimentological and palaeontological evidence for a complex sequence of minor changes, culminating in the Windermere Interstadial and Loch Lomond Stadial towards the close of the Devensian. However, the Coombe Deposits occurring within some of the Chiltern scarp-slope dry valleys contain buried thin humic soils (rendzinas), and studies of terrestrial gastropods (land snails) from the soils and the slope deposits above and below them have provided evidence for a history of environmental change for the Chiltern area during and since the Late Devensian.

The first of these buried soils to be discovered were in the superficial deposits of Pegsdon Valley (TL 1129) near Hexton (Sparks and Lewis, 1957) and a small coombe (SP 948146) subsequently destroyed by excavation of the Icknield Way Chalk Quarry on the north-western side of Pitstone Hill (Brown, 1964). Later, other buried soils in coombes of the Pitstone area were investigated by Evans (1966). In samples from a section in a coombe adjacent to Brook's Statnalls Wood (SP 947149), which was partly lost to later expansion of Pitstone chalk quarry, Evans (1966) identified infrequent shells of the molluscs *Pupilla muscorum, Vitrina pellucida, Vallonia costata, Vallonia pulchella, Punctum pygmaeum, Retinella radiatula, Helicella itala* and *Euconulus fulvus* and internal plates of Limacidae (slugs) in the uppermost part of the Coombe Deposit attributed to the Dimlington Stadial. In the overlying buried soil, attributed to the Windermere Interstadial (then described as the Allerød Interstadial), the same land snails increased greatly in abundance and were accompanied by four new species, *Hygromia hispida, Catinella arenaria, Cochlicopa lubricella* and *Cochlicopa lubrica*. The assemblage as a whole indicates a sparse open vegetation. The soil consisted of a 2.5 cm-thick black (10YR 2/1) humic horizon with numerous charcoal fragments over a less humic light grey (10YR 7/1) chalk mud; brown iron staining resulting from seasonal waterlogging during development of the soil extended down into the uppermost 20 cm of the Coombe Rock. In places the soil consisted of two distinct humic horizons with separate peaks in molluscan abundance, suggesting a warm-cool-warm climatic oscillation within the Windermere Interstadial. At this site the soil was buried by a bedded chalk and flint gravel up to 2 m thick and yielding a very sparse mollusc fauna consisting only of *Pupilla muscorum, Vallonia costata* and *Punctum pygmaeum*.

Plate 56. Ver valley near Redbournbury (TL 123094) in winter, showing naleds (depressions created by deposition of gravel around masses of surface ice on the valley floor in the Late Devensian).

This deposit was interpreted as the head deposit of the Loch Lomond Stadial. It was overlain by up to 2 m of light brownish grey (10YR 6/2) humic chalk mud, at the base of which were sherds of Iron Age pottery. Evans (1966) described this deposit, which contained a rich land snail fauna indicative of dry open grassland, as late Holocene ploughwash or colluvium.

Fluvial deposits

Although the Late Devensian winters were so cold that the ground throughout the county was frozen from the surface downwards for many metres, surface thawing in most summers produced sufficient meltwater that streams would have flowed temporarily in many valleys, including those of chalkland areas that are now dry. The meltwater streams were able to flow over the surface because the chalk was still frozen beneath the thawed upper layer, so that ground-ice filled most of the pores and fissures, making the Chalk impermeable. The main sediments deposited by such streams were valley gravels derived principally from gelifluction deposits on the valley floors. As a result they can be difficult to distinguish from the gelifluction deposits, especially as fossils characteristic of either environment are unknown. In higher parts of the Chiltern valleys, the valley gravels are composed mainly of angular chalk and flint fragments, often with some Palaeogene flint pebbles. Sherlock (1922, Plate I) provided a photograph of an

exposure of such gravels in the Wendover Gap, from which remains of mammoth were recorded (Sherlock, 1922, p. 52). Many of the stones in this exposure were aligned vertically, suggesting post-depositional disturbance in periglacial conditions. Elsewhere the gravels consist mainly of the stones and coarser sand components from the local head deposits, whose finer particles (fine sand, silt and clay) were probably removed downstream by nival floods. For example, where the lower Gade valley cuts through older terrace deposits of the proto-Thames below Kings Langley, the valley gravels contain quartzite pebbles (Sherlock, 1922, p. 49), which were probably derived by gelifluction from the terrace gravels exposed on the upper valley sides. Locally the fluvial valley gravels are irregularly interbedded with layers of typical unsorted head, which was probably deposited at times between the fluvial episodes.

The mixed gelifluction deposits and fluvial gravels are almost always overlain by much less stony loams containing abundant freshwater molluscs and other fossils or by thin peat beds indicating deposition in the warmer conditions of the Holocene. Sequences of this type were described in the early 20th century from temporary exposures in the Colne valley at Watford (TQ 117957) (Lones, 1904) and the Gade valley between Hunton Bridge (TL 0800) and Kings Langley Station (TL 080020) (Lones, 1905). There must also have been numerous other exposures, as the valley floors have been extensively disturbed by gravel workings or by urban and industrial development, but few geological descriptions have been published other than the general accounts in the earlier British Geological Survey memoirs (Sherlock, 1922; Sherlock and Noble, 1922; Sherlock and Pocock, 1924). Some chalkland valley floors were also disturbed by construction of watercress beds or, in the Bulbourne and lower Gade valleys, by digging of the Grand Union Canal. In the earlier BGS publications for Hertfordshire, the fluvial gravels were often interpreted as a lower part of the Holocene alluvium. But it is unlikely that the gentle flow regime of Hertfordshire rivers during the early Holocene would have resulted in such coarse deposits.

Naleds. At several grassland (i.e. unploughed) sites in the Chiltern valleys, such as the Gade valley near Boxmoor (TL 037060) and the Ver valley near Shafford Farm (TL 122097), there are irregularly shaped enclosed hollows in the surface of the fluvial gravels (Plate 56). The hollows often contain thin (<3 m) accumulations of Holocene peat and lacustrine muds, and in prolonged periods of wet weather may be temporarily water-filled today. They probably originated under periglacial conditions in the Late Devensian where extensive masses of ice formed on valley floors when groundwater emerged as springs from thawed layers (taliks) in the permanently frozen Chalk. Similar accumulations of surface ice, known as icings, naleds or aufeis, occur today on valley floors in many arctic regions, such as northern Canada. Gravel would have been deposited around them during periods of river flow and, when the ice masses melted because of climatic change during or at the end of the Late Devensian, their former positions were marked by wet depressions in which the peat and muds have since accumulated. Similar fossil naleds may originally have been a common feature of Chiltern valleys, but on cultivated land they have probably been erased by repeated ploughing. Those at Moorend Farm Meadows (Boxmoor), which are preserved in long established grassland owned by the Boxmoor Trust, are a designated RIGS (Hertfordshire RIGS Group, 2003).

Devensian river terraces. Some of the fluvial gravels in Hertfordshire valleys form recognizable terraces. For example, in the Stort and Ash valleys they form two fairly distinct terraces, at 1-2 m and 3-4.5 m above the modern floodplain. The ages of these terraces are uncertain, though they probably date from the Devensian and Wolstonian cold stages. In the lower Lea valley two distinct gravel terraces were identified by Sherlock and Pocock (1924, p. 49) on the west bank below Great Amwell. The upper terrace, reaching a height of 54 m OD northwest of Great Amwell (TL 3711) (Fig. 6.8), was thought to correspond with the Taplow Terrace (MISs 8-6) of the Thames. The lower terrace, correlated with the then undifferentiated Flood Plain Terrace of the Thames (MISs 4-2), was traced upstream from Waltham Cross (TL 3500) through Cheshunt (TL 3603), southern parts of Ware (TL 3514) and northern Hertford (TL 3313) as far as Bayfordbury (TL 3111) and also into the tributary Mimram Valley as far as Hertingfordbury (TL 3012). Downstream from Waltham Cross on the North London geological sheet (British Geological Survey, 1993),

the lower terrace was correlated with the Kempton Park Gravel (MIS 4-3), and areas of it in Hertfordshire are shown as such in Fig. 6.8. According to Sherlock and Pocock (1924, pp. 50-51), the Taplow Gravel is up to 7 m thick and the Flood Plain (Kempton Park) Gravel 4-5 m thick. Both are overlain by several metres of brickearth (loess). However, if the lower Lea originated by diversion of the proto-Thames from the Mid-Essex Depression during the Anglian Stage (Section 6.6), it is surprising that no post-Anglian record older than the Taplow Terrace has been recognized anywhere in the valley. In particular there are no known equivalents of the Boyn Hill and Lynch Hill Gravels.

River terraces that can be correlated with those of the Thames on the basis of height have also been recognized in the Colne Valley beyond the county boundary south of Rickmansworth. In this area the gravels of four weakly expressed terraces younger than the late Anglian Smug Oak Gravel (equivalent to the Black Park Gravel of Thames) were recognized by Gibbard (1994), and have been described as separate members of the Colne Formation (Gibbard, 1999, p. 53). The oldest, thought to be the lateral equivalent of the Boyn Hill Gravel, is the Broom Warren Gravel, which was previously exposed in excavations for the M25 1 km south of Junction 16 (TQ 024845) near Iver Heath, Buckinghamshire. The Gould's Green Gravel, probably equivalent to the Lynch Hill Gravel of the Thames, was previously exposed about 1 km west of Hayes (TQ 082808) in Middlesex, and an extensive area of the Denham Village Gravel, equated with the Taplow Gravel (Fig. 6.8), was previously exposed near Denham (TQ 041863), Buckinghamshire (see cover photo). Finally, the Horton Close Gravel, Sand and Silt, probably of Ipswichian age, was recorded 1 km east of Yiewsley (TQ 070802), Middlesex. The post-Anglian sequence of the Colne is therefore more complete than that of the lower Lea.

Peat. Beds of peat and black organic clay within the Flood Plain (Kempton Park) Gravel are known from several sites in the lower Lea Valley. They were first recorded by Warren (1912, 1916, 1923) at Ponders End (TQ 3595), but have since been recognized also at Broxbourne (TL 3707) and Stratford (TQ 387828) (Allison *et al.*, 1952) and at Deepham's Sewerage Works (TQ 357936) near Pickett's Lock (Hayward, 1956). On the BGS Hertford Sheet (239), they are also shown on the western side of the Lea valley at Cheshunt (TL 3501, and between TL 366012 and TL 366035). Because of the remains of arctic herbs, grasses, sedges, mosses and dwarf species of birch (*Betula nana*) and willow (*Salix herbacea*), the deposit has become known as the Lea Valley Arctic Plant Bed (Reid, 1949; Godwin, 1956). It has also yielded molluscs indicating a cold climate, such as *Pupilla muscorum* and *Columella columella*, and bones of cold tolerant mammals, including mammoth (*Mammuthus primigenius*), woolly rhinoceros (*Coelodonta antiquitatus*), reindeer (*Rangifer tarandus*), elk (*Alces machlis*), horse (*Equus* sp.), wild boar (*Sus scrofa*) and Norway lemming (*Lemmus lemmus*). Remains of some of these mammals have also been found in the overlying brickearth (Warren, 1912, p. 228). At Deepham's Sewerage Works, Coope and Tallon (1983) recorded an impoverished insect assemblage similar to the present insect fauna of the open tundra in parts of arctic Russia. Wells drilled at Cheshunt showed that the plant bed is there at least 6 m thick (Sherlock and Pocock, 1924, p. 51). Uncalibrated radiocarbon dates for the deposit range from 21,580 ± 480 (Coope and Tallon, 1983) to 28,000 ± 1500BP (Godwin, 1956), suggesting correlation with either the youngest part of the Kempton Park Gravel or the oldest part of the Lower Floodplain Terrace (Shepperton Gravel) of MIS 2, though some of the dates may not be accurate.

In the uppermost part of the Colne valley at Colney Heath (TL 197059), organic deposits similar to the Lea Valley Arctic Plant Bed were studied by Pearson (1962) and Godwin (1964). Here they occurred as disturbed blocks within fluvial sands that rested on an irregular surface of chalky till, probably Ware Till, and were covered by a thin bed of Holocene alluvium deposited by the Colne. The blocks were probably eroded from a peat originally situated upstream, and were transported in a frozen condition and deposited within the Late Devensian fluvial sands. The blocks contained arctic beetles and pollen and macroscopic remains of marsh plants, such as *Filipendula ulmaria*, *Valeriana officinalis* and *Caltha palustris*, and of shrubs and herbs of drier ground, including juniper (*Juniperus communis*), willow (*Salix herabacea*), mugwort (*Artemisia*), *Armeria*, *Helianthemum*, *Alchemilla*, *Plantago*, *Jasione*, *Scleranthus*, *Sanguisorba*, *Geranium* and *Polemonium*. Fragments of willow and juniper wood gave a radiocarbon date of 13,560 ± 210 BP (*c*. 16,860 calendar years), i.e. late in the Dimlington Stadial.

Scour hollows. Another group of features, thought to have originated in periglacial conditions during the Late Devensian or earlier cold stages, are known as scour hollows (Berry, 1979). These occur where the Kempton Park and Shepperton terrace gravels overlie London Clay in the Thames, lower Lea, Ravensbourne and Roding valleys. In central London, they have been encountered in tunnels and other engineering works since the mid 19th century. The hollows are oval in plan, 20-150 m wide and up to 1 km long. They have steep, sometimes almost vertical sides, and are often very deep (up to 33 m), occasionally penetrating considerable thicknesses of basal London Clay to reach older Palaeogene formations (usually Woolwich and Reading Formations) beneath. As they are often filled with the terrace gravel, they are very permeable, certainly in contrast to the surrounding London Clay, and therefore can conduct groundwater into the sandy Palaeogene deposits, which in turn are often in hydrological continuity with the Chalk aquifer beneath. Some contain alluvial deposits with Ipswichian pollen sequences, and therefore originated before this interglacial.

Berry (1979) proposed that the hollows were eroded by water scouring the river bed at the beginning of an interglacial or interstadial, when river flow was greatly increased by summer meltwater from snow and ice fields. However, Hutchinson (1980) noted that the Woolwich and Reading Formations have risen diapirically by 6-12 m into the base of some hollows, and suggested an alternative

origin involving the formation of open-system pingos. These are lenticular masses of ground ice formed below the ground surface within the permafrost by freezing of groundwater injected upwards from the aquifer through cracks in the London Clay. De Freitas (2009) has suggested that fault planes could have provided pathways of this type. On thawing, the pingo collapsed and scour occurred where the gravel and London Clay had been disturbed and weakened. The upper parts are therefore scour hollows, as Berry (1979) suggested, but their lower parts are often the eroded roots of pingos. Later, Hutchinson (1991) recognized five types of hollow: (a) simple scour hollows with no hydraulic connection with the aquifer; (b) scour hollows with incipient uplift and cracking of London Clay; (c) scour hollows over a diapir of disturbed London Clay; (d) scour hollows over a diapir involving also Woolwich and Reading Beds; and (e) subsidence hollows resulting from subsurface dissolution of Chalk. Types and c and d have considerable significance for groundwater movement (Section 9.2).

The origin of Chiltern dry valleys

As elsewhere on the Chalk outcrop of England, two main types of dry valley can be distinguished in the Chilterns. Most of those dissecting the dip-slope are long and meandering (Fig. 5.6), 0.2-1.0 km wide, with gently to moderately sloping sides (up to 15°) and heads that terminate gradually at various levels on the plateau surface (Section 5.6); some have heads very close to the scarp crest. In contrast, those of the scarp-slope southwest of Hitchin are shorter and narrower, have notably steeper sides (up to 30°) and steep (10-20°), abrupt heads close to the scarp crest. Most of the scarp-face valleys are straight, though a few show sharp (near 90°) bends. Flat floors are a common, though not ubiquitous, feature in both types, and many have short tributary coombes or gullies. As Lewis (1949) and Sparks and Lewis (1957) demonstrated for the scarp-face dry valleys at Pegsdon (TL 1129), Hexton (the Ravensburgh Valley, TL 1029) and Barton (TL 0829), a few kilometres west of Hitchin, the flat floors can be attributed to partial infill with Late Devensian coombe deposits and Holocene colluvium (Section 6.11), though the flatness has often been accentuated by late Holocene soil cultivation. The Chalk bedrock surface beneath is actually V- or U-shaped, suggesting previous development by fluvial erosion. The Ravensburgh Valley and adjacent parts of the Chalk scarp were designated a RIGS by Hertfordshire RIGS Group (2003).

As suggested in Section 5.6, the fluvial erosion resulting in the trellised and dendritic pattern of long dip-slope dry valleys probably started when the Chalk water table was much closer to the surface because relative sea level was higher prior to the progressive tectonic uplift of southeast England during the Quaternary. Chandler (1909) and Fagg (1923) proposed other reasons why the Chalk water table may have been somewhat higher in the past. But their suggested mechanisms would not have raised the water table sufficiently to initiate downcutting close to the plateau (exhumed Sub-Palaeogene) surface, even where this is lower

Plate 57. Typical asymmetric Chiltern valley – the Gade Valley near Hudnall, looking north-westwards; steeper south-west facing slope to right.

in south-eastern parts of the Chilterns.

Many of the dip-slope valleys have asymmetrical cross sections, the S-, SW- and W-facing sides being noticeably steeper than those facing N, NE or E (Plate 57), and this has been interpreted as a result of differential erosion in periglacial conditions during cold stages of the Pleistocene (Ollier and Thomasson, 1957; French, 1972). As the emerging Chiltern landscape was uplifted to heights well above sea level, the decline in water table level would eventually have resulted in desiccation of the dip-slope valley system, at least in the warm climate of interglacial stages. However, during cold stages of the Pleistocene, the presence of permafrost made the Chalk less permeable at the surface, so that a nival surface drainage network independent of the groundwater table was re-established periodically. During periods of summer thaw in this periglacial environment, the active layer would have developed more readily on the valley sides facing S, SW or W, as these were subject to more frequent changes of temperature (freeze-thaw cycles) because they received greater insolation than the shadier and more permanently frozen N-, NE- and E-facing slopes (Fig. 6.21). The gelifluction deposits accumulating preferentially below the S-, SW- or W-facing slopes were then removed down valley by torrential flows of seasonal meltwater, which also caused rapid downcutting. Repeated cycles of gelifluction, downcutting and removal of the footslope deposits led to progressive undercutting and steepening of the slopes facing S, SW or W, whereas those

facing N, NE or E were subject to less gelifluction and therefore remained more stable. French (1972) suggested that asymmetry resulting from unequal insolation began to develop once the valley slopes exceeded 7-9°.

Unequal gelifluction on the opposing valley sides is indicated by the asymmetric distribution of gelifluction deposits, which is shown most clearly by the 1:63,360 Aylesbury sheet of the Soil Survey of England and Wales (Avery, 1964). Soils derived from the gelifluction deposits, such as the Charity and Coombe series, are widespread on the gentler N-, NE- and E-facing valley sides in this part of the Chilterns, but are almost completely absent from the steeper S-, SW- and W-facing slopes, which carry mainly thin rendzinas (Icknield series) with Chalk bedrock usually lying within 30 cm depth (Section 7.7).

Late Pleistocene gelifluction was also important in the final shaping of the shorter scarp-slope dry valleys, as these are again partly infilled by Coombe Deposits, which extend as fan-shaped accumulations onto the low ground below the scarp. The excavation of similar coombes in Kent (Kerney *et al.*, 1964) and Oxfordshire (Paterson, 1977) has been attributed almost entirely to severe gelifluction in the Loch Lomond Stadial at the end of the Devensian cold stage, as the large fans of chalky head extending from their mouths are almost equal in volume to the coombes and overlie buried soils dated to the Windermere Interstadial. However, the evidence for such a short-lived periglacial origin is less clear in Hertfordshire.

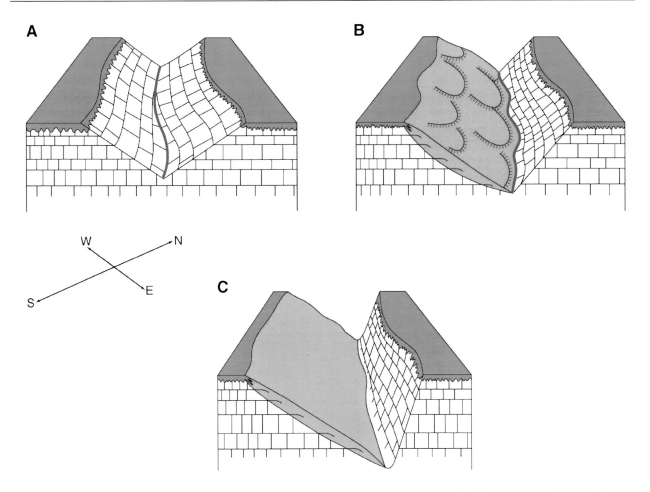

Fig. 6.21. Development of typical Chiltern asymmetric dry valley (C) cut through Plateau Drift (dark brown) into Chalk (white) from originally symmetric wet valley (A). Gelifluction deposits (orange) accumulating under periglacial conditions are preserved on north- and east-facing slopes. South- and west-facing slopes have lost these deposits by erosion because of increased thawing, downslope sludging and removal by periglacial rivers flowing over impermeable permafrost.

For the valleys near Pegsdon, Hexton and Barton in northeast Hertfordshire, Lewis (1949) and Sparks and Lewis (1957) favoured initial formation by the process of spring sapping. As originally suggested by Hopkinson (1899, p. 69), the continual turbulent flow of groundwater from a spring slowly enlarges fissures in the adjacent Chalk, so that any rising ground behind the spring is progressively undercut, then collapses and is gradually eroded back to form an amphitheatre-headed valley. Many of the scarp-slope dry valleys in chalkland areas presently contain small springs where water emerges over the outcrop of less permeable beds, such as the West Melbury Marly Chalk Formation, and the springs could have been larger, more active and at higher levels on the scarp-slope in past periods of temperate climate when the groundwater table was higher. Spring sapping may also have accelerated in cold periods when the saturated chalk close to the spring was subject to increased seasonal frost-shattering (gelifraction). Perhaps the most convincing example in the Hertfordshire area of spring sapping producing a steep scarp-face valley is Well Head (SP 999204) near Dunstable (Plate 58), which is a source of the River Ouzel. The same process may also have created the small amphitheatre undercutting the main street in Ashwell (TL 270398); the water from this

spring is a source of the River Rhee or Cam, but the original amphitheatre has probably been enlarged by mediaeval quarrying of Totternhoe Stone. Oakley (1936) also invoked spring sapping to account for Steps Coombe or Incombe Hole (SP 959156), a spectacular scarp-face dry valley near Ivinghoe, Buckinghamshire (Plate 59), though Barrow and Green (1921b) had previously suggested that it was cut by meltwater from snow and possibly even a local ice cap on the Chilterns.

Yet another theory for the origin of the scarp-face dry valleys is the process of nivation during cold stages of the Pleistocene. This involves erosion at the margins of snow patches, where repeated seasonal or even daily thawing of the snow produces water that soaks into the underlying chalk. When the water refreezes at night or in the winter, the chalk is broken into small pieces by gelifraction, which are then washed away in the next thawing episode or moved down the scarp-slope by gelifluction. Near the crests of slopes in modern periglacial regions, nivation is known to produce shallow depressions, which sometimes coalesce along the slope to produce almost flat terrace-like features known as altiplanation terraces. However, the depth of erosion is much less than that of the scarp-face coombes, so nivation is a possible reason only for their initiation and siting.

179

Plate 58. Well Head Valley (SP 999203) near Dunstable, formed by spring sapping.

Plate 59. Steps Coombe or Incombe Hole (SP 959156) near Ivinghoe – a scarp face coombe with right-angle bends.

Plate 60. View of Dagnall Gap (SP 9916) at the head of the Gade valley from near Ivinghoe Beacon.

Steps Coombe (Plate 59) and two of the scarp-face valleys in northeast Hertfordshire (the Ravensburgh and Barton Valleys) show right-angle bends, which have been attributed to some form of structural control on erosion during their formation. Oakley (1936), Lewis (1949), Sparks and Lewis (1957) and Small (1965) have all suggested that these sharp changes in direction reflect the rectangular pattern of joints in the local Chalk. Joints would probably influence the direction of spring sapping by controlling the movement of water leading to the springs and also creating loose blocks that might break away once undermined. However, none of these workers actually demonstrated a correlation between the directions of valley segments and those of measured joints. Brown (1969) did make measurements of both in the Ivinghoe area, but found no correlation between them. Instead, he concluded that most of the dry valley axes were parallel to the direction of maximum slope of the scarp, which could have directed erosion by meltwater or gelifluction, though zones of weakness in the Chalk associated with faults observable in the area could also have guided the direction of either periglacial erosion or spring sapping.

The exact mode of origin of the scarp-face dry valleys of the Chilterns therefore remains obscure. Almost certainly much of their development can be attributed to Late Devensian gelifluction, but this probably followed earlier nivation, incision by meltwater from snow and ice or headward erosion by spring sapping, the last continuing slowly today where the valley floor intersects the water table.

An unusual dendritic network of small scarp-slope dry valleys occurs in Tring Park (SP 9210). Here a single valley about 10 m deep and 150 m wide, which traverses the Middle Chalk outcrop on the eastern side of the town, divides southwards (upslope) in the park into about five tributary valleys that terminate near the foot of the steep Middle Chalk scarp. Near the scarp the tributary valleys are incised into a gently sloping bench occupying an amphitheatre about 800 m wide, which may have been created by erosion at the edge of the glacier that occupied the Vale of Aylesbury in MIS 12 or MIS 10 (Section 6.8).

The Chiltern through-valleys

A few of the dip-slope valleys of the Chilterns southwest of the Anglian ice margin are unlike the remainder in that they contain perennial rivers, at least in their lower (south-eastern) reaches, and also continue north-westwards through the scarp as dry 'wind gaps'. Because of this they are sometimes described as 'through-valleys'. The main examples in the Hertfordshire area are the Misbourne valley, leading to the Wendover gap, the Bulbourne valley to the Tring gap, the Gade valley to the Dagnall gap (Plate 60), the Ver valley to the Dunstable gap and the upper Lea valley to the Luton gap. In the glaciated area of northeast Hertfordshire, the drainage pattern was greatly modified during the Anglian Stage, either by subglacial erosion or by glacial deposition (Section 6.6). Nevertheless, other through-valleys may have existed here before the glaciation. These could have included pre-Anglian equivalents of the present Rivers Mimram, Beane, Rib, Quin and Stort, all of which are represented by buried valleys cut in the Chalk bedrock beneath the Anglian glacial deposits (Fig. 6.9). The first two lead to the Lilley Bottom and Hitchin-Stevenage gaps, respectively. The others may have led to pre-Anglian gaps near Royston, Barley and Chrishall, respectively, but the borehole data in these areas is insufficient to confirm this.

In the uppermost reaches of the through-valleys close to the Chiltern scarp, the valley floors cut in lower parts of the Chalk fall north-westwards until they reach the Gault Clay floor of the Vale of Aylesbury, but do not extend beyond this. Consequently, the through-valleys have humped profiles, which could be explained by subglacial erosion for those in the glaciated north-eastern part of the county, but not for those south of the ice limit. The latter are back-to-back dry valleys, with long reaches declining south-eastwards backing onto much shorter reaches falling to the northwest. For at least 1 km on either side of this meeting point, both valleys are now dry, with no historical evidence for streams other than very short-lived flows created by surface runoff in heavy rain.

Various theories have been put forward to explain the origin of the through-valleys. Like the dry valleys, they were considerably modified by periglacial processes in the Devensian and probably also some earlier cold stages. They must have originated before the Anglian glaciation in MIS 12, because some are recognizable in the sub-Anglian surface (Fig. 6.9) and are buried by Anglian glacial deposits. Also, the NW-SE course of the Ver was diverted southwards near Sopwell (TL1505) around the western margin of the ice lobe in the Vale of St Albans (Wooldridge, 1953). Apart from this evidence for age, none of the valleys contains any known datable deposits, so any pre-Anglian history is conjectural at present.

Harmer (1907) suggested that the Wendover, Tring and Dagnall gaps were cut by water overflowing from a large glacially impounded lake (Lake Oxford) west of the Chalk escarpment, and this idea was accepted by Sherlock (1922, p. 50) and Oakley (1936). But there are no known lake deposits in the Vale of Aylesbury and areas to the west, and the gravels in the through-valleys contain no far-travelled rocks. Also the floors of the wind gaps are at a wide range of heights (125-215 m OD.), and cannot have been cut by overflow from a lake with a single water level (Gregory, 1914).

Gregory (1894) had previously concluded that the through-valleys were cut by pre-glacial rivers and, as suggested in Section 6.6, these seem to have been left-bank tributaries of the proto-Thames before it was diverted out of the Vale of St Albans by the Anglian glaciation. As with the dip-slope dry valleys, this explanation requires a water table high enough in the pre-Anglian period to initiate and maintain flow in the through-valleys. Assuming the Chalk scarp receded a considerable distance during the late Neogene and Quaternary, and assuming the dip of the Chalk continued north-westwards at approximately its present angle, a higher water table could have resulted simply from the increased elevation of the scarp crest. However, as we now know that the Chiltern area has been progressively uplifted by as much as 160 m in relation to sea level during the Quaternary (Sections 5.2 and 6.2), the water table would

then have been much closer to the land surface, and this probably provides the best explanation for the origin of the through-valleys. Periglacial erosion of the frost-susceptible Chalk in cold stages of the Quaternary was probably the main process of erosion, but the driving force that initiated and maintained the downcutting to create both the deep through-valleys and the dip-slope dry valleys of the Chilterns was almost certainly tectonic uplift.

Unfortunately there is no depositional or geomorphological (erosional) evidence for extension of any of the through-valleys west of the Chiltern scarp. The evidence from the Marsworth area (Section 6.8), immediately west of the Tring Gap, suggests that the Chiltern scarp has remained in approximately its present position since at least MIS 7, and perhaps even since the glaciation of the Vale of Aylesbury in MIS 10 or 12. Previously, the scarp could have extended further to the west, and subsequent scarp recession, perhaps by repeated periglacial erosion, may have beheaded the through-valleys, removing any evidence for their north-westward extension. But it has to be admitted that this is pure speculation. The north-westward inclination of the now dry short north-western reaches of the valleys probably resulted from periglacial slope erosion in post-Anglian cold stages, which created for example the Wolstonian coombe deposits at Marsworth.

The longitudinal profiles (talwegs) of the through-valleys are not regular, but show a series of knick-points separating reaches, each of which approximates to a logarithmic curve steepening up-valley (Culling, 1956a). No remnants of depositional terraces can be recognized in any of the valleys, other than gently sloping surfaces slightly above the valley floors, which were probably formed by Devensian gelifluction. However, by extrapolating the graded reaches above each knick-point downstream, Culling (1956a) was able to show that those in lower parts of the through-valleys can be correlated with terraces of the Middle Thames dating back to the Winter Hill (early Anglian) stage. For example, in the Ver and Harpenden valleys he correlated successive reaches with the Boyn Hill, Black Park and Winter Hill terraces, and in the Chess and Gade valleys there are also equivalents of the 'Upper Taplow' (Lynch Hill?) Terrace. The reaches dating from the Anglian (MIS 12) in the Chess, Gade, Ver and Harpenden valleys may have been graded to the proglacial Moor Mill Lake in the Vale of St Albans (Section 6.6).

Above the reaches correlated with the Winter Hill terrace, Culling (1956b) was unable to resolve graded sections in any of the Chiltern through-valleys. This was attributed either to elimination of knick-points by increased stream flow in the steeper upper parts of the talwegs or to severe erosion by meltwater from the glacier occupying the Vale of Aylesbury, but periglacial erosion during and since MIS 12 is perhaps a more likely reason. So, although Culling's work seems to confirm that the valleys existed in some form before MIS 12 (i.e. before about 0.5 Ma), it provides no evidence for a definite pre-Anglian history or a date for the original cutting of the valleys.

Brown (1964) speculated that the rivers which cut the

Chiltern through-valleys originated as consequent streams flowing down the sloping surface exposed when the Plio-Pleistocene (Red Crag) sea withdrew to the east. This marine regression would have occurred soon after 2.6 Ma. There is certainly no evidence in the Chilterns for such a long pre-Anglian history, but a similar through-valley in the western North Downs south of Croydon (the Wandle Valley leading southwards to the Merstham Gap) probably existed in a shallow high-level form before deposition of the Red Crag (Peake, 1983).

6.11. The Holocene

The boundary between the Devensian and Holocene (or Flandrian Stage), which is also the boundary between the Pleistocene and Holocene, has long been drawn at a rapid, worldwide climatic warming, which is dated by the radiocarbon method to 10,000 years BP. However, calibration of ^{14}C dates for deposits close to this boundary and dating of the first evidence for warming in Greenland ice cores (Walker *et al.*, 2009) suggests that, in calendar years, the warming occurred about 11,700 years ago, and this date is now internationally accepted as the boundary between the Pleistocene and Holocene. Coleopteran (beetle) assemblages from British deposits that span the boundary indicate an increase of about 10°C in mean annual temperature over only a few decades (Atkinson *et al.*, 1987). Together with evidence from pollen, molluscs and other animals, the beetles also suggest that mean temperatures then rose more slowly and irregularly to a maximum of 1-3°C above present values at approximately 6000 calendar years ago (Bell and Walker, 2005, p. 90). Following this 'Holocene climatic optimum', there was an irregular cooling, culminating in the 'Little Ice Age' between about 1400 AD and the late 19th century, when temperatures across the northern hemisphere as a whole were approximately 0.5°C lower than in the mid-20th century (Bradley, 2000).

In the past, subdivision of Holocene time has been based mainly on the recognition of five pollen assemblage biozones that were originally identified in Scandinavian peat sequences; these are named (in order of decreasing age) the Pre-Boreal, Boreal, Atlantic, Sub-Boreal and Sub-Atlantic periods. However, the boundaries between the biozones are diachronous, because of the slow migration of trees in response to minor climatic changes. Also the vegetation characteristics on which they are based were strongly influenced by local human activities, especially deforestation. In fact, it is now recognized that forest vegetation has varied almost continually in both time and space throughout the Holocene and, as a result, there is little value in using pollen assemblages for subdividing and dating Holocene sequences.

Nevertheless, radiocarbon dating of Holocene lake sediments and peat deposits in various parts of lowland Britain has indicated that, following the rapid warming at the beginning of the Holocene, there was a sudden expansion of juniper (*Juniperus communis*) scrub, quickly followed by the northward spread of birch (*Betula*), willow

(*Salix*) and hazel (*Corylus*). Other broad-leaved components of the early Holocene mixed oak forest invaded later, elm (*Ulmus*) by about 10,900, oak (*Quercus*) by 10,300 and lime (*Tilia*) and alder (*Alnus*) by 8575 calendar years ago (Birks, 1989). Minor localized deforestation, by Mesolithic hunters and food-gatherers, probably began before 9000 calendar years ago, but there was much more extensive woodland clearance by the Neolithic farming communities after approximately 6000 calendar years ago, and again in the early Bronze Age (soon after 4200 calendar years ago) and Iron Age (after 2800 calendar years ago). It is therefore likely that, by the time of the Roman invasion, most of lowland Britain, including much of Hertfordshire, had lost its natural forest cover.

The two principal Holocene sediments in Hertfordshire, colluvium (ploughwash or fieldwash) and alluvium, almost certainly resulted from soil erosion following cultivation for early arable farm crops from the Neolithic period (approximately coincident with the Holocene climatic optimum) onwards. Under the natural forest of the earlier Holocene, there would have been almost no downslope movement of sediment to form colluvium, and therefore very little input to rivers and streams, so that they ran clear and deposited almost no alluvium. In some valleys and poorly-drained upland sites within the county, small amounts of peat may have accumulated in the early Holocene. But elsewhere the oldest sediments overlying the Late Devensian gelifluction deposits and periglacial river gravels are probably no older than about 6000 calendar years, and most are likely to be considerably younger.

Alluvium

The Holocene alluvial deposits in Hertfordshire form ribbon-shaped outcrops, usually 300-500 m wide, along the floors of valleys containing rivers or streams. Most are less than 3 m thick, but locally they exceed 7 m, and in the higher reaches of many valleys they are often less than 30 cm thick. They are composed almost entirely of fine sediment (clay and silt) with very little coarser material of sand and gravel size. On the floors of wet valleys draining the Chilterns, such those of the Chess, Bulbourne, Gade, Ver and Colne (below its confluence with the Ver), they are mainly silty and strongly calcareous, with some shelly layers, though peat beds are locally interbedded with or overlie the alluvium. This composition reflects the dominance of bedrock chalk and chalky Devensian gelifluction deposits in the valley catchments, the gelifluction deposits often containing silt (loess) as the main non-calcareous component. A section in the Colne alluvium at Watford (TL 117957) was described by Lones (1904); in its lower part it contained many land snails and freshwater molluscs; bones of domesticated animals, such as ox, horse and pig, were reported from higher layers.

Further east, the alluvium of rivers with catchments dominated by Anglian till, such as the Colne (above its confluence with the Ver), Lea, Mimram, Beane, Rib, Stort and Hiz, are much less calcareous and dominantly clayey, again with local patches of peat occurring in the wettest areas of the floodplain, such as abandoned river meanders.

Peat up to 1 m thick is widespread at Oughtonhead Common (TL 1630) in the valley of the River Oughton near Hitchin, and there are smaller patches in the valleys of the River Ivel (TL 240349) north of Baldock and the River Hiz at Ickleford Common (TL 1833).

In the lower Lea valley below St Margarets, the floodplain widens to 1-2 km. Below its surface, there is a complex pattern of abandoned channels filled with shelly sands, clays, marls and peat, many of which have been partially destroyed by excavation of artificial waterways since the late Mediaeval period or gravel working over the last century. The successions exposed at several sites, including Deepham's Sewage Works (TQ 360930) near Pickett's Lock, Rammey Marsh (TQ 373995) near Waltham Abbey, Carthagena Lock (TL 380071) near Broxbourne and Rikof's Pit (TL 381075) near Broxbourne, were recorded by Hayward (1956), who listed numerous species of freshwater molluscs, ostracods and other animal and plant fossils from some of the beds. A dugout canoe of Romano-British type with shells of *Planorbis acronicus* and *Bithynia leachi* attached to the underside (Holmes and Hayward, 1955) was found in peat at Rammey Marsh, but there is no other evidence for the exact age of these deposits. The infilled channels are overlain by a thin grey 'marsh clay', which extends over most of the floodplain, and was probably deposited during episodes of overbank flooding at various times over the last two millennia.

Peat. The almost permanently wet conditions necessary for peat accumulation usually result from the groundwater table lying close to the land surface, but locally peat has also formed where the water table is perched on a slowly permeable substrate such as till, as for example at Biggin Moor (TL 380336) south of Barkway (Hopson *et al.*, 1996, p. 110). At Ridlins Mire (TL 263222), south of Stevenage, up to 1.8 m of Holocene peat has accumulated in an unusual position on the upper slope of a valley cut in Chalk, where groundwater emerging from a layer of glacial gravel is perched over till (Tinsley and Cosgrove, 1991).

Tufa. In the upper Lea valley near Coldharbour Farm (TL 141159), Harper (1940) recorded a roadside section exposing 2 m of tufa resting on Chalk and overlain by colluvium. The tufa was probably deposited in the Early Holocene by a spring seeping from the Chalk into a marsh on the valley floor. It yielded 29 species of molluscs, mainly small gastropods typical of marsh conditions or flowing water. Thin patchy accumulations of Holocene tufa also occur in the alluvial squences of many other valleys.

Colluvium

Loamy colluvial, hillwash or ploughwash deposits of late Holocene age have a very patchy distribution on valley floors and footslopes, mainly occurring below extensive slopes that have been cultivated over long periods. They are known mainly in chalkland areas, where they often contain land snails indicating changes in the vegetation resulting from deforestation and early agricultural activities. The most widespread are on the floors of dry valleys, especially those cut into the Chiltern scarp-slope, but they also occur in some of the wet dip-slope valleys, such as those of the Rivers Gade and Ver.

Evans (1966) recorded the sequence of land snail assemblages through typical chalkland colluvial deposits in scarp-face dry valleys near Pitstone. In buried soils, ditch infills of possible Neolithic age and humic chalk muds beneath the colluvium, he found an assemblage, with species such as *Vertigo pulsilla*, *Hygromia striolata*, *Columella edentula* and *Lauria cylindracea*, characteristic of closed woodland. In contrast, the fauna in lower parts of the overlying colluvium indicated dry open grassland, with an abundance of *Vallonia excentrica*, which is common today on nearby chalk grasslands. Higher in the colluvium the assemblage was dominated by *Ceciloides acicula*, with declining numbers of *Vallonia excentrica* and other grassland species, suggesting the occurrence of ploughed soils upslope. This sequence indicates an early Holocene period of closed woodland, followed by deposition of colluvium as a result of woodland clearance initially for pasture and finally ploughing of the grassland slopes. In the uppermost 15 cm, the colluvium contained *Monacha cantiana* and *Helix aspersa*, which were introduced to Britain early in the Roman period, and at the very top of the deposit the Mediaeval introductions *Hygromia hispida*, *Helicella virgata*, *H. caperata* and *H. gigaxi* were recorded. These suggest that most of the colluvium accumulated before the Roman period, with very little since Mediaeval times.

In two dry valleys in northeast Hertfordshire, Coombe Bottom (TL 3138) and Wing Hall (TL 3339) near Royston, Waton (1982) described buried Holocene soils beneath chalky colluvium. The land snail faunas from the buried soils were either typical of woodland or contained equal amounts of shade-loving (tall grassland and scrub) and open country (bare soil or short grassland) species. In comparison, the assemblages from the overlying hillwash were greatly impoverished, and contained only species typical of short grassland or bare soil.

The approximate time of deposition of the colluvium is sometimes indicated by included pottery fragments, and the time of initial woodland clearance by burning has been obtained by radiocarbon dating of charcoal in the buried soils. For example, in the Pitstone area, Evans and Valentine (1974) recorded Iron Age and Romano-British pottery from the colluvium, and charcoal from the buried woodland soil suggested an initial clearance phase around 4000 BP. This evidence for age agrees with that suggested by the presence of molluscs introduced at various times.

Chapter 7.

Soils, ecology and agriculture

John Catt, Trevor James and the late Brian Avery

7.1. Introduction

Descriptions of soils are rarely found in accounts of regional geology, but there are several reasons why it is considered appropriate for a book on the geology of Hertfordshire. First, soils link geology to a range of other natural sciences, such as ecology, hydrology and agriculture, which are important for understanding the county's overall environment. This understanding is essential for local and county-wide planning decisions concerning exploitation of the county's natural resources and conservation of its valuable features. Second, it enhances knowledge of the distribution of thin later Quaternary deposits that are identifiable only within the soil profile. Third, it clarifies the history of landscape development during the later Quaternary by identifying soils that have developed over long and short periods of time, thus indicating areas where the land surface has remained stable for different lengths of time. These three factors together provide a basis for linking the county's landscape features to its broader geological history (Section 7.7), which is much more detailed than any that can be derived from our inevitably restricted knowledge of local geology based on the limited number of exposures in quarries, road- and railway-cuttings and temporary excavations.

In addition, Hertfordshire figured prominently in the development of studies on soil genesis, composition and classification during the 20th century. This work was based mainly at Rothamsted Experimental Station, Harpenden, where extensive fundamental research has also been conducted on the influence of soil properties on the growth and yields of arable farm crops. Within the county, important field experimental work on arable and horticultural crops was also done during the 20th century at the Hertfordshire Institute of Agriculture (Oaklands College, near St Albans), the John Innes Institute (previously at Bayford), the Lee Valley Experimental Horticulture Station (Hoddesdon), the Cheshunt Research Station (incorporated since 1954 into the Glasshouse Crops Research Institute at Littlehampton) and demonstration farms run by *Farmer and Stockbreeder* (Hall Farm, Little Hadham) and by *Farmers Weekly* (Grove Farm, Tring).

The first account of Hertfordshire soils was in the introduction to an early general account of the county by Norden (1593, pp. 1-2). He wrote:

'Concerning the Soyle: It is for the most part, chalkie, though the upper crust in the south and west parts, be for the most part of redde earth mixed with gravel, which yet by reason of the white marle under it, yeeldeth good wheat and oates: But of its own nature most enclined to wood, and coupisses, affording also faire wayes. In the North part of the Shire, as in the hundreds of Hitche, and Oddesey, the soyle is very apt to yeeld corne, and dertie wayes, especially that part which is accompted parcell of a vayle called of the countrie men the Vayle of Ring-tayle or Wring-tayle or rather Ringdale, which extendeth it selfe also into Cambridg-shire. And affordeth no small store of wheat and malte towards the provision of London.' ... 'To speake of the Soyle as indeede it is most generally, for my part I take it but a barraine countrie, in respect of some other Shires, without the industrious toyle & charge of the thirstie husbandman.'

This chapter deals in general terms first with the nature and origin of soil types that occur in the county, then with the history of their classification and mapping. This is followed by more detailed accounts of the occurrence of the numerous soil types known in Hertfordshire and of properties that influence ecology (mainly the semi-natural vegetation) and the use of land for agriculture.

7.2. Soil profiles and their development

Soils result from the operation of various complex processes, which modify the near-surface layers of the earth wherever the ground is stabilized beneath a cover of vegetation and is not subject to rapid erosion or deposition of fresh sediment. In Britain these soil-forming processes include:

a) addition, decomposition and incorporation of plant and animal residues (organic matter)
b) structural reorganization (changes in the spatial arrangement of solid particles and voids), which results from seasonal wetting, drying and freezing, the activities of soil animals and the growth and decay of roots
c) weathering (chemical alteration) of mineral particles, especially through the agency of percolating water charged with oxygen, carbon dioxide and soluble products of organic matter decay
d) downward leaching of soluble components in percolating

water, often with reprecipitation at depth
e) downward movement of fine solid particles dispersed in the soil water (illuviation)
f) reduction of iron oxides and other compounds where permanent or seasonal saturation with water greatly decreases the usual contact with atmospheric oxygen (gleying).

Prolonged action of these processes results in the development of more or less distinct soil horizons, which are approximately parallel to the land surface and together constitute the soil profile.

In order to identify or map the soils of an area such as Hertfordshire, it is necessary to adopt some form of classification, and most modern systems of soil classification use the soil profile as the unit of study. This is defined as the sequence of soil horizons beneath a limited area (usually 1m²) of land surface. Adjacent soil profiles often show the same horizon sequence, but where the sequence changes significantly a line between two soil types can be drawn on a soil map.

7.3. Soil horizons

Soil horizons differ from one another and from unaltered material below in properties such as colour, texture (particle size distribution), amount and type of organic matter, calcium carbonate content, degree of root development and structure. Soil structure is defined as the size and shape of aggregates of solid particles and of the voids between them.

In some places the unaltered material beneath the soil profile can be equated with the parent material in which the soil horizons have developed. But elsewhere the horizons have developed in a different material or have been superimposed on a succession of originally distinct layers. There are also situations in which the soil consists wholly or partly of material that has been excavated and replaced in its present position, as in restored quarries, gravel pits and other mineral workings.

It is convenient to describe soil horizons using a letter notation (e.g. Hodgson, 1976), whereby the same symbol is applied to analogous horizons in profiles of the same general type. Thus superficial and usually dry organic horizons (litter layers) in uncultivated soils are designated L (undecomposed litter), F (partially decomposed litter) or H (strongly decomposed or humified material). These are differentiated from generally thicker O horizons, which consist of more or less decomposed peat that accumulated under waterlogged conditions. Dark-coloured surface or near-surface horizons containing <20-30% incorporated organic matter (depending on the clay content) are denoted by the symbol A, and subjacent mineral horizons clearly affected by soil-forming processes by E or B. E denotes a relatively light-coloured eluvial subsurface horizon that has lost silicate clay or other fine consituents by downward movement (illuviation); it is normally underlain by an illuvial B horizon in which redeposition of the fine constituents has occurred. Where no detectable

illuviation has occurred, an A horizon either overlies a B horizon showing evidence of weathering and/or structural modification only, or rests directly on a little-altered substrate, which is designated C if unconsolidated or R if hard consolidated bedrock.

More specific kinds of soil horizons are indicated by letter suffixes. For example, Ap denotes the ploughed and consequently homogenized surface layer of a cultivated soil, Bw a well aerated non-illuvial B horizon (weathered B) and Bt (from German *Ton* = clay) an illuvial B horizon enriched in silicate clay. Horizons with greyish and ochreous mottles attributable to reduction of iron and its removal or segregation under periodically water-saturated conditions (gleying) are identified by the suffix g (gleyed), for example Eg or Btg. Permanently waterlogged horizons lying beneath a near-surface water table and therefore subject to intense reduction of iron have predominantly greyish or bluish-grey colours; these are indicated by an additional capital G (e.g. CG).

7.4. Soil types

The type of soil, as expressed by its profile characteristics, that occurs in any particular place depends partly on the physical and mineralogical composition of the parent material/s, partly on past and present environmental factors (climate, vegetation, animals and hydrological conditions, which together regulate the nature and intensity of soil-forming processes), and partly on the length of time these processes have operated, as determined by the age and stability of the ground surface. Also in long-inhabited areas, where the natural equilibria between soil, vegetation, animals and hydrological conditions have been disturbed by farming or forestry, the upper soil horizons in particular take on new characteristics, which depend on past and present land uses and mask the influence of earlier natural vegetation.

In Hertfordshire, as in southeast England generally, climatic conditions are fairly uniform and soil differences reflect the integrated effects of parent material, time and relief, with superimposed differences arising from land use. Over most of the county, unconsolidated Quaternary deposits (drift deposits) of glacial, fluvial, aeolian, gelifluction or colluvial origin form a nearly continuous mantle obscuring the older (solid or bedrock) strata, such as the Gault Clay, Chalk, Reading Beds and London Clay. Consequently the bedrock gives rise to the soil in only limited areas where the drift cover is thin or absent. Such areas occur chiefly on and north of the Chiltern (Chalk) scarp-slope and on London Clay in the south-eastern part of the county.

The Quaternary soil parent materials contain sand (>0.06 mm), silt (0.002-0.06 mm) and clay (<0.002 mm), chalk fragments and flint or quartz stones in greatly varying proportions. The soils formed from them usually contain similar amounts of these components, because apart from chalk most of the components are resistant to the weak weathering and leaching processes that have occurred in the temperate and moderately humid climate. Weathering is mainly limited to dissolution of chalk, oxidation and reduction of iron-containing minerals and minor modification of clay minerals under acidic soil conditions. Leaching is confined to the winter half of the year, as evapotranspiration normally exceeds rainfall from March or April to September or October (Section 9.2). Therefore, except in a few places where the water table remains within the rooting depth of plants, the soils dry out during the summer to varying degrees.

The various Quaternary deposits were emplaced at different stages in the evolution of the landscape (Chapter 6), and have therefore been subject to pedogenic modification for varying lengths of time. Soils in Holocene alluvium and colluvium rarely show well-defined horizons attributable to weathering and leaching *in situ*, and soils on upper slopes subject to recent erosion have lost one or more pre-existing horizons so that they are thinner than soils on uneroded sites nearby. In contrast, soils on Devensian or older Quaternary deposits generally exhibit clearly differentiated horizons, and are thicker than other soils, often showing evidence of alteration well below the main rooting zone. Although periglacial conditions prevailing during the Devensian Stage caused widespread disruption or removal of pre-existing soils by cryoturbation and gelifluction, many of the soils in Anglian or older deposits retain the impress of soil-forming processes that operated during the Ipswichian or earlier interglacials. The resulting horizons are much redder and more clay-enriched and often thicker even than those formed in Devensian deposits. In the system of soil classification currently used in England and Wales (Section 7.5), they are defined as paleo-argillic B horizons.

Where soils have formed wholly or mainly in pre-Quaternary bedrock formations, the ground surfaces concerned are usually Late Quaternary (probably Late Devensian) erosion surfaces. Consequently the extent of pedogenic alteration that they show is no greater than that of soils formed in Late Devensian deposits of broadly similar composition. The main exceptions are the thick, well-developed soils with paleo-argillic B horizons, widespread on the plateau surface of the Chiltern Hills, which are formed in Plateau Drift and Clay-with-flints *sensu stricto*, materials derived mainly from a veneer of the Reading and Upnor formations left on the Sub-Palaeogene Surface during late Tertiary or early Quaternary denudation of the Chilterns (Section 5.3).

As soil parent materials, chalk or fragmented chalk (e.g. Coombe Deposits) are unique, as they are composed almost entirely of calcium carbonate, which dissolves readily in acidic water percolating through the soil. Weathering and dissolution of chalk-rich deposits releases small amounts of insoluble residue, mostly clay and flint nodules or fragments of nodules, but this accumulates to form a soil with a B horizon of significant thickness only if the land surface remains undisturbed for a very long period. Hence Chalk or very chalky Quaternary deposits usually form soils consisting of A and C (or R) horizons only.

Plants acquire the nutrients needed for growth from various sources. The process known as photosynthesis involves conversion of carbon dioxide from the atmosphere into carbohydrates (sugars and starch) using energy from sunlight in the presence of the chlorophyll present in green leaves. The macronutrients nitrogen, phosphorus, potassium, magnesium and calcium and numerous micronutrients are taken up in solution as the plant sucks in water through its roots. Their immediate source is the water that partially or completely fills pores between the solid soil particles. Some contributions of these macronutrients and micronutrients come from the bacterial decomposition (mineralization) of soil organic matter. Others are provided by soluble artificial fertilizers added to the soil by farmers or gardeners, and a third source consists of the ions released by natural decomposition of weatherable minerals in the soil. But as the decomposition of soil minerals by weathering processes is very slow, almost all wild plant species have developed methods of increasing the rate of mineral breakdown by a symbiotic relationship with soil fungi known as mycorrhizae, which grow in close association with their roots. The mycorrhizae are able to release nutrients from mineral particles more rapidly than by other (non-biological) weathering processes, so that the dissolved nutrients can be taken up through the plant's roots, and in return the plant provides carbohydrates to sustain the mycorrhizae. They are especially important in the provision of plant-available phosphorus, and for the establishment and growth of orchids. Compared with wild plants, modern cultivated farm crops are usually less dependent on mycorrhizae because sufficient nutrients are provided by artificial fertilizers.

7.5. Classification and mapping of Hertfordshire soils

The first attempt to classify and map the soils of Hertfordshire was by the local (North Mymms) farmer Arthur Young (1804), who assessed the agricultural potential of the county at the request of the government-funded Board of Agriculture and Internal Improvement. From his own experience and evidence provided by other Hertfordshire landowners, he divided the county into six areas with broadly different soil types:

a) Northeast Hertfordshire – chalky soils
b) East Hertfordshire – loamy clay soils resembling those in Essex
c) Lower Lea valley – rich loam soils
d) South Hertfordshire (Hatfield, North Mymms and Northaw areas) – poor gravelly soils
e) Southwest Hertfordshire (Elstree, Aldenham and Barnet areas) – clay soils resembling those of Middlesex and heavier than those in east Hertfordshire
f) Central Hertfordshire (as far east as Ware and Stevenage) and northwest Hertfordshire (including the Chilterns) – loamy and often very flinty soils.

The distribution of these was shown on a hand-coloured map of the county in the 1804 publication, but in the 1813 and 1971 reprints of his book the map was reproduced in black and white. The six types were based essentially on the characteristics of the cultivated surface (Ap) horizons, with little knowledge of subsurface characteristics. Young recognized that his map was an over-simplification, stating that the six types 'mix and run into each other in a remarkable manner'. Nevertheless, his account subsequently proved surprisingly accurate, especially as it pre-dated any consistent or detailed account of the surface geology of the county. It was also very perceptive in terms of the relative agricultural capabilities of the six areas; for example, he described the rich loam soils of the lower Lea valley as the 'best land that I have seen in the county', and the gravel soils of south Hertfordshire as 'the most infertile that we find in the south of England' and best adapted to woodland.

In addition to the natural short-range variation of Hertfordshire soils, Evershed (1864) emphasized that a wide variety of management techniques have increased the complexity of their characteristics. He wrote 'In general, on every variety of soil, good and bad management are blended together with such slight shades of difference that a picture of their general aspect could hardly be drawn, and if drawn would be unreadable'.

No significant improvement on Young's map was made until after soil surveys based on field examination and sampling of soil profiles had been initiated in the 1920s. Following contemporary American usage, soil series were adopted about this time as the basic units of classification and mapping, and were named according to localities where they were first identified or most extensive. By 1939, when the Soil Survey of England and Wales was formally recognized, soil series maps based on field surveys using the 1:10,560 Ordnance Survey sheets had already been made in a few widely scattered localities throughout the country. The surveys involved field examination of soil profiles in quarry faces or specially dug pits and by hand-drilling with a soil auger. Some characteristics of each horizon (e.g. colour and structure) were determined in the field, but supplementary information on particle size distribution, carbonate content and other chemical properties for representative profiles was obtained by laboratory analyses of bulk samples taken during the fieldwork. Each soil series was conceived as a set of soils with similar profiles developed under similar conditions from similar parent materials. To show their relationships, the series were grouped into broader genetic classes termed major soil groups (e.g. brown earths, podzols, calcareous soils, gley soils and organic soils).

To extend the national coverage of soil information, several reconnaissance surveys were also made during and after the 1939-45 war. For this purpose sample areas throughout the country were selected on a geological basis (i.e. where important parent materials are extensive), and were mapped in detail to identify the soil series present and their mode of occurrence. Knowledge gained in this way was then used in conjunction with less intensive surveys of other areas to construct smaller scale maps showing the boundaries of compound soil-landscape units or soil associations, each characterized by a particular combination of geographically associated series.

The earliest of such surveys in Hertfordshire were begun in the winter of 1944-45, and resulted in soil series maps of Rothamsted Experimental Station near Harpenden, the then Hertfordshire Farm Institute at Oaklands near St Albans, and larger sample areas located near Long Marston, Aldbury, Sandridge, Shenley and Little Berkhamsted. A soil association map of the southern part of the county was also produced. In 1945 a national headquarters for the Soil Survey of England and Wales was established at Rothamsted, and this led to much detailed work being done in the county. By the early 1960s additional detailed soil maps were available for much of the north-western part of the county covered by Ordnance Survey 3rd Edition Sheet 238 (Avery, 1964) and smaller blocks elsewhere. Also reconnaissance surveys of areas north of a line from Redbourn (TL 110100) to Stanstead Abbotts (TL 400100) had been completed (King, 1969; Thomasson, 1969). The various surveys were then used to compile an account of the soils of the county illustrated by a 1:250,000 map showing the boundaries of twelve soil associations (Thomasson and Avery, 1963, 1970). Twenty eight soil series were identified as significant components of one or more of the associations, and were placed in two broad classes of calcareous and leached (carbonate-free) soils. The former were subdivided into rendzinas, brown calcareous soils and calcareous gley soils, and the latter into brown earths and non-calcareous gley soils. Podzols and gley-podzols (q.v.) were also noted, but no corresponding soil series were identified as they occupy very limited areas. The same classification was used by Gardner (1967) in his agricultural survey of Hertfordshire.

From 1973 the Soil Survey of England and Wales began to use a more comprehensive and detailed soil classification system (Avery, 1973, 1980; Clayden and Hollis, 1984), in which major soil groups, soil groups, soil subgroups and soil series are defined by progressive division using observable or measurable soil characteristics as differentiating criteria. These criteria include the composition of the soil material and the presence or absence of 'diagnostic horizons', both within specified depths. Diagnostic horizons are surface or subsurface horizons defined according to the type and degree of pedogenetic alteration of the parent material, including incorporation of humus (organic matter), illuviation of clay, sesquioxides and organic matter, oxidative weathering of primary minerals, gleying and permeability. They have strictly defined limits of thickness, depth, colour, organic content and other aspects of composition (Avery, 1980). Soil series were then redefined as divisions within subgroups with limited ranges of lithology (including texture, stoniness, certain mineralogical characteristics and depth to specified substrata), but without reference to stratigraphic age, at least of pre-Quaternary parent materials. The previously used textural classes of the United States Department of Agriculture (Fig. 7.1A) were also replaced by newly defined particle size classes (Fig. 7.1B) based on the particle size grades of the British Standards Institution (1975). For differentiating soil series, these classes were grouped as in Fig. 7.1C.

The new classification system was first fully utilized in

a)

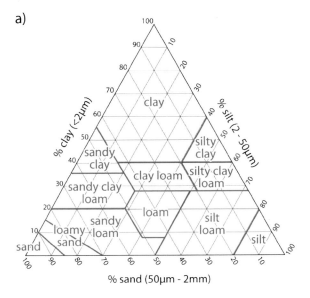

% sand (50μm - 2mm)

b)

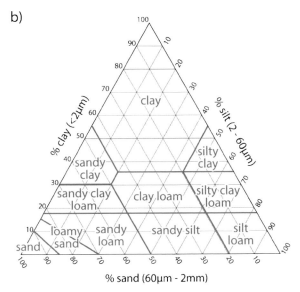

% sand (60μm - 2mm)

c)

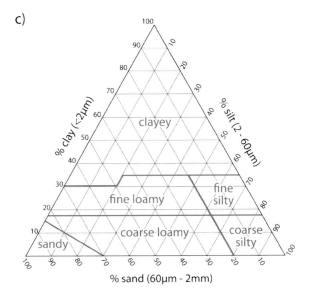

% sand (60μm - 2mm)

Fig. 7.1. Soil particle size classes (<2 mm) according to a) United States Department of Agriculture, b) British Standards Institute and c) Soil Survey of England and Wales.

compiling a national 1:250,000 soil association map of England and Wales, in which associations were identified as hitherto, using the names of the dominant or most distinctive soil series that each contained. In Hertfordshire 91 series were identified as major or minor components of one or more of the 39 associations in the county. The distribution of these associations is shown on Sheets 4 and 6 of the national 1:250,000 map, both of which cover the county, and were described in detail by Hodge *et al.* (1984) and Jarvis *et al.* (1984), respectively. They were drawn from information gathered in the earlier surveys, supplemented by additional sampling and profile descriptions on a grid basis. The soil association map of the county shown in Figure 7.2 is a simplified version of the national 1:250,000 map.

Table 7.1 summarizes the specifications of the major soil groups, soil groups, soil subgroups and soil series occurring in Hertfordshire. The soil series listed are those identified as major or minor components of the soil associations shown on the national 1:250,000 map. Full definitions of the classes in major soil groups, soil groups and soil subgroups were given by Avery (1980), and those of the soil series by Clayden and Hollis (1984). The 1:250,000 soil association maps covering Hertfordshire and adjacent counties are available from the National Soil and Land Resource Institute, whose headquarters are now at Cranfield University, Bedfordshire.

7.6. Description, occurrence and ecology of the Major soil groups

Major soil group 1. Terrestrial raw soils

Lacking distinct pedogenic horizons of significant thickness, these are soils only in the sense that they consist of unconsolidated mineral material at the ground surface, and are normally colonized by plants wherever the surface is sufficiently stable and other conditions permit. In Hertfordshire they are restricted mainly to places where pre-existing soil has been removed by quarrying or earth-moving operations to expose unmodified hard rock or unconsolidated sediment (Raw skeletal soils and Raw earths, respectively) and where accumulations of artificially displaced non-soil materials of various types (Man-made raw soils) occur in similar situations. Although no soil subgroups or soil series are defined within the Terrestrial raw soils, it is possible to divide these three groups in Hertfordshire according to the presence or absence of calcium carbonate, and therefore the influence of pH and free (plant-available) Ca on pioneer plant communities.

Raw skeletal soils on chalk. In old chalk quarries, such as the Hertfordshire and Middlesex Wildlife Trust nature reserves at Hexton Chalk Pit (TL 107299) and Ashwell Quarry (TL 253395) (James, 1992) and deep cuttings in chalk, these soils are extremely calcareous but lack plant nutrients other than calcium. They are also subject to large variations in temperature and to dry surface conditions in summer. This

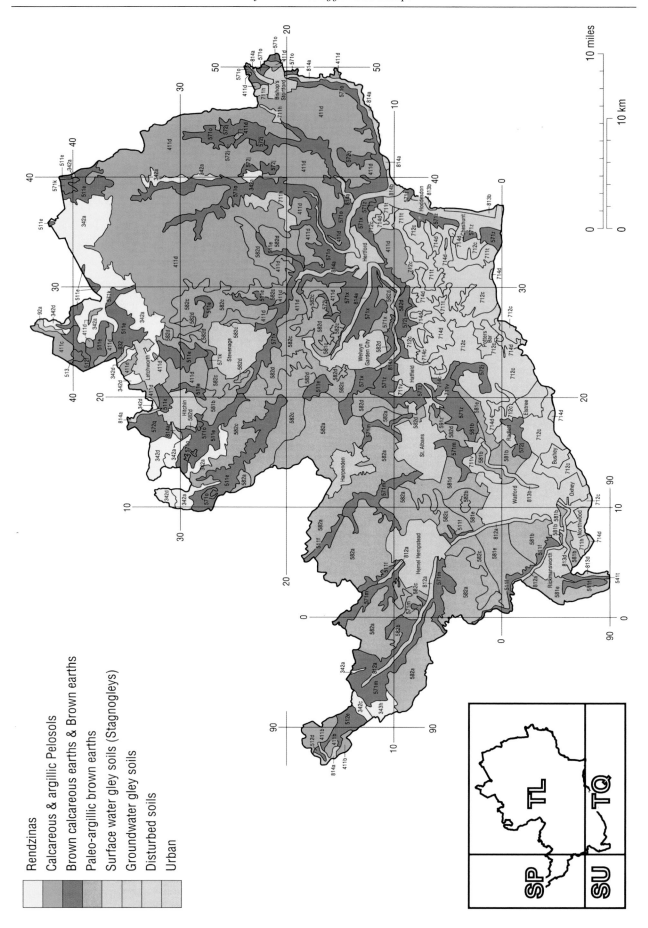

Fig. 7.2. Soil association map of Hertfordshire, redrawn from Soil Survey of England and Wales 1:250,000 map Sheet 6 (South East England) 1983.

Rendzinas

Calcareous & argillic Pelosols

Brown calcareous earths & Brown earths

Paleo-argillic brown earths

Surface water gley soils (Stagnogleys)

Groundwater gley soils

Disturbed soils

Urban

Major soil groups	Soil groups	Soil subgroups	Soil series
1 **Terrestrial raw soils**: mineral soils without diagnostic horizons; not consisting wholly or partly of displaced material from pre-existing soil horizons	1.3 **Raw skeletal soils**: with naturally occurring bedrock or fragmented hard rock at 30 cm or less	None defined	None defined
	1.4 **Raw earths**: with naturally occurring loamy or clayey material other than recent alluvium extending to at least 30 cm depth	None defined	None defined
	1.5 **Man-made raw soils**: consisting of artificially displaced material	None defined	None defined
3 **Lithomorphic soils**: with distinct humose or peaty topsoil and no diagnostic B or gleyed subsurface horizon containing <40% CaCO$_3$	3.4 **Rendzinas**: on extremely calcareous (>40% CaCO$_3$) material other than recent alluvium	3.41 **Humic rendzinas**: with very dark humose A horizon	**Icknield**: loamy; lithoskeletal chalk (chalk or >40% chalk fragments within 30 cm depth)
		3.42 **Grey rendzinas**: with greyish non-humose A horizon	**Upton**: loamy; lithoskeletal chalk **Wantage**: loamy; over chalk at 30-80 cm depth
		3.43 **Brown rendzinas**: with brown or reddish brown A and/or thin Bw horizon containing <40% CaCO$_3$	**Andover**: silty; lithoskeletal chalk **Newmarket**: coarse loamy; lithoskeletal chalk **Rudham**: fine loamy; lithoskeletal chalk **Wallop**: clayey; lithoskeletal chalk
		3.44 **Colluvial rendzinas**: in recent colluvium >40 cm thick	**Gore**: chalky; loamy
		3.45 **Gleyic rendzinas**: with non-humose A horizon and ochreous mottles within 60 cm depth; shallow groundwater table	**Burwell**: loamy; passing to soft chalk **Ford End**: loamy; chalky drift **Gubblecote**: fine loamy over calcareous gravel
		3.47 **Stagnogleyic rendzinas**: with non-humose A horizon and ochreous mottles within 60 cm depth; slowly permeable	**Lode**: glauconitic clayey passing to clay or soft mudstone
4 **Pelosols**: slowly permeable clayey soils with diagnostic B horizon; subject to seasonal cracking; no loamy surface horizon >15 cm thick with <30% clay; no non-calcareous gleyed subsurface horizon extending below 40 cm depth	4.1 **Calcareous pelosols**: calcareous in or directly below a Bw or Bg horizon	4.11 **Typical calcareous pelosols**: includes all Calcareous pelosols	**Evesham**: swelling clayey passing to clay or soft mudstone **Hanslope**: on chalky drift
	4.3 **Argillic pelosols**: with diagnostic Bt (argillic) horizon	4.31 **Typical argillic pelosols**: includes all Argillic pelosols	**Faulkbourne**: on chalky drift
5 **Brown soils**: mineral soils excluding pelosols with diagnostic Bw or Bt horizon and no diagnostic gleyed subsurface horizon within 40 cm depth	5.1 **Brown calcareous earths**: with loamy or clayey Bw horizon in and/or over calcareous material other than recent alluvium	5.11 **Typical brown calcareous earths**: without gleying in upper 60 cm	**Badsey**: fine loamy over calcareous gravel **Coombe**: fine silty on chalky drift **Panholes**: fine silty over chalk within 80 cm **Soham**: fine loamy over chalk within 80 cm **Stretham**: clayey on chalky drift **Swaffham Prior**: coarse loamy over chalk within 80 cm

Major soil groups	Soil groups	Soil subgroups	Soil series
		5.12 **Gleyic brown calcareous earths**: with some gleying within upper 60 cm; shallow groundwater table	**Block**: fine loamy on chalky drift **Grove**: fine loamy over calcareous gravel **Milton**: fine loamy over flinty terrace deposits
		5.13 **Stagnogleyic brown calcareous earths**: with some gleying within upper 60 cm; slowly permeable within 80 cm	**Cannamore**: fine loamy over chalky drift **St Lawrence**: fine loamy or silty over clayey; passing to clay or soft mudstone
		5.14 **Colluvial brown calcareous earths**: in recent colluvium >40 cm thick	**Millington**: chalky; fine silty
	5.3 **Brown calcareous alluvial soils**: with loamy or clayey Bw horizon in recent alluvium; calcareous within 40 cm depth	5.32 **Gleyic brown calcareous alluvial soils**: predominantly loamy; some gleying within 60 cm depth	**Usher**: fine loamy in river alluvium
		5.33 **Pelogleyic brown calcareous alluvial soils**: predominantly clayey, with no loamy surface horizon 15 cm or more thick containing <30% clay	**Uffington**: in river alluvium
	5.4 **Brown earths**: with loamy or clayey Bw horizon in non-calcareous material other than recent alluvium	5.41 **Typical brown earths**: without gleying in upper 60 cm	**Hall**: coarse loamy over non-calcareous gravel **Wick**: coarse loamy in drift with siliceous stones
	5.5 **Brown sands**: non-calcareous sandy with no loamy surface horizon 30 cm or more thick	5.51 **Typical brown sands**: without diagnostic Bt (argillic) horizon; no gleying in upper 60 cm	**Newport**: in drift with siliceous stones
		5.54 **Argillic brown sands**: with diagnostic Bt (argillic) horizon; no gleying in upper 60 cm	**Ebstree**: in drift with siliceous stones **St Albans**: sandy-gravelly; with siliceous stones
	5.7 **Argillic brown earths**: predominantly loamy or clayey with diagnostic Bt (argillic) horizon not qualifying as paleo-argillic	5.71 **Typical argillic brown earths**: without gleying in upper 60 cm	**Charity**: fine silty in drift with siliceous stones **Efford**: fine loamy over non-calcareous gravel **Frilsham**: fine loamy over chalk **Garston**: fine silty over chalk **Hamble**: silty in stoneless drift **Ludford**: fine loamy in drift with siliceous stones **Maplestead**: coarse loamy in drift with siliceous stones **Melford**: fine loamy over clayey on chalky drift **Moulton**: coarse loamy on chalky drift **Weasenham**: fine loamy on chalky drift
		5.72 **Stagnogleyic argillic brown earths**: with gleying within upper 60 cm; slowly permeable within 80 cm	**Ashley**: fine loamy over clayey on chalky drift **Burlingham**: fine loamy on chalky drift **Bursledon:** fine loamy passing to loam or interbedded sand and clay **Loshes**: coarse loamy over clayey passing to clay **Oxpasture**: fine loamy or fine silty drift over clayey passing to clay **Ratsborough**: fine silty over clayey in drift with siliceous stones

Major soil groups	Soil groups	Soil subgroups	Soil series
		5.73 **Gleyic argillic brown earths**: with gleying within upper 60 cm; no slowly permeable subsurface horizon within 80 cm depth; shallow groundwater table	**Ellingham**: coarse loamy passing to loam or interbedded sand and clay **Hook**: silty in stoneless drift **Tidmarsh**: loamy-gravelly; with siliceous stones
	5.8 **Paleo-argillic brown earths**: predominantly loamy or clayey with diagnostic paleo-argillic Bt horizon	5.81: **Typical paleo-argillic brown earths**: without gleying in upper 60 cm	**Barrow**: coarse loamy over clayey on chalky drift **Bockmer**: loamy-gravelly; with siliceous stones **Carstens**: fine silty over clayey in drift with siliceous stones **Givendale**: clayey in drift with siliceous stones **Marlow**: fine loamy over clayey in drift with siliceous stones **Maxted**: coarse loamy in drift with siliceous stones **Sonning**: coarse loamy over non-calcareous gravel **Winchester**: clayey with siliceous stones
		5.82 **Stagnogleyic paleo-argillic brown earths**: with gleying within upper 60 cm; slowly permeable within 80 cm depth	**Batcombe**: fine silty over clayey in drift with siliceous stones **Berkhamsted**: coarse loamy over clayey in drift with siliceous stones **Hornbeam**: fine loamy over clayey in drift with siliceous stones **Horseley**: coarse loamy in drift with siliceous stones
6 **Podzolic soils**: with diagnostic podzolic B (Bh and/or Bs and/or Bf) horizon enriched in poorly ordered (amorphous) colloidal materials containing organic matter or aluminium and iron	6.3 **Podzols (*sensu stricto*)**: with light-coloured eluvial (Ea) horizon and/or Bh horizon and no peaty topsoil, thin ironpan (Bf) or immediately underlying gleyed horizon	6.34 **Paleo-argillic podzols**: with diagnostic paleo-argillic Bt horizon below the podzolic B	**Southampton**: sandy-gravelly; with siliceous stones
	6.4 **Gley podzols**: with diagnostic gleyed horizon below the podzolic B and no thin ironpan	6.43 **Stagnogley podzols**: with slowly permeable subsurface horizon within 80 cm depth	**Haldon**: coarse loamy over clayey in drift with siliceous stones
7 **Surface-water gley soils**: slowly permeable soils, excluding pelosols, in mineral materials other than recent alluvium; with non-calcareous gleyed subsurface (B or E and B) horizons starting within and extending below 40 cm depth; no immediately underlying relatively permeable gleyed horizon affected by mobile groundwater	7.1 **Stagnogley soils**: with distinct (non-humose, non-peaty) topsoil	7.11 **Typical stagnogley soils**: with loamy surface horizon at least 15 cm thick and a diagnostic Btg (argillic) horizon not qualifying as paleo-argillic	**Beccles**: fine loamy over clayey on chalky drift **Kings Newton**: coarse loamy over clayey passing to clay or soft mudstone **Prolleymoor**: fine silty over clayey in drift with siliceous stones **Wickham**: fine loamy or fine silty over clayey passing to clay or soft mudstone
		7.12 **Pelo-stagnogley soils**: predominantly clayey with no loamy surface horizon that is >15 cm thick and contains <30% clay; no paleo-argillic Btg horizon	**Denchworth**: swelling-clayey passing to clay or soft mudstone **Lawford**: swelling-clayey drift passing to clay or soft mudstone **Ragdale**: on chalky drift **Windsor**: swelling-clayey passing to brownish clay

Major soil groups	Soil groups	Soil subgroups	Soil series
		7.14 Paleo-argillic stagnogley soils: with paleo-argillic Btg horizon	**Essendon**: coarse loamy over clayey in drift with siliceous stones **Oak**: fine loamy over clayey in drift with siliceous stones
8 Groundwater gley soils: with distinct humose or peaty topsoil and gleyed subsurface horizons in recent alluvium and/or CG or relatively pervious Cg horizons affected by mobile groundwater	**8.1 Alluvial gley soils**: with distinct (non-humose, non-peaty) topsoil in loamy or clayey alluvium >30 cm thick	**8.11 Typical alluvial gley soils**: loamy; non-calcareous to at least 40 cm depth	**Conway**: fine silty in river alluvium **Enborne**: fine loamy in river alluvium **Racton**: silty over calcareous gravel
		8.12 Calcareous alluvial gley soils: loamy; calcareous within 40 cm depth	**Frome**: silty over calcareous gravel
		8.13 Pelo-alluvial gley soils: clayey; non-calcareous to at least 40 cm depth	**Fladbury**: in river alluvium **Midelney**: in river alluvium over peat
		8.14 Pelo-calcareous alluvial gley soils: clayey; calcareous within 40 cm depth	**Thames**: in river alluvium **Windrush**: in river alluvium over peat
	8.3 Cambic gley soils: with distinct (non-humose, non-peaty) topsoil and loamy or clayey Bg horizon in material other than recent alluvium	**8.32 Calcaro-cambic gley soils**: with loamy Bg horizon; calcareous within 40 cm depth	**Kelmscot**: fine loamy over calcareous gravel
		8.33 Pelo-cambic gley soils: with non-calcareous Bg horizon extending below 40 cm depth	**Carswell**: clayey over calcareous gravel
	8.4 Argillic gley soils: with distinct (non-humose, non-peaty) topsoil and diagnostic Btg (argillic) horizon	**8.41 Typical argillic gley soils**: with loamy topsoil	**Binstead**: loamy-gravelly; with siliceous stones **Curdridge**: coarse loamy passing to sand or soft sandstone **Hurst**: coarse loamy over non-calcareous gravel **Park Gate**: silty in stoneless drift
	8.5 Humic-alluvial gley soils: with humose or peaty topsoil; in loamy or clayey recent alluvium >30 cm thick	**8.52. Calcareous humic-alluvial gley soils**: calcareous within 40 cm of the mineral soil surface	**Gade**: silty over calcareous gravel
9 Man-made soils: with thick (>40 cm) man-made A horizon and/or disturbed soil material extending below 40 cm depth	**9.1 Man-made humus soils**: with thick man-made A horizon	**9.11 Sandy man-made humus soils**: sandy with or without >70% stones in at least half the upper 80 cm	None defined
		9.12 Earthy man-made humus soils: finer than sandy in more than half the upper 80 cm	None defined
	9.2 Disturbed soils: without thick man-made A horizon	None defined	None defined
10 Peat soils: with >40 cm of organic material within the upper 80 cm; no overlying mineral subsurface horizon extending below 30 cm depth	**10.2 Earthy peat soils**: with well decomposed earthy topsoil or mineral surface layer that does not pass through the fingers when a sample is squeezed in the hand	**10.22 Earthy eu-fibrous peat soils**: with partially decomposed (semifibrous or fibrous) peat at least 30 cm thick starting within 60 cm depth; pH (in $CaCl_2$) >4.0 in some part	**Altcar**: grass-sedge peat
		10.24 Earthy eutro-amorphous peat soils: with well-developed (amorphous) peat extending to at least 60 cm depth; pH (in $CaCl_2$) >4.0 in some part	**Adventurers**: humified peat

Table 7.1. Classification of Hertfordshire soils.

hostile environment strongly influences the way in which plant communities develop. Colonization also depends on the nature of the chalk itself. It is slower on harder layers, such as hardgrounds, than on softer layers that fragment easily under frost action to form a powdery mass (Smith, 1980), and the non-calcareous clay constituents in the West Melbury Marly Chalk Formation produce slightly different plant communities from those on the purer chalk of overlying formations.

Initial colonization on chalk is mainly by algae and bryophytes able to withstand surface desiccation in summer droughts. Early colonization also occurs from pioneer vascular plants, the species present depending on local seed sources, aspect and the characteristics of the chalk. Many initial pioneers, such as flattened meadow grass (*Poa compressa*) and the ephemeral weeds prickly sow-thistle (*Sonchus asper*) and common poppy (*Papaver rhoeas*), are not necessarily limited to calcareous substrates. However, many are, including several species of Asteraceae with basal rosettes that enhance survival in hostile conditions, or with strong tap-roots providing access to the water in subsurface pores and fissures. They include mouse-ear hawkweed (*Pilosella officinarum*), rough hawkbit (*Leontodon hispidus*) and greater knapweed (*Centaurea scabiosa*). Other pioneer species include leguminous plants able to fix nitrogen from the atmosphere, such as black medick (*Medicago lupulina*), kidney vetch (*Anthyllis vulneraria*) and bird's-foot trefoil (*Lotus corniculatus*), as well as calcium-loving species, such as common rest-harrow (*Ononis repens*). However, the nitrogen-fixing plants are vulnerable to excessive nitrogen migrating from strongly fertilized arable fields nearby. Descriptions and illustrations of these and other plants mentioned in this section are included in the Flora of Hertfordshire (James, 2009). Kidney vetch is important as the food plant of the small blue butterfly (*Cupido minimus*).

With the build-up of humus from the decay of initial colonizers and acquisition of nutrients from the atmosphere, some other calcicolous species may be able to colonize, if the site is near seed sources. These may include salad burnet (*Sanguisorba minor*), dwarf thistle (*Cirsium acaule*), fairy flax (*Linum catharticum*), ploughman's spikenard (*Inula conyzae*), common toadflax (*Linaria vulgaris*), autumn gentian (*Gentianella amarella*), blue fleabane (*Erigeron acer*) and wild carrot (*Daucus carota*). If the substrate is damp, colt's-foot (*Tussilago farfara*) can often be abundant for the first few years. If the site is near sources of woody species, the early colonizers may also include traveller's-joy (*Clematis vitalba*), wayfaring tree (*Viburnum lantana*) and wild privet (*Ligustrum vulgare*), or even large tree species such as sycamore (*Acer pseudoplatanus*). Some orchids, notably the bee orchid (*Ophrys apifera*) and pyramidal orchid (*Anacamptis pyramidalis*), are also common in the early successional stages on chalk, though they may not be evident for several years.

Even without nearby sources of woody species, the later succession from the short-herb vegetational stages usually progresses to include hawthorn (*Crataegus monogyna*), ash (*Fraxinus excelsior*), buckthorn (*Rhamnus cathartica*), dog rose (*Rosa canina*), common blackberry (*Rubus ulmifolius*)

and dewberry (*Rubus caesius*). Elder (*Sambucus nigra*), hazel (*Corylus avellana*) and common nettle (*Urtica dioica*) also colonize rapidly where nitrogen levels are high. Recently, non-native species, including walnut (*Juglans regia*) and butterfly-bush or buddleia (*Buddleja davidii*), have joined the list of woody species locally occurring on bare chalk.

Raw skeletal soils on non-calcareous gravels. On the well-drained Raw skeletal soils of abandoned gravel pits, free calcium is less abundant or absent, resulting in plant communities that are very different from those on chalk. Where calcium is completely absent, as on the weathered siliceous gravels of proto-Thames terraces, initial colonization is by nitrogen-fixing plants, such as white clover (*Trifolium repens*). The humus formed by their decomposition encourages other weeds typical of disturbed ground, including rosebay willowherb (*Chamaenerion angustifolium*), square-stalked willowherb (*Epilobium tetragonum*), american willowherb (*E. ciliatum*), white melilot (*Melilotus albus*), ribbed melilot (*M. officinalis*), curled dock (*Rumex crispus*), broad-leaved dock (*R. obtusifolius*), weld (*Reseda luteola*), common ragwort (*Senecio jacobaea*), creeping buttercup (*Ranunculus repens*), creeping cinquefoil (*Potentilla reptans*) and creeping thistle (*Cirsium arvense*), to establish themselves in the interstices between the pebbles. Later, rough grassland of false oat grass (*Arrhenatherum elatius*) with cock's-foot (*Dactylis glomerata*), hogweed (*Heracleum sphondylium*), yarrow (*Achillea millefolium*) and occasional bugloss (*Anchusa arvensis*) comes to dominate. Finally, species-poor scrub dominated by common hawthorn, elder and ash is characteristic, often including the introduced himalayan giant blackberry (*Rubus armeniacus*). Locally, where conditions are more acidic, creeping soft-grass (*Holcus mollis*) eventually takes over from the initial pioneers, and woody shrubs, including gorse (*Ulex europaeus*), broom (*Cytisus scoparius*), silver birch, sycamore and elder, may appear later.

Where the water table is near the surface, the vegetation is often more characteristic of semi-natural wetlands, and is dominated even from early stages by various willow (*Salix*) species, rushes (*Juncus* spp.), great willowherb (*Epilobium hirsutum*), the commoner sedges (*Carex* spp.), water figwort (*Scrophularia auriculata*), water forget-me-not (*Myosotis scorpioides*) and reed canary-grass (*Phalaris arundinacea*). A typical example of this assemblage was described at Amwell Quarry (TL 3712) in the lower Lea valley by James (1990).

Raw skeletal soils on glacial gravels. The glacial gravels excavated in parts of east and central Hertfordshire often contain chalk, other limestones and non-siliceous far-travelled rocks, and consequently have more free calcium and some other mineral nutrients than the proto-Thames gravels. Typical colonizing plants on these substrates include blue fleabane (*Erigeron acer*), early forget-me-not (*Myosotis ramosissima*), common stork's-bill (*Erodium cicutarium*), black medick (*Medicago lupulina*), wild carrot (*Daucus carota*), wild strawberry (*Fragaria vesca*), common centaury (*Centaurium erythraea*), ploughman's spikenard (*Inula conyzae*) and other plants characteristic of the Raw skeletal soils in abandoned chalk pits. Later stages of the succession on these gravels where the water table is near the surface are indicated by the HMWT reserves in the long abandoned gravel pits at Broad Colney (TL 177034) and Stocker's Lake, Rickmansworth (TL 044931). Stocker's Lake has marginal areas of reed and sedge marsh, and small areas of willow scrub and alder carr.

Raw earths. If the substrate is sandy or loamy rather than gravelly, pioneering quasi-heathland communities may develop on the resulting Raw earths, including foxglove (*Digitalis purpurea*), wood sage (*Teucrium scorodonia*), heath speedwell (*Veronica officinalis*), sheep's sorrel (*Rumex acetosella*) and eventually bracken (*Pteridium aquilinum*). In these situations, bramble is often again aggressively dominant, but is more likely to be the native *Rubus echinatus* typical of hedgerows.

Raw earths also occur locally on areas of exposed clay-rich deposits, such as road cuttings in London Clay or chalky till, abandoned brickpits and spoil tips of till associated with extraction of glacial gravels. The vegetation that develops on these also varies according to pH and the availability of free calcium. Neutral to acidic clay-rich deposits, such as those in abandoned areas of Bovingdon brickpit (TL 0103), have a quite distinctive flora, with abundant smaller willowherb species, including square-stalked willowherb (*Epilobium tetragonum*), bugle (*Ajuga reptans*), red bartsia (*Odontites vernus*), sheep's sorrel (*Rumex acetosella*), creeping soft-grass (*Holcus mollis*) and creeping bent grass (*Agrostis stolonifera*). On tips of calcareous clays, such as chalky till, another distinctive colonizing plant assemblage, including cowslip (*Primula veris*), glaucous sedge (*Carex flacca*) and bee orchid (*Ophrys apifera*), often develops.

Dry, thinly vegetated gravelly and sandy surfaces in abandoned pits often provide a suitable habitat for reptiles, such as common lizard (*Lacerta vivipara*), slow worm (*Anguis fragilis*) and grass snake (*Natrix natrix*), and flooded areas are often favoured by Daubenton's bat (*Myotis daubentonii*) (Clark, 2001).

Man-made raw soils. Occurring on many 'brownfield sites', these soils comprise a mixed bag of substrates, including brick rubble, mortar, plaster, broken concrete and waste tarmac from demolition of industrial or urban sites, waste from furnaces and coal-fired power stations and railway ballast. As a result, they show a wide range of colonizing vegetation types. Those associated with railway ballast, for example on some of the county's abandoned railway lines, including the HMWT reserve at Uxbridge Alderglade (TQ 056854), often contain rat's-tail fescue (*Vulpia myuros*), Oxford ragwort (*Senecio squalidus*), Canadian fleabane (*Conyza canadensis*), bird's-foot trefoil (*Lotus corniculatus*) and, less commonly, pale toadflax (*Linaria repens*). A mixed woody vegetation including goat willow (*Salix caprea*), silver birch, buddleia, himalayan giant blackberry (*Rubus armeniacus*), rosebay willowherb (*Chamaenerion*

angustofolium), common ragwort (*Senecio jacobaea*) and false oat-grass (*Arrhenatherum elatius*) frequently develops on concrete waste and other substrates with moderate calcium levels. Because concrete, mortar and plaster often contain fairly reactive calcium minerals other than carbonates, such as portlandite ($Ca(OH)_2$), gypsum ($CaSO_4.2H_2O$) and some calcium silicates, the calcium ions they release on weathering can combine with carbon dioxide and sequestrate it as insoluble calcite ($CaCO_3$), a process that may be valuable in mitigating the effects of increasing atmospheric carbon dioxide on global warming (Manning *et al.*, 2009).

Tips of pulverized fuel ash or 'fly-ash' removed from coal-fired power stations can develop unusual vegetation covers, especially where the material is deposited in damp sites. It is initially very alkaline (pH 10-11) but weathers rapidly, releasing mineral nutrients (K, P, Ca and some micronutrients) and becoming less alkaline within a few decades. Shaw (1990, 1992) studied soil and vegetation development on fly-ash dumped at various times over more than twenty years into lagoons in a disused gravel pit in the lower Lea valley close to Rye House power station (now closed) near Hoddesdon (TL 388088). The pioneer vegetation consisted mainly of nitrogen-fixers, such as white clover (*Trifolium repens*) and common vetch (*Vicia sativa*), with colt's-foot (*Tussillago farfara*), mugwort (*Artemisia vulgaris*), creeping thistle (*Cirsium arvense*) and the grasses cock's-foot (*Dactylis glomerata*), Yorkshire fog (*Holcus lanatus*) and red fescue (*Festuca rubra*) appearing later. After 10-15 years, some areas were invaded by white willow (*Salix alba*), osier (*S. viminalis*) and silver birch, with the occasional appearance of red campion (*Silene dioica*), various dandelions (*Taraxacum* spp.), black medick (*Medicago lupulina*) and orchids such as southern marsh-orchid (*Dactylorhiza praetermissa*), early marsh-orchid (*Dactylorhiza incarnata*) and common spotted-orchid (*Dactylorhiza fuchsii*). Rapid release of nutrients by weathering of the mineral-rich material in a damp environment apparently enables these orchids to thrive in the absence of the fungal mycorrhizae that normally supply nutrients from natural soils.

Major soil group 2 (Raw gley soils) is not present in Hertfordshire. Such soils occur in mineral sediment that has remained waterlogged since deposition, such as intertidal flats and other coastal situations.

Major soil group 3. Lithomorphic soils

These soils overlie bedrock or little altered unconsolidated material within 30 cm depth, and differ from Terrestrial raw soils in having prominent organo-mineral (A) or organic (O) surface horizons. In Hertfordshire, they are represented only by rendzinas on Chalk or chalky drift, which occur mainly on the Chiltern scarp and the steep sides of dry valleys incised into the Chiltern plateau. On the scarp they occur on both the gentle slopes of the marly Grey Chalk outcrop and on the steeper slopes cut in the overlying White Chalk.

Humic rendzinas, typifying this group, are almost entirely confined to areas that remain under semi-natural vegetation, including woodland, scrub and grassland communities (Smith 1980; Sawford 1990; James 1991, 1992) containing calcicoles that are rare or absent on non-calcareous soils nearby. They have very dark-coloured humus-rich A horizons (Plate 65), and generally give way in arable land to Grey or Brown rendzinas, which contain less organic matter because repeated shallow disturbance by ploughing has removed much of the original humus by oxidation. In Grey rendzinas the Ap horizons contain much finely divided chalk brought up by ploughing, and consequently appear almost white when dry, whereas the Brown rendzinas have less calcareous brown or reddish brown A horizons developed in very thin loamy or clayey superficial deposits. The Humic and Grey rendzinas have loamy A horizons, but the Brown rendzinas are more variable in texture, ranging from coarse loamy to clayey. In many parts of the county the Brown rendzinas are silty and probably derived from a thin layer of Late Devensian loess over the Chalk, but on the gently undulating chalklands between Baldock and Royston in northeast Hertfordshire they are coarse loamy because of a coversand component.

Colluvial, gleyic and stagnogleyic subgroups are also recognized, but occupy very limited areas. The first are in Late Holocene chalky colluvium, which has accumulated in minor valley bottoms and at the base of slopes long subject to repeated water erosion under cultivation. Organic matter contents are mainly derived from eroded topsoils upslope and consequently decrease gradually or irregularly with depth. Buried A horizons, marking earlier (late Devensian or early Holocene) ground surfaces, are locally discernible. Gleyic and stagnogleyic rendzinas are distinguished by the occurrence of yellowish or ochreous mottles indicative of gleying within 60 cm depth. The former are confined to low ground on the Grey Chalk or on chalky drift, where the groundwater table is close to the surface or is retained above impervious bedrock. The latter are restricted to rare erosional sites, where the topsoil is immediately underlain by very calcareous but relatively impermeable material, such as compact chalky till.

Agriculture. In arable cultivation the topsoil of most Rendzinas is puffy and difficult to consolidate to a firm seedbed, with the result that germination is poor in dry conditions. Also young plants can be damaged by frost heave or wind exposure in winter and early spring. Generous fertilizer applications to improve N, P and K levels are necessary for high yields of many arable crops, and Mg deficiency can occur in cereals. Although the Rendzinas are much thinner than other chalkland soils, crops usually maintain good growth during periods of spring and summer drought. This is because, even on steep, well-drained slopes, plant roots can access the large supplies of water retained in the very fine matrix pores of the White Chalk. The arable fields have a characteristic range of weeds, including common toadflax (*Linaria vulgaris*), small toadflax (*Chaenorhinum minus*), henbit dead-nettle (*Lamium amplexicaule*), venus's looking-glass (*Legousia hybrida*) and the rare sharp-fruited corn-salad (*Valerianella dentata*) (James, 2009).

Chalk grassland. The areas of the Humic rendzinas under grass have considerable scientific interest because of their unusually diverse, species-rich herb communities and large soil mesofaunal populations, including earthworms, ants, mites, millipedes and woodlice (Avery, 1964; Smith, 1980). They occur mainly on the Chiltern scarp-slope between Tring and Royston, but there are several small areas elsewhere in the county. The grassland of similar soils on Chalk in northwest Kent was immortalized by Darwin (1859) in his famous book on the origin of species.

The reason for the large reserves of soil organic matter in the Rendzinas is uncertain. Until recently, it was thought that it accumulated under a dense woodland cover that dominated the English chalklands for much of the early Holocene. But pollen and land snail records suggest that in some areas grassland has persisted since the Late Devensian, possibly because of grazing by large herbivores (Vera, 2004). A mosaic of closed woodland, open (park) woodland and grassland, as suggested by Allen and Gardiner (2009), may explain the occurrence of the discrete, species-rich communities characteristic of Rendzinas on steep slopes such as the Chalk scarp. Many chalkland areas were certainly deforested for Neolithic and Bronze Age cultivation of arable crops, which would have caused erosion and depleted nutrients. They were then either used for pasture or were abandoned and developed into secondary woodland, and soil organic matter could have increased under both of these land uses.

Grazing stock, including sheep, cattle and goats, subsequently maintained open conditions in many areas, though shifting patterns of cultivation have maintained an overall diversity of vegetation since pre-Roman times. In some areas, only certain specialized plants could survive the shallow dry soils and exposure as well as the grazing pressures. The Norman introduction of rabbits may have added to pressure on the grassland, but also prevented growth of scrub. By burrowing, the rabbits have also created small areas of bare soil (scrapes), which are important for maintaining the presence of less competitive pioneer species. Scrapes also form around badger (*Meles meles*) setts, which commonly occur on upper valley slopes adjacent to the margins of woodland established on clayey non-calcareous (Paleo-argillic brown earth) soils of the Chiltern plateau (Clark, 2001, p. 180).

In the county, the true extent of chalk grassland that has survived intact through many or all of these land use changes is uncertain. Mediaeval periods may have seen extensive arable cultivation, but by Tudor times extensive sheep rearing was prevalent. Since then, there has been a progressive decrease in the total area of chalk grassland, through inclosure of common grazing during the late 18th century and the effects of ploughing for arable agriculture during and after the Napoleonic Wars (1790-1815). More recently, the intensive agricultural activity after the Second World War (1939-45) again reduced the extent of old chalk grassland. A decline in sheep farming since the mid-20th century and reduced rabbit grazing through the introduction of myxomatosis in the 1950s have also led to the overgrowth of much chalk grassland and its loss to scrub. Only 177 ha of even moderately degraded forms of this habitat remain, and most sites are less than 1 ha in area (Cuming, 1997). They include parts of the HMWT reserves at Therfield Heath (TL 335400), Alpine Meadow (SP 989102) and Aldbury Nowers (SP 949140 and SP 952129), and other sites at Telegraph Hill (TL 117288) and Chorleywood Dell (TQ 038971). Over the last 20-30 years there have been attempts to enhance some sites and extend the habitat by reintroducing grazing in limited areas, for example on Roughdown Common (TL 0405) near Boxmoor, Coombe Bottom (TL 3138) near Kelshall, Therfield Heath, Aldbury Nowers, Tring Park (SP 9210) and Ivinghoe Hills (SP 9616). However, these have met with variable success.

Indicators of ancient grassland. The existing patches of chalk grassland have a range of highly characteristic plant species, many of which occur in no other part of the county, though they can be found on limestones in other parts of Britain. Some of these species are often regarded as indicators of ancient grassland, though the uncertainty over survival of the habitat at most sites makes identification of the indicator species somewhat uncertain. Many may have recently recolonized the disturbed ground of animal scrapes from nearby sources of seed. Nevertheless, there are several plants that seem to be limited to ancient sites, including the pasque flower (*Pulsatilla vulgaris*), lesser meadow-rue (*Thalictrum minus*), bastard-toadflax (*Thesium humifusum*), purple milk-vetch (*Astragalus danicus*), field fleawort (*Tephroseris integrifolia*), meadow oat-grass (*Helictotrichon pratense*), crested hair-grass (*Koeleria macrantha*), horseshoe vetch (*Hippocrepis comosa*), squinancywort (*Asperula cynanchica*), common rock-rose (*Helianthemum nummularium*) and dropwort (*Filipendula vulgaris*).

Other grassland species. Numerous other species characteristic of chalk grassland, and often limited to it, are probably present because they are better able to colonize open or disturbed ground and may not be true indicators of ancient grassland. These include wild thyme (*Thymus polytrichus*), basil thyme (*Clinopodium acinos*), large thyme (*T. pulegioides*), wild marjoram (*Origanum vulgare*), common eyebright (*Euphrasia nemorosa*), chalk eyebright (*Euphrasia pseudokerneri*), harebell (*Campanula rotundifolia*), clustered bellflower (*Campanula glomerata*), lady's bedstraw (*Galium verum*), carline thistle (*Carlina vulgaris*), welted thistle (*Carduus crispus*), woolly thistle (*Cirsium eriophorum*), dwarf thistle (*Cirsium acaule*), spotted cat's-ear (*Hypochaeris maculata*), rough hawkbit (*Leontodon hispidus*), hawkweed oxtongue (*Picris hieracioides*), mouse-ear hawkweed (*Pilosella officinarum*), grassland hawkweed (*Hieracium nemophilum*), ploughman's spikenard (*Inula conyzae*), quaking-grass (*Briza media*), sheep's fescue (*Festuca ovina*), downy oatgrass (*Helictotrichon pubescens*), upright brome (*Bromopsis erecta*), tor-grass (*Brachypodium rupestre*), bulbous buttercup (*Ranunculus bulbosus*), thyme-leaved sandwort (*Arenaria serpyllifolia*), hairy violet (*Viola hirta*), wild mignonette (*Reseda lutea*), cowslip

(*Primula veris*), meadow saxifrage (*Saxifraga granulata*), salad burnet (*Sanguisorba minor*), sainfoin (*Onobrychis viciifolia*), kidney vetch (*Anthyllis vulneraria*), bird's-foot trefoil (*Lotus corniculatus*), common rest-harrow (*Ononis repens*), black medick (*Medicago lupulina*), perennial flax (*Linum perenne*), fairy flax (*Linum catharticum*), yellow-wort (*Blackstonia perfoliata*), common milkwort (*Polygala vulgaris*), hoary plantain (*Plantago media*), field scabious (*Knautia arvensis*), small scabious (*Scabiosa columbaria*), wild candytuft (*Iberis amara*), greater knapweed (*Centaurea scabiosa*), its parasite knapweed broomrape (*Orobanche elatior*), autumn gentian (*Gentianella amarella*), chiltern gentian (*Gentianella germanica*) and various dandelions (*Taraxacum* spp.).

Chalk grassland also supports a range of orchids (Bateman, 1981), including common twayblade (*Neottia ovata*), common spotted orchid (*Dactylorhiza fuchsii*), and the rare man orchid (*Orchis anthropophora*) and burnt orchid (*Neotinea ustulata*). Some are found especially in formerly disturbed sites, such as the bee orchid (*Ophrys apifera*), pyramidal orchid (*Anacamptis pyramidalis*) and the rare downland fragrant-orchid (*Gymnadenia conopsea*).

Many insect species, limited by their food plants or other requirements, are also found only on chalk grassland, including the chalkhill blue butterfly (*Lysandra coridou*), whose larval food plant is horseshoe vetch, and the leaf beetle (*Timarcha goettingensis*).

Chalk scrub. Areas invaded by scrub because of decreased grazing usually contain ubiquitous species, mainly common hawthorn (*Crataegus monogyna*), but may also include species common on calcareous substrates, such as wayfaring tree (*Viburnum lantana*), whitebeam (*Sorbus aria*), spindle (*Euonymus europaeus*), sweet-briar (*Rosa rubiginosa*), wild privet (*Ligustrum vulgare*), spurge laurel (*Daphne laureola*) and buckthorn (*Rhamnus cathartica*), the last of which is the food plant of the brimstone butterfly (*Gonepteryx rhamni*). There are also rare occurrences of juniper (*Juniperus communis*); on the chalk, it now occurs only at Sheethanger Common, Roughdown Common and Aldbury Nowers (James, 2009), but it was probably more widespread in the past. In addition, box (*Buxus sempervirens*) may have been common in the past, but it no longer occurs as a genuinely wild species in Hertfordshire. Small groves of box at Ivinghoe (SP 966157) are probably the remains of an 18th century plantation by the Duke of Bridgwater (Mead, 2003, pp. 1 & 84). Although yew (*Taxus baccata*) forms very characteristic stands on chalk in some other parts of the country, it does not seem to have done so in Hertfordshire, though it is now widespread as a secondary colonist.

Major soil group 4. Pelosols

These are heavy clay soils formed from argillaceous bedrock formations (e.g. Gault Clay) or fine-textured Pleistocene deposits (e.g. chalky till), and named from the Greek word *pelos* (= clay). They differ from the related Pelo-stagnogley soils of Major soil group 7 in lacking a non-calcareous Bg or Btg horizon starting within and extending below 40 cm depth. Three Pelosol groups have been distinguished nationally and are not further divided at subgroup level, but of these only Calcareous and Argillic pelosols have been recognized in Hertfordshire.

Calcareous pelosols. These are extensive on the Anglian chalky tills in eastern parts of the county, and also occur on Gault Clay northwest of Tring and north of Ashwell. They have dark A horizons overlying brown or olive-coloured Bw and/or Bg horizons, which have been only weakly decalcified by leaching. Fine ochreous and greyish mottling appears at depths ranging from 30 to 60 cm, and becomes more pronounced in the greyer Bcg and more calcareous C horizons. The substrate below 1-2 m can be virtually impervious, but the upper subsoil is penetrated by a network of shrinkage cracks, which divide it into prismatic or angular blocky aggregates of varying size. The cracks open following rain-free periods in spring and summer, permitting ingress of air and water. But during autumn and winter they progressively close as the clay swells, so that, once the considerable capacity of the dried soil to absorb water is satisfied, the upper horizons are subject to waterlogging unless there is effective artificial drainage. Because drainage is restricted in this way, calcium carbonate leached from the upper (A and Bw) horizons is partly reprecipitated as whitish nodules or incoherent segregations usually at depths between 60 and 120 cm.

Argillic pelosols. Characterized by a clayey Bt (argillic) horizon, these Pelosols are associated with the Calcareous pelosols on chalky tills forming gently undulating plateaux in eastern parts of the county. In contrast to the Calcareous pelosols, the B horizon of Argillic pelosols is completely or almost completely decalcified and contains significantly more clay than horizons above and below. However, the additional clay makes little difference to the drainage characteristics which, as in the Calcareous pelosols, are determined mainly by the seasonal subsurface crack patterns.

Agriculture. The clayey topsoils of Pelosols can be cultivated satisfactorily only over a narrow range of moisture contents, so careful timing of soil preparation is important in arable farming. As there are few opportunities for spring cultivation, the preferred crops are autumn-sown cereals and oilseed rape. Indeed, these soils provide probably the most extensive areas of cereal cultivation in the county. Characteristic weeds of the arable fields include Babington's poppy (*Papaver dubium* ssp. *lecoquii*), night-flowering catchfly (*Silene noctiflora*), broad-leaved spurge (*Euphorbia platyphyllos*) and round-leaved fluellen (*Kickxia spuria*).

Some of the land is in grass, but winter stocking is restricted by the risk of poaching (formation of water-filled depressions by animal hooves) in wet conditions. The main grasses of unimproved pasture are tall fescue (*Festuca arundinacea*) and meadow foxtail (*Alopecurus pratensis*), which are often accompanied by strawberry clover (*Trifolium fragiferum*), sulphur clover (*T. ochroleucon*), meadow crane's-bill (*Geranium columbinum*), greater

burnet-saxifrage (*Pimpinella major*), devil's-bit scabious (*Succisa pratensis*) and hoary ragwort (*Senecio erucifolius*) (James, 2009). In wetter areas, false fox-sedge (*Carex otrubae*) and pendulous sedge (*Carex pendula*) often occur. The HMWT reserve and SSSI at Blagrove Common (TL 328337) near Sandon is a rare area of unimproved marshy and dry grassland on Pelosols derived from chalky till. It has been grazed by cattle and other animals for several centuries, the wetter, poached areas providing an important habitat for various marsh orchids, such as the southern marsh orchid (*Dactylorhiza pratermissa*) and early marsh orchid (*Dactylorhiza incarnata*).

Woodlands. In northeast Hertfordshire, the Pelosols on chalky till support numerous small areas of ancient (Mediaeval or older) ash-field maple-hazel woodland, which have been extensively coppiced in the past. Examples include Great Hormead Park Wood (TL 4129), Broadfield Great Wood (TL 3231) near Throcking, Capons Wood (TL 3632) near Chipping, Friars Wood (TL 3232) near Rushden and Northey Wood (TL 4033) at Anstey. Where the Argillic pelosols have slightly acidic A horizons, as in northern parts of the HMWT reserve at Balls Wood (TL 3410) and the western part of the HMWT reserve of Pryor's Wood (TL 2626) on the eastern side of Stevenage, coppiced hornbeam (*Carpinus betulus*) replaces much of the field maple, and pedunculate oak (*Quercus robur*) may also occur.

The shrub layer of these woodlands usually includes midland hawthorne (*Crataegus laevigata*), blackthorn (*Prunus spinosa*), dogwood (*Swida sanguinea*), hybrid dog-rose (*Rosa × scabriuscula*), dewberry (*Rubus caesius*) and elder (*Sambucus nigra*), sometimes also wild privet (*Ligustrum vulgare*), wayfaring tree (*Viburnum lantana*) and spindle (*Euonymus europaeus*). Many of the woods have a fairly diverse ground flora, including primrose (*Primula vulgaris*), early dog-violet (*Viola reichenbachiana*), early purple orchid (*Orchis mascula*), common twayblade (*Neottia ovata*), wood anemone (*Anemone nemorosa*), sanicle (*Sanicula europaea*), glaucous sedge (*Carex flacca*), the woodland subspecies of tufted hair-grass (*Deschampsia cespitosa* ssp. *parviflora*) and occasionally herb paris (*Paris quadrifolia*), greater butterfly-orchid (*Platanthera chlorantha*) and oxlip (*Primula elatior*). However, because of the decline in coppicing in recent decades, with less light reaching the woodland floor, and an increase in fallow deer populations, the ground flora of some woods has been greatly reduced since the 1960s, and now consists of a dense mat of dog's mercury (*Mercurialis perennis*), perhaps with a few bluebells (*Hyacinthoides non-scripta*), though nowhere do the bluebells form a complete carpet, as in some Chiltern woods.

Major soil group 5. Brown soils

These are soils, excluding Pelosols, with Bw or Bt horizons, usually brown or reddish brown, that extend below 30 cm depth and have no diagnostic gleyed horizon within 40 cm depth. Other properties, including texture and base status, vary greatly depending on the parent material and the kind and degree of alteration it has undergone. Of the eight soil groups distinguished nationally, six are represented in Hertfordshire. Of these, the Brown calcareous earths and Brown calcareous alluvial soils have Bw horizons developed in calcareous sediments, and remain calcareous throughout or below 40-50 cm depth. In contrast, the Brown earths, Brown sands, Argillic brown earths and Paleo-argillic brown earths comprise originally non-calcareous or more deeply decalcified soils, which are acidic unless ground chalk or agricultural lime has recently been added. Each soil group is typified by freely draining profiles showing little or no evidence for gleying. However, variants transitional to Surface-water gley soils and Groundwater gley soils are placed in stagnogleyic and gleyic subgroups respectively. Variants in Late Holocene calcareous colluvial deposits are also set apart at subgroup level as Colluvial brown calcareous earths.

Brown calcareous earths. In Hertfordshire these soils have formed in chalky drifts containing variable proportions of loamy or clayey material. Most are in head (gelifluction) deposits occurring on the floors of broad dry chalkland through-valleys and on low ground northwest of the Chiltern scarp. Apart from the colluvial variants, they are partly decalcified by leaching, and are distinguished from associated Rendzinas by the appearance of a brown Bw horizon similar in texture to the A horizon and differentiated from the underlying parent material by colour and development of soil structure. Typical brown calcareous earths with good drainage and no evidence of gleying in the upper 60 cm of the profile are more widespread than those occurring in the gleyic and stagnogleyic subgroups. On the chalky till in east Hertfordshire they occur mainly on the edges of interfluves, where the till is more permeable because it thins over gravel or chalk. The Gleyic brown calcareous earths form small areas near streams where the groundwater table is close to the surface, and the Stagnogleyic brown calcareous earths occur where slowly permeable calcareous clay (e.g. Gault Clay) or chalky till occurs within 80 cm depth.

Brown calcareous alluvial soils. These form narrow strips in loamy calcareous Holocene alluvium, often on natural levées slightly elevated above areas occupied by other alluvial soils. Where the alluvium is clayey to the surface, polygonal crack patterns often develop in dry seasons.

Brown earths. Soils of this group have loamy surface and Bw horizons often overlying non-calcareous flint-rich Pleistocene gravels forming low river terraces. They lack evidence of gleying in the upper 60 cm. Where the loamy upper deposits are absent or replaced by sandy sediments, Brown earths give way to Brown sands, which are often Argillic brown sands with a weakly developed Bt (argillic) horizon enriched in illuvial clay. Argillic brown earths with loamy or silty A and clay-enriched Bt horizons are widespread on a range of deposits in Hertfordshire, including Chalk, Reading Beds, chalky and flinty Pleistocene

deposits and loess. Stagnogleyic variants with evidence of gleying in the upper 60 cm occur where slowly permeable clay occurs within 80 cm depth, and Gleyic argillic brown earths exist locally on lower ground where the groundwater table rises into the subsoil in winter. In thin section, the additional (illuvial) clay deposited in the Bt horizon can be recognized as strongly birefringent (well-orientated) coatings on the walls of the pores and channels that conduct water percolating through the soil.

Paleo-argillic brown earths. These soils are characterized by a diagnostic paleo-argillic Bt horizon formed in one or more interglacial periods of the Pleistocene on parent materials deposited before the Ipswichian Stage (MIS 5e). As defined by Avery (1980, pp. 30-31), this horizon differs from the argillic Bt (Late Devensian to Holocene in age) in possessing (a) redder matrix colours or mottles not inherited from a red or red-mottled pre-Quaternary rock, and (b) greater concentrations of bright yellow or red illuvial clay, which in thin section is often seen to be no longer associated with the original subsoil pores and channels in which the clay was deposited. The incorporation of fragmentary illuvial clay bodies into the soil matrix probably resulted from periglacial disturbance of the interglacial soil during the Devensian or possibly earlier cold stages of the Pleistocene. The widespread occurrence of Paleo-argillic brown earths on the Chilterns and in other parts of the county explains why Chauncy (1826, Vol. 1, p. 2) described the soil of Hertfordshire as consisting 'in many places of a red earth mixt with gravel'.

Typical paleo-argillic brown earths, with no evidence of gleying in the upper 60 cm of the profile, occur on chalky tills in areas where aeolian sand has been incorporated into the upper layers, on flinty glaciofluvial and river terrace gravels, often also with admixtures of aeolian sand or silt (loess), and over Upper Chalk where a thin (<1 m) layer of Clay-with-flints *sensu stricto* emerges from beneath the Plateau Drift of the Chiltern dip-slope interfluves (e.g. on the upper slopes of dry valleys) (Plate 26).

Stagnogleyic paleo-argillic brown earths, with evidence of gleying within the upper 60 cm of the profile, are extensive where the Plateau Drift is thicker and also slowly permeable below 80 cm because it is derived principally from a cover of Reading Beds clay. They occur mainly on higher parts of the Chilterns between the Beane valley and the south-western county boundary near the Bulbourne valley, but also extend onto parts of the Chilterns in the adjacent county of Buckinghamshire. Late Devensian loess is extensively incorporated into upper layers of the Plateau Drift, with the result that most of the Stagnogleyic paleo-argillic brown earths of the Chiltern interfluves have silty or loamy upper (A and E) horizons. Between St Albans and Baldock, Stagnogleyic paleo-argillic brown earths also occur on chalky till covering the Chalk on lower footslopes of the Chilterns at heights of 100-125 m OD.

Agriculture. Most soils in the Brown earth, Brown sands, Argillic brown earth and Paleo-argillic brown earth groups have silty or loamy surface horizons, and are easily worked with plenty of opportunities for spring and autumn cultivations in most years. However, the timing of cultivation is more critical where the topsoils are clayey, for example on chalky till in eastern parts of the county. Consequently many areas are used for arable cultivation, principally for cereals, but there are various limitations in arable agriculture. First, they are all naturally acidic and require frequent liming. Second, the Brown sands retain little water available to plants, with the result that in dry summer periods grass and arable crops grow poorly for lack of water. Third, crops grown on the Brown sands can also suffer from deficiencies of mineral nutrients, especially K, Mg and some trace elements. Fourth, the periods available for cultivation of the Stagnogleyic paleo-argillic brown earths are more restricted than for other Brown soils, especially in spring, and subsoil waterlogging can decrease crop yields compared with most of the better drained soils. Finally, the abundance of flints in soils derived from gravels and Plateau Drift increase the wear rate of farm implements (ploughs, harrows, etc) and tractor tyres, and can cause damage to mechanically harvested root crops, such as potatoes and sugar beet.

In arable cultivation the Brown sands present additional problems resulting from the weak structure of their surface (Ap) horizon, which leads to crusting or capping (the formation under heavy rain of a thin hard surface layer that germinating seedlings often find impenetrable) and to erosion by surface runoff under heavy rain. The eroded soil is often an environmental hazard, damaging wildlife by introducing fertilizers and pesticides into streams, ponds and lakes, and in extreme circumstances blocking roads and drainage systems or swamping houses built in footslope positions. Because of the wide range of problems associated with Brown sands, they are really unsuitable for arable cultivation, and should be restricted to pasture or woodland.

Soil acidity. In Hertfordshire the problem of soil acidity has long been counteracted by application of chalk. In areas where chalk occurs near the land surface, this was obtained from small quarries and carted short distances for spreading on fields. But for the Stagnogleyic paleo-argillic brown earths occurring on more extensive parts of the Chiltern plateau, long-distance transportation from the nearest chalk pit was often avoided by excavating chalk from special pits dug by hand beneath the thick cover of Plateau Drift. This work was usually done by itinerant gangs of men known as chalk-drawers (Plate 61), who were paid initially to sink a shaft 10 m or more through the Plateau Drift and uppermost layers of soft puggy or putty chalk, then to raise the underlying hard chalk to the surface by pulley and rope and finally spread it on adjacent fields. With repeated use, some of the pits developed into large 'chalk mines' (Section 10.3). Arthur Young (1804) described the method in detail and regarded it as characteristic of Hertfordshire, though it has probably been used also in other areas where the Chalk is covered by thick Plateau Drift, such as the North Downs in Kent and Surrey. As a trade it continued until the 1930s, by which time transportation over longer distances had become possible by lorry or tractor-drawn cart. Re-application of

Plate 61. Gang of chalk drawers at Rothamsted Farm 1913 (Copyright Rothamsted Research).

chalk was usually necessary every 10-20 years, and over this time the shaft partly collapsed, leaving a surface depression several metres across. This often provided easier access for future operations, but since their last use many such depressions have been progressively infilled, though some sites remain as shallow 'dell-holes' near field margins. On the Chilterns, the word *dell* is often incorporated into farmer's names for fields where chalk was extracted in this way (e.g. Chalkdell Field) (Gover *et al.*, 1938). In addition to counteracting soil acidity, chalking also made heavy clay soils easier to plough, removed acidophilous weeds, such as common sorrel (*Rumex acetosa*) and scentless mayweed (*Tripleurospermum inodorum*), and decreased the incidence of slugs (Evershed, 1864).

Woodlands. On higher parts of the Chiltern plateau the various soil limitations to crop growth are also accompanied by minor climatic limitations (wind exposure and increased frost frequency). Consequently many areas of Paleo-argillic brown earths in these areas remain under old semi-natural beech (*Fagus sylvatica*) and mixed oak woodlands (James, 2009). The beech woods often have a calcifuge flora including holly (*Ilex aquifolium*), rowan (*Sorbus aucuparia*), broad buckler-fern (*Dryopteris dilatata*), wood-sorrel (*Oxalis acetosella*), honeysuckle (*Lonicera periclymenum*), foxglove (*Digitalis purpurea*), common dog-violet (*Viola riviniana*), wood melick (*Melica uniflora*), slender St John's wort (*Hypericum pulchrum*) and bracken (*Pteridium aquilinum*). Orchids such as the violet helleborine (*Epipactis purpurata*) also occur occasionally (Bateman, 1981).

Where the beechwoods extend downslope onto base-rich Brown calcareous earths and Humic rendzinas on the scarp-slope and dry-valley sides, other tree and shrub species occur alongside beech, including wild cherry (*Prunus avium*), ash (*Fraxinus excelsior*), hazel (*Corylus avellana*), and sometimes field maple (*Acer campestre*), spindle (*Euonymus europaeus*), whitebeam (*Sorbus aria*), wayfaring tree (*Viburnum lantana*), dogwood (*Swida sanguinea*) and guelder rose (*Viburnum opulus*). The ground flora also changes, with the appearance of primrose (*Primula vulgaris*), early dog-violet (*Viola reichenbachiana*), wood false-brome (*Brachypodium sylvaticum*), sanicle (*Sanicula europaea*), deadly nightshade (*Atropa belladonna*) and fly orchid (*Ophrys insectifera*).

In the mixed oak woodlands, which rarely extend downslope onto the base-rich soils, stands of pedunculate oak (*Quercus robur*) are usually accompanied by subordinate ash (*Fraxinus excelsior*), with areas of coppiced hazel (*Corylus avellana*) and a field layer of bramble. The bramble is usually the woodland species *Rubus rufescens*, but may also include others, some of which (e.g. *R. pedemontanus*) are rare beyond the Chilterns. Bluebell (*Hyacinthoides non-scripta*) is usually abundant, and other common plants include yellow archangel (*Lamiastrum galeobdolon*, ssp. *montanum*), wood millet (*Milium effusum*), greater stitchwort (*Stellaria holostea*), enchanter's nightshade (*Circaea lutetiana*), wood spurge (*Euphorbia amygdaloides*), pignut (*Conopodium majus*) and common

hemp-nettle (*Galeopsis tetrahit*). Locally hornbeam (*Carpinus betulus*) can occur, and the woodland is then transitional to those common in central Hertfordshire, which usually occur on Stagnogleyic paleo-argillic brown earths derived from chalky till. In the Chiltern oakwoods, hornbeam is close to its northern limit in southeast England.

The differences in woodland composition between the acidic Paleo-argillic brown earths on the Chiltern plateau and the more alkaline Brown calcareous earths and Humic rendzinas of the valley sides are found also in the roadside hedgerows. In parts of northwest Hertfordshire between the M1, Hemel Hempstead and the northern county boundary, the hedgerows were surveyed botanically by Kingsbury (1987). He showed that oak (*Quercus robur*), ash (*Fraxinus excelsior*), hornbeam (*Carpinus betulus*) and wild cherry (*Prunus avium*) are more common in hedgerows on the plateau, whereas field maple (*Acer campestre*), wayfaring tree (*Virburnum lantana*), buckthorn (*Rhamnus catharticus*), spindle (*Euonymus europaeus*) and dogwood (*Swida sanguinea*) prefer soils on the valley sides.

In parts of southern Hertfordshire and north London, some long-established hornbeam woodlands remain in areas where Brown sands on Reading Beds sand, Pebble Gravels or proto-Thames terrace gravels have soil limitations (acidity, low water retention, insufficient mineral nutrients) too severe for arable cultivation. The hornbeam (*Carpinus betulus*) is here accompanied mainly by sessile oak (*Quercus petraea*), with subordinate alder buckthorn (*Frangula alnus*) and buckthorn (*Rhamnus cathartica*). Examples occur in parts of Symondshyde Great Wood (TL 1910), Sherrardspark Wood (TL 2313), Broxbourne Woods (TL 0889) and Ruislip Woods (TQ 0889) (Salisbury, 1916, 1918). Hornbeam-rich woodlands also occur on less acidic clay-rich soils (mainly Pelosols on chalky till and Pelo-stagnogley soils on London Clay) in eastern parts of the county, but these differ in containing abundant pedunculate oak (*Quercus robur*) instead of sessile oak and also in numerous minor components of the tree, shrub and herb layers.

The Rothamsted 'wilderness' sites. The succession of secondary woodland communities likely to develop naturally on the Paleo-argillic brown earths of the Chilterns after arable use is indicated by two areas of 'wilderness' at Rothamsted Experimental Station, which were set aside from previous arable land in the 1880s and have remained under scientific observation but with no human intervention up to the present day (Harmer *et al.*, 2001). One of these, Geescroft Wilderness (TL 132128), had previously been part of an experimental site growing field beans (*Vicia faba*) continuously from 1847 to 1878 and a grass-clover mixture from 1883 to 1885, and had a neutral soil (pH 7.0-7.1) in 1883. Since the land was fenced off in 1886 the soil pH has gradually decreased and had reached 4.4 in 1999 (Poulton *et al.*, 2003). The woodland is now mainly pedunculate oak (*Quercus robur*) with subordinate ash (*Fraxinus excelsior*), hawthorn (*Crataegus monogyna*), field maple (*Acer campestre*), wild cherry (*Prunus avium*), holly (*Ilex aquifolium*) and English elm (*Ulmus procera*). The ground flora is sparse, consisting mainly of bluebell (*Hyacinthoides non-scripta*), ivy (*Hedera helix*) and bramble (*Rubus fruticosus* group).

The other, Broadbalk Wilderness (TL 121136) (Plate 62), was part of the famous Broadbalk Winter Wheat Experiment from 1843 to 1881, and here the soil was originally alkaline (pH 7.9-8.1 in 1881) because it had previously been generously chalked. It is now slightly less alkaline (pH 7.4 in 1999), and the woodland is dominated by ash with some hawthorn, sycamore (*Acer pseudoplanatus*), field maple and pedunculate oak, and an understory consisting mainly of ivy with some bramble and dog's mercury (*Mercurialis perennis*). Changes recorded in the vegetation of the two wilderness sites over the century or so of their history were detailed by Harmer *et al.* (2001). The botanical differences between them can be attributed mainly to the different pH values inherited from the previous arable management.

Grasslands. Semi-natural grassland is rare on the Palaeo-argillic brown earths and Calcareous brown earths of the Chilterns, owing to the expansion of arable agriculture and pasture improvement, but where it does exist it includes some distinctive plant assemblages. The deeper Palaeo-argillic brown earths developed on Plateau Drift have a somewhat calcifuge flora dominated by common bent grass (*Agrostis capillaris*) and red fescue (*Festuca rubra*), with subordinate sweet vernal grass (*Anthoxanthum odoratum*), Yorkshire fog (*Holcus lanatus*) and occasional creeping bent (*Agrostis stolonifera*), cock's-foot (*Dactylis glomerata*) and field wood-rush (*Luzula campestris*). Associated herbs include common knapweed (*Centaurea nigra*), common cat's ear (*Hypochaeris radicata*), sheep's sorrel (*Rumex acetosella*), pignut (*Conopodium majus*), lesser stitchwort (*Stellaria graminea*) and occasional harebell (*Campanula rotundifolia*), upright tormentil (*Potentilla erecta*) and heath bedstraw (*Galium saxatile*). On the Calcareous brown earths, the assemblage changes to one more akin to chalk grassland, with an increase in red fescue and the appearance of yellow oat-grass (*Trisetum flavescens*), downy oat-grass (*Helictotrichon pubescens*) and quaking grass (*Briza media*), and herbs such as field scabious (*Knautia arvensis*), lady's bedstraw (*Galium verum*), rough hawkbit (*Leontodon hispidus*), lesser hawkbit (*L. saxatilis*), agrimony (*Agrimonia eupatoria*) and germander speedwell (*Veronica chamaedrys*). If the grassland is well grazed, species even more typical of downland may survive, including hoary plantain (*Plantago media*), crested hair-grass (*Koeleria macrantha*), sheep's fescue (*Festuca ovina*), common eyebright (*Euphrasia nemorosa*), large thyme (*Thymus pulegioides*) and fairy flax (*Linum catharticum*).

In present-day agriculture, pastures are strongly affected by nutrients applied as fertilizers. The range of grassland communities that can exist on the Paleo-argillic brown earths under various fertilizer treatments is demonstrated by the plots of the Park Grass Experiment at Rothamsted (TL 123129) (Plate 63). Before this experiment was laid out by John Lawes and Henry Gilbert in 1856, the field had been in pasture for at least a century, and the pH was probably about 5.7. The fertilizer treatments were initially intended to improve the growth of herbage and its nutritional value

Plate 62. Aerial view of Broadbalk Winter Wheat Experiment, Rothamsted, with Broadbalk Wilderness in foreground (Copyright Rothamsted Research). Parts of the wilderness to the left of the woodland section (1882) have been grazed since 1960 (centre) or mown since 1957 (left).

for grazing animals, but were soon observed to influence the botanical composition of the sward. The differences continued to develop during the late 19th century and were extended in the 20th century by a range of pH effects, so that the field is now the most famous experiment in the world on grassland ecology. Use of ammonium sulphate as a source of nitrogen led to increasing soil acidity, which was initially counteracted by periodic applications of lime over the whole site. However, since 1965 each of the plots with different fertilizer treatments has been divided into four subplots, three of which now receive chalk calculated to give pH values of 5.0, 6.0 and 7.0; the fourth remains unchalked, its soil pH values ranging from 3.4 to 5.7 depending on fertilizer treatment. The main botanical effects of fertilizers and liming are:

1. The unfertilized plots (Plate 64) have the most diverse flora, with 35-45 species of grass and herbs. The main grasses are common bent (*Agrostis capillaris*) and red fescue (*Festuca rubra*), and the main herbs are common

Plate 63. Aerial view of Park Grass Experiment, Rothamsted (Copyright Rothamsted Research).

Plate 64. Close-up of herbage on Plot 3d (unfertilized and unlimed since 1854), Park Grass Experiment, Rothamsted (Copyright Rothamsted Research).

knapweed (*Centaurea nigra*), rough hawkbit (*Leontodon hispidus*), meadow vetchling (*Lathyris pratensis*), red clover (*Trifolium pratense*), with less abundant ribwort plantain (*Plantago lanceolata*), salad burnet (*Sanguisorba minor*) and bugle (*Ajuga reptans*). These swards probably resemble the field as it was before 1856, except that progressive impoverishment of soil nutrients by repeated removal of hay has caused decreases in the abundance of perennial rye-grass (*Lolium perenne*) and Yorkshire fog (*Holcus lanatus*) and increases in common bent grass, red fescue, rough hawkbit and salad burnet. At higher pH values the nutrient depletion has also decreased common bent and red fescue but increased downy oat grass (*Helictotrichon pubescens*).

2. Treatment with fertilizer containing P alone has increased common sorrel (*Rumex acetosa*) and meadow buttercup (*Ranunculus acris*).

3. A mixture of the mineral nutrients P, K, Na and Mg has increased legumes (red clover and meadow vetchling) and false oat-grass (*Arrhenatherum elatius*), especially at higher pH values.

4. On most of the fertilizer treatments, hogweed (*Heracleum spondylium*), buttercups (*Ranunculus* spp.) and dandelions (*Taraxacum* spp.) also increase with increasing pH.

5. P, Na and Mg (without K) have slightly increased the abundance of ribwort plantain (*Plantago lanceolata*).

6. On the unlimed subplots treated with ammonium sulphate as a source of N but with no added P (pH 3.8-4.1) the herbage is almost completely dominated by common bent and sweet vernal grass, with occasional specimens of other acid-tolerant grasses, such as red fescue, Yorkshire fog and false oat; herbs are absent.

7. On the limed parts of plots receiving ammonium sulphate but no mineral nutrients there is a wider range of grasses, including cock's-foot, downy oat grass, red fescue, false oat grass, quaking grass (*Briza media*) and meadow foxtail (*Alopecurus pratensis*).

8. Where P has been applied with ammonium sulphate but without K or lime (pH 3.8), sweet vernal grass (*Anthoxanthum odoratum*) is dominant, and where K has been added the sward is composed almost entirely of Yorkshire fog.

9. Where sodium nitrate has been applied as a source of N, there are 32-34 species present. Where mineral nutrients are also applied, false oat grass and meadow foxtail increase considerably in abundance.

Major soil group 6. Podzolic soils

These soils have diagnostic podzolic B horizons enriched in organic matter and poorly crystallized iron and aluminium oxides as a result of leaching under acidic conditions. They are rare in Hertfordshire and have decreased in area over the past 50-100 years because of agricultural expansion, gravel extraction and nutrient enrichment by scrub invasion. At present, they occupy only about 21 ha in the county (Cuming, 1997). One subgroup (the Paleo-argillic podzols) occurs on ancient common land, where the paleo-argillic Bt horizon developed in older flinty gravels of glaciofluvial or river terrace origins is not overlain by silty or loamy aeolian deposits. The other (the Stagnogley podzols) forms small patches where flinty clay-rich Quaternary deposits overlie London Clay in some east Hertfordshire woodlands. In the Paleo-argillic podzols, the diagnostic podzolic B horizon overlies a paleo-argillic Bt and is often overlain by a light-coloured E horizon from which organic matter, iron and aluminium have been lost by leaching during the Holocene. In contrast, in the Stagnogley podzols a gleyed horizon replaces the paleo-argillic Bt. Because of the moderately acidic topsoil conditions, neither soil type is suitable for modern agriculture, and almost all remaining areas now have semi-natural vegetation.

Heathland communities. The Paleo-argillic podzols are well drained and, where long uncultivated, have dry heathland plant communities including heather (*Calluna vulgaris*) and heathland grasses, such as common bent (*Agrostis capillaris*) early hair-grass (*Aira praecox*), fine-leaved sheep's fescue (*Festuca filiformis*) and heath-grass (*Danthonia decumbens*). Other common herbs include heath bedstraw (*Galium saxatile*), sheep's sorrel (*Rumex acetosella*), harebell (*Campanula rotundifolia*), upright tormentil (*Potentilla erecta*), meadow buttercup (*Ranunculus acris*), mouse-ear hawkweed (*Pilosella officinarum*) and common cat's-ear (*Hypochaeris radicata*) (James, 2009). Rarer species include dwarf gorse (*Ulex minor*), bird's-foot (*Ornithopus perpusillus*), trailing tormentil (*Potentilla anglica*) and petty whin (*Genista anglica*). Heathland lichens of the genus *Cladonia* are often common.

Left ungrazed, this community is rapidly colonized by gorse, and subsequently by pedunculate oak and silver birch, along with various brambles, including some heathland specialist species. However, such colonization enriches the nutrient pool and in time alters the soil profile characteristics. Examples of dry heathland communities occur on Nomansland Common (TL 1712), Gustardwood Common (TL 1716), Mardley Heath (TL 2418), Symondshyde Great Wood (TL 1911) and the HMWT reserve on Pebble Gravel at Rowley Green Common (TQ 216960). The pale coloured sandy surfaces of these soils are often quite thinly vegetated, and provide a favourable habitat for reptiles such as the common lizard (*Lacerta vivipara*) (Clark, 2001).

Stagnogley podzols. These are less well drained and locally carry wet heathland, which is similar in composition to the dry heathland communities on Palaeo-argillic podzols in containing heather, upright tormentil and heath bedstraw, but also includes purple moor-grass (*Molinia caerulea*), velvet bent grass (*Agrostis canina*), mat-grass (*Nardus stricta*), common yellow sedge (*Carex viridula* ssp. *oedocarpa*), alder buckthorn (*Frangula alnus*), green-ribbed sedge (*Carex binervis*), pill sedge (*Carex pilulifera*), bulbous rush (*Juncus bulbosus*) and various species of *Sphagnum* moss. Herbs in this community may include the heath spotted-orchid (*Dactylorhiza maculata*), sneezewort

(*Achillea ptarmica*), lousewort (*Pedicularis sylvatica*) and devil's-bit scabious (*Succisa pratensis*). Examples of wet heaths occur at Hertford Heath (TL 350106 and TL 354111) and Patmore Heath (TL 443258), which are HMWT reserves and SSSIs, and on parts of Bricket Wood Common (TL 1200) (Dony, 1967), also a SSSI.

Major soil group 7. Surface-water gley soils

These soils have gleyed subsurface (E and/or B) horizons starting within 40 cm depth, which are saturated by rainwater or lateral flow of water perched over slowly permeable clay-rich B or C horizons. They have formed in clay-rich Pleistocene or older deposits, sometimes overlain by thin loamy or even sandy deposits, which were originally non-calcareous or have been decalcified to at least 40 cm depth. However, they exclude similar soils formed in recent alluvium, which are separated as the Alluvial gley soil group. Clayey soils which crack in dry summer periods and contain carbonate within 40 cm depth (Pelosols) are also excluded, though intergrades in which clayey non-calcareous horizons above 40 cm are subject to seasonal cracking are separated at subgroup level as Pelo-stagnogley soils. Two groups (Stagnogley soils and Stagnohumic gley soils) are recognized nationally, but only the former occur in Hertfordshire. The Stagnohumic gley soils occur mainly in wetter upland regions of Britain and have a (humose or peaty) surface horizon rich in organic matter, whereas the Stagnogley soils have a distinct topsoil that usually contains no more organic matter than associated better drained Brown soils.

Within the Stagnogley soils, three subgroups can be recognized in Hertfordshire. The first, the Typical stagnogley soils, includes those with a loamy surface horizon at least 15 cm thick and a gleyed argillic B (Btg) horizon, which lacks paleo-argillic characteristics. These occur in minor depressions on the chalky till interfluves in eastern parts of the county, on thin till resting at 1-2 m depth on gravels in the St Albans area, and on lower slope positions on the London Clay outcrop in the south of the county. The second, the Pelo-stagnogley soils, are mainly clayey and any loamy surface horizon containing less than 30% clay (<2 μm) is less than 15 cm thick. They occur where the main clay formations of the county (Gault and London Clays and chalky till) crop out immediately beneath Devensian erosion surfaces and are covered by little or no overlying aeolian or other Late Quaternary deposits. Soils of the third subgroup, the Paleo-argillic stagnogley soils, are extensive on level surfaces between Hatfield, Barnet and Hoddesdon in south Hertfordshire, where chalky till overlies London Clay or Early/Mid Pleistocene gravels and interglacial paleo-argillic Btg horizons were not completely removed by Devensian surface erosion. Loamy upper horizons containing Late Devensian aeolian drift are also preserved.

Unless they are artificially drained, all the Stagnogley soils are waterlogged for long periods in winter. Autumn cultivations are often possible, but there are few suitable days in spring, so autumn-sown cereals are the main arable crop. Some of the land is under grass, but the Pelo-stagnogley soils in particular are prone to poaching and associated structural damage (compaction) by animal hooves in wet periods.

Until the late 20th century spread of dutch elm disease, elm species (*Ulmus* spp.) were common on these soils, especially in northeast Hertfordshire and around Barnet. Long established woodland may also include local stands of alder (*Alnus glutinosa*), aspen (*Populus tremula*) and goat willow (*Salix caprea*). Where the soils are less acidic, woodland sedges, such as thin-spiked wood-sedge (*Carex strigosa*) and false fox-sedge (*C. otrubae*), may occur, along with wild angelica (*Angelica sylvestris*) and bugle (*Ajuga reptans*). On the Palaeo-argillic stagnogley soils in south Hertfordshire, woodlands often have extensive areas of pendulous sedge (*Carex pendula*) or tufted hair-grass (*Deschampsia cespitosa*). Hard rush (*Juncus inflexus*), soft rush (*J. effusus*), clustered rush (*J. conglomeratus*) and tufted forget-me-not (*Myosotis laxa*) are common in damp pastures. Black poplar (*Populus nigra*) is a characteristic hedgerow tree on the Pelo-stagnogley soils on Gault Clay in north-western extremities of the county.

Major soil group 8. Groundwater gley soils

These poorly-drained soils occur close to rivers and in other situations where the groundwater table approaches the surface, and have gleyed subsurface (CG or Cg) horizons influenced by the mobile groundwater. In the Alluvial gley group, the parent material is Holocene alluvium more than 30 cm thick and the topsoil is silty, loamy or clayey; the Humic alluvial gley soils are similar, but the topsoil is humose or peaty. In other soil groups (Cambic gley and Argillic gley soils) the parent material is Late Pleistocene gravel or brickearth (loess or fluvially reworked loess) occurring on valley floors close to but usually slightly above river level.

Alluvial gley soils. Four subgroups are recognized in the Alluvial gley soil group. The Typical alluvial gley soils are formed from silty or loamy alluvium and are non-calcareous to at least 40 cm depth. In this subgroup the alluvium usually exceeds 1.5 m in thickness, but may form a thinner silty layer over calcareous gravel. The Calcareous alluvial gley soils are also silty over calcareous gravel, but are calcareous within 40 cm of the surface. They occur mainly in the lower reaches of valleys containing seasonal or perennial rivers draining the Chilterns, such as the Chess, Bulbourne and Gade. In these valleys they are often associated with the Humic-alluvial gley soils, which are also calcareous within 40 cm of the surface. The two remaining subgroups are in clayey alluvium, which cracks in dry periods, and is either non-calcareous to at least 40 cm depth (Pelo-alluvial gley soils) or calcareous within 40 cm (Pelo-calcareous alluvial gley soils). The Pelo-alluvial gley soils occur in the Colne valley between Colney Street and Denham, in the Lea valley from Hertford to Cheshunt and in the Rib valley downstream from Barwick (TL 3819). The Pelo-calcareous alluvial gley soils are typical of the Stort valley between Stansted Mountfitchet and Harlow, and also occur in higher parts of the Lea valley between Hertford and Stanborough

(TL 2211), the Mimram valley downstream from Welwyn, the Beane valley downstream from Woodhall Park (TL 3118) and the Ash valley downstream from Wareside (TL 3915).

Other Groundwater gley soils. The Cambic gley soils in Hertfordshire have either loamy upper (A and Bg) horizons, which are calcareous within 40 cm depth (Calcaro-cambic gley soils), or clayey cracking upper horizons which are non-calcareous to below 40 cm depth (Pelo-cambic gley soils). In both, calcareous (chalk and other limestone) gravel occurs within 1.5 m depth. They occur only on a low-lying terrace of the Ivel valley between Baldock and Henlow.

The Argillic gley soils also occur in deposits other than Holocene alluvium, and have loamy or silty upper horizons and clay-enriched Btg (argillic) subsoil horizons over gravel or stoneless brickearth in river valleys, or over Reading Beds sand on footslopes of the Tertiary outliers. The largest areas are on the sides of upper reaches of the Ash, Rib and Stort valleys.

Alder carr. Some areas of Groundwater gley soils, for example in parts of the Purwell and Oughton valleys near Hitchin, support one of the rarest ancient woodland types in Hertfordshire, the alder (*Alnus glutinosa*) carr. Subordinate tree species include ash (*Fraxinus excelsior*), grey willow (*Salix cinerea*), downy birch (*Betula pubescens*), hybrid elm (*Ulmus glabra × minor*) and occasionally pedunculate oak (*Quercus robur*). The ground flora includes wetland plants, such as marsh marigold (*Caltha palustris*), wild angelica (*Angelica sylvestris*), yellow iris (*Iris pseudacorus*), great horsetail (*Equisetum telmateia*), southern marsh-orchid (*Dactylorhiza praetermissa*), rushes and sedges, especially lesser pond-sedge (*Carex acutiformis*) and occasionally brown sedge (*Carex disticha*). Woodland plants characteristic of this vegetation include broad buckler-fern (*Dryopteris dilatata*) and lesser celandine (*Ranunculus ficaria*). Examples include St Ippollitts Alder Swamp (TL 1927) and the HMWT reserves at Oughton Head (TL 166304) and Purwell Ninesprings (TL 206293).

Major soil group 9. Man-made soils

These occur either (a) in areas where a humus-rich A horizon more than 40 cm thick (thick man-made A horizon) has been created by repeated application of organic manures or occupation residues, by unusually deep cultivation or by re-emplacement of topsoil, or (b) where the natural soil has been disturbed or artificially displaced to depths exceeding 40 cm. Soils of the first group (Man-made humus soils) occur locally in old gardens, on long-established market-garden land or on old settlements and other archaeological sites. They are often rich in mineral nutrients, especially phosphorus. In Hertfordshire, small areas are associated with Roman settlements at St Albans (Verulamium), Baldock and elsewhere.

The second group (Disturbed soils) consists of mixed material from pre-existing O, A, E or B horizons, and differs in this respect from the disturbed rock waste of Man-made raw soils (Major soil group 1). In Hertfordshire they occur mainly in areas where land has been restored for agriculture, forest plantations or amenity woodland following gravel extraction or quarrying, often with land-filling. Areas of substandard restoration, where the redistributed soil material is less than 40 cm thick over landfill or undisturbed rock or gravel, are classed as Man-made raw soils.

No soil subgroups are formally recognized in the Disturbed soils group, but the first group (Man-made humus soils) are separated into Sandy man-made humus soils (sandy or sandy with >70% stones in at least half the upper 80 cm) and Earthy man-made humus soils (finer than sandy in more than half the upper 80 cm).

The presence of frequent common nettle (*Urtica dioica*), along with other plants of disturbed ground, such as ground elder (*Aegopodium podagraria*), cow parsley (*Anthriscus sylvestris*), field bindweed (*Convolvulus arvensis*), goosegrass (*Galium aparine*) and shrubs like elder (*Sambucus nigra*) or trees that prefer enriched soils, such as English elm (*Ulmus procera*) and sycamore (*Acer pseudoplatanus*), is often indicative of these soils.

Major soil group 10. Peat soils

These occur very locally in Hertfordshire, usually where Holocene peat has accumulated in very wet valley bottom conditions, because the water table is close to or above the surface for most of the year and little or no mineral sediment is deposited. To qualify as a Peat soil, peat must form at least half the upper 80 cm of the profile. Where it underlies a mineral surface layer, the latter should not exceed 30 cm in thickness, and the peat need be no thicker than 30 cm where it rests directly on a mineral substratum of gravel. Like most Peat soils in other parts of lowland Britain (e.g. the Fenland and Somerset Levels), those occurring in Hertfordshire are eutrophic (rich in mineral nutrients, especially Ca), often with pH values >7.0, though surface layers leached at times of low groundwater level may become moderately acidic (pH < 4.0). All are in the group of Earthy peat soils with a mineral surface horizon. Two subgroups are distinguished based upon the degree of decomposition of the peat layer. Earthy eu-fibrous peat soils are recognized where the peat is fibrous or semifibrous (partially decomposed) and formed mainly of sedge remains, and Earthy eutro-amorphous peat soils occur where the peat is amorphous (humified with few identifiable plant remains).

Both subgroups form small irregularly distributed patches associated with Alluvial gley soils along valleys such as those of the Lea, Stort, Rib, Beane, Mimram and Hiz, often where groundwater from the Chalk rises as clear springs containing little or no suspended sediment. Small areas also occur over chalk and flint gravel in lower reaches of Chiltern valleys, such as the Ver near Shafford Farm (TL 1209), the Gade at Hunton Bridge (TL 0800) and the Bulbourne at Boxmoor (TL 0306), where accumulations of surface ice from temporary valley-floor springs (naleds or aufeis) resulted in minor surface depressions in the periglacial gravels deposited during the Late Devensian (Section 6.10). The HMWT reserve at Ridlins Mire near Stevenage (TL 263222) is unusual in that a thick (1.8 m) dome of mid and late

Holocene fen peat (a rheotrophic hangmire) has developed on the upper western side of the Aston Dene valley where springs emerge from between gravel and chalky till overlying the Chalk (Tinsley and Cosgrove, 1991). Similar features occur at Sandon Moor (TL 325328) and Biggin Moor (TL 380336) near Buckland. The total area of Peat soils in the county is only 113 ha (Cuming,1997).

Marsh vegetation. Most areas of Peat soils are under meadow or rough pasture with sedges, such as lesser pond-sedge (*Carex acutiformis*), common sedge (*Carex nigra*), slender tufted sedge (*Carex acuta*) and greater tussock-sedge (*Carex paniculata*), and grasses of wet habitats, such as purple moor-grass (*Molinia caerulea*) or reed canary-grass (*Phalaris arundinacea*). Common reed (*Phragmites australis*) and marsh marigold (*Caltha palustris*) may also occur in the wetter swampy areas, and some patches have been invaded by alder- or willow-carr. Many of the surviving semi-natural sites are important for scarce wild plants, including marsh valerian (*Valeriana dioica*), marsh willowherb (*Epilobium palustre*), marsh pennywort (*Hydrocotyle vulgaris*), lesser spearwort (*Ranunculus flammula*), common meadow-rue (*Thalictrum flavum*), fen bedstraw (*Galium uliginosum*), blunt-flowered rush (*Juncus subnodulosus*), marsh arrow grass (*Triglochin palustre*), great horsetail (*Equisetum telmateia*) and marsh horsetail (*E. palustre*). The precise assemblage of species present depends on the amounts of free calcium in the percolating water. Southern marsh-orchid (*Dactylorhiza praetermissa*) occurs in such sites, and very rarely the marsh helleborine (*Epipactis palustris*), but Hertfordshire does not have some other orchids that occur on natural peatlands elsewhere. Other plants of this habitat, such as common cotton-grass (*Eriophorum angustifolium*), grass-of-parnassus (*Parnassia palustris*) and marsh stitchwort (*Stellaria palustris*), have probably become extinct in the county since the 19th century because of declining groundwater levels. The marsh plants often support a wide range of invertebrates; for example, at Ridlins Mire Nellist (1989) recorded over 50 species of spider.

7.7. Description, occurrence and agricultural characteristics of the soil associations

Soil associations are groupings of several, often very diverse, soil series, which consistently occur together in the landscape and form map units suitable for delineation at scales smaller than approximately 1:10,000. All but one of the 39 soil associations identified in Hertfordshire (Fig. 7.2) consist of three or more soil series. Some series are more extensive than others, though none exceeds 50% by area of an association. The associations are named after the single most common series (the eponymous series). The various series within each association usually occur in characteristic landscape situations within the delineated map units of the association (e.g. less well-drained soils in minor valleys cut into the plateau on which the more extensive and better-drained eponymous series occurs). In the following accounts of associations the eponymous and other important series are described in detail and their topographic relationships are outlined in general terms. A more detailed account of the distribution of different series in the county is impossible at present because the patterns of soil variation are too complex. The association names and alphanumeric codes are taken from the national 1:250,000 soil association map. The alphanumeric code indicates the Soil subgroup (Table 7.1) in which the most extensive (eponymous) soil series occurs.

Association 92a: Disturbed Soils

This association occurs mainly in a narrow strip up to 500 m wide extending from Ashwell End (TL 2540) along the eastern side of the Rhee valley, and also beyond the northern county boundary in Cambridgeshire. It consists of land restored after 19th century strip quarrying of the Lower Cenomanian Cambridge Greensand (Section 2.8) for phosphatic nodules ('coprolites') to make superphosphate fertilizer (Jukes-Browne, 1875; Barraud, 1951). The area is flat and drained by ditches leading into the River Rhee.

To extract coprolites, trenches were dug to depths of up to 7 metres, often through part of the West Melbury Marly Chalk Formation into the thin bed of Cambridge Greensand overlying the Gault Clay. After they were removed, the coprolites were washed on site and transported to mills for crushing and grinding before treatment with sulphuric acid to form superphosphate. The unwanted slurry was spread on adjacent land, and the trenches were then backfilled and levelled. As the backfill was consequently quite variable in composition, no soil series are distinguished, but over most of the area a greyish-brown calcareous clay loam overlies greyish mottled very calcareous clay, both layers often containing dark green to black glauconite pellets derived from the Greensand.

The soils are usually waterlogged in winter and, as the organic matter content is often small, they suffer from problems associated with a weak topsoil structure, such as compaction by winter trafficking and formation of a hard silty surface crust on seedbeds that dry after heavy rain. However, because of the coprolite mining, the soils are usually very rich in available phosphorus (Gardner, 1967, p. 112).

Association 342a: Upton

This association of thin well-drained silty soils is extensive on undulating areas of the Chalk outcrop in north-eastern Hertfordshire, especially in northern parts of Royston, Ashwell, Bygrave, Reed, Barkway, Therfield (including Therfield Heath), Kelshall, Sandon, Wallington, Clothall, Weston and Letchworth parishes. Further west it is also present in parts of Pirton, Lilley, Preston, Offley and Hexton parishes, and where the Chalk is exposed along the sides of the Quin Valley in eastern Hertfordshire it occurs in parts of Anstey, Braughing, Standon and Hormead parishes.

The most common soil in the association is the Upton series, a very calcareous Grey rendzina with Chalk (often frost-shattered) at <30 cm depth, which occurs mainly on cultivated and eroded slopes. Icknield series, a less calcareous Humic rendzina with dark greyish brown topsoil, is restricted to small areas under long-established woodland or grassland (Plate 65), which have not suffered as much erosion. Andover series, a less calcareous silty Brown

Plate 65. Profile of Humic rendzina (Icknield series) under grass, Whipsnade (SP 999185).

rendzina formed in a thin but distinct layer of Devensian loess, also occurs in cultivated but less eroded sites such as ridge crests. North-eastwards from Hitchin, Letchworth and Baldock towards Royston, all three series become progressively less silty and more sandy, probably reflecting a slight regional coarsening in the Devensian aeolian sediment.

On concave slopes in coombes and on lower slopes of the Chalk escarpment, slightly thicker soils with brown subsoil (Bw) horizons and Chalk at up to 80 cm depth occur where thin periglacial slope (gelifluction) deposits have been preserved from erosion. Panholes series occurs near Baldock where these soils are fine silty in texture, but towards Royston it gives way first to Soham series (fine loamy) and then to Swaffham Prior series (coarse loamy) as the aeolian sediment component (coversand) becomes more sandy. Even deeper soils of the Coombe series occur in patches on valley floors where the chalky gelifluction deposits exceed 80 cm in thickness. Where soil erosion caused by late Holocene cultivation has resulted in valley floor accumulations of calcareous colluvium (hillwash) more than 80 cm thick, Millington series occurs if the colluvium is fine silty and Gore series if it is slightly coarser (loamy).

Agriculture. All soils in Association 342a are well drained and easily cultivated, though the small amounts of topsoil organic matter in long-cultivated areas can lead to compaction if cultivated in wet spring periods or crusting and poor germination after heavy rain. Because of their pale colour and high albedo, the Upton soils warm slowly in spring, and this can also delay germination. Consequently the association is better suited to autumn-sown than spring-sown crops. Although most of the soils are thin, crops other than grass suffer little from summer drought, as their roots can penetrate the shattered Chalk beneath and extract large amounts of water from its fine pores. However, in very dry summers, yellow or brown parchmarks can appear in grassland where the soil is composed mainly of coversand, which retains little water and dries rapidly. The marks often indicate the presence of periglacial soil structures, such as polygonal ice wedge casts filled with coversand. Archaeologically important marks may also occur where stone or brick foundations lie close to the surface, as for example at Quickswood (TL 276330) near Clothall, a 16th century hunting lodge demolished in 1780 (Dalton, 2007, Plates 2.1 and 2.2).

Association 342c: Wantage 1

This association forms a narrow strip of gently sloping land on the outcrop of the West Melbury Marly Chalk Formation at the foot of the main Chalk escarpment northwest of Tring, and consists mainly of loamy Grey rendzinas (Wantage series). The strip also extends along the Chiltern scarp foot in parts of southeast Bedfordshire close to the county boundary with Hertfordshire (e.g. around the villages of Marsworth, Pitstone, Ivinghoe, Houghton Regis, Sharpenhoe and Barton-le-Clay). A subsidiary soil, the Burwell series (a Gleyic rendzina with yellow mottles

appearing within 60 cm depth) occurs on the floors of shallow valleys, which have been cut into the West Melbury Marly Chalk Formation by small seasonal streams fed by springs rising from the Totternhoe Stone and other parts of the Zig Zag Chalk Formation. Upton series (see Association 342a) occurs on the convex upper sides of these valleys.

Agriculture. Apart from the narrow strips of Burwell series, the association is generally well drained, but the soils are strongly moisture-retentive and provide few opportunities for cultivation in winter and early spring. There are sufficient reserves of plant available water (Section 9.2) for good growth of winter cereal crops, but summer growth of grass is sometimes limited by drought.

Association 342d: Wantage 2

This association occupies small areas close to the north-eastern border of Hertfordshire on the northern side of Letchworth and in the parishes of Pirton, Hexton, Ashwell and Holwell. However, it is more extensive in adjacent parts of Bedfordshire and Cambridgeshire. Like Association 342c, it occurs on the outcrop of the West Melbury Marly Chalk Formation and includes mainly loamy Grey rendzinas of the Wantage series, with Gleyic rendzinas of the Burwell series and slightly stony shallow Grey rendzinas of the Upton series in the valleys of small seasonal streams. However, it also includes thicker Typical brown calcareous earths of the Swaffham Prior, Soham and Coombe series (see Association 342a) on higher ground between the valleys and seasonally waterlogged, clayey Stagnogleyic rendzinas with glauconitic subsoils (Lode series) where the valleys are incised into the clay-rich Upper Greensand.

Agriculture. The agricultural characteristics of the association are similar to those of Association 342c. Winter wheat and barley are grown extensively, often with a break crop of beans, peas or oilseed rape every 2-3 years to avoid the build-up of cereal diseases. Sugar beet is sometimes grown on areas of the Typical brown calcareous earths.

Association 343h: Andover

This association is widespread on the Berkshire, Hampshire and South Downs and also on the Yorkshire and Lincolnshire Wolds, but is restricted in Hertfordshire to a small area of rolling Middle Chalk (Holywell Nodular Chalk Formation) land immediately west and northwest of Tring and extending onto the moderately or steeply sloping scarp between Tring Park (SP 9210) and West Leith Farm (SP 915103) close to the county boundary south of the town. Nearby there are also small areas on similar land close to the villages of Ivinghoe (Buckinghamshire) and Whipsnade (Bedfordshire).

The principal soil of the area is Andover series, a silty Brown rendzina formed in a thin layer of Devensian loess over Chalk, which occurs mainly on arable land extending northwards from West Leith Farm towards Miswell Farm (SP 913120) and on the recently built housing estates of western Tring. Under old grassland and woodland in Tring Park, this is replaced by Humic rendzinas of the Icknield series, and on the floors of the dry valleys running northwards through Tring Park and north-eastwards through the centre of the town there are deeper silty Typical brown calcareous earths formed in Devensian Coombe Deposits (chalky gelifluction deposits), either Panholes series where carbonate occurs within 40 cm depth or Coombe series if decalcified to 40-80 cm depth. In higher parts of the dry valleys in Tring Park there are also silty flinty soils of the Charity series (silty Typical argillic brown earth, non-calcareous to more than 80 cm depth) where the Coombe Deposits are derived partly from flinty clay on the Chalk plateau above.

Agriculture. All the soils overlie permeable Chalk and are well drained. The Andover series is also well structured and easy to cultivate soon after rain, but is naturally deficient in mineral nutrients, such as phosphorus, potassium and magnesium, and also in some trace elements, including copper and cobalt. Under grass the Icknield series suffers little from poaching, and cattle can remain outdoors through the winter in Tring Park. A small area of steep deforested slope within the woodland at Oddy Hill (SP 934108) was previously grazed to assist reinstatement of species-rich chalk grassland, but has become overgrown with scrub vegetation.

Association 411b: Evesham 2

The soils of this association occur on the flat or gently undulating land of the Gault Clay outcrop at 80-85 m OD south of Puttenham and north of Long Marston in the extension of Hertfordshire beyond the Chiltern scarp northwest of Tring (Fig. 7.3). They consist mainly of Typical calcareous pelosols of the Evesham series, which have a dark grey clayey topsoil and olive-coloured subsoil overlying calcareous Gault Clay at a depth of less than 40 cm. There is no evidence in the Evesham series of even thin Quaternary deposits, though the surface layers of clay have probably been disturbed by frost action. The topsoil is strongly structured and cracks on drying in summer to form vertical fissures, which assist infiltration of rain. However, in wetter periods and for most of the winter the soil swells again to close the cracks, thus greatly decreasing permeability.

Pelo-stagnogley soils occur where the clay has been decalcified to more than 40 cm depth (Denchworth series) or where a superficial layer of clayey drift is indicated by the presence of occasional flint fragments and other stones (Lawford series). Typical Stagnogley soils of the

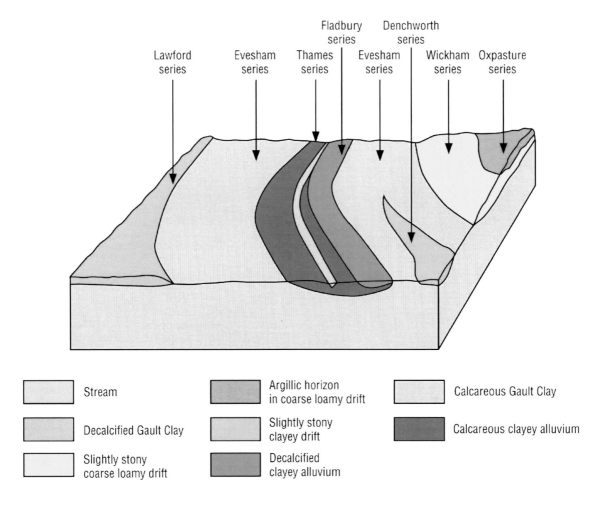

Fig. 7.3. Relationships between constituent soil series in Association 411b (Evesham 2) on Gault Clay northwest of Tring.

Wickham series and Stagnogleyic argillic brown earths of the Oxpasture series occur where the superficial drift layer is slightly coarser (fine loamy) in texture. The soil pattern is also diversified by narrow strips of clayey alluvium associated with present or former streams. These areas are occupied mainly by Pelo-alluvial gley soils (Fladbury series) and Pelo-calcareous alluvial gley soils (Thames series).

Agriculture. All soils in the association are poorly drained and frequently waterlogged in winter. They are mainly under grass, but the occasional presence of ridge-and-furrow (e.g. at Rectory Farm, Puttenham, SP 884146) suggests that some areas were cultivated in the mediaeval period, and a few fields on Wickham and Oxpasture series have been cultivated since World War II. Today the main arable crops are winter cereals, with oilseed rape or field beans grown every 2-3 years as a break crop to prevent build-up of cereal diseases. The Evesham and Oxpasture series respond better to artificial field drainage than either the alluvial soils or the more deeply decalcified Denchworth, Lawford and Wickham series. All the soils require heavy dressings of phosphorus and nitrogen, but they contain adequate natural reserves of potassium and trace elements. Under grass there is an appreciable risk of poaching in winter, and this shortens the safe grazing period.

Association 411c: Evesham 3

These soils resemble those of Association 411b, but occur on the Gault Clay outcrop in the north-eastern part of the county in the northern part of Hinxworth parish and the north-western part of Ashwell parish. Evesham series is again the most common soil type, occupying about 40% of the land, and Denchworth and Lawford series are also present. However, thin drift deposits, probably derived from a nearby outcrop of chalky till on slightly higher ground to the west, are more extensive and often thicker than in Association 411b, and give rise to fine loamy Stagnogleyic brown calcareous earths of the St Lawrence series as well as Stagnogleyic argillic brown earths of the Oxpasture series. Consequently the area is slightly better drained and subject to rather fewer cultivation and grazing problems than Association 411b in the geologically similar part of the county near Tring.

Association 411d: Hanslope

This association is the most extensive in Hertfordshire and provides a very large area of pasture and cereal growing land in the east of the county. It extends across the almost continuous plateau formed of chalky till east of a line between Hitchin, Stevenage, Hertford and Bayford, and south of the area between Royston and Baldock occupied by Association 342a. The main soils are Calcareous pelosols of the Hanslope series, which occupy almost half of the area and have a slightly stony, dark greyish brown swelling clay topsoil and an olive brown calcareous clay subsoil at less than 40 cm depth. On level sites they are accompanied by Typical argillic pelosols of the Faulkbourne series and Pelo-

stagnogley soils of the Ragdale series, both also clayey to the surface, and by fine loamy Stagnogleyic argillic brown earths (Ashley series) or Typical stagnogley soils (Beccles series).

The pattern of soil variation on the plateau is irregular and difficult to explain. It could be related to lateral variation in the till, or the loamy topsoils may contain a minor component of Devensian loess. Unlike soils on the chalky till further east in Essex (Sturdy *et al.*, 1979), none of those in east Hertfordshire contains features inherited from interglacial pedogenesis, so the plateau must have been swept completely clean of earlier soils by periglacial erosion in the Devensian cold stage. On slopes leading to valleys, which are better drained than the plateau areas, there are patches of either Typical brown calcareous earths with clayey surface horizons (Stretham series) or Stagnogleyic brown calcareous earths (Cannamore series) with fine loamy topsoils (Fig. 7.4).

Agriculture. Despite the clay-rich surface horizons and gleyed, slowly permeable subsurface horizons of most soils in the association, waterlogging is not a frequent problem, probably because stones in the till assist drainage and the subsoil carbonate content helps maintain a soil structure with a pattern of sub-vertical fissures that are more stable and persistent than in non-calcareous clays. In addition, all the soils respond well to artificial drainage with outfalls into ditches at field boundaries, a system which has been in widespread use for centuries. Originally hollow drains were hand-dug and filled with straw or bushes to maintain flow and stability (Young 1804), but today cylindrical channels (mole drains) are drawn with a bullet-shaped mole plough and either left empty or stabilized by infilling with fine gravel. With such drainage improvement, the soils can usually be worked in the autumn until mid-December and again in the spring from late March onwards. The natural nutrient status is generally good, but cereal crops require large spring dressings of nitrogen for the highest yields and treatment with superphosphate fertilizer every 2-3 years to resist root fungal diseases. Sugarbeet, potatoes, beans, peas, oilseed rape and brassicas are grown periodically as break crops. The late 19th and early 20th century expansion of pasture for dairy farming, to supply milk to London, terminated abruptly in World War II, in response to the campaign to increase land under arable production.

Association 511e: Swaffham Prior

This association of chalkland soils occurs in north Hertfordshire, mainly as a wide NE-SW strip on the undulating outcrops of the Zig-Zag and Holywell Nodular Chalk Formations forming the Chalk scarp between Royston and Lilley (TL 1126). It also extends south-eastwards in the long dry through-valleys (windgaps) dissecting the Chalk outcrop, such as Lilley Bottom. The largest patches are in the parishes of Barley, Barkway, Ashwell, Newnham, Bygrave, Letchworth, Graveley, Hitchin, Offley, Preston, Ippollitts, Hexton, Lilley, King's Walden, St Paul's Walden, Codicote and Ayot St Lawrence.

The association differs from others on this part of the

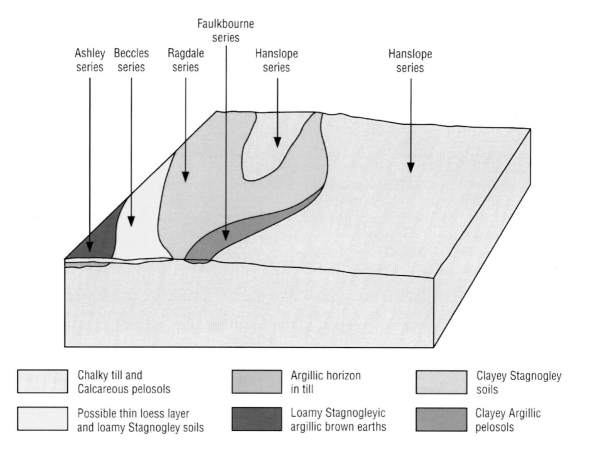

Fig. 7.4. Relationships between constituent soil series in Association 411d (Hanslope) on chalky till in northeast Hertfordshire.

Chalk outcrop in being dominated by Brown calcareous earths rather than Rendzinas. Freshly ploughed surfaces are normally brown in colour rather than the predominantly grey colours of Associations 342a, 342c and 342d, so the land is consequently often known as "redland". In the north-eastern parts of the county, the main soil is the Swaffham Prior series, a coarse loamy Typical brown calcareous earth, but west and south of Baldock, this is replaced by fine loamy Typical brown calcareous earths of the Soham series, the change in textural class resulting from the same transition in particle size distribution of Devensian periglacial aeolian sediments (from coversand to loess) to that seen in the adjacent Association 342d. Coombe series (fine silty Typical brown calcareous earth) is common on the floors of valleys and Rudham series (fine loamy Brown rendzina) and Upton series (fine loamy Grey rendzina) on valley sides in the area dominated by Soham series. Elsewhere the main accompanying soils are Moulton series (coarse loamy Typical argillic brown earth) and Newmarket series (coarse loamy Brown rendzina).

Agriculture. As in Association 342a, short-range soil variation often results from periglacial soil patterns inherited from the Late Devensian, with mainly polygonal patterns on flat or gently sloping surfaces and stripes on slightly steeper slopes. The polygons result from ice-wedge casts filled mainly with aeolian sediment (the deeper

Swaffham Prior, Moulton or Soham series) surrounding areas with chalk closer to the surface (Rudham and Newmarket series). The stripes probably result from downslope stretching of the polygons by mass movement (gelifluction) of surface layers during the Devensian. Both features can be seen in aerial photographs of bare soil, but in dry spring and summer periods they also appear as crop patterns (Plate 55). At these times growth is more restricted on the thicker soils, because there are smaller reserves of available water.

All the soils are well drained and easy to cultivate in both spring and autumn. Consequently they are mainly used for winter and spring cereals, oilseed rape, sugar beet, potatoes and peas, and there is little grassland. The areas of remaining woodland are also quite small, though some, such as Tingley Wood (TL 1330) near Pirton, have been partly replanted and extended.

Association 511f: Coombe

This association (Fig. 7.5) occurs on the floors and lower south-facing slopes of the Gade valley from the M25 Motorway near Kings Langley (TL 0701), through Hemel Hempstead to the county boundary near Hudnall Corner (TL 0213), and also the Ver valley between the M1 Motorway at Friar's Wash (TL 0814) and the county boundary northwest of Markyate (TL 0517). The dominant soil is Coombe series

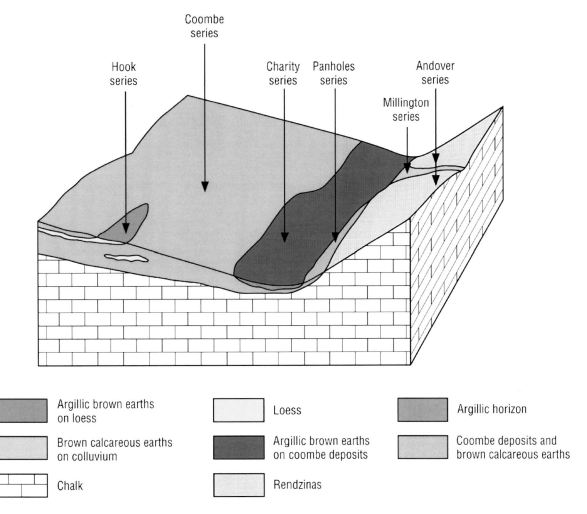

Fig. 7.5. Relationships between constituent soil series in Association 511f (Coombe) in dry upper reaches of the Gade and Ver valleys.

(fine silty Typical brown calcareous earth) developed in thick (>0.8 m) chalky and flinty gelifluction deposits (Coombe Deposits), usually with a major loess component. The loess sometimes forms almost stonefree lenticular streaks, which give rise to small patches of silty Typical argillic brown earths (Hamble series) if they occur at the surface. Fine silty Typical argillic brown earths (Charity series) often occur in central parts of the valley floor and on side slopes facing north, where the Coombe Deposits have been decalcified to 40-80 cm depth in the Holocene. On the lower valley sides facing south, where the Coombe Deposits are much thinner over undisturbed chalk, Panholes series (fine silty Typical brown calcareous earth with chalk at <80 cm depth) and Rendzinas such as Andover and Upton series are present. Fine silty Colluvial brown calcareous earths (Millington series) occur on footslopes where Late Holocene colluvium (hillwash) is more than 40 cm thick.

Agriculture. All the soils are well drained and also drought resistant because of the large silt contents. Cultivation is possible throughout the autumn and for much of the spring, and the main arable crops are cereals, though much of the land is under permanent or short-term grass. However, the topsoils can be temporarily compacted if trafficked

by heavy machinery in wet periods, and the abundance of angular (frost-shattered) flint fragments in many of the soils accelerates the wear of tractor tyres, ploughs and other farm machinery. The valley floors are also vulnerable to spring frosts, which can damage sensitive crops, such as topfruit. At present there is a single vineyard at Frithsden (TL 020098), but the similarities of aspect and soil type to vineyards in the Champagne region of France suggest that in future these soils might profitably be used more extensively for viticulture and wine production.

Grassland. The effects of aspect and soil variation on grassland vegetation and semi-natural woodland in the Coombe Association are demonstrated around the margins of the HMWT reserve at Long Deans (TL 076050), Hemel Hempstead. For example, the southeast-facing slopes with thin Coombe Deposits over chalk, have fairly typical chalk grassland, but the northwest-facing slopes on Charity series have neutral grassland.

Association 512d: Grove

In Hertfordshire this association is restricted to a small level area adjacent to the Thistle Brook north of Folly Farm (SP

877160), close to the county boundary northwest of Tring, but is more extensive in nearby parts of Buckinghamshire south and east of Aylesbury and south of Leighton Buzzard. It occurs where thin river terrace gravels composed mainly of angular brown-stained flint and subrounded (waterworn) chalk clasts derived from the Chilterns overlie Gault Clay. The gravel was probably deposited during the Late Devensian cold stage when minor periglacial rivers flowing across the Vale of Aylesbury were fed by torrential seasonal meltwater streams issuing from Chiltern scarp-slope coombes and windgaps such as the Bulbourne valley. It has a calcareous sandy matrix and ranges in thickness from a few centimetres to over 1.5 m, often within very short distances. The variation in thickness mainly results from Late Devensian cryoturbation, though the thickest accumulations sometimes occur in elongated troughs, which could have originated as stream channels. The gravel is overlain by a much less stony layer of clay loam or silty clay loam up to 0.5 m thick, which probably represents a final phase of quiet fluvial aggradation in the Holocene after inputs of periglacial gravel and sand had ceased. Drainage of the soils is impeded by the substratum of Gault Clay, so that the gravel and loamy horizons above are periodically or permanently waterlogged.

The main soils, occupying approximately equal proportions of the association where the gravel is thickest, are fine loamy Gleyic brown calcareous earths (Grove series) and fine loamy Calcaro-cambic gley soils (Kelmscot series). Where the gravel layer is thin or intermittent, these are replaced by patches of fine loamy Stagnogleyic brown calcareous earths (St Lawrence series), Pelo-stagnogley soils (Lawford series) or Typical calcareous pelosols (Evesham series).

Agriculture. The Grove and Kelmscot series are easily improved by artificial field drainage, as water quickly moves laterally through the gravel. However, infiltration through the fine loamy surface horizons can be reduced by compaction resulting from poaching or trafficking during or immediately after prolonged periods of wet weather, so opportunities for winter or spring cultivation and grazing are few. Apart from permanent grass, the main crops are winter cereals, oilseed rape and field beans. In places older arable land was cultivated by ridge and furrow, the soils on ridges having thicker and slightly better drained loamy surface horizons than those in the furrows.

Association 512e: Block

In Hertfordshire this association also occurs only northwest of Tring, where it occupies a gently undulating area northwest of Association 342c (Wantage 1) and extending between the two map units of Association 411b (Evesham 2) south of Puttenham and north of Long Marston, respectively. The area extends from Whitwell Farm (SP 882170) south-eastwards across the Gault Clay outcrop onto the gently rising ground formed by the West Melbury Marly Chalk Formation between Drayton Beauchamp (SP 9012) and Startop's End (SP 9214). Near the county boundary west of Tring the area includes Wilstone Reservoir (SP 9013).

The association is more extensive in adjacent counties, forming a narrow strip along the Chiltern scarp footslope north-eastwards to Houghton Regis and south-westwards to Wendover.

The soil parent material consists of thick chalky and often slightly flinty gelifluction deposits (head) derived from the nearby slopes of the Zig-Zag and Holywell Nodular Chalk Formations. As these superficial deposits overlie slowly permeable Gault and marly chalk, the soils are seasonally affected by groundwater and consist mainly of fine loamy Gleyic brown calcareous earths (Block series) and loamy Gleyic rendzinas (Ford End series). Both soils are calcareous to the surface, with dark greyish brown slightly stony topsoils and pale grey to white subsoil horizons with ochreous mottles. On slightly elevated areas, where the head deposits are thinner and marly chalk occurs at 40 cm depth or less, loamy Gleyic rendzinas of the Burwell series occur. Locally associated with Block series are fine loamy Gleyic rendzinas (Gubblecote series) and Gleyic brown calcareous earths (Grove series), both with subsoil horizons consisting of waterlain flinty gravel occurring within 80 cm depth. It is therefore possible that in the Late Devensian the narrow SE-NW strip of Association 512e extending between Long Marston and Puttenham was a gelifluction lobe feeding the stream that deposited the terrace gravel of Association 512d.

Agriculture. Where they are undrained, the Block, Burwell and Grove series are often waterlogged in winter, but not as frequently as the Ford End series, which can have surface flooding in wet periods. Much of the land has been successfully drained by mole and pipe systems feeding into ditches, and can be cultivated in autumn and dry spring periods. Grass is the main crop but some winter cereals are also grown, though they can suffer from manganese deficiency.

Association 512f: Milton

This association consists of fine loamy calcareous soils occurring near the northern county boundary on terrace remnants of the River Rhee overlying Gault Clay and West Melbury Marly Chalk Formation in parts of Hinxworth, Caldecote and Ashwell parishes. It is more extensive in parts of Cambridgeshire along the Cam and Granta valleys. The principal soils are the Milton and Block series, both Gleyic brown calcareous earths with slightly stony calcareous sandy clay loam or clay loam surface horizons. The Milton series has brown loamy subsoil horizons derived from chalky and slightly flinty terrace deposits, whereas the Block series has a pale greyish brown to grey, more calcareous subsoil derived from marly chalk or chalky gelifluction deposits. Gleyic rendzinas of the Burwell series occur locally in association with the Block soils. On the terrace gravels, the Milton soils are often associated with better drained Typical brown calcareous earths of the Badsey series, which have coarse loamy or sandy and very stony subsoil horizons. The two often form polygonal soil patterns, probably originating under periglacial conditions in the Late Devensian. The Milton soils forming the polygon margins retain more water than the Badsey soils within the polygons, often leading to polygonal patterns of differential crop growth in dry spring and early summer periods. Where the terrace deposits are very thin over Gault Clay near margins of the terrace remnants, Stagnogleyic brown calcareous earths with grey clayey subsoil horizons (St Lawrence series) are present.

Agriculture. Apart from the Badsey series, all soils of this association are waterlogged at least occasionally, but are easily cultivated, especially in the autumn, and are used for a wide range of crops, including cereals, sugar beet, potatoes and grass. However, growth is often retarded in periods of drought, especially where the terrace deposits are thickest (Badsey and Milton series).

Association 513: Cannamore

In Hertfordshire this association is restricted to a small area in Hinxworth parish, though it is more extensive in Bedfordshire south and east of Biggleswade. Around Hinxworth village (TL 2340) it occurs on the crest of a ridge capped by chalky till, which overlies an outlier of West Melbury Marly Chalk Formation. The till here is slightly more sandy than elsewhere in the county, probably because the glacier had moved along the outcrop of the Upper Greensand or crossed the Lower Greensand inlier southwest of Kingston (TL 3455). Consequently the most common soil (Cannamore series) is a fine loamy Stagnogleyic brown calcareous earth rather than the clay soils occurring on the chalky till elsewhere in Hertfordshire (see Association 411d). A typical profile has a sandy clay loam or clay loam texture throughout and contains chalk fragments even in the dark grey topsoil. The subsoil horizons are yellowish brown with greyish mottles appearing at depths below 40 cm. The subsidiary soils are mainly fine loamy over clayey Stagnogleyic argillic brown earths (Ashley series), and less commonly Typical calcareous pelosols (Hanslope series) and Typical brown calcareous earths (Stretham series) where the till is clayey to the surface.

Agriculture. The soils are more easily worked than those of Association 411d, though there can be as many as 70 days between mid-December and late March in the average winter when the land is too wet for safe use of heavy machinery. The main crops grown are winter cereals with some sugar beet and small areas of grass.

Association 571k: Moulton

This association occurs mainly on the floors of minor chalkland valleys in north Hertfordshire, including the valley of Cat Ditch north of Wallington and two valleys in Barley parish east of Royston, which contain minor streams tributary to the River Rhee. The patches north of Barley extend for 6-7 km into Cambridgeshire on either side of the A505 as far as Duxford Airfield. There is also a small area of the same association east of the A1(M) between Stevenage and Graveley.

The dominant soils, forming about 30% of these mapped

areas, are coarse loamy Typical argillic brown earths of the Moulton series, with brown subsoil horizons over chalky gelifluction deposits (Coombe Deposits) resting on chalk of the New Pit and Lewes Nodular Chalk Formations. They are accompanied by similar textured soils of the Maplestead series where the Coombe Deposits are slightly flinty, by fine loamy Typical argillic brown earths of the Frilsham series, and by Typical brown calcareous earths of the Swaffham Prior series (also coarse loamy) and Soham series (fine loamy) where the Coombe Deposits are less than 80 cm thick over chalk and have not been decalcified. On the slightly steeper valley sides, where the Coombe Deposits are even thinner or absent, so that chalk occurs within 30 cm depth, there are coarse loamy Brown rendzinas of the Newmarket series.

Agriculture. All soils in the association are well drained and can be cultivated in all but the wettest winter and spring periods. Reserves of plant available water are moderate to high because of the loamy texture of the subsoil horizons and the porous chalky substrates, both of which can readily be exploited by plant roots. The land is mainly cultivated for cereals and sugar beet, but there are some areas of permanent grassland.

Association 571m: Charity

This association is typical of chalkland valleys dissecting areas southwest of the upper Lea valley, where the interfluves are covered with Plateau Drift and Clay-with-flints *sensu stricto* (Fig. 7.6). The soils are developed in chalky and often very flinty gelifluction or head deposits (Coombe Deposits) derived partly from the Plateau Drift and partly from chalk exposed on the valley sides. A considerable loess component is also present, so that most of the soils are silty in texture. The association is extensive in the Tring and Dagnall areas, and extends down the Bulbourne and Gade valleys as far as Hemel Hempstead. It is also present in the Ver and adjoining valleys between the M1 at Friars Wash (TL 0914) and St Albans, and occupies the floors of narrow but fairly shallow dry valleys between St Albans, Harpenden and Wheathampstead.

The main soils are deep fine silty Typical argillic brown earths of the Charity series, which occur on the valley floors where the head deposits are thickest, often adjacent to narrow river floodplains with alluvial soils. On the steeper (south- and west-facing) valley sides, where the head is thinner (40-80 cm) over chalk, the shallower but otherwise similar Garston series occurs, and Rendzinas (mainly Andover series) are present on the steepest parts of the slope where the Coombe Deposits are absent. Coombe series (fine silty Typical Brown calcareous earths) and the similar but thinner Panholes series, with chalk or rubbly chalk at 40-80 cm depth, also occur on valley sides where the head deposits have not been decalcified.

Agriculture. All soils in the association are well drained, but have a weak structure and are prone to compaction when wet. The high silt content can also allow crusting,

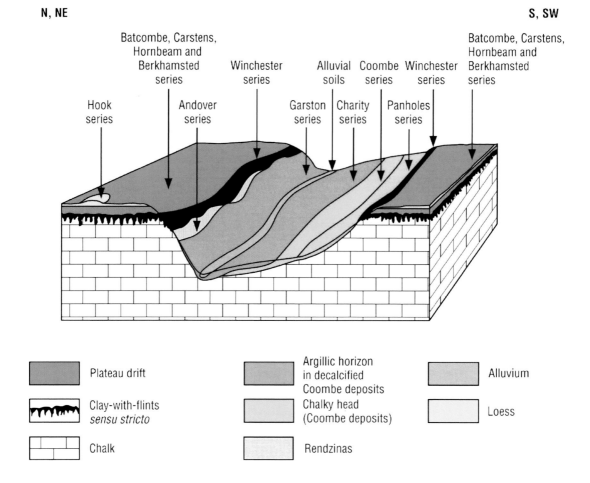

N, NE

Hook
series

Batcombe, Carstens,
Hornbeam and
Berkhamsted
series

Andover
series

Winchester
series

Garston
series

Charity
series

Alluvial
soils

Coombe
series

Winchester
series

Panholes
series

Batcombe, Carstens,
Hornbeam and
Berkhamsted
series

S, SW

	Plateau drift		Argillic horizon in decalcified Coombe deposits		Alluvium
	Clay-with-flints *sensu stricto*		Chalky head (Coombe deposits)		Loess
	Chalk		Rendzinas		

Fig. 7.6. Relationships between constituent soil series in Associations 571m (Charity) and 582a (Batcombe) in a typical Chiltern valley and adjacent parts of the Chiltern plateau in Hertfordshire.

which leads to localized runoff and erosion when the soil is exposed to periods of heavy rain. The flat or gently sloping valley floors are often suitable for cultivation of cereals, but the Charity and Garston soils are sometimes less suitable because they can be very flinty, and this decreases plant available water and causes implement wear. Like the steeper valley sides, these areas are suited only to permanent grass or woodland.

Association 5710: Melford

The soils of this association occur in valleys cut into the chalky till plateau of east Hertfordshire, including those of the rivers Beane, Rib, Quin, Ash and Stort. They are mainly fine loamy or clayey soils developed in thin till or head overlying chalk of the Lewes and Seaford Formations, and occur on moderate or gentle valley-side slopes. The principal soils are Typical argillic brown earths of the Melford series (fine loamy over clayey) and Weasenham series (fine loamy throughout). Both have dark brown slightly stony topsoils and yellowish brown subsoil horizons overlying brown till or head containing chalk fragments at depths of less than 1 m. The main subsidiary soils are fine loamy Typical argillic brown earths of the Ludford series and coarse loamy Typical brown earths of the Hall series, both developed on head

derived from till upslope. Where eroded remnants of the till are slightly thicker, there are also fine loamy or fine loamy over clayey Stagnogleyic argillic brown earths (Burlingham and Ashley series, respectively). Typical brown sands of the Newport series occur where Kesgrave Sands and Gravels or glaciofluvial gravels underlying the chalky till are exposed on upper parts of the valley sides. Marlow series (fine loamy Typical paleo-argillic brown earth) and Barrow series (coarse loamy Typical paleo-argillic brown earth), both with reddish clayey paleo-argillic Bt subsoil horizons, also occur locally in small patches. They are probably formed in head derived from pre-existing interglacial soils on the till.

Agriculture. Apart from the small areas of Burlingham and Ashley series, the whole association is well drained and can be cultivated until late December in most years, though there may be cultivation problems in wet springs. Available moisture reserves are moderately large for deeper rooting crops, such as cereals, oilseed rape and sugar beet, but grass, potatoes and other shallow rooting crops can suffer from drought in prolonged dry spells. Consequently the main cropping sequence is 3-4 years continuous cereals followed by oilseed rape, sugar beet or field beans as a break crop to avoid build-up of fungal root diseases in the cereals.

Heathland. The small areas of gravelly Newport series are too dry and stony for arable use, and often retain a semi-natural grass heath vegetation, which probably developed under common grazing regimes. At the HMWT reserve and SSSI of Patmore Heath (TL 443257), the gravels (Stoke Row Gravels of the proto-Thames, within the Kesgrave Sand and Gravel Formation) overlie impermeable clay of the Reading Formation, and are waterlogged in winter around nine small ponds (probably abandoned gravel pits). Consequently the reserve has a patchwork of dry and wet heath vegetation types, some of the latter containing small areas of *Sphagnum*, soft rush (*Juncus effusus*) and heath rush (*Juncus squarrosus*). The larvae of the moth *Coleophora alticollela* feed on the seed capsules of soft rush (Plant, 2008), and the ponds are important in supporting breeding populations of frog, toad and all three species of British newts, as well as various aquatic beetles.

Association 571x: Ludford

This association occurs in the Lea valley between Wheathampstead and Hertford, the Mimram valley east of Welwyn, the Beane valley south of White Hall (TL 2821) and in Langley Bottom from near Almshoe Bury (TL 2025) to where it joins the Beane valley southeast of Stevenage. The soils are mainly fine loamy Typical argillic brown earths (Ludford series) and coarse loamy Typical argillic brown earths (Maplestead series) formed in thin flinty gelifluction (head) deposits overlying the Lewes and Seaford Chalk Formations. The upper soil horizons often contain loess, and where this exceeds 1 m in thickness, principally in the Lea valley between Hatfield and Hertford, silty and almost stonefree Typical argillic brown earths of the Hamble series occur. The valleys also contain glaciofluvial and river terrace sands and flint gravels, in which Typical brown sands (Newport series), Argillic brown sands (Ebstree series), very flinty Argillic brown sands (St Albans series) and coarse loamy Typical brown earths over gravel (Hall series) are developed. St Albans series is most extensive in the Mimram valley near Panshanger (TL 2513) on the eastern side of Welwyn Garden City.

Agriculture. All soils in the association are well drained and can be cultivated in most years until mid or late December and again in early March. They are mainly under arable crops, such as cereals, oilseed rape, sugar beet and potatoes, but growth in dry spring and summer periods is poor and yields are reduced, especially on the Newport, Ebstree and St Albans series which retain little water. In contrast, the Hamble series has a much larger available water capacity and rarely suffers drought problems. Consequently in dry spells patterns of variable crop growth are usually evident. Although most of the association is on flat or gently sloping land, water erosion can occur locally on slightly steeper slopes if there is heavy rain before the soil has acquired a protective crop cover.

Association 571z: Hamble

The thick stoneless silty soils of this association occur in two main areas in Hertfordshire, one along the western side of the Lea valley south of Hertford and the other in the Vale of St Albans east of the city between Colney Street (TL 1502) and Stanborough (TL 2211). The thick loess (brickearth) parent material, the Spring Wood Silt of Gibbard (1977) (Section 6.10, Plate 54), mainly overlies flinty river terrace gravels of the Lea, upper Colne and proto-Thames. Silty Typical argillic brown earths (Hamble series) occupy slightly elevated interfluves and silty Gleyic argillic brown earths (Hook series) occur close to rivers, where the groundwater table rises in winter to within 60 cm of the surface. These two soils together occupy about 70% of the land. Where the brickearth is thinner than 80 cm over the non-calcareous gravel, the main subsidiary soil is the Efford series (fine loamy Typical argillic brown earth). Ratsborough series (fine silty over clayey Stagnogleyic argillic brown earth) occurs sporadically in the Vale of St Albans where thin brickearth is separated from the gravel beneath by a thin layer of clayey drift such as chalky till.

Agriculture. Because they are easily cultivated, mainly well drained and also have large reserves of available water, the soils of this association provide some of the most valuable farmland in the county. They equate to Young's (1804) rich loam of the lower Lea valley, which he described as possessing 'adhesion without tenacity, and friability without looseness: equal to all the productions of the climate'. However, since Young's time much of the land has been disturbed by gravel working. In the lower Lea valley extensive areas of abandoned workings are now flooded and used for leisure purposes or as nature reserves, such as Amwell Quarry (TL 3712). In the Vale of St Albans, they have been used mainly as landfill sites and subsequent restoration has often been poor, so that present soil quality does not match that of the original.

On undisturbed land a wide range of crops can be grown, including cereals, sugar beet, potatoes, vegetables, soft fruit, salad crops and flowers, though some of these benefit from irrigation in dry spring and summer periods. However, the topsoil structure is weak, especially where prolonged cultivation has depleted the organic matter content, and this can result in the formation of a hard surface crust, which may prevent the emergence of seedlings. Subsequently under heavy rain the crust can cause runoff, formation of erosion rills and removal of young plants. To avoid these problems and also warm the soils to encourage early growth of salad crops and flowers for the London market, they have long been protected under glass. Until the early part of the 20th century, horse manure swept from London streets was regularly applied to maintain organic matter levels and fertility, but under glass plant nutrients are now applied in irrigation water (fertigation). The glasshouses are also heated in winter to provide crops throughout the year. The most extensive glasshouse areas remaining in Hertfordshire are in the lower Lea valley near Great Amwell (TL 3612), Hailey (TL 3610), Hammond Street (TL 3204) and Goffs

Plate 66. Glasshouse complex on Hamble Association, Smallford (TL 1907) near St Albans (published with the permission of Glinwell plc).

Oak (TL 3302), though there are larger areas on similar soils east of the river in Essex. There are also small glasshouse complexes on the Hamble Association in the Vale of St Albans at Smallford (TL 1907) (Plate 66).

In view of the current desire to minimize the distances ('food miles') that crops are transported to consumers, especially in winter, expansion of the glasshouse industry on this soil association is likely in the future. It would be especially beneficial if such developments could be linked to nearby heavy industries, from which carbon dioxide emissions and waste heat could be fed to the glasshouses.

Association 572j: Bursledon

In Hertfordshire the Bursledon Association occurs on the narrow outcrop of the Reading Beds in southern parts of the county between Bushey and Brookmans Park, and also near Essendon. Small patches also occur on the sides of the Stort, Ash and Rib valleys where these have cut through the chalky till into the Reading Beds. The soils are mainly fine loamy Stagnogleyic argillic brown earths of the Bursledon series, where the Reading Beds consist of interbedded sands and clays, and Oxpasture series, where loamy drift rests on yellowish brown Reading Beds clay. Stagnogleyic argillic brown earths of the Loshes series occur where the thin drift overlying Reading Beds clay is coarse loamy. In low-lying areas there are also small areas of more poorly drained Typical stagnogley soils (Wickham series) where Reading Beds clay is overlain by fine loamy or fine silty drift, and of Typical argillic gley soils (Curdridge series) where coarse loamy drift overlies sands or soft sandstones within the Reading Beds.

Agriculture. All soils in this association have seasonally or permanently waterlogged subsoil horizons and require artificial drainage for successful arable cultivation. This is usually least successful with the Wickham soils, which are consequently under pasture though poaching problems are common. The main arable crops are cereals with break crops of oilseed rape, potatoes, sugar beet or field beans every 3-4 years to limit cereal diseases.

Association 572q: Ashley

The Ashley Association occurs in two small parts of Hertfordshire, an undulating area in Holwell, Ickleford and Pirton parishes near the northern county boundary, and a broad minor valley extending from the chalky till plateau south of Widford (TL 4215) towards the Stort valley south of Hunsdon. In both areas the soils are derived mainly from Anglian chalky till. The principal soil, the Ashley series, is a Stagnogleyic argillic brown earth with fine loamy upper horizons probably containing Late Devensian loess over a clayey subsoil derived from the till. The main subsidiary soils are Typical calcareous pelosols (Hanslope series), Argillic pelosols (Faulkbourne series) and Typical stagnogley soils (Beccles series), all of which occur on convex slopes where erosion has removed the loamy upper layer and the topsoil consists of weathered clayey till.

Agriculture. Because of the slowly permeable clayey subsoil horizons, all the soils are seasonally waterlogged, but can be readily improved by mole and pipe drainage systems. In autumn the Ashley soils in particular can be worked until late November, but opportunities for spring cultivation are often inadequate for establishment of spring-sown crops. Consequently the association is best suited to autumn-sown cereals and oilseed rape.

Association 581b: Sonning

The soils of this association are mainly Paleo-argillic brown earths occurring on patches of proto-Thames and Colne river terrace gravels in the Vale of St Albans south of Rickmansworth and Croxley Green, between Chorleywood and Watford, and on either side of the River Colne from the M1 near Aldenham (TQ 1398) to the M25 north of Shenleybury (TL 1801). There is also an area on Anglian glaciofluvial gravels around St Ippollitts and Gosmore south of Hitchin, extending as far south as the ruined Minsden Chapel (TL 1924).

The principal soil (Sonning series) is a coarse loamy Typical paleo-argillic brown earth. In south Hertfordshire this is associated mainly with coarse loamy over clayey Stagnogleyic paleo-argillic brown earths of the Berkhamsted series, but near Hitchin loamy-gravelly Typical paleo-argillic brown earths (Bockmer series) are more common. Deep coarse loamy Stagnogleyic paleo-argillic brown earths (Horseley series) and fine loamy over clayey Typical paleo-argillic brown earths (Marlow series) occur locally. There are also small areas of Argillic brown sands (Ebstree and St Albans series), coarse loamy Typical brown earths (Hall series), coarse loamy Typical argillic brown earths (Maplestead series) and fine loamy Typical argillic brown earths (Efford series).

Agriculture. The Sonning, Marlow, Bockmer, Ebstree, St Albans, Hall and Maplestead soils are all well drained, but subsoil horizons of the Berkhamsted and Horseley series are less permeable and often waterlogged in winter. The Bockmer, Ebstree and St Albans soils have small reserves of available water, and crop yields are limited by drought more than on the other soils. Another problem in arable farming is the large flint content of topsoils, which causes rapid implement and tyre wear and damages root crops during harvesting. Consequently much of the land is under grass or woodland rather than arable crops. Although there is little risk of poaching, the slow growth of grass in dry spring and summer periods can limit stocking rates.

Association 581d: Carstens

The mainly Paleo-argillic brown earths of this association occur on lower parts of the Chiltern plateau on the western side of the Ver and Colne valleys between the eastern end of Punchbowl Lane where it joins Watling Street (TL 118102) and the eastern side of Woodside (TL 1101) adjacent to the A405 south of Garston Crematorium. The most extensive soil, the Carstens series (fine silty over clayey Typical paleo-argillic brown earth) is formed in thin Late Devensian loess overlying Plateau Drift, which in turn rests at depths of several metres on chalk of the Seaford and Newhaven Formations. Where the superficial loess layer is absent, clayey Typical paleo-argillic brown earths of the Givendale series occur. Clayey Typical paleo-argillic brown earths (Winchester series) also occur on spurs at the edge of the plateau, where Clay-with-flints *sensu stricto* emerges from beneath the Plateau Drift and chalk is present within 1 m depth. Fine silty Typical argillic brown earths (Charity series) occur on the floors of dry valleys, where gelifluction (head) deposits composed partly of loess eroded from the adjacent plateau have accumulated.

Agriculture. All these soils are well drained because their clayey subsoil horizons have a strongly developed structure with numerous vertical fissures leading to the underlying chalk. This structure was probably inherited from interglacial pedogenesis. Consequently most of the land can be readily worked in autumn and early winter, though in wet spring periods there are fewer opportunities for cultivation, especially on the rather sticky Givendale and Winchester series. The soils are naturally acidic and need periodic dressings of lime to maintain crop yields, especially of barley. Most of the land is under arable cultivation, usually winter wheat or winter barley with break crops of oilseed rape or potatoes.

Association 581e: Marlow

This association, also consisting mainly of Paleo-argillic brown earths, occurs on lower parts of the Chiltern dip-slope, but southwest of the area occupied by the Carstens Association (581d). The main area extends from the Chess valley between Loudwater (TQ 0596) and Latimer (TQ 0098) north-eastwards as far as Bricket Wood (TL 1202)

and Potters Crouch (TL 1105). There is also a narrow strip extending along the foot of the Tertiary scarp from Hill Farm (TL 151008) north of Radlett to Walsingham Wood (TL 2104), and a small area between Welwyn (TL 2316) and Digswell (TL 2415).

The principal soil, Marlow series, is a fine loamy over clayey Typical paleo-argillic brown earth. It is associated mainly with Hornbeam and Berkhamsted series, which are fine loamy over clayey and coarse loamy over clayey Stagnogleyic argillic brown earths, respectively. In all three series the reddish brown Plateau Drift is overlain by a thin layer of Late Devensian loess. Where this is absent because of erosion on upper slopes of valleys incised into the plateau, clayey Typical paleo-argillic brown earths of the Givendale and Winchester series are present, as in Association 581d. The Plateau Drift often overlies proto-Thames terrace gravels, such as the Gerrards Cross and Beaconsfield Gravels, probably because it was soliflucted over them from higher parts of the Chiltern dip-slope during cold stages of the later Mid and Late Pleistocene.

Soil drainage and other characteristics important for agriculture are similar to those of the Carstens Association (581d).

Association 582a: Batcombe

The Stagnogleyic paleo-argillic brown earths of this association (Fig. 7.6) are extensive on higher parts of the Chiltern dip-slope between the county boundary southwest of the Bulbourne valley and the dry valley (Whiteway Bottom) running north-westwards from Kimpton (TL 1718) to the county boundary near Winch Hill Farm (TL 1321) northeast of Luton Airport. As in Associations 581d and 581e the surface horizons contain loess, which overlies reddish brown clayey subsoil horizons derived from Plateau Drift, with chalk of the Seaford and Newhaven Formations at depths of several metres.

The principal soil, Batcombe series, is a fine silty over clayey Stagnogleyic paleo-argillic brown earth with grey mottled subsoil horizons. Carstens series (fine silty over clayey Typical paleo-argillic brown earth lacking grey subsoil mottles), Hornbeam series (fine loamy over clayey Stagnogleyic paleo-argillic brown earth) and Berkhamsted series (coarse loamy over clayey Stagnogleyic paleo-argillic brown earth) are the main subsidiary soils on the plateau surface. As well as angular flint fragments, the Berkhamsted soils often contain abundant small black flint pebbles derived ultimately from the Reading Beds, and Hook series (silty almost stonefree Gleyic argillic brown earth) occurs where the loess cover is thicker than 1 m. As in Associations 581d and 581e, the Winchester series occurs where Clay-with-flints *sensu stricto* emerges from beneath the Plateau Drift on the upper slopes of valleys (Plate 26).

Agriculture and forestry. Many soil characteristics important for agriculture are similar to those of Associations 581d and 581e, but subsoil permeability is generally slower, which restricts opportunities for late autumn and spring cultivation to a greater extent. Also the structure of the silty (loess-containing) topsoils of the Batcombe, Carstens and Hook soils is weak, so that the soil can be compacted if cultivated in wet periods. Because of these problems, much of the land is wooded or pasture. The main arable crops are autumn sown cereals, though some vegetables and soft fruit are grown where the silty or fine loamy surface horizons are thicker. The growth of beech (*Fagus sylvatica*) is better on all these plateau soils, including the Winchester series, than on the steeper scarp and valley-side slopes occupied by thin rendzinas of the Upton (342a), Wantage 1 (342c) and Andover (343h) Associations (Brown, 1953; 1964). However, the effect of soil type is often overridden by aspect and degree of exposure, as forestry records show that the growth rate on Winchester series on sheltered slopes facing south-east is almost twice that on the same soil series on north-facing slopes of the exposed escarpment brow.

Association 582b: Hornbeam 1

In Hertfordshire this association forms two small areas, one on Plateau Drift of the Chiltern plateau north of Berkhamsted (SP 9909), and the other on proto-Thames terrace gravels (Stoke Row Gravels) surrounding the village of Bedmond (TL 0903). North of Berkhamsted the Plateau Drift rests partly on Chalk and partly on Reading Beds, and includes the Plio-Pleistocene sands and gravels formerly worked at Little Heath (Section 5.2). In both areas the association is very heterogeneous, showing intricate patterns in which the main soil type is the Hornbeam series (fine loamy over clayey Stagnogleyic paleo-argillic brown earth) and subsidiary soils include Berkhamsted series (coarse loamy over clayey Stagnogleyic paleo-argillic brown earth), Marlow series (fine loamy over clayey Typical paleo-argillic brown earth), Bockmer series (loamy-gravelly Typical paleo-argillic brown earth), Southampton series (sandy-gravelly Paleo-argillic podzol) and St Albans series (Argillic brown sand). Winchester series (clayey Typical paleo-argillic brown earth) occurs in strips up to 400 m wide at the edges of the plateau north of Berkhamsted.

Agriculture. The Marlow, Bockmer, Southampton, St Albans and Winchester soils are all well drained, but the Hornbeam and Berkhamsted series have less permeable clayey subsoils, which can cause waterlogging in winter and restrict opportunities for spring cultivation. All the soils are naturally acidic and require periodic liming under arable cultivation. Also the available water reserves of the St Albans and Southampton soils are too small for good growth of grass and arable crops. Consequently they are mainly under woodland, though these areas are often a complex of small pits where gravel has been dug in the past. Growth of beech is poor on the most acidic soils (Southampton series).

Association 582c: Hornbeam 2

This association occurs in various parts of west and central Hertfordshire, including lower parts of the Chiltern dip-slope between Flaunden (TL 0100) and Praewood Farm (TL 128068), between the Mimram valley and Burnham

Green (TL 2616) east of Digswell and on Perrywood Farm (TL 293180) and Great Gobions Farm (TL 298173) east of Bramfield Woods. It is also extensive on the slopes of the Lilley Bottom valley between the county boundary east of Luton south-eastwards to Welwyn and then south-westwards to the Lea valley east of Wheathampstead, and on either side of the Beane valley southwards from Weston (TL 2630) to Watton at Stone (TL 3019). It also forms a large area extending from Rook's Nest Farm (TL 2426) northwards to the Weston Hills (TL 2532) south of Baldock.

The soils are mainly Stagnogleyic paleo-argillic brown earths with loamy upper horizons containing Late Devensian loess over subsoil horizons composed of flinty clayey Plateau Drift, which is turn rests at irregular depths on chalk of the Seaford and Newhaven formations. As in Association 582b, the dominant soil is Hornbeam series and the main subsidiary series are Typical paleo-argillic brown earths of the Marlow and Carstens series. However, there are also minor areas of fine loamy over clayey Paleo-argillic stagnogley soils (Oak series) where the Plateau Drift is less permeable, and Givendale series (clayey Typical paleo-argillic brown earth) occurs locally where the superficial loamy aeolian drift is absent. Ludford series (fine loamy Typical argillic brown earth) occurs where the loamy drift is thicker than usual, and Charity series (fine silty Typical argillic brown earth) on the floors of minor valleys where mixed silty and flinty head deposits have accumulated. Marlow and Givendale series are most abundant in central parts of the county between Welwyn and Baldock.

Agriculture. Subsoil permeability ranges from fairly rapid in areas of Marlow, Carstens, Givendale, Ludford and Charity series to slow on Oak series. Most of the land is used for autumn-sown cereals with oilseed rape or potatoes grown every 3-4 years as a break crop to avoid diseases building up. There are also many areas of permanent grass and deciduous woodland, especially on Oak series. The Hornbeam, Marlow and Charity soils are often very flinty, which causes excessive tyre wear of farm machinery.

Association 582d: Hornbeam 3

In Hertfordshire this association occurs on chalky till in numerous small areas from the southern side of St Albans eastwards towards Hertford and northwards to the Chalk plateau between Weston (TL 2630) and Baldock. The largest patches occur (a) on the eastern side of St Albans northwards to Wheathampstead, (b) on either side of the Lea valley between Hatfield Hyde (TL 2410), Letty Green (TL 2810), Hillend Farm (TL 256093) and Howe Green (TL 2809), (c) between Burnham Green (TL 2616), Datchworth (TL 2619) and Woolmer Green (TL 2518), (d) between Knebworth (TL 2420), Rusling End Farm (TL 208213) and Pottersheath (TL 2318), (e) from the Beane valley near Woodhall Park (TL 3118) northwards to Nasty (TL 3524) and (f) between Sacombe Green (TL 3419) and Levens Green (TL 3522).

Hornbeam series (fine loamy over clayey Stagnogleyic paleo-argillic brown earth), formed in a thin superficial layer containing Late Devensian loess over the till, occupies about 30% of most of these areas, but the proportion increases south-westwards. The main subsidiary soils are the less well drained Oak series (fine loamy over clayey Paleo-argillic stagnogley soil), Batcombe series (fine silty over clayey Stagnogleyic paleo-argillic brown earth) and less strongly developed soils with calcareous clayey (chalky till) horizons occurring within 80 cm depth, such as the Ashley series (fine loamy over clayey Stagnogleyic argillic brown earth) and Faulkbourne series (Typical argillic pelosol). The latter has no superficial loess component. Hook series (silty Gleyic argillic brown earth) occurs locally where the loess layer exceeds 1 m in thickness.

Agriculture and woodlands. All the soils have slowly permeable clayey subsoil horizons and are subject to winter waterlogging, but apart from the Oak series can readily be drained for arable agriculture. However, there are few opportunities for spring cultivation, so the main crops grown are autumn-sown cereals, with oilseed rape, potatoes and field beans as break crops. Woodland is common, especially on the wetter Oak soils, and consists mainly of hornbeam (*Carpinus betulus*), often with subsidiary pedunculate oak (*Quercus robur*), ash (*Fraxinus excelsior*), field maple (*Acer campestre*), downy birch (*Betula pubescens*), silver birch (*Betula pendula*) and hazel (*Corylus avellana*) (James, 1991). Many of the woodland areas were previously coppiced and some, such as parts of Symondshyde Great Wood (TL 1910), Bramfield Wood (TL 2816), Graffidge Wood (TL 2121) and Newton Wood (TL 2222), are still very extensive.

Association 711h: Wickham

The soils of this association occur where Palaeogene (London and Reading Beds) clays are exposed on the sides of valleys cutting through the chalky till on the east Hertfordshire plateau, mainly on the western side of the Rib valley from Mentley Farm (TL 376236) near Puckeridge southwards to Badger's Eye Plantation (TL 3719) near Colliers End and westwards to Potterscroft Wood (TL 352198) near Sacombe Green. There are also two small areas west of Bishop's Stortford near Wickham Hall (TL 474230) and in the Blackthorn Spring valley between Hadham Lodge (TL 468222) and Bury Green (TL 4521).

The dominant soil (Wickham series) is a Typical stagnogley soil with fine loamy or fine silty surface horizons developed on gently sloping valleys sides and footslopes in a thin head deposit overlying grey and ochreous mottled clay subsoil. Pelo-stagnogley soils of the Denchworth and Windsor series are the main accompanying soils, occurring on moderately steep upper slopes where the head is thin or absent. The Windsor soils have a brown clay subsoil, whereas the Denchworth soils have grey and ochreous mottles throughout the profile.

Agriculture. All three series are poorly drained and difficult to cultivate even after underdrainage has decreased the extent of winter waterlogging. Consequently autumn cereals

are the main arable crop. The soils are naturally acidic, and the Wickham and Windsor series in particular need regular liming.

Association 711t: Beccles

The Beccles association occurs in an irregular arcuate area west of the Lower Lea valley extending from near Hoddesdon and Cheshunt westwards to Epping Green (TL 2906) and Coldharbour Farm (TL 280056). This area is essentially a dissected ridge composed of London Clay overlain by Pebble Gravel and capped by chalky till. The principal soil is Beccles series, a fine loamy over clayey Typical stagnogley soil, with a dark greyish brown A horizon and mottled upper subsoil horizons composed of Late Devensian loess mixed with weathered till. This is accompanied mainly by the slightly better drained Ashley series (fine loamy over clayey Stagnogleyic argillic brown earth), occurring where the till is thinner over Pebble Gravel, and by Hanslope series (Typical calcareous pelosol, clayey throughout) and Ragdale series (Pelo-stagnogley soil, also clayey throughout) on convex slopes at the edges of the ridge, where the superficial loess-containing layer is absent because of erosion. Coarse loamy Typical brown earths of the Wick series occur locally on patches of glaciofluvial gravels or where glacial deposits are absent and Pebble Gravel emerges at the surface.

Agriculture and woodlands. The Beccles and Ragdale soils are poorly drained and subject to winter waterlogging. They respond fairly well to underdrainage, but they are best suited to pasture or autumn cultivation of cereals, and some areas are under woodland. As in parts of Broxbourne Wood (TL 3207) and the HMWT reserves of Fir Wood (TL 276011) and Pond Wood (TL 279004) near Potters Bar, the woodland consists mainly of pedunculate oak (*Quercus robur*) and hornbeam (*Carpinus betulus*), with some silver birch (*Betula pendula*), rowan (*Sorbus aucuparia*) and beech (*Fagus sylvatica*). The Wick, Ashley and Hanslope soils are waterlogged for much shorter periods in winter and can often be cultivated in spring. They are less suited to pasture because reserves of available water are small and growth of grass is poor in periods of spring and summer drought.

Association 711v: Gresham

This association occurs in three small almost flat areas near St Albans, one extending northwards from Bricket Wood Common (TL 1200) to How Wood (TL 1403), another near Courser's Farm (TL 205047) and a third on the now disused Hatfield Aerodrome (TL 2008). The total area is only 7 km². The soils are derived from an almost stonefree Late Devensian loess layer overlying weathered Anglian till, which forms the clayey subsoil horizons below a minimum depth of 60 cm. The main soil (Gresham series) is a fine silty over clayey Typical stagnogley soil with greyish mottles within 40 cm depth. It is accompanied mainly by the better drained Hook series (silty Gleyic argillic brown earth) and by Prolleymoor series (fine silty over clayey Typical stagnogley soil), the latter occurring where the upper, loess-containing layer is less than 60 cm thick. The weathered till layer is often thin, resting on sand or gravel at 1-2 m depth.

Agriculture. Although the Gresham and Prolleymoor soils are poorly drained because of the clay subsoil, they respond well to artificial drainage and, like the Hook series, can easily be cultivated for arable crops throughout the autumn and early winter as well as in drier spring periods. The whole association includes some of the county's most productive soils, suitable for cereals, root crops and field vegetables, but much of it is under woodland, especially in the Bricket Wood area.

Association 712c: Windsor

The Windsor Association is extensive on the undulating, strongly dissected land of the London Clay and Claygate Beds outcrops in south Hertfordshire, from Moor Park (TQ 0893) eastwards to the edge of the Lea valley west of Cheshunt, Hoddesdon and Hertford Heath (TL 3411). The soils are mainly Pelo-stagnogleys of the Windsor series, where Quaternary deposits are absent, and the Lawford series, developed in thick clayey head deposits overlying London Clay. Both have grey, olive and ochreous mottled subsurface horizons, which pass downwards into brown, less-mottled subsoil horizons (oxidized London Clay). Wickham series (fine loamy over clayey Typical stagnogley soil) occurs where thin loamy or silty drift deposits overlie the clay, and Denchworth series (Pelo-stagnogley soil similar to the Windsor series but with grey rather than brown subsoil horizons) occurs on clay beds within the Claygate Beds. The Lawford soils occur mainly on footslopes and valley floors, Wickham series is most common on interfluve crests and Windsor series on the steeper valley sides.

Agriculture and woodlands. All the soils are waterlogged and inaccessible to machinery and livestock for most of the winter. Even in summer the clayey topsoils become sticky and plastic during and immediately after rain, so that trafficking can lead to compaction. Consequently any cultivation for arable crops must be carefully timed even in autumn. In many years there are almost no days suitable for work between mid-October and late April. Autumn-sown cereals with winter oilseed rape as a break crop are grown in some areas, though regular liming of the naturally acidic topsoil is essential. The land is not suitable for root crops, and much of it is under permanent grass or woodland. However, poaching is a common problem in winter, and grazing is best confined to late spring, summer and early autumn. Some woodland areas consisting mainly of sessile oak (*Quercus petraea*), hornbeam (*Carpinus betulus*) and downy birch (*Betula pubescens*), such as Scratch Wood (TQ 2094) and parts of Northaw Great Wood (TL 2804), Wormley Wood (TL 3206) and Hoddesdon Park Wood (TL 3508), are important local nature reserves. The shrub layer and ground flora of these *Quercus-Carpinus* woodlands were described in detail by Salisbury (1916).

Association 714c: Oak

In Hertfordshire the Paleo-argillic soils of this association occur only in two small areas, a patch west of Welham Green (TL 2205) and a narrow strip beside the A1000 between Old Hatfield (TL 2308) and Marshmoor (TL 2306) on the western side of Hatfield Park. They are developed in thin Late Devensian loess overlying chalky till weathered in one or more interglacials. The main soil is Oak series (Paleo-argillic stagnogley), which has dark greyish brown and yellowish brown fine loamy upper horizons over strong brown, grey and red mottled clayey subsoil horizons and chalky till occurring at depths of 1-2.5 m. Subsidiary soils include better drained Stagnogleyic paleo-argillic brown earths of the Hornbeam series (fine loamy over clayey) and Batcombe series (fine silty over clayey) and Typical argillic pelosols of the Faulkbourne series, the last with subsoil horizons composed of little-weathered chalky till.

Agriculture. The Oak series is poorly suited to agriculture because of the seasonally waterlogged subsoil. Consequently the two areas are mainly under woodland. However, the Hornbeam, Batcombe and Faulkbourne soils are better drained and can be used for pasture or cultivation of winter cereals. Like other Paleo-argillic soils, the Oak, Hornbeam and Batcombe series are naturally acidic in all horizons above the chalky till, and consequently require applications of lime every few years when in arable use.

Association 714d: Essendon

In Hertfordshire the Paleo-argillic stagnogley soils of this association occur mainly on plateaux and narrow ridges above approximately 100 m OD. south and west of the Lea valley from Hatfield southwards to the county boundary near Potters Bar. The ridges mainly extend eastwards from the north-south plateau, the best example being The Ridgeway between Brookmans Park (TL 2504) and Cuffley (TL 2903), which includes the higher (southern) part of Northaw Great Wood Country Park. Further west there are additional small patches between Green Street (TQ 1998), Ridge (TL 2100) and Shenley (TL 1800), on the northern side of Elstree (TQ 1795 and TQ 1895) and on Caldecote Hill (TQ 1594) between Bushey Heath and the M1. The association also occurs near Harefield (Middlesex) and is extensive in Buckinghamshire around Beaconsfield, Denham, Iver Heath and Stoke Poges. Further east it also widespread in southern Essex.

The main soils are Essendon series (coarse loamy over clayey) and Oak series (fine loamy over clayey), both with red-mottled paleo-argillic subsoil horizons formed by interglacial weathering of thin till or head (gelifluction) deposits over Pebble Gravel or proto-Thames terrace gravels, which in turn rest on London Clay. There are also better drained Stagnogleyic paleo-argillic brown earths of the Hornbeam series (fine loamy over clayey) and Berkhamsted series (coarse loamy over clayey). Where the Quaternary deposits are thin over London Clay, mainly on the upper slopes of valleys, there are small patches of Wickham series (fine loamy or fine silty over clayey Typical stagnogley soil).

The drainage characteristics, natural acidity and other properties of soils in the Essendon Association are similar to those of the Oak Association. Consequently the range of land uses is also similar.

Association 812a: Frome

The chalky and often gravelly Alluvial gley soils of the Frome Association occur on the floors of major valleys draining the Chilterns, such as the Bulbourne valley between Bulbourne (SO 9313) and Hemel Hempstead, the Gade valley between The Hoo Lodge (TL 0212) and Croxley Green (TQ 0794) and the Chess valley from Rickmansworth (TQ 0694) upstream to Latimer (TQ 0098).

The distribution of different soil series is complex and variable. Silty over gravelly Calcareous alluvial gley soils of Frome series are the dominant type, and the main subsidiary soils are the Racton series (non-calcareous silty over gravelly Typical alluvial gley soils) and Gade series (silty over gravelly Calcareous humic alluvial gley soils, often with a peaty topsoil). Earthy eutro-amorphous peat soils of the Adventurers' series occur in small patches where the peat layers, usually interbedded with calcareous alluvium, are thick enough in total to form more than half the upper 80 cm of the profile.

Grassland and watercress beds. All the soils show grey and ochreous subsoil mottling and are waterlogged

for much of the year, especially in lower reaches of the valleys. The Adventurers series and Gade soils with peaty topsoils are wet even for much of the spring and summer growing season. Consequently most of the land is under permanent grass or locally woodland. However, some areas were previously disturbed by gravel working and are now flooded, for example in the Bulbourne valley upstream from Boxmoor and in the Gade valley near Kings Langley. Other areas used to be maintained in a flooded state for cultivation of watercress, for example in the Gade valley between Great Gaddesden and Water End (TL 0310). According to Clutterbuck (1864, pp. 312-313), watercress cultivation in Hertfordshire commenced at West Hyde near Rickmansworth in the middle of the 19th century. But the industry has declined in recent decades, and the only productive beds still remaining are in the Mimram valley at Whitwell (TL 180212) and Kimpton Mill (TL 197185) (Plate 67). Initially the native watercress species (*Rorippa nasturtium-aquaticum*) was grown, but recently the main commercial product has been the hybrid *Rorippa nasturium-aquaticum* × *Rorippa microphylla* (James, 2009). The effect of short-range soil variation on grassland types is indicated by the HMWT reserve and SSSI of Frogmore Meadow (TQ 022988) beside the River Chess near Chenies. In Cassiobury Park (TQ 089973), between Watford and Rickmansworth, abandoned watercress beds have developed into marshland with lagoons and areas of wet woodland (mainly willow and alder).

Plate 67. Watercress beds near Kimpton Mill (TL 197185), upper Mimram valley.

Association 813b: Fladbury 1

The clayey Alluvial gley soils of this association occur on the floodplains of the lower Lea valley from Hertford (TL 3213) downstream to Holdbrook (TL 3600), the Rib valley from Barwick Ford (TL 3818) downstream to Hertford and the Colne valley from Colney Street (TL 1501) to central Watford (TQ 1196). This distribution mainly reflects the occurrence of clay-rich calcareous source deposits, especially chalky till, in the various catchments. The dominant soil (Fladbury series) is a Pelo-alluvial gley soil, clayey throughout the profile, decalcified to at least 40 cm depth and with prominent grey and ochreous mottles below a dark greyish brown topsoil. Associated soils include Pelo-calcareous alluvial gley soils (Thames series), which are similar to the Fladbury series but calcareous within 40 cm depth, and less commonly Pelo-alluvial gley soils of the Midelney series and Pelo-calcareous alluvial gley soils of the Windrush series where the clayey alluvium overlies peat.

Grassland. All the soils are affected by groundwater, the levels of which fluctuate seasonally with changes in river level. Because the land is flat and close to river level, soil drainage is difficult to improve. Also many areas are flooded several times per year, especially in winter, though the duration of most floods is short. The land is almost entirely under permanent pasture, but poaching is a common problem in all but dry summer periods, and grazing in spring and autumn may be curtailed by flooding. The growth of grass is rarely limited by lack of water, but manganese deficiency can be a problem. Together with the poor drainage, manganese deficiency also limits the suitability of the soils for cereals (Gardner, 1967, p. 112), especially those sown in the autumn, but small areas of spring-sown cereals are grown locally. The HMWT reserve and SSSI of Rye Meads (TL 387106) is an old seasonally flooded meadow showing the mosaic of marshy grassland with reedbeds and fen vegetation typical of this association.

Association 813d: Fladbury 3

In Hertfordshire the clayey Alluvial gley soils of this association occur only on the floodplain of the Colne valley between Oxhey Park (TQ 1195) and the county boundary south of West Hyde (TQ 0390). As in Association 813b, Fladbury series is the dominant soil, but is mainly accompanied by fine silty Typical alluvial gley soils (Conway series) and fine loamy Typical alluvial gley soils (Enborne series). The slightly coarser sediment contributing to these soils probably originates from tributaries of the Colne, especially the Gade and Chess. Peat has also accumulated locally, giving small areas of Adventurers' series (Earthy eutro-amorphous peat soils), Midelney series (clayey over peaty Pelo-alluvial gley soils) and Windrush series (Pelo-calcareous alluvial gley soils in clayey alluvium, calcareous within 40 cm depth, over peat).

Grassland. The Fladbury, Adventurers', Midelney and Windrush soils are waterlogged for long periods in winter

and frequently into spring and summer growing periods as well. Surface flooding is common in winter, though usually for short periods only. The peat soils often occur in rushy backswamp depressions, which are almost permanently waterlogged. The Conway and Enborne soils are also waterlogged in winter, but their subsoil horizons drain slightly more rapidly than those of the other series, so that waterlogging persists for shorter periods and less commonly into the growing season. Much of the land is under permanent grass, but periods suitable for grazing are curtailed by flooding and risk of poaching. There are also a few small areas of woodland. However, the Holocene alluvium and peat of the Colne valley are underlain by Devensian gravels, which have been extensively excavated, leaving numerous large shallow lakes. Some of these, such as the HMWT reserve at Stocker's Lake (TQ 044931), near Rickmansworth, are important as bird reserves.

Association 814a: Thames

In Hertfordshire the clayey Alluvial gley soils of the Thames Association occur on the floors of river valleys upstream from Hertford, such as the Lea valley below Stanborough (TL 2211), the Mimram valley below Welwyn (TL 2316) and the Beane valley below Woodhall Park (TL 3118). The association also occurs along the Stort valley upstream of Stansted Bury, and on the floor of the Hiz valley and its tributaries from the source at Wellhead (TL 175276) northwards to the county boundary west of Arlesey (TL 1735). The dominant soil, Thames series, is a Pelo-calcareous alluvial gley soil, which is clayey throughout the profile and calcareous within 40 cm depth. The clay and carbonate contents reflect derivation of the alluvium mainly from chalky till within the various catchments. The main subsidiary soil is Fladbury series (non-calcareous Pelo-alluvial gley soil). Adventurers' series (Earthy eutro-amorphous peat soil) and Windrush series (clayey over peaty Pelo-calcareous alluvial gley soil) occur in the wettest areas, such as backswamp depressions in abandoned meanders, or marshes fed by springs rising from the Chalk. On slightly raised sites, such as narrow levees, better drained soils often occur (Fig. 7.7). These include Pelogleyic brown calcareous alluvial soils (Uffington series) in predominantly clayey alluvium, and Gleyic brown calcareous alluvial soils (Usher series) where the alluvium is fine loamy. Both soils are calcareous within 40 cm depth.

Grassland. All except the Uffington and Usher soils are affected by periodic flooding and a high groundwater table throughout the winter, often extending into the growing season. Consequently most of the land is under permanent grass or woodland. Grazing is usually restricted to summer because of the risk of poaching or flooding. Small areas are cultivated for winter cereals, but can be difficult to manage.

The wettest areas are under semi-natural willow woodland or reed marsh, as at the HMWT reserves of Stanborough Reed Marsh (TL 230105), Welwyn Garden City and Sawbridgeworth Marsh (TL 492158). Some wet areas were previously used as watercress beds, for example at

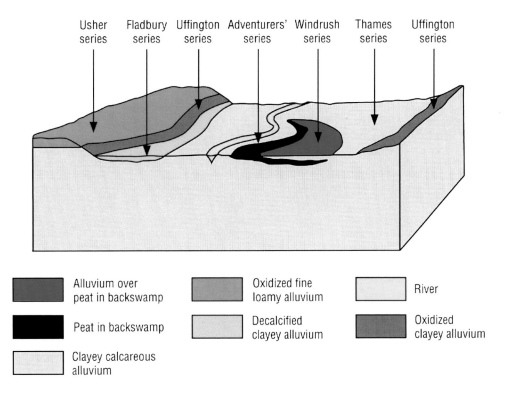

Usher series   Fladbury series   Uffington series   Adventurers' series   Windrush series   Thames series   Uffington series

Alluvium over peat in backswamp

Peat in backswamp

Clayey calcareous alluvium

Oxidized fine loamy alluvium

Decalcified clayey alluvium

River

Oxidized clayey alluvium

Fig. 7.7. Relationships between constituent soil series in Association 814a (Thames) on calcareous clayey alluvium in east Hertfordshire river valleys.

Lemsford Springs (TL 222123), now a small HMWT bird reserve. Another HMWT reserve and SSSI, Hunsdon Mead (TL 416108), is an example of the very diverse grassland flora that can develop on soils of this association after several centuries of hay production. The fen vegetation of small spring-fed marshes in valleys tributary to the River Hiz at Norton Common (TL 218332), Letchworth and Oughtonhead Common (TL 166304), Hitchin, have been described in detail by Sawford (1974) and James (1980), respectively. In recent decades, both of these areas have suffered slight desiccation, possibly because of lowering of the water table in the Chalk, and this has decreased the species diversity.

Association 832: Kelmscot

In Hertfordshire the Groundwater gley soils of the Kelmscot Association occupy only a small area in the valley of the River Ivel between Baldock (TL 2434) and the county boundary near Radwell (TL 2235). Elsewhere they occur mainly on low (Late Devensian) gravel terraces of the River Thames upstream of Oxford. The main soil, Kelmscot series, is a Calcaro-cambic gley soil developed in fine loamy calcareous alluvium overlying the limestone gravel of low

terraces. This is accompanied by better drained soils, mainly fine loamy over gravelly Gleyic brown calcareous earths (Grove series), fine loamy over gravelly Typical brown calcareous earths (Badsey series) and fine loamy Gleyic brown calcareous earths (Milton series), the last where the loamy alluvium is thicker than 1 m. On the lower ground of the floodplain close to the river, these are replaced by silty over gravelly Calcareous alluvial gley soils (Frome series) and clayey Pelo-calcareous alluvial gley soils (Thames series). Gade series (silty over gravelly Calcareous humic alluvial gley soils, often with a humose topsoil) occurs in shallow depressions on the floodplain.

Agriculture. The low terrace soils have subsoil horizons of gravel and any waterlogging is confined to short periods in winter, but the Frome, Thames and Gade soils are subject to occasional flooding and prolonged waterlogging, often extending into the growing season. There are usually some opportunities for autumn cultivation, but few in the spring before the end of April, even on the terrace soils. Consequently some of the higher land is cultivated for winter cereals or oilseed rape, but the floodplain is under woodland or permanent grass.

Chapter 8.

Prehistoric archaeology and human occupation of Hertfordshire

John Catt, Brian Perry, Isobel Thompson and Stewart Bryant

8.1. Introduction

As with soils, regional geological descriptions rarely include accounts of local archaeology. But again Hertfordshire is an important exception, because it was the pioneering work of John Evans (1823-1908), the famous Hertfordshire geologist and archaeologist, that initiated the complex task of integrating the evidence for early human activities with later geological events. When Evans was awarded the London Geological Society's Lyell Medal in 1880, the Society's President paid tribute to Evans' efforts in this interdisciplinary field with the words: 'We can now scarcely say where archaeology ends and geology begins, nor whether to rank and value you most as an antiquary or a geologist' (Sorby, 1880).

This chapter is concerned with later parts of the Quaternary period (the later Mid and Late Pleistocene and the Holocene), during which Hertfordshire has been occupied by an increasingly large human population. For the first 400,000+ years of the area's occupation, humans had little or no impact on the landscape because the population was small and human activities were limited. But in the last few thousand years there has been a rapidly increasing human impact on the landscape because of an expanding population and technological developments. The chapter will describe the evidence for a human presence in Hertfordshire throughout the later Quaternary up to 43 CE, and will also consider relationships between human activities and areas of occupation on the one hand, and geology and soils on the other. Hertfordshire is one of the best parts of lowland Britain for studying the influence of geology on human occupation in various periods.

Fossil remains of prehistoric humans (the species *Homo sapiens* and various ancestors), such as bones and teeth, are very rare. Much more common are tools (artefacts) produced by early humans, initially of stone (principally flint) but later of a wider range of materials, including other hard rocks, bone, antler, wood and the metals bronze and iron. In Hertfordshire, the oldest datable flint artefacts (handaxes from the Hitchin area) are from deposits of the Hoxnian Interglacial (Marine Isotope Stage 11), and are therefore approximately 400,000 years old (Section 6.7). Yet older artefacts are known from other parts of southern England, the earliest of which (sharp flint flakes and the cores from which they were struck) are thought to date from

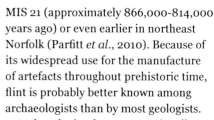

MIS 21 (approximately 866,000-814,000 years ago) or even earlier in northeast Norfolk (Parfitt *et al.*, 2010). Because of its widespread use for the manufacture of artefacts throughout prehistoric time, flint is probably better known among archaeologists than by most geologists.

Archaeologists have conventionally divided prehistoric time into three main periods, the Stone Age, Bronze Age and Iron Age. Although this terminology is still widely used, the three 'ages' are more correctly a sequence of cultures based upon evolving technologies, which to some extent overlapped in time. Except within specific areas, they do not conform consistently to clearly defined periods of time. In southern Britain the Stone Age corresponds with the Mid and Late Pleistocene plus the early Holocene, and the Bronze and Iron Ages with later parts of the Holocene prior to the second Roman invasion in 43 CE. Worldwide, the Stone Age has been subdivided in turn into three – the Palaeolithic (older Stone Age), Mesolithic (middle Stone Age) and Neolithic (newer Stone Age) – and the Palaeolithic has been further divided into three parts (Lower, Middle and Upper), each representing successive developments in stone-working technology. Bearing in mind the same caveat that these are evolving cultures rather than ages with specific time boundaries, the Palaeolithic in Britain roughly corresponds with the Mid and Late Pleistocene, the Mesolithic with the early Holocene before *c.* 6000 calendar years ago, though starting locally in the Loch Lomond Stadial some time between *c.* 13,000 and *c.* 11,700 calendar years ago, and the Neolithic with the later Holocene after *c.* 6000 calendar years ago. The Bronze Age in Britain commenced *c.* 4200 and the Iron Age *c.* 2800 calendar years ago.

The main feature of Neolithic culture was agriculture, both pastoral and arable. Many Neolithic artefacts are tools, such as primitive ploughs, hoes and sickles, necessary for agricultural work. The preceding Mesolithic and Palaeolithic peoples lived as essentially nomadic hunter-gatherers, often migrating in response to climate change, whereas the Neolithic and later cultures gradually led to development of settlements (permanent farms, villages and later towns) in the temperate climate of the later Holocene.

8.2. The Lower Palaeolithic

The earliest (Lower Palaeolithic) cultures in Britain, the Clactonian and Acheulian, are associated with (a) chopper-core and flake tools and (b) handaxes and waste flakes, respectively. Assemblages of Clactonian tools (Fig. 8.1 a & b) are usually characterized by flakes with prominent striking platforms and bulbs of percussion, which were sometimes trimmed for use as knives, scrapers or woodshaves. Clactonian cores are typically biconical, sometimes with part of the original flint cortex retained, and were probably used as chopping tools. No handaxes were produced. In contrast, the main purpose of Acheulian knapping was production of handaxes (Fig. 8.1 c-e), and the flakes removed in this activity were rarely retouched. Acheulian assemblages also include cleavers (Fig. 8.1 f), which have a single wide straight cutting edge perpendicular to the long axis. Current evidence from various sites in Britain and other parts of Europe suggests that these two cultures overlapped in time, the Clactonian being the English equivalent of a culture widespread in Asia and eastern Europe, whereas the Acheulian was confined to western and southern Europe. As both types of tool are found at certain Hoxnian sites in southeast England, such as Swanscombe in northwest Kent, it is likely that Britain was at the frontier of two different Lower Palaeolithic cultural provinces at this time. Tools of Acheulian type were probably the work of the Mid-Pleistocene hominin species *Homo heidelbergensis*, who

had a larger brain than the ancestral African species *Homo erectus*.

Clactonian assemblages are rare in Hertfordshire, but Acheulian artefacts are well represented, mainly as chance (isolated) finds of handaxes or flakes found in the surface soil or incorporated into fluvial gravels. More rarely, they have been found as groups preserved within a stratigraphic sequence of Middle Pleistocene deposits and sometimes representing an occupation or workshop level. Roe (1968a, pp. 120-128) listed 107 sites in Hertfordshire yielding a total of 881 handaxes and even larger numbers of waste or reject flakes produced during their manufacture.

Handaxes were produced by chipping flakes from all surfaces of a flint nodule or cobble initially using another stone as a hammer. The tool was then flattened and sharpened by removing thin flakes, often by carefully directed blows with an antler, heavy stick or bone. Although handaxes are widely regarded as all-purpose tools used for chopping, cutting, scraping, etc they show a variety of sizes and shapes (Fig. 8.1 c-e), suggesting some degree of specialization in use that was lacking in the more clumsy chopper-core and flake artefacts. However, at many sites the handaxes tend to be of one particular type, so shape may reflect a degree of standardization by local cultural influences as much as for intended purpose. Originally, it was thought that handaxes show a progressive refinement over time, so that shape could be used for dating purposes. But at sites with a long history of Lower Palaeolithic occupation, such as Olduvai Gorge in Tanzania, there is no clear upward trend of handaxe improvement (Wymer, 1982). At present all that can be said is that handaxes of various types appeared at different times and places; they provide evidence only of Lower Palaeolithic occupation, which needs to be dated independently by geological methods at each site. In Britain as a whole, the periods of probably intermittent occupation span much of the Middle Pleistocene, between about 700 and 150 ka, but in other countries handaxes are also known from older and younger deposits.

Lower Palaeolithic sites in the Colne catchment

Long Valley Wood. Several sites in the Colne Valley near Rickmansworth are among the most prolific Lower Palaeolithic localities in the Hertfordshire area. Perhaps the most famous is the extensive gravel pit at Long Valley Wood (TQ 075948), which is situated close to the confluences of the Rivers Chess and Gade with the Colne on the southern side of Croxley Green. This pit is still open though much degraded and overgrown by woodland. In the early part of the 20th century it yielded numerous artefacts of both Acheulian and Clactonian type, including at least 32 Acheulian handaxes and several hundred flakes. These have been divided between numerous collections, including those of the British Museum and other museums at Rickmansworth (Plate 68), St Albans, Letchworth, Oxford and Stroud. According to Evans (1907), who published two photographs of the exposure, the first artefacts were found there by Robert Barker in 1904. Subsequently the

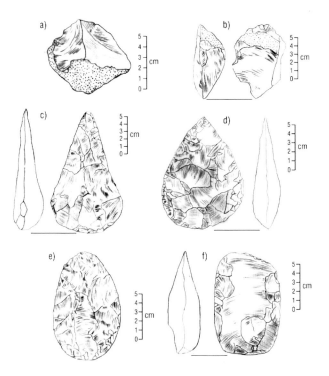

Fig. 8.1. Examples of typical Lower Palaeolithic flint implements: a) Clactonian chopper-core, Clacton-on-Sea, Essex; b) Clactonian flake with secondary reworking, Clacton-on-Sea, Essex; c) pointed Acheulian handaxe, Swanscombe, Kent; d) cordate Acheulian handaxe, Hoxne, Suffolk; e) ovate Acheulian handaxe, Abbeville, northern France; f) cleaver, Whitlingham, near Norwich, Norfolk. Redrawn from Wymer (1982).

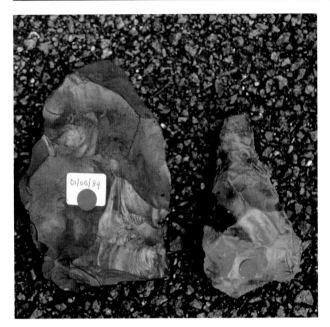

Plate 68. Acheulian handaxes from Long Valley Wood (with thanks to Rickmansworth Museum).

site was described by Hopkinson and Kidner (1908), Kidner (1910a), Smith and Dewey (1915), Oakley (1947, p. 248), Roe (1968a, 1981), Wymer (1968), Gibbard (1985) and Wessex Archaeology (1996). As part of a recent re-examination of the site by the local archaeologist David Harding, the stratigraphy and age have been briefly reviewed by Green (2006) and Schreve (2006), respectively.

The artefacts from Long Valley Wood have come mainly, though not exclusively, from a thin (1-2 m) bed of unstratified gravel resting on Chalk bedrock at *c*. 60 m OD, approximately 18 m above the modern River Colne. This and the overlying 6-10 m of current-bedded sand and gravel were probably deposited by the Colne but derived at least partly from late Anglian glacial outwash gravel (Smug Oak Gravel) upstream. Before quarrying operations, the gravel was overlain by 'brickearth' (probably Devensian loess), and in part of the quarry it rested on a sequence of Palaeogene deposits, mainly Reading Beds containing large sarsenstones (Kidner, 1910a). It is likely that the Palaeogene deposits originally filled a solution pipe in the Chalk, the supporting walls of which were removed by dissolution and general lowering of the Chalk surface beneath the gravel, thus allowing the gravel to slump down on either side of the pipe infill (Anon., 1908a; Hopkinson, 1910, p. 46). This would account for arching of the gravels over the Palaeogene deposits, as reported by various authors. A sarsenstone from Long Valley Wood was incorporated into the collection of the Museum of St Albans in Hatfield Road (TL 151075) (Plate 69).

Age. Gibbard (1985) regarded the gravel as part of the Denham Village Gravel of the Colne, which is probably equivalent to the Taplow Gravel (MIS 8-6) of the Middle Thames (Section 6.10). However, the map of Thames terrace remnants by Bridgland (1994, Fig. 3.1, redrawn in this book as Fig. 6.8) suggests that it is equivalent to the early Anglian Winter Hill Terrace (MIS 12). The only fossils reported from the site are a tusk and molar of straight-tusked elephant (*Palaeoloxodon antiquus*), and a tooth of woolly mammoth

Plate 69. Sarsenstone brought from Long Valley Wood, Hatfield Road Museum, St Albans (with thanks to St Albans Museum Service).

(*Mammuthus primigenius*), but these do not help date the deposit very precisely. Smith and Dewey (1915) noted similarities between many of the artefacts and those from Swanscombe, which suggests they are Hoxnian (MIS 11) in age, a date perhaps supported by the mixed Acheulian-Clactonian assemblage. However, many are mildly abraded and could have been derived from earlier deposits.

Other Colne valley sites. Gravel yielding further implements was described by Smith and Dewey (1915) from a nearby site known as Croxleyhall Wood Pit, Pratt's Pit or Miss Beasley's Pit. This was a short distance to the west of the Long Valley Wood site (probably near TQ 072948), and is similarly wooded today. A third site described by Smith and Dewey (1915) was at Mill End (TQ 046943), about 3 km west of Long Valley Wood and now part of Rickmansworth. The gravels here lie on a Chalk surface approximately 10 m lower than at Long Valley Wood, and have yielded at least 77 handaxes. Unlike Long Valley Wood, the assemblage from Mill End seems to be entirely Acheulian with no Clactonian component. Together with the lower height of the underlying Chalk platform, this suggests it is different in age, perhaps slightly younger. Mill End Pit has been levelled but not completely infilled, and is now a school playing field. Artefacts from this site are held in numerous museum collections, including those at Luton, St Albans, Oxford, Stroud, Norwich, Birmingham, Cambridge, Grantham, Hayes and Harlington, Hull and the Institute of Archaeology, University College London, as well as the British Museum.

In addition to the numbers of artefacts already mentioned, at least 397 handaxes and almost 500 flakes, some of them retouched, are known from the area (Roe, 1968a), and are distributed among the collections of at least 28 museums. Most are probably from the Long Valley Wood, Croxleyhall Wood and Mill End Pits, but as they are located no more precisely than 'Rickmansworth' or 'Croxley Green', there could be yet other important Palaeolithic sites in this part of Hertfordshire.

Isolated finds of Acheulian handaxes have been recorded by Roe (1968a), Wessex Archaeology (1996) and others from numerous additional sites in and near the valleys of the Colne and its tributaries in Hertfordshire, including:

various parts of St Albans (TL 174097, TL 154084, TL
    145068, TL 155069, TL 144034, TL 142036, TL 142034,
    TL 160035, TL 124060, TL 150070, TL 156090),
Old Parkbury Farm near Colney Street (TL 161022),
Redbourn (TL 118098),
Nash Mills (TL 065047),
Colney Heath (TL 206068),
Hatfield (TL 230090),
North Mymms (TL 230050, TL 222061),
Aldenham (TQ 162984, TL 160000, TL 124001),
Bedmond (TL 095035),
Watford (TQ 107992, TQ 104983, TQ 120957, TQ 110970)
    and
Bushey (TL 123961, TQ 135950).

Most were chance finds on the present land surface or in disturbed gravel workings.

Lower Palaeolithic sites in the Lea catchment

Caddington. On parts of the Chiltern plateau in the upper Lea catchment near Dunstable and Luton, there are several nationally important Lower Palaeolithic sites, which yielded large numbers of artefacts in the late 19th and early 20th centuries. The most famous of these included several brickpits close to the village of Caddington, from which Smith (1894) made large collections of artefacts over many years following his move for health reasons from London to Dunstable in 1885. They included sites described as Pit A (TL 049196), Pit B (TL 050192), the Cottages Pit or Pit C (TL 055193), Pit D (TL 062195), Folly Pit or Pit E (TL 062200) and Buncer's Farm or Pit F (TL 063197) (Fig. 8.2). Some of these pits were originally in Hertfordshire and some in Bedfordshire, but since 1897, when the county boundary was moved to unite the parish of Caddington within a single county, they are all within Bedfordshire, though close to the Hertfordshire border.

The brickearth from which most of the Caddington artefacts were obtained was the 'true brickearth' of Barrow (1919a, pp. 31-34), which is composed partly of pre-Ipswichian loess (Avery *et al.*, 1982) and typically occurs within funnel-shaped depressions (sinkholes or dolines) penetrating Plateau Drift that was itself derived from an original cover of basal Palaeogene sediments overlying the Chalk (Section 5.4; see also Catt and Hagen, 1978). Unfortunately all the Caddington pits have been infilled or levelled, and a subsequent attempt by Sampson (1978) to reopen a site near one of them (Pit C) led to the discovery of only one new artefact (a small retouched flake), probably because the brickearth filling each doline was almost completely exhausted for brickmaking during or soon after the time when Smith was collecting in the Caddington area.

Smith's detailed drawings of the deposits exposed in the Caddington pits and Sampson's reinvestigation of a doline infill close to Smith's Pit C showed that the brickearth in which the artefacts were found is often concealed beneath a thin cover of contorted flint gravel or flinty clay resembling the Plateau Drift (Fig. 8.3). These deposits are

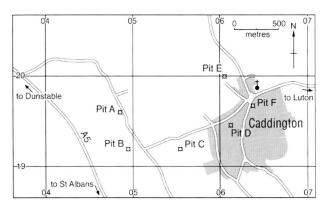

Fig. 8.2. Location of Pits A-F of Smith (1894) at Caddington, Bedfordshire.

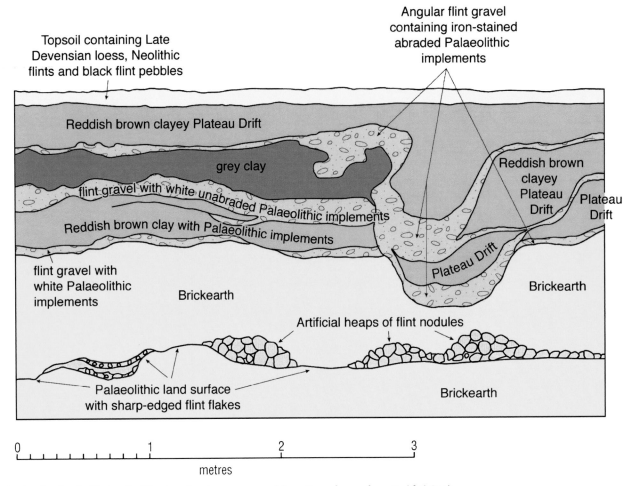

Topsoil containing Late
Devensian loess, Neolithic
flints and black flint pebbles

Angular flint gravel
containing iron-stained
abraded Palaeolithic
implements

Reddish brown clayey Plateau Drift

grey clay

flint gravel with white unabraded Palaeolithic implements

Reddish brown clay with Palaeolithic implements

flint gravel with
white Palaeolithic
implements

Brickearth

Reddish brown
clayey
Plateau
Drift

Plateau
Drift

Plateau Drift

Brickearth

Artificial heaps of flint nodules

Palaeolithic land surface
with sharp-edged flint flakes

Brickearth

0   1   2   3

metres

Fig. 8.3. Section in Pit A at Caddington showing sequence of deposits, redrawn from Smith (1894).

in turn overlain by the usual silty surface layer present in many Chiltern soils (Chapter 7), which consists mainly of Late Devensian loess. Smith referred to the layers of gravel and flinty clay as 'contorted drift'. Both contained occasional flint artefacts, which resembled those from the brickearth beneath, except that most of them had a white cortex resulting from weathering, and those in the flinty clay were usually iron-stained and scratched by lateral movement during deposition. Smith's drawings clearly show that the contorted drift was disturbed by cryoturbations, involutions and plications (involutions distorted and stretched by downslope movement), so it is probably best interpreted as a gelifluction deposit derived from adjacent land surfaces strewn with weathered and abraded artefacts. As the gelifluction deposit predates deposition of the Late Devensian loess, it could have accumulated earlier in the Devensian (MIS 4 or 3) or in a preceding cold stage (e.g. MIS 6) after the period of Lower Palaeolithic human occupation.

Age of Caddington sites. Pollen analysis of samples collected during Sampson's excavation near Pit C (Campbell and Hubbard, 1978) suggested that, at this site at least, the brickearth accumulated in a warm episode with a mixed grassland and woodland vegetation, the woodland components suggesting similarity to those of IpII, the Early temperate period of the Ipswichian (MIS 5e). However, it

is now known that the Ipswichian woodland in southern England was very similar in composition to that of the previous interglacial (MIS 7), so the pollen does not provide unequivocal evidence of age. On the south-eastern flank of the doline excavated near Pit C, a layer of coarse flint gravel interbedded with the brickearth also yielded fragmentary mammal remains, including an elephantid bone and tooth, a bone of rhinoceros and several cervid antler fragments (Campbell and Hubbard, 1978). More specific identification was impossible because the remains were all very poorly preserved, so this assemblage could also date from either MIS 7 or MIS 5e. The only fossil remains recorded by Smith (1894, pp. 166-167) from Caddington were teeth found by workmen digging in Pit C, who described them as like those of horse (*Equus*). The teeth were put on one side out of doors by the workmen to await Smith's next visit, but they disintegrated and the fragments were blown away before he saw them. Nevertherless, assuming the identification was correct, it suggests an MIS 7 rather than Ipswichian (MIS 5e) age, as present evidence from better dated sites suggests that *Equus* was present in Britain during MIS 7 but not in the Ipswichian (Section 6.3). As the same was true of *Homo*, the abundance of artefacts also suggests an MIS 7 and not an MIS 5e age.

A pre-MIS 7 age is probably ruled out by the fact that, as Roe (1981, pp. 194-195) noted on re-examining Smith's collection, many of the Caddington artefacts show incipient use of the Levallois technique. In the Thames valley terrace sequence, the earliest occurrence of this technique is in the Mucking (= Taplow) Gravel, which dates from early MIS 7, about 250 ka (Schreve, 2004). The Levallois technique involved removing flakes from the entire cortex of a flint nodule to produce an oval flint core, then preparing a striking platform at one end, and finally detaching a large flake by a carefully directed heavy blow on the platform (Wymer, 1982, Fig. 27). This left behind a characteristic 'tortoise core' with a single concave inner surface and a multifacetted convex outer surface. The technique was probably introduced by a new human species, *Homo neanderthalensis*, which had a larger brain, lighter jaw and less prominent brow ridges than *H. heidelbergensis*, but larger brow ridges, heavier jaw and less upright forehead than modern man (*Homo sapiens*). In the hands of *H. neanderthalensis*, the Levallois technique led in time to the Mousterian culture. This was characterized by a variable abundance of the final types of handaxe, which were small and either cordate or subtriangular in shape, and were perhaps used as spearheads. Although recorded from Mid Devensian deposits, such as Wookey Hole cave in the Mendip Hills, Somerset (Currant and Jacobi, 2004), these handaxes and other Mousterian flint tools have yet to be found in Hertfordshire.

The Palaeolithic 'floor'. The careful records made by Smith (1894) at Caddington indicated that the artefacts within the brickearth occurred mainly in a thin layer at 4-5 m depth, which he referred to as a land surface or 'floor'. Hundreds of the thin sharp flakes found in Pit A were associated with raised heaps of flint nodules on the floor (Smith, 1894, Fig. 46) (Fig. 8.3), which were thought to be stockpiles of raw material for knapping. Elsewhere narrow vertical fissures, interpreted as sun-cracks, descended from the buried land surface (Smith, 1894, Fig. 49). As the 'floor' occurred at approximately the same depth in each pit, he assumed that a single continuous buried land surface extended throughout the Caddington area, and was even preserved at more distant sites with similar concentrations of artefacts, such as Stoke Newington in east London. However, as the various brickearth pits at Caddington were probably located within separate dolines, the assumption of a continuous land surface was incorrect, though it is certainly clear that within each doline the floors represent exposed sediment surfaces on which the worked flints were deposited.

Conjoined artefacts. All the flakes found by Smith were in mint condition, and over 500 of those collected at various times from Pit C could be refitted so as to reconstruct in reverse order the successive stages in the knapping process (Smith, 1894, pp. 126-157; O'Connor, 2007, p. 97) (Fig. 8.4). One set of 13 flakes found on various dates in 1890 were refitted around a space that, when filled with plaster of Paris, produced a facsimile of the partially finished chopper-like tool that the knapper was intending to produce (Smith, 1894, pp. 151-152); however, the final implement itself was never found. The large number of refitted or 'conjoined'

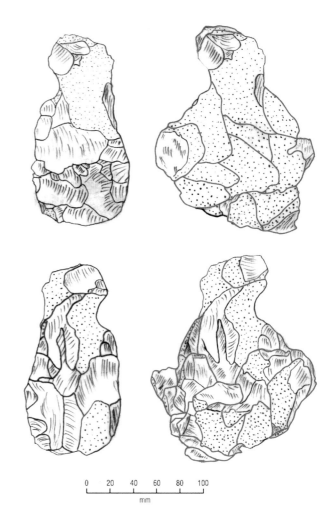

0   20   40   60   80   100
mm

Fig. 8.4. Conjoined Lower Palaeolithic implements from Caddington, Bedfordshire, redrawn from Smith (1894). Red lines outline flakes replaced onto the finished artefact.

flakes show unequivocally that the 'floors' were undisturbed knapping sites. Numerous handaxes were recovered from the pits but few cores or retouched flakes were found, so the industry was mainly, if not entirely, Acheulian. The handaxes were of two main shapes, ovate and roughly triangular (Plate 70).

The most likely sequence of events at Caddington can be reconstructed as follows (Fig. 8.5):

a) deposition of an older loess during the Anglian (MIS 12) or an early Wolstonian cold stage (MIS 10 or 8) on a land (erosion) surface cut across undisturbed basal Palaeogene deposits,

b) partial conversion of the Palaeogene deposits to Plateau Drift by soil development in a forested landscape during MIS 7, and formation of dolines by collapse following localized dissolution of chalk beneath,

c) also in MIS 7, washing of loess into the dolines by streams flowing over the Palaeogene deposits, and simultaneous occupation of the area by Lower Palaeolithic people, who practised Acheulian and primitive Levallois tool-making techniques on temporarily dry land surfaces (floors)

within the dolines,

d) in a subsequent cold stage (MIS 6, 4 or 3), gelifluction across the partially infilled dolines of weathered flint gravel and Plateau Drift containing abraded artefacts from adjacent land surfaces, and

e) deposition of a younger (Late Devensian, MIS 2) loess cover over the entire Chiltern landscape.

Other Lea valley sites. At several other important Lower Palaeolithic sites in the upper Lea catchment, artefacts have been recorded from similar sequences of brickearth, often clearly contained within doline-like depressions penetrating the Plateau Drift to depths of 6-12 m, and from thin overlying layers of gelifluted Plateau Drift (Scott-Jackson, 2000, pp. 36-47). They include pits at:

Slip End (TL 078185) (Smith, 1894, pp. 95 and 99),

Plate 70. Lower Palaeolithic flint handaxes from Caddington and Gaddesden Row. Right: roughly triangular handaxe from Caddington Pit C; left: ovate handaxe from Gaddesden Row. Images provided by Museums Luton.

Blake (or Bleak) Hall, Kensworth (TL 033176), which yielded 11 handaxes and 169 flakes (Smith, 1919),

Leverstock Green (TL 075080), where 6 ovate handaxes were obtained from Plateau Drift overlying brickearth (Evans, 1908),

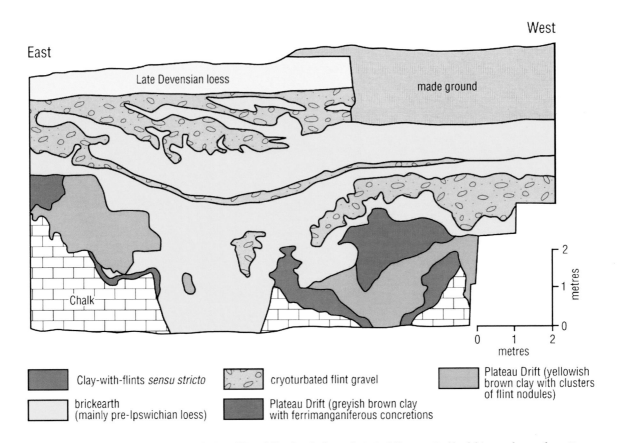

Fig. 8.5. Section in brickearth and 'contorted drift' infilling doline in Chalk at Pit C, Caddington, Bedfordshire, redrawn from Sampson (1978).

232

Butterfield's Pit at Gaddesden Row (TL 038134), where
50 handaxes and 56 flakes have been found (Smith, 1916;
Wymer, 1980; Roe, 1981; Bridgland and Harding, 1989);
many of the handaxes are ovate (Plate 70),

and several sites in nearby parts of south Bedfordshire,
including:

Round Green, Luton (TL 101226), which has yielded
26 handaxes (Smith, 1916),
Ramridge End, Luton (TL 105233), where 11 handaxes have
been recorded (Smith, 1916),
Stopsley Common (TL 100239), where 5 handaxes have been
found (Roe, 1968a, p. 6) and
Mixieshill Field (TL 098234) near Round Green, where
Smith (1916) reported sharp flakes, antlers of red deer
(*Cervus elaphus*) and other animal bones.

These sites are could be similar in age to those at
Caddington, though none has provided any dating evidence,
and at Gaddesden Row there is no evidence of intentional
use of Levallois technique (Wymer, 1980).

At the Gaddesden Row and Kensworth sites, Smith (1916)
and Smith (1919) described successions of 7-8 artefact-
yielding 'floors' within the brickearth. But White (1997,
pp. 922 & 925) has suggested that there was in fact only
one layer at each site, the mode of brickearth excavation
(in successive steps 1-2 m deep) and the inclination of the
artefact-containing layer parallel to the sloping edge of the
doline giving the impression of multiple layers as digging
progressed.

Possible human remains. Mixieshill pit is famous as the
site of what was probably a complete human skeleton of
Lower Palaeolithic age (Smith, 1906, 1916, pp. 67-68).
This was found by Joseph Ford and other workmen 'some
years before 1905', but was never actually seen by Smith.
Ford reported that it lay close to the animal bones at a
depth of approximately 7 m, which must preclude a recent
inhumation. Also the state of preservation, very friable
and dark brown in colour, was similar to that of the animal
bones, and the skull disintegrated when touched, so an
age similar to that of the brickearth is likely. Although this
record relies only on the evidence of one workman with no
training in archaeology, Smith (1906) regarded it as having
'every mark of probability'. Together with the abundance
of artefacts, which provide clear evidence of on-site flint
working, it therefore emphasizes the great potential that the
numerous Chiltern brickearth sites offer for early human
history in Britain.

Unfortunately, all the pits mentioned above have been
closed and infilled. From time to time local brickmakers still
open pits in other silty doline infills, such as those exploited
in recent years near Bovingdon Brickworks (TL 004030).
However, no artefacts or bones have been recorded from
them, mainly because careful searching is discouraged by
modern mechanized digging, which has replaced the hand-
digging of a century or more ago when Smith made his
discoveries.

Lower Palaeolithic artefacts that are probably somewhat
older than the Caddington assemblage were reported
from the Hoxnian (MIS 11) lacustrine deposits at Fishers
Green, Stevenage (TL 224260) by Evans (1896, Plate XI,
No 3; 1897, p. 602), Oakley (1947, p. 252) and Roe (1968a,
p. 127). These included four pointed handaxes and two
flakes. The Hoxnian Interglacial lake deposits (*Chara* marl)
and overlying brickearth at Hitchin have also yielded thin
triangular or ovate handaxes mostly in mint condition, i.e.
produced at or near the site (Evans, 1896, Plate XII; Oakley,
1947). Plate 51 shows an example now in Verulamium
Museum. These two sites are described more fully in
Section 6.7.

Surface finds. Numerous abraded Lower Palaeolithic
artefacts, probably derived from geliflucted Plateau Drift,
have been found on the surface of ploughed fields in many
parts of the Chilterns, but their ages are uncertain. There are
records of this type from:

Caddington Common (TL 060175) where 6 handaxes have
been found (Oakley, 1947, p. 251),
Woodside (TL 075190) (Roe, 1968a, p. 6),
Kinsbourne Green (TL 105160) (Roe, 1968a, p. 124),
Redbourn (TL 092130) (Oakley, 1947, p. 252) and
St Paul's Walden (TL 174217) (Shephard-Thorn and Wymer,
1996).

Also in the Lea catchment are numerous records of Lower
Palaeolithic artefacts found on the soil surface in or near
river valleys (Wessex Archaeology, 1996), and probably
derived either from fluvial gravels or, in east Hertfordshire,
possibly from Anglian glacial deposits. These include several
sites near Luton, such as:

Biscot (TL 080230), where 5 handaxes have been found
(Roe, 1968a, pp. 5-6),
Leagrave Marsh (TL 060240) (Smith, 1894, pp. 90 and 179),
Limbury gravel pit (TL 077244), where 17 handaxes were
recorded by Roe (1968a, p. 5) and
an unlocated site on the New Bedford Road (4 handaxes
reported by Roe, 1968a, pp. 5-6).

Other Lea catchment sites in Hertfordshire include:

Harpenden (TL 140150) (Smith, 1894, p. 180, Oakley, 1947),
Nomansland Common near Wheathampstead (TL 070126)
(Evans, 1892; Smith, 1894, pp. 180-183; Evans, 1896, Plate
XI, No. 4; Oakley, 1947; Roe, 1968a, p. 129),
Stevenage (TL 237243 and TL 233248) (Evans, 1892),
Langley (TL 215225) (Oakley, 1947),
Knebworth (TL 250195), where 7 handaxes have been
recorded from gravels exposed at the southern end of the
railway cutting (Evans, 1896, Plate VII; Roe, 1968a, p. 124),
Codicote (TL 215185) (Oakley, 1947),
Ayot St Peter (TL 222144 and TL 220160) (Smith, 1894,
p. 184),
Welwyn Cemetery (TL 228164) (Roe, 1968a, p. 128),
Welwyn Workhouse Pit (TL 231162) (Oakley, 1947),

Digswell (TL 240150) (Roe, 1968a, p. 120),

Hertford (TL 313128),

Bengeo (TL 325135) (Smith, 1894, pp. 184-185; Oakley, 1947),

Ware (TL 370150) (Smith, 1894, p. 185; Oakley 1947),

Hall Green near Standon (TL 371220),

Stocking Pelham (TL 455290) (Oakley, 1947),

Bishop's Stortford (TL 503239 and TL 490225) (Evans, 1892, 1897, p. 602),

Broxbourne (TL 365090) (Evans, 1897, p. 603; Oakley, 1947),

Bayford (TL 315085) (Evans, 1892),

Cheshunt (TL 360005 and TL 345035) (Evans, 1892; Smith, 1894, pp. 185-186; Oakley, 1947),

Turnford (TL 360044) (Oakley, 1947, p. 253) and

Waltham Cross (TL 343003) (Evans, 1897, p. 603).

In summary, there is abundant evidence in many parts of Hertfordshire (Fig. 8.6) and south Bedfordshire for a fluctuating and probably sporadic human (Lower Palaeolithic) presence over a long period of Mid Pleistocene

time, certainly from the Hoxnian (MIS 11) until probably MIS 7, and possibly also in the Anglian (MIS 12). The main factor influencing Lower Palaeolithic occupation was probably the presence of water, mainly in the form of the county's major rivers, but also as ephemeral ponds occupying dolines on the Chiltern plateau, which were probably fed by minor streams flowing over impermeable Palaeocene clays before the clays were fully transformed into Plateau Drift.

After MIS 7 there is no evidence in the county for later Lower or Middle Palaeolithic human activity in MISs 6-4. A few late Middle Palaeolithic artefacts associated with animal bones dated to the Mid Devensian (the later part of MIS 3, between about 48,000 and 28,000 BP) have been recorded from limestone caves in the Midlands, Wales and southwest England. These were probably the work of *Homo neanderthalensis* shortly before this species was replaced by *Homo sapiens* (modern man). But no artefacts of this type are known from Hertfordshire, which has no limestone caves. Almost certainly the climate throughout most of MIS 3 was too cold for regular habitation at other (open) sites.

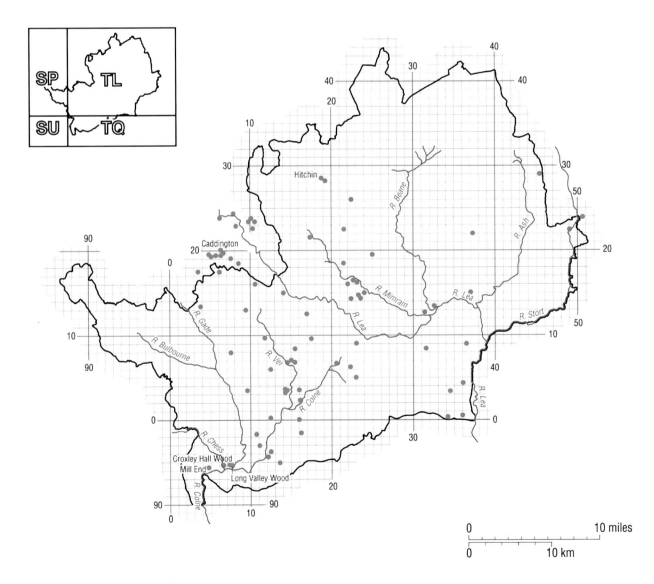

Fig. 8.6. Distribution of sites yielding Lower Palaeolithic artefacts in the Hertfordshire area.

8.3. The Upper Palaeolithic

The Upper Palaeolithic is sometimes known as the Leptolithic (or light-stone age), because many of the flint artefacts produced at this time by early *Homo sapiens* are long, thin delicate blades, which were often fashioned into highly specialized tools. For example, early in the Upper Palaeolithic (the Aurignacian), they included the sharply pointed leaf-shaped blades, known as *Blattspitzen* in central and eastern Europe, which were probably lashed to wooden handles for use as hunting spears. The blades were produced in large numbers by initially hammering a pointed punch close to the edge of a flat prepared surface of flint. They were then carefully shaped by detaching small flakes from the blade's edges using pressure from a bone or antler. Other tools, such as barbed harpoons, needles and awls, were also fashioned directly from bone and antler.

In time terms, the Upper Palaeolithic was broadly equivalent to the Late Devensian (MIS 2, 26-11.5 ka BP), though some of the earliest Upper Palaeolithic artefacts in Britain and other parts of northwest Europe may date from the later millennia of MIS 3 (Jacobi, 2007). As these two periods were even colder than earlier parts of MIS 3, they were again unsuitable for habitation at open sites in Britain, and almost all the British Upper Palaeolithic artefacts have been found in caves, such as Kent's Cavern in south Devon and Soldier's Hole in Cheddar Gorge, Somerset. Radiocarbon dating of associated animal (mainly mammoth, horse, woolly rhinoceros, giant deer and reindeer) bones has shown that the caves were inhabited either (a) just before the Dimlington Stadial glaciation (the earlier Upper Palaeolithic) or (b) during and after the Windermere Interstadial that followed the glaciation (the later Upper Palaeolithic), but not in the intervening period between about 22,000 and 12,750 BP (14,700 calendar years ago) at the height of the Dimlington Stadial glaciation (Jacobi, 1980a, p. 15). The artefacts of these two periods show some similarities with the better known Aurignacian and Magdalenian cultures, respectively, of the French Upper Palaeolithic. The later Upper Palaeolithic culture in Britain is often referred to as the Creswellian, on account of Magdalenian type artefacts, including some recently discovered examples of rock art, found in caves in the Permian Magnesian Limestone at Creswell Crags, on the Derbyshire-Nottinghamshire border.

There are a few open Upper Palaeolithic sites in East Anglia and southeast England, most of them dating from the Windermere Interstadial (later Upper Palaeolithic), though some, including Broxbourne in the lower Lea valley of Hertfordshire, are thought to be earlier Upper Palaeolithic (Dimlington Stadial) in age because of the presence of fine leaf-shaped flint artefacts similar to those of the French Aurignacian culture. The Broxbourne site was originally described by Warren (1938), who found a leaf-shaped spearhead in sand (probably part of the Kempton Park Gravel) exposed at Rikof's Pit (TL 379069). Peat overlying the sand yielded a pollen assemblage dominated by pine (*Pinus*) and birch (*Betula*) (Allison *et al.*, 1952), and later gave an early Holocene radiocarbon date of 9657 ± 200 BP

(Jacobi, 1978, p. 300), equivalent to approximately 11,100 calendar years ago, though Kerney (1977) suggested that the terrestrial molluscs in the peat indicate a slightly earlier (Loch Lomond Stadial) age. Jacobi (1980a, pp. 18-19) reported a further leaf point from a site nearby.

These two earlier Upper Palaeolithic artefacts may represent nothing more than a temporary, perhaps summer season hunting campsite, as the Broxbourne sites have yielded no other evidence for contemporary human activity. Elsewhere in Europe where caves were not available and there were no trees to provide timber for makeshift shelters, Upper Palaeolithic hunters are thought to have built tents from animal skins, bones and tusks (Wymer, 1982, Chapter 7). They could have survived in a similar fashion in the lower Lea valley during the intensely cold early part of the Dimlington Stadial, but these materials would probably not have been preserved in sand leached by water passing through overlying peat.

Later Upper Palaeolithic artefacts have been recorded from another site at Broxbourne (Jacobi, 1980a, pp. 80-81) and also from the Colne valley at Three Ways Wharf in Uxbridge, northwest London (Cotton, 1991, p. 151; Lewis *et al.*, 1992, pp. 238-239). The Uxbridge site yielded over 700 Upper Palaeolithic flint artefacts of the type known as long blades. Bones of horse and reindeer from the Uxbridge site were dated by radiocarbon to late in the Loch Lomond Stadial (10,320 ± 100 and 10,050 ± 120 BP, i.e. about 11,750-12,100 calendar years ago), so here again there is evidence for outdoor Upper Palaeolithic human presence in a very cold part of the Late Devensian. However, dates on bone material are often inaccurate and these may be revised in due course. At another site in the Colne valley, Sandy Lodge Golf Course (TQ 091935) near Oxhey, a few typical Upper Palaeolithic flints have been recorded, but the site was disturbed before it could be studied.

It is surprising that as yet there are no known later Upper Palaeolithic sites in the Hertfordshire area dating from the warmer Windermere Interstadial. The total human population of Hertfordshire in both the earlier and later Upper Palaeolithic definitely seems to have been very small, probably only a dozen or so at any one time, and certainly much less than in the Lower Palaeolithic. As in the Lower Palaeolithic, the few Upper Palaeolithic sites in Hertfordshire seem to be associated with rivers as sources of water and food from animals attracted to the rivers.

8.4. The Mesolithic

The rapid climatic amelioration at the beginning of the Holocene about 10,000 radiocarbon years BP (11,700 calendar years ago) encouraged repopulation of Britain, then still part of the European land mass, probably by migration from continental Europe. The beginning of the Mesolithic period is conventionally placed at this time. According to Cavalli-Sforza *et al.* (1994, p. 262), the human population of Britain then increased to between 3000 and 9000. This estimate is of course very approximate; it indicates perhaps a few hundred people living in Hertfordshire, although the numbers of known surviving artefacts suggest more than this. The lifestyle remained essentially similar to that of the Upper Palaeolithic, a non-sedentary nomadic style of seasonal hunting and food gathering (Mithen, 1999), although there is evidence for semi-permanent encampments in many parts of the country.

Changes in artefact typology included the introduction of (a) microlithic industries, in which large numbers of small narrow flint blades were produced, often for mounting in wood as tips and barbs of arrowheads, or for cutting, boring or engraving tools (burins), (b) barbed bone and antler spears and fishing harpoons, and (c) flint axeheads for felling trees and shaping timbers. In Hertfordshire, the most common type of axehead was the adze, tranchet or transversely sharpened axe, which was hafted with the cutting edge at right angles to the handle. Because it occurs frequently in areas surrounding the Thames valley, it is sometimes referred to as the Thames pick. This assemblage of tools was characteristic of a Mesolithic culture known as the Maglemosian, which came to lowland areas of southern and eastern England from Denmark, north Germany and Estonia by migration across the southern North Sea. Apart from an anastomosing system of shallow river channels in the Dover Straits, there was probably a persistent land connection with Europe after late MIS 5 even until the early Holocene about 6800 calendar years ago, when the worldwide (eustatic) rise of sea level resulting from melting of glaciers eventually flooded the southern North Sea and English Channel. There is considerable evidence for Mesolithic occupation of the southern North Sea from artefacts brought up by trawlers and from detailed seismic mapping (Gaffney *et al.*, 2007). The rapid rise of sea level after 6800 year ago probably led to inland retreat and an increase in the population of Hertfordshire and other parts of Britain.

In northern Europe as a whole, the Maglemosian people often seem to have occupied semi-permanent encampments beside lakes or rivers. In the densely wooded landscape of the early Holocene, these could have supplied water, fish, meat from the wildfowl and animals that came to drink, reeds for thatching buildings, and communication by boat. The forest also supplied timber and food such as hazel nuts, the shell fragments of which are common at many Mesolithic sites. Deforestation, which may have assisted hunting, was probably limited to small areas on dry, better drained soils. In southern England generally, the microlithic industry occurs mainly on areas of coarse sandy soil, which were possibly more congenial (drier and warmer) as occupation sites and often had a more sparse shrub understorey that made hunting easier (Mellars and Reinhardt, 1978). However, in the same broad region, the tranchet axeheads used for felling occur most frequently on the Chalk outcrop, probably because the Chalk provided a ready supply of good quality fresh flint.

Because of the frequent seasonal hunting movements of the Maglemosian people, their artefacts are even more widely distributed over the land surface than those of Lower Palaeolithic age (Wymer, 1977). In Hertfordshire, this is especially true of the abundant microliths, isolated examples

of which can be found by careful search of cultivated field surfaces in almost any part of the county where the soil is well drained (e.g. on glacial or river terrace gravels) or even moderately well drained (e.g. on the Chiltern plateau). However, concentrations of Mesolithic artefacts are known from several sites in the county, which may represent longer term encampments.

Early Mesolithic. British Mesolithic flint assemblages are divided into two main types, those with broad-bladed microliths, which date from the early Holocene (11,700-9000 calendar years ago), and those with more carefully made geometric, narrow-bladed microliths, dating from 9000-6000 calendar years ago (Jacobi, 1973, pp. 237-238). The only known early Mesolithic sites in Hertfordshire are in the lower Lea valley, where Warren *et al.* (1934) recorded a small assemblage of typical early Mesolithic flint blades and microliths in Rikof's Pit (TL 378069), and a butchery site at Dobbs Weir (TL 380081) with food remains of cattle and red deer, which have been radiocarbon-dated to 9350 ± 120 BP (approximately 10,700 calendar years ago). However, more abundant early Mesolithic evidence is available nearby at two sites in north London. The Three Ways Wharf excavation at Uxbridge (Cotton, 1991; Lewis *et al.*, 1992) produced about 7000 early Mesolithic flints, and at a site on Hampstead Heath (Collins and Lorimer, 1989) over 60,000 flints were found, a burnt example giving a thermoluminescence date of 9640 ± 900.

Late Mesolithic. In Hertfordshire, late Mesolithic implements have been found at numerous sites (Fig. 8.7), many of which are in or on well drained sands overlying Late Devensian river terrace gravels but covered by later Holocene alluvium. Sites of this type are perhaps best known in the lower Lea valley in east Hertfordshire, where they have been recorded at:

Rikof's Pit, Broxbourne (TQ 379069) (Warren *et al.*, 1934),
Broxbourne Church of England School (Sanger, 1937),
Dobb's Weir (TL 380081 and TL 379080) and Rye Meads (TL 382107) near Hoddesdon (Holgate, 1988, pp. 217 and 224),
Waltham Cross (TL 373000),
Turnford (TL 362043) (Oakley, 1947, p. 254),
Cheshunt (TL 359044) (Moss-Eccardt, 1970),
Ware (TL 353145) (O'Brien and Roberts, 2005),
St Margarets (TL 381116) and
Stanstead Abbotts (TL 389116) (Davies *et al.*, 1982).

The assemblages from Broxbourne and Stanstead Abbotts are dated approximately by the fact that they were from sands buried beneath peat with pollen of mid-Holocene age. More precise dating is available for the slightly later assemblage at Dobb's Weir, where an underlying peat gave a radiocarbon date of 7880 ± 120 BP (*c.* 8600 calendar years ago) (Jacobi, 1980b). The Broxbourne assemblage described by Warren *et al.* (1934), now in the British Museum, includes three tranchet axeheads.

Other sites close to rivers, often buried by alluvium or on

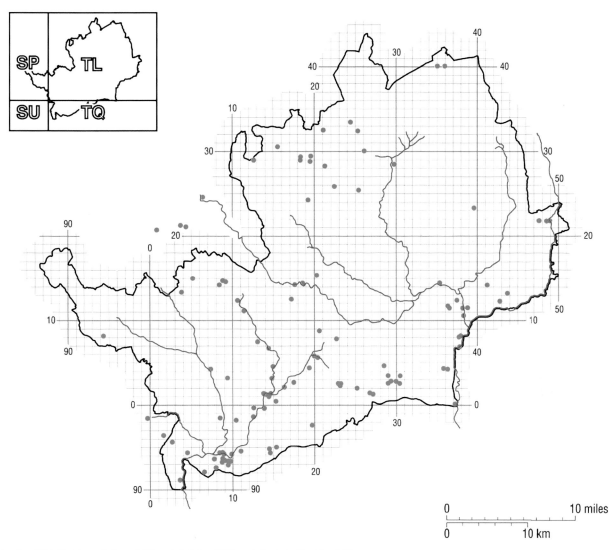

Fig. 8.7. Distribution of sites yielding late Mesolithic artefacts in Hertfordshire.

low terraces, are known in the upper Lea valley at:
  Wheathampstead churchyard (TL 176140) (Saunders and
  Havercroft, 1982a)
  and Aldwickbury Golf Course (TL 155144), Harpenden
  (West, 2008).
in the Stort valley at:
  Silver Leys (TL 477219) and The Meads (TL 489219) close
  to Bishop's Stortford (Gibson, 1968),
in the Colne valley at:
  West Hyde (TQ 036911) near Maple Cross (Lacaille, 1961),
  Hampermill, Watford (TQ 098941) (Derricourt and
  Jacobi, 1970),
  Merchant Taylors' School (TQ 089943), Rickmansworth,
  Sandy Lodge Golf Course (TQ 089934, TQ 090935,
  TQ 092930, TQ 092933, TQ 094936 and TQ 095933) near
  Oxhey,
  Otterspool (TQ 128987) and other sites (TL 143011,
  TQ 139999 and TQ 125998) near Aldenham,
  Old Parkbury (TL 163020) near Colney Street (Holgate,
  1988, pp. 216 and 223),
  London Colney (TL 174027),
  Bricket Wood (TL 139014) (Saunders and Havercroft,
  1977),

Smug Oak (TL 140013),
Tyttenhanger (TL 193043) and
Oxhey (TQ 110947) (Rawlins, 1977),
in the Chess valley at:
  Latimer Park Farm (SU 998986) near Latimer (Stainton,
  1995),
in the Gade valley at:
  The Grove Estate, Watford (TQ 085986),
in the Ver valley at:
  Redbourn (TL 107123 and TL 113111) (Saunders and
  Havercroft, 1979, pp. 54-64; West, 2005),
  Ver Lodge, St Albans (TL 143068) (Saunders and
  Havercroft, 1979, p. 16) and
  Friars Wash (TL 090147) (West 1993),
in the Rib valley at:
  Standon (TL 393231),
and in the Mimram valley at Welwyn.

Most of the artefacts from these sites are microliths, flakes
and the cores from which they were struck (Plate 71). But
tranchet axeheads are also quite common; for example,
four were reported from the Old Parkbury site (Holgate,
1988, p. 223). The Ashmolean Museum (Oxford) has several

examples of tranchet axeheads collected by Sir John Evans from imprecisely located sites in the Abbots Langley, Bedmond, Nash Mills and Markyate areas (Rawlins, 1980), and there are others from St Albans, Aldenham, Nomansland, Bushey, Ridge and Hertford Heath in Verulamium Museum (Plate 72), from Gaddesden Row in Luton Museum, from Mill End in Gunnersbury Museum and from Chorleywood in Aylesbury Museum (Wymer, 1977, pp. 128-133).

Plate 71. Mesolithic core and microliths from Sandy Lodge Golf Course (TQ 090933).

On less well-drained soils (on the London Clay, Reading Beds clay and chalky till), late Mesolithic assemblages have been reported at:

Thornton's Farm (TL 292030), Hemp's Hill (TL 290027), Cuffley Hills Farm (TL 294029) and Tolmers Road (TL 305034), Cuffley (Brown, 1970; Lee, 1977, 1987),
Cromer Hall (TL 297285) near Ardeley,
Tiverton Road (TL 270014 and TL 269015) and The Avenue (TL 251020), Potters Bar (Warren, 1982),
on the A1(M) northwest of Potters Bar (TL 231026 and TL 230026) (Warren, 1982),
Bathend Clump, Moor Park Golf Course (TQ 080928), and various sites in and near Rickmansworth, including Moor End (TQ 080927, Askew Road (TQ 088937), South Approach (TQ 087932), Westbury Road (TQ 093931) and Tolpits Lane (TQ 084943 and TQ 087945) (Jacobi, 1966, 1975; Castle, 1971; Holgate, 1988, pp. 216 and 223),
Bushey (TQ 144950, TQ 158951 and TQ 146947),
Hill Farm (TL 154005) near Radlett (Rawlins, 1980),
Gilston Park (TL 438134) near Harlow,
Eastwick Hall (TL 428124) near Harlow,
Hare Street (TL 307299),
Hunsdon (TL 4114),
Standon (TL 393231),
The Glaxo factory, Ware (TL 352145),
Weston (TL 260300) (Westell, 1926, p. 279; Burkitt, 1926; Moss-Eccardt, 1970),
Letchworth (TL 210324),
Great Wymondley (TL 2128),
Hatfield Aerodrome (TL 207088) and
Wheathampstead by-pass (TL 1985142) (Saunders and Havercroft, 1982b, Fig. 6).

Plate 72. Mesolithic tranchet axeheads from – top: St Germain's House, St Albans; centre: Maynes Farm, St Albans; bottom: Otterspool near Aldenham (with thanks to the St Albans Museum Service).

An interesting component of the artefact assemblage from Thornton's Farm were numerous 'pot boilers', cracked flints thought to have been used for cooking or boiling water after heating them in a fire, though no hearth was found at the site. A tranchet axehead from Bathend Clump is in Watford Museum.

On well drained soils of the Chalk outcrop in and near

northern parts of the county, there are other important later
Mesolithic sites at:

Wigginton (SP 9408),
Letchworth (TL 210324),
Little Offley (TL 126290),
Royston (TL 360400) (Moss-Eccardt, 1970),
Zouches Farm (TL 041213), Caddington (Holgate, 1991a),
Five Knolls (TL 006210), Dunstable Downs (Holgate,
   1991b),
Baldock (TL 252321),
Pirton (TL 153307) (Hudspith, 1999),
Hitchin (TL 195289, TL 182290 and TL 196295) and
Waulud's Bank (TL 062245), Leagrave (Holgate, 1988,
   pp. 215 and 223).

This part of the Chilterns marks the northern limit of
the known distribution of Mesolithic tranchet axeheads
in Britain. Examples from Weston, Letchworth and
Cottered are in Letchworth Museum and others from Great
Wymondley and Royston are in Hertford Museum (Wymer,
1977). The Ashmolean Museum has a flint chisel found by
William Whitaker near Baldock, and Luton Museum has a
Thames pick from Wigginton. A finely barbed Maglemosian
bone spearhead, originally recorded by Westerby (1931) as
from Royston, probably originated instead at Barrington,
Cambridgeshire (Jacobi, 1987).

   The distribution of precisely located late Mesolithic
finds, based upon data from the Hertfordshire Historic
Environment Record, is shown in Figure 8.7. Detailed
comparison of the distribution with the county Soil
Association map (Fig. 7.2) shows that about 18% of the sites
are in areas now occupied by groundwater gley (alluvial)
soil associations (mainly Fladbury 1), though the evidence
from most of these sites indicates that the alluvium has
been deposited since the period of occupation. Other late
Mesolithic sites, often with single isolated finds, are spread
widely around the county. Perhaps surprisingly, the greatest
abundance of sites (28%) is on the poorly drained soils,
mainly Windsor Association, of the Palaeogene clay outcrop
in southern Hertfordshire, though this may partly reflect
the work of local collectors in the Rickmansworth and
Potters Bar areas. There are also many sites (24%) on soils
developed on the Plateau Drift and higher proto-Thames
terraces of the Chilterns dip-slope, and on the slightly better
drained soil types developed on chalky till in northeast
Hertfordshire (12%, mainly on Hanslope and Melford Soil
Associations). The remaining sites are on thick loess soils
(7% on Hamble 2 Association), coombe deposits in Chiltern
valleys (8%, mainly on Charity 2 Association), thin soils over
Chalk (1% on Wantage 2 and Swaffham Prior Associations in
north Hertfordshire) and gravels in the Vale of St Albans (1%
on Ludford Association).

   In summary, most of the larger assemblages of artefacts
suggest that later Mesolithic occupation in Hertfordshire
was on the drier soils of low sandy and gravelly river terraces
that were subsequently flooded and covered by alluvium
in the Neolithic and later Holocene periods. However,
many of the smaller assemblages and individual artefacts

are from sites on a wide range of soil types remote from
rivers, including poorly drained associations in southern
Hertfordshire and slightly better drained associations in
north-eastern parts of the county or on higher parts of the
Chilterns. This type of distribution probably reflects a need
to live for most of the time close to rivers, mainly to provide
day-to-day sources of water and food, but with a tendency to
roam widely and perhaps set up temporary summer camps
in distant parts of the early Holocene forest, in order to hunt
animals, gather plant food from other sources and obtain
fresh flint to manufacture artefacts. Expeditions of this
type may have served to broaden the diet and bring in food
supplies for over-winter storage.

8.5. The Neolithic

The Neolithic period in Britain began 6000-6500 calendar
years ago with the first evidence for agricultural activities in
many parts of the country. This has long been attributed to
the arrival of seaborne immigrants originating ultimately in
the Middle East and bringing agricultural skills previously
unknown in Britain. Evison (1999) detected a SE-NW
gradient in modern human DNA characteristics across
Europe, which he attributed to this migration, as it was
probably the only time when a large enough population from
the southeast mixed with a sufficiently small indigenous
European population. Later immigrations into southern
Britain were probably insufficient to obscure this trend in
modern gene distributions. However, it is likely that the
appearance of agriculture in Britain partly involved other
factors and pressures, such as increasing demands for food
for an expanding population.

   The gradual spread of farming practices resulted in
removal of increasingly large areas of the mixed oak forest
that had developed naturally in Britain since the beginning
of the Holocene (Brown, 1997). The earliest farming
was probably pastoral (for sheep, cattle and pigs), as the
decreases in tree pollen seen at this time in Holocene peat
and lacustrine sequences were accompanied by the first
appearance of pollen from typical pasture weeds, such as
ribwort plantain (*Plantago lanceolata*) and dock (*Rumex*
spp.). This decline in tree pollen has been observed in
Hertfordshire, for example at Stanstead St Margarets
in the lower Lea valley (Scaife, 2002). Somewhat later
soil cultivation for arable farming, indicated by the first
appearance of cereal pollen, resulted in soil erosion on
slopes, the accumulation of footslope colluvium and
deposition of river alluvium that contained more mineral
material than in the earlier Holocene (Section 6.11). The
main cereals grown are thought to have been emmer
wheat (*Triticum dicoccum*) and barley (*Hordeum vulgare*)
(Hillman, 1981).

   Deforestation became more efficient in the Neolithic
through the invention of ground or polished axeheads,
which were made from a wide range of igneous and other
hard rocks as well as flint. The Neolithic also resulted in
the introduction of new crafts, notably pottery, greatly
improved technology based on stone, bone and antler,

and the construction of artificial earthworks, such as embankments for enclosures and burial mounds. Farming may have gradually produced a more sedentary lifestyle than the predominantly nomadic lifestyle of the Mesolithic and earlier periods. However, archaeological evidence for static field systems does not appear until the Bronze Age, and even then they do not accompany permanent domestic settlements.

Early Neolithic. In Britain, the Neolithic period is divided into two on the basis of differences in flint artefacts, styles of pottery and types of earthworks and monuments (Smith, 1974; Whittle, 1980). The early Neolithic is characterized by 'plain bowl' pottery (Holgate, 1988, Fig. 2.2), interrupted ditch or causewayed enclosures (in which the surrounding bank and ditch are interrupted by several unexcavated sections), long barrows (earth mounds approximately 15 m wide and 50-100 m long, often elongated roughly E-W and flanked by ditches) and flint assemblages dominated by ground flint axeheads (replacing the tranchet axeheads of the Mesolithic), leaf-shaped arrowheads (replacing the Mesolithic microliths as projectile points), knives and ovate

scrapers (Holgate, 1988, Figs 5.1 and 5.2). Early Neolithic pottery is rare, probably because it was softer than most later pottery and consequently disintegrated after burial, but Holgate (1988, p. 281) recorded a 'plain bowl' vessel found in 1974 during road construction at Chorleywood (TQ 037947). Radiocarbon dating has demonstrated that the characteristic large monuments, which represent organized effort on a large scale, appeared quite suddenly in the 200 years between *c.* 5800 and 5600 calendar years ago.

In the Hertfordshire area, evidence for the early Neolithic (*c.* 6000 – *c.* 5400 calendar years ago) is sparse (Fig. 8.8). It begins with a dugout longboat found at Old Parkbury (TL 160022) close to the River Colne, and dated to 5950 ^{14}C BP (6800 calendar years ago). The longboat was accompanied by early Neolithic potsherds (Niblett 2001a), and had been used for a human and animal cremation. It indicates that Hertfordshire rivers were used for at least local transportation at the beginning of the Neolithic, and probably even earlier.

In terms of earthworks, there are five long barrows, two in Hertfordshire itself (Plate 73) and three on the Chilterns in south Bedfordshire (Table 8.1). There are also

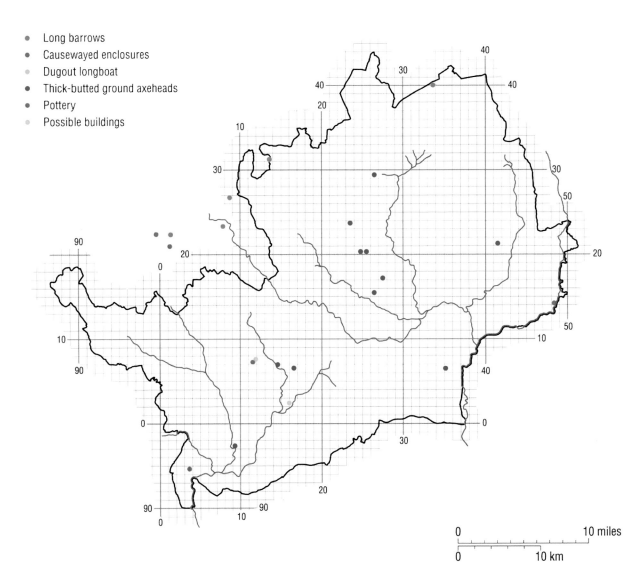

- Long barrows
- Causewayed enclosures
- Dugout longboat
- Thick-butted ground axeheads
- Pottery
- Possible buildings

Fig. 8.8. Distribution of sites in Hertfordshire with early Neolithic artefacts.

Plate 73. Early Neolithic long barrow, Therfield Heath (TL 341402).

numerous oval cropmarks, which were identified by the Air Photography Unit of RCHME (1992, p. 41; Fenner, 1996), and may represent long barrows degraded by ploughing and erosion. Most of the long barrows and cropmarks are on the Chalk outcrop, but a few uncertain examples are in the Stort and Lea valleys.

Possible early Neolithic causewayed enclosures have been identified in Hertfordshire at Sawbridgeworth (TL

Location	Grid reference	County	References and comments
Therfield Heath	TL 341401	Hertfordshire	Excavated along spine in 1855; the scar still visible. A few inhumation remains found. Later excavation (Phillips, 1935) found a turf core overlain by chalk rubble dug from surrounding ditch; no bones or artefacts, and no evidence of the internal timber construction found in such mounds elsewhere
Knocking Knoll	TL 133310	Herts/Beds boundary	Excavated 1856, almost completely destroyed
Dunstable	TL 012222	Bedfordshire	Dyer (1959, p. 14)
Biscot Mill	TL 079232	Bedfordshire	Dyer (1959, p. 14)
Streatley	TL 086268	Bedfordshire	Dyer (1959, p. 14)
Tea Green, Offley	TL 142241	Hertfordshire	Cropmark on Chalk
Clothall, Bird Hill	TL 270333	Hertfordshire	Cropmark on Chalk
Clothall	TL 263340	Hertfordshire	Cropmark on Chalk
Ashwell, Newnham Hill	TL 251392	Hertfordshire	Cropmark on Chalk
Ashwell	TL 272393	Hertfordshire	Cropmark on Chalk
Ashwell	TL 269406	Hertfordshire	Cropmark on Chalk
Ashwell, Highley Hill	TL 287380	Hertfordshire	Cropmark on Chalk
Ashwell, Claybush Hill	TL 267382	Hertfordshire	Cropmark on Chalk
Letchworth	TL 197322	Hertfordshire	Cropmark on Chalk
Wheathampstead	TL 194137	Hertfordshire	Cropmark on Chalk
Sawbridgeworth	TL 485153	Hertfordshire	Cropmark, Stort Valley
Ware	TL 337148	Hertfordshire	Cropmark, Lea valley

Table 8.1. Early Neolithic long barrows and oval cropmarks in the Hertfordshire area.

483139) (Palmer, 1976, p. 184), Bragbury End, Stevenage (TL 260207) and Bell Bar (TL 252049), and in south Bedfordshire at Maiden Bower (SP 996225) near Totternhoe (Smith, 1904). Excavations at Maiden Bower have produced 'plain bowl' pottery and a comb made from antler. These enclosures are thought to be meeting places of ritual or social importance rather than domestic sites; evidence for domestic sites of this period is virtually unknown. A rectangular pattern of gullies, apparently the footings of a building, were found during excavation of a Roman villa at Gorhambury (TL 111077) near St Albans (Neal *et al.*, 1990, pp. 7-8), but it is not known if this had a domestic function. There were associated flint tools and fragments of 'plain bowl' pottery, which was hardened (tempered) by incorporation of crushed flint. Charcoal from the gullies gave a late Neolithic radiocarbon date of 4860 ± 80 BP (c. 4810 calendar years ago), but this could have been incorporated some time after the gullies were dug.

Typical early Neolithic (thick-butted) ground and polished flint axeheads have been found at Knebworth (TL 253202), Tewin (TL 262156), Weston (TL 263295), Stevenage (TL 235238), Bull's Green (TL 272171), Watford (TQ 092973), Wormley (TL 350062), St Albans Abbey (TL 145070), The Camp, St Albans (TL 166067) and other less precisely located sites (Evans, 1902; Holgate, 1988). Many of these were probably produced outside Hertfordshire; some may have come from flint mines in Sussex or Norfolk. There are also axeheads of other stone types. A polished axehead made of Lake District (Langdale) tuff was found at Chorleywood (TQ 018956), and others of basalt have been recorded from Hitchin (TL 172295) and Buntingford. Three made of jadeite, thought to derive from the Italian Alps (Woolley *et al.*, 1979; Sheridan, 2007), have been found at Ashwell, Knebworth Station Hotel (TL 248202) and Bromleyhall Farm, Standon (TL 413212). Precisely how and why fine polished axeheads of rare and beautiful stones reached Hertfordshire is still obscure, but they are part of broader cultural links, which can be traced across Britain and into western Europe.

Late Neolithic. This period (c. 5400 – c. 4200 calendar years ago, 3400-2200 BCE) was characterized by a more decorated pottery style known as Peterborough Ware (Smith, 1974, p. 111; Holgate, 1988, Fig. 2.2); less elongate (oval) and round barrows with surrounding ring-ditches replaced the long barrows of the early Neolithic, and henge monuments made their first appearance. In addition, there was a more restricted range of flint implements than those produced in the early Neolithic, including transverse (chisel-shaped) or lozenge-shaped rather than leaf-shaped arrowheads, thin-butted axeheads and ground-edged knives and chisels (Holgate, 1988, Figs 5.1 and 5.2). The flintwork was less carefully produced than that of the early Neolithic, in that almost any quality of flint was used and flakes were usually struck from a more crudely prepared striking platform. This may reflect a decreased interest in flint resulting from the growing emphasis on arable farming, which needed additional raw materials such as antler and timber.

In Hertfordshire, thin-butted ground axeheads have

been recorded from Church End, Redbourn (TL 098118) (Stageman, 1983), Sandy Lodge Lane (TQ 0893) near Oxhey, Mill End (TL 3332) near Buntingford (Holgate, 1988, Tables 16 and 17) and numerous other sites (Fig. 8.9). A small hoard of four edge-ground flint axeheads was also found near Balls Park (TL 331117), Hertford (Holgate, 1988, p. 285). Ground flint chisels have been recorded from the Gade valley at Rickmansworth (now in Gunnersbury Park Museum, London) and Temple Mills (TQ 375852) in the lower Lea valley. Transverse arrowheads and a grain rubber, an early form of quern for grinding grain to produce flour, were recorded by Lee (1977) from Cuffley Hill Farm (TL 300029).

Waulud's Bank (TL 062245), Leagrave, is probably a late Neolithic henge monument situated near the head of the River Lea. Excavations there have produced Peterborough Ware (Dyer, 1964; Selkirk, 1972), and a thin-butted axehead, now in Luton Museum, was found nearby. Other possible henge monuments are suggested by cropmarks near Weston (TL 256319), Titmore Green (TL 214258), Stanstead St Margarets (TL 373113), Ashwell (TL 268382), Buckland (TL 387382), Ardeley (TL 314265) and House Lane (SP 951105) near Northchurch (McDonald, 1995).

Late Neolithic domestic sites are suggested only by scatters of flint implements. Although flint for at least the larger implements probably continued to be imported in the late Neolithic from outside the county, such as Grimes Graves in Norfolk (Holgate, 1991c), some may have come from local sources, such as the six flint mines at Pitstone Hill (SP 950140) near Tring (Dyer and Hales, 1961).

The known distribution of late Neolithic artefacts found in Hertfordshire, based on the Historic Environment Record, is shown in Figure 8.9. Detailed comparison with the county Soil Association map (Fig. 7.2) shows a rather different relationship between soils and evidence of Neolithic human presence from that inferred for the Mesolithic (Section 8.4). Over half (58%) the Neolithic sites are on the Plateau Drift of the Chiltern dip-slope (23%, mainly Hornbeam 2 Association), the higher proto-Thames terraces (10%, mainly Sonning 1 Association) and the thin Chalk soils in northern parts of the county. Of the last, 11% are on Rendzinas (mainly Upton 1 Association) and 14% on Typical brown calcareous earths (mainly Swaffham Prior Association). In percentage terms, Mesolithic finds are much less common, a total of only 33%, on these soils. In contrast, only 14% of Neolithic finds are from alluvial sites and other poorly drained soils, such as those on Palaeogene clays (essentially Windsor Association) in southern parts of the county, whereas 46% of the Mesolithic finds are from poorly-drained sites. The percentage of finds on the chalky till plateau (mainly Hanslope Association) in north-eastern parts of the county is the same (12%) in both periods. Thus, in the Neolithic there was a distinct move away from poorly drained soils, including those of riverside sites, onto the better drained soils of the Chiltern escarpment throughout the county. This probably resulted from the need to find soils that provided drier pasture or could be cultivated easily in wet weather for production of arable crops.

Very few of the round barrows have been dated to the late

- Thin-butted ground axeheads, adzes and transverse chisels
- Arrowheads, spearheads
- Grain rubbers/saddle querns
- Henge monuments
- Pottery
- Flint mines
- Pits
- Concentrations of flint implements suggesting domestic settlements

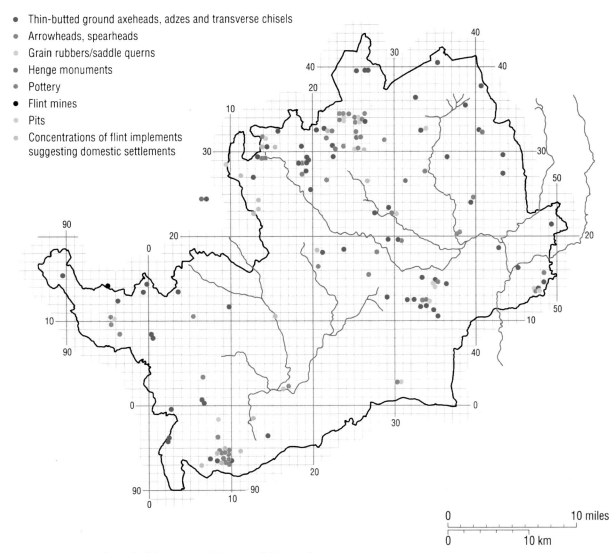

Fig. 8.9. Distribution of Hertfordshire sites with late Neolithic artefacts.

Neolithic; most are probably early Bronze Age. However, a ring ditch at Ayot St Lawrence (TL 206165) produced late Neolithic pottery (Anon., 1971), and others may be of a similar age.

The transitional period from the late Neolithic to the Bronze Age has been named the beaker period from a distinctive type of pottery drinking vessel or 'beaker', such as the one found at Ware and now in Hertford Museum (Clarke, 1970, p. 38). A few beakers have been found in round barrows, but not in Hertfordshire.

8.6. The Bronze Age

The Bronze Age spans the period between the end of the Neolithic (*c.* 2200 BCE) and the beginning of the Iron Age (*c.* 800 BCE). It was a period of more rapid change that saw a transformation in religion and beliefs, and led to the emergence of organized tribes living in settled agricultural communities, which were also engaged in trade and exchange. These changes are reflected in the nature of the archaeological evidence in Hertfordshire, the earlier

Bronze Age (*c.* 2200 – *c.* 1400 BCE) being dominated by ritual and burial monuments, and the later Bronze Age (*c.* 1400 – *c.* 800 BCE) by domestic settlements, evidence of agriculture and metalwork. The use of bone, flint and other stone tools continued, but the introduction of metal tools, initially copper and later bronze (copper fused with tin and other metals), brought increased efficiency in woodland clearance, farming and other industries. The demand for metal ores enabled trade, perhaps established in the Neolithic, to develop on a more extensive scale, in particular with Cornwall, Wales and Ireland (Cunliffe, 2001), and this may have led to establishment of a network of long distance trackways.

Early Bronze Age. The main landscape feature of this period (though some may be late Neolithic) are the round barrows, which are 10-40 m in diameter and surrounded by single or double ring-ditches. In the Hertfordshire area, about 50 upstanding round barrows still exist (Fig. 8.10). Many are arranged in clusters on or near the crest of the Chiltern escarpment, for example the Five Knolls near Dunstable (TL 007210) (Dyer, 1991), and other groups near Ivinghoe

- Circular soil/crop marks, possible ring-ditches
- Round barrows

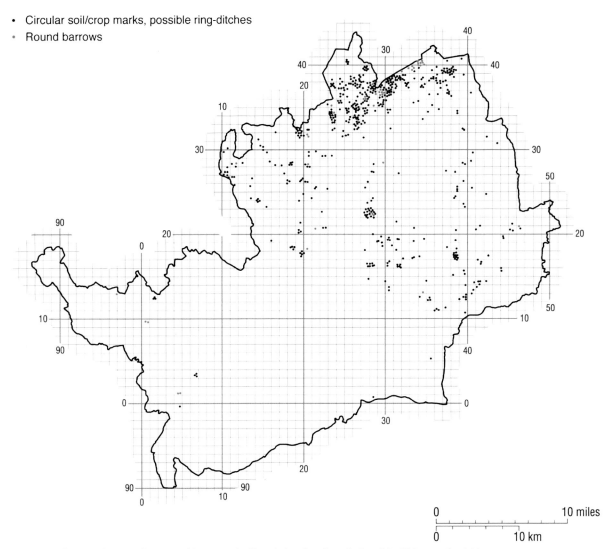

Fig. 8.10. Distribution of upstanding round barrows (red) and circular ring-ditches (black) in Hertfordshire.

(SP 9616), Letchworth (TL 205318), Odsey (TL 2936), Bygrave (TL 276360) and on Therfield Heath (Stevenson, 1987; Holgate, 1995, Fig. 10) and the Barton Hills (Dyer, 1974; Clark, 1991). Isolated examples occur, for example, at Chipperfield Common (TL 046012), Nettleden (TL 005099 and TL 005100), Aldbury Common (SP 970130), Winter Wood (TL 214208) near Crouch Green and on Telegraph Hill (TL 118285), and there are others in the Mimram, Beane and other valleys. The partial clustering of round barrows might suggest proximity to settlements but, as in other parts of England (Brown and Murphy, 1997, p. 14), there is little direct evidence for early Bronze Age settlements in the county. Any settlements were probably still seasonal, lacking permanent structures.

However, most of the round barrows have been obliterated by soil cultivation and remain only as ring-ditches visible in aerial photographs as soil patterns or cropmarks (Fenner, 1996). At least 540 of these have been recognized throughout the county (Fig. 8.10), and many others may have been completely destroyed. The large number suggests a considerably increased population compared with the Neolithic period. Comparison of their distribution with

the soil association map of the county (Fig. 7.2) shows that approximately 60% are situated on thin chalky soils in north Hertfordshire, mainly Grey rendzinas of the Upton 1 Association and Typical brown calcareous earths of the Swaffham Prior Association. Another 10% are on the Palaeo-argillic brown earths (mainly Hornbeam 2 and Hornbeam 3 Associations) of the Chiltern plateau east, south and west of Stevenage. So, as in the Neolithic, the human population in the early Bronze Age was probably concentrated on the thin well-drained soils over Chalk in north-eastern Hertfordshire, but also extended onto nearby areas of the heavier but still workable soils on the Plateau Drift. The proportion (16%) of barrows and ring-ditches occurring in groups or as isolated examples on the Typical calcareous pelosols (Hanslope Association) of the chalky till outcrop in north-eastern Hertfordshire suggests that this area was more densely populated than in the Neolithic and Mesolithic.

Possible trackways. Many of the groups of upstanding round barrows are spaced at fairly regular intervals along the Icknield Way on the scarp-slope of the Chilterns. This trackway has long been thought to be a prehistoric

244

route following the Chalk scarp from East Anglia through northwest Hertfordshire to Wiltshire. It probably consisted of several subparallel trackways spread over a belt of well-drained, thinly wooded country up to 5 km wide. This and other 'ridgeways' were thought to have formed a network of routes along which goods were carried, though Harrison (2003) has cast doubt on the existence of such long-distance routes in prehistory. Local trackways almost certainly existed, and the main Roman roads were evidently engineered versions of older routes, but there is a lack of archaeological evidence for long-distance prehistoric trackways. It is likely that some goods were transported by water, and shallow-draught dugout longboats like the one found at Old Parkbury could certainly have negotiated the Hertfordshire river system, providing access to the Thames and thus to the sea.

Flint artefacts. Early Bronze Age flint implements, such as barbed and tanged arrowheads, are widely distributed throughout the county but are much less abundant than those of the Mesolithic and Neolithic periods, presumably reflecting a continuing decline in the use of flint for production of tools once metals were being used for this purpose. The flint tools are sometimes associated with the flint scatters that may indicate late Neolithic domestic sites, so it is possible that late Neolithic settlements continued to be used into the early Bronze Age.

Late Bronze Age. In contrast, there is more evidence for settlement of Hertfordshire during the late Bronze Age. Much of this has been obtained from excavations made in the last 15 years. Settlements of timber roundhouses with evidence of agriculture are now known from most parts of the county apart from the London Clay area in the south. Many are enclosed by substantial banks and ditches, emphasizing a change to more permanent settlements. There was an expansion onto the chalky till areas of east Hertfordshire, for instance at Thorley (TL 475191), Bishop's Stortford (TL 509217 and TL 485191) and Wood End, Ardeley (TL 330260), and recent excavations at Stansted Airport have demonstrated a sharp increase in activity in the middle of the Bronze Age (Cooke *et al.*, 2008). Settlement also became more common along the river valleys, with particular concentrations along the Lea and Gade. Along the Lea, later Bronze Age agricultural settlements have been found at Cole Green (TL 299119) near Hertford and John Warner School (TL 379102), Hoddesdon, and important evidence for bronze manufacturing is known from Prior's Wood (TL 353114), Hertford Heath. In the Gade and Colne valleys, excavations at The Grove, (TQ 080985), Watford and Gadebridge (TL 046080), Hemel Hempstead, and at Apsley (TL 052049), Oakwood, (SP 974072) and Bottom House Lane (SP 951105) on the A41 by-pass, have also produced evidence of later Bronze Age settlements (McDonald, 1995; Bryant, 1995).

Burials. A feature of these and other late Bronze Age settlements in Hertfordshire is the presence of human burials and deposits in pits and ditches near or within the settlements. The burial practices of the late Bronze Age differ from those of the early Bronze Age in consisting mainly of cremation remains placed in urns unaccompanied by other grave goods and not usually marked or covered by mounds. A globular collared urn dated to the beginning of the late Bronze Age (*c.* 1400-1200 BCE), probably from Cromwell Road, Hertford (TL 341132) (Davies and Petchey, 1977) is in Hertford Museum, and collared cremation urns of similar date have been found near Codicote (TL 205183), Willian (TL 221306), Spinney Farm, Stotfold (TL 227383) and at Foxholes Farm (TL 345123), Hertford.

Hillforts. Another feature of the late Bronze Age is the growing diversity of settlement types, some of which are highly visible in the landscape. They include hillforts with defensive earthworks, such as those at Ivinghoe Beacon (SP 960168), Buckinghamshire, Wilbury Hill (TL 205324) near Letchworth and Arbury Banks (TL 261387) near Ashwell. Previously, all hillforts were thought to have originated in the Iron Age, but recent excavations have indicated that these three and possibly others existed in rudimentary forms in the late Bronze Age. Ivinghoe Beacon had a single ditch 2.5 m deep and 2.5 m wide, enclosing an area of 2.4 ha, with an internal 'box rampart'. This probably consisted of a box-framed timber structure 1-2 m wide and 2-3 m high, strengthened by interlacing timbers and filled with earth and rubble from the ditch (Cotton and Frere, 1968). At Wilbury Hill, the single ditch was approximately 6 m wide and 2 m deep (Applebaum, 1949, p. 21). The large double-ditched enclosure or 'ringwork' at Whiteley Hill (TL 376391) near Royston is probably a late Bronze Age domestic site (Bryant, 1993), and a single enclosure at Great Westwood Quarry (TQ 075985) near Sarratt is probably also late Bronze Age.

The foundations of buildings are known from various late Bronze Age sites. At the Ivinghoe Beacon and Wilbury Hill hillforts, at the Puddlehill (TL 006236), Cole Green, Pea Lane (SP 946083) and Bottomhouse Lane (SP 951105) settlements and at Bishops Park (TL 470208) near Bishop's Stortford, roundhouses with posthole foundations were probably domestic in origin. Other rectangular structures built on either four or six posts were probably used as grain stores, and rectangular palisaded enclosures may have been stockpens.

Agriculture. Changes in agricultural practices during the Bronze Age led to a more diverse range of arable crops than those grown in the Neolithic, including bread wheat (*Triticum aestivo-compactum*), oats (*Avena* spp.), rye (*Secale cereale*) and legumes. This range was typical of agriculture in southern Britain for the rest of prehistory. The assemblages of bones from many late Bronze Age sites are dominated by domesticated animals, such as sheep, cattle, pigs and horses, with fewer from wild animals, suggesting that hunting had become less important than animal husbandry in meeting dietary needs.

In several parts of south Hertfordshire (Fig. 8.11), there is evidence in the landscape for co-axial field systems, which were probably used mainly for pasture and are thought to date from the late Bronze Age (Dyson-Bruce *et al.*, 2006).

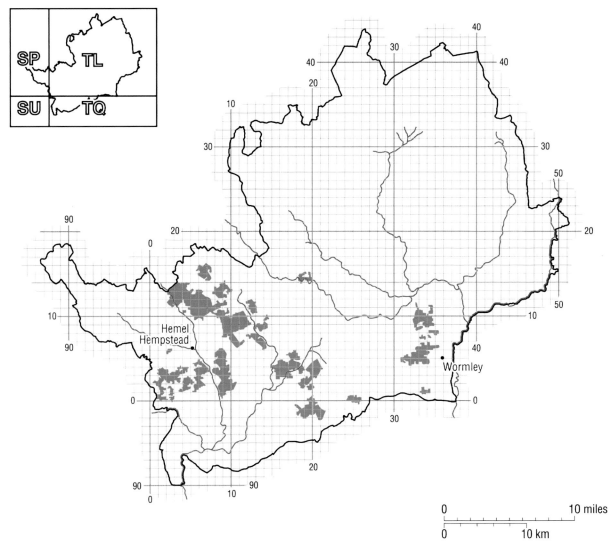

Fig. 8.11. Distribution of possible co-axial field systems in Hertfordshire, some of which may be Late Bronze Age (redrawn from Dyson-Bruce et al., 2006).

They consist of groups of long, narrow, parallel fields with straight or sinuous long boundaries, often aligned up and down valley sides perpendicular to rivers, which presumably served as water sources for animals. For example, in the Wormley area between Tanfield Stud Farm (TL 325050) and Broxbourne Wood (TL 3207), the fields are aligned E-W on the western side of the lower Lea valley (Bryant *et al.*, 2005), and on the north-eastern side of the Gade valley northwest of Hemel Hempstead they are orientated NE-SW. The Wormley system may have been associated with a high-status late Bronze Age settlement at Turnford (Bryant *et al.*, 2005). The evidence for co-axial field systems is best preserved in areas of ancient (mediaeval or earlier) semi-natural woodland. A late Bronze Age origin is suggested by similarities with prehistoric field patterns in south Essex (Rodwell, 1978), south Norfolk (Williamson, 1998) and parts of the Thames valley (Yates, 1999), and by a pollen assemblage from the buried soil beneath a bank associated with the co-axial field system in Wormley Wood (TL 316063) (Bryant *et al.*, 2005). The field boundaries of the systems determined the positions of many Hertfordshire parish

boundaries, which were fixed no later than the late 12th century (Winchester, 2000).

Pottery. In the late Bronze Age, the pottery commonly found on domestic sites is characteristically flint-tempered, i.e. crushed flint grit was fired with the clay to give the pottery added strength and abrasion resistance. Shouldered jars and bowls with rounded profiles were made in the first few centuries of the late Bronze Age; most were plain and undecorated, but some had a simple ring of fingerprint decoration. In the Hertfordshire area, examples of this type are known from the hillfort at Ivinghoe Beacon (Cotton and Frere, 1968), and from settlement sites at Totternhoe (Hawkes, 1940), Puddlehill (TL 006236) near Houghton Regis (Matthews, 1976), Gadebridge, Hemel Hempstead, and at the Bottom House Lane (SP 951105), Crawley's Lane (SP 955098) and Pea Lane (SP 946083) sites near Berkhamsted described by Bryant (1995).

The pottery produced in the final centuries of the late Bronze Age (1000-800 BCE) contained flint that was more finely ground than previously. This allowed larger and

246

thinner-walled vessels to be produced, often with carinated profiles (angular ridges around the sides) and greater finger decoration (Bryant, 1995). In Hertfordshire examples are known from the hillfort at Wilbury Hill (Applebaum, 1949) and from other settlements at Moles Farm (TL 361162) near Thundridge (Kiln, 1970), Ware (Kiln, 1973), Blackhorse Road (TL 233336), Letchworth (Birley, 1988), King Harry Lane (TL 136063), St Albans (Longworth, 1989), Halfhide Lane, Turnford (TL 226318), Foxholes Farm, Hertford (Partridge, 1989), Cole Green (TL 2911) (McDonald, 2004a) and Buncefield Lane (TL 082080), Hemel Hempstead (McDonald, 2004b).

Metalwork. Bronze artefacts are occasionally found on domestic sites, and almost all date from the very end of the Bronze Age, *c.* 900-800 BCE (Bryant, 1995, p. 19). However, most are from hoards not associated with settlements, as at Prior's Wood (TL 353114) Hertford Heath, Cumberlow Green near Rushden (TL 3030), Clothall (TL 2433), Stockbridge Farm near Ware (TL 3515), Rickmansworth (TQ 055949), Watford (TQ 090955) and Lowerfield near Royston (TL 3840). Typical bronze artefacts include spearheads, palstaves, swords, rapiers, socketed axeheads, winged axeheads, buckets, cauldrons, chisels, sickles, daggers, pins, razors and items of personal ornament, though most of the bronze found is obviously scrap material. The hoards were probably either caches of personal wealth or the stock-in-trade of bronze workers or itinerant tinkers, perhaps buried at a time when bronze production and trade networks collapsed across much of northern Europe. Two probable bronze manufacturing sites are known, one at Halfhide Lane, Turnford, where fragments of crucibles, hearths and clay moulds were found, and the other at Prior's Wood, which yielded socketed and winged axeheads and ingot fragments from a sooty earth with blackened stones (Partridge, 1980a).

8.7. The Iron Age

The period between about 800 BCE and the Roman invasion of Britain in 43 CE is known as the Iron Age, because of the use of iron as well as bronze and stone artefacts. Techniques for iron smelting were either introduced into eastern England by links with mainland Europe (Thompson, 2005, p. 24) or arose through the inventiveness of the existing (late Bronze Age) population. The latter is more likely for the introduction of iron than for copper and bronze, because iron ores are much more widely distributed than those of copper and tin; indeed some were probably obtained in or close to Hertfordshire. The development of iron-working technology, although more complex than the manufacture of bronze, allowed production of sharper edged tools, and a wider range of agricultural implements. In southern Britain, the Iron Age has been divided into three, but recent work has partially conflated the early Iron Age and later Bronze Age, as the change from bronze to iron seems to have occurred gradually between 800 and 600 BCE. In the Hertfordshire area, the approximate dates are: early Iron

Age *c.* 800 – *c.* 400 BCE; middle Iron Age *c.* 400-100 BCE; late Iron Age 100 BCE to 43 CE.

The flint-tempered coarse pottery fabric of the later Bronze Age persisted throughout the early Iron Age, but with the addition of fine decorated bowls of a distinctive angular type known as the Chinnor-Wandlebury style, which are found only in north Hertfordshire and the Chilterns from *c.* 600 BCE. The middle Iron Age is characterized by simple rounded forms, plain and tempered mainly with sand rather than flint. This type of pottery is found across much of the region, though there are only a few known sites in Hertfordshire.

In the early and middle Iron Ages, iron artefacts, mainly agricultural tools, knives and brooches, were rare, and the dead were not buried formally, but were probably cremated and the ashes scattered. However, in the late Iron Age there were large changes. Iron smelting and the production of agricultural tools, knives, weapons and brooches made from iron became more firmly established. During the first century BCE, the introduction from the European continent of the fast potter's wheel and the use of 'grog' (ground fragments of previously fired pot) as a tempering material resulted in the development of new and distinctive pottery forms, including pedestalled jars, bowls, cups and plates. Pottery made in Gaul began to arrive towards the end of the first century BCE, and was both used and copied in Hertfordshire. Luxury goods, such as wine in large containers (amphorae), were imported from the Mediterranean area. Cremation became the normal burial rite, with ashes buried in and/or accompanied by urns and other artefacts. In addition, coins were introduced in the late Iron Age. The earliest, manufactured from gold, were brought from north-eastern France (Gaul) and Belgium, and are thought to represent gifts between tribal chieftains rather than trade. Later gold, silver and bronze coins were minted in Britain (Allen, 1962; Haselgrove, 1987), and at the close of the Iron Age, the indigenous coinage often provides evidence for named tribal leaders and the locations of their mints.

The source of ironstone as a raw material for the iron industry in Hertfordshire is uncertain. The county has no significant ironstone resources, though small amounts could undoubtedly have been found in iron-rich soil layers (iron pans) and ferruginous nodules of pedological origin, as in upper parts of the Plateau Drift of the Chilterns or in the alluvial soils of river valleys. More likely sources are the geological ironstones found in the Woburn Sand Formation (Lower Cretaceous) of south Bedfordshire and the Middle Lias (Lower Jurassic) exposed further to the northwest.

Earlier Iron Age earthworks

Hillforts. The most impressive effect of the early and middle Iron Age population on the landscape of the Hertfordshire area was the development of an extensive network of hillforts (Table 8.2; Fig. 8.12). The term is a general one, covering a range of monument types. Some, on the Chiltern scarp, originated in the late Bronze Age (e.g. Arbury Banks, Ivinghoe Beacon and Wilbury Hill). Most of the later ones

Site name	Grid reference	County	References and comments
Arbury Banks	TL 261387	Hertfordshire	Bivallate; includes roundhouses; Dyer (1981)
Ivinghoe Beacon	SP 961169	Buckinghamshire	Cotton and Frere (1968), Farley (2010)
Wilbury Hill	TL 205324	Hertfordshire	Univallate; includes roundhouses; Applebaum (1949)
Maiden Bower	SP 997225	S. Bedfordshire	Matthews (1976)
Sharpenhoe Clappers	TL 066302	S. Bedfordshire	Matthews (1976)
Cholesbury Camp	SP 930073	Buckinghamshire	Kimble (1933)
Whelpley Hill	SP 980053	Buckinghamshire	
Bulstrode Park	SU 994880	Buckinghamshire	
Bulpit Hill	SP 831050	Buckinghamshire	
Boddington Hill	SP 882080	Buckinghamshire	
Bush Hill	TQ 321957	N. London	
Ravensburgh Castle	TL 099295	Hertfordshire	Bivallate; sub-rectangular; four phases; Dyer (1976)
?Widbury Hill	TL 372138	Hertfordshire	Fragmentary; uncertain
?Caley Wood (Westland Green Camp)	TL 421215	Hertfordshire	On slope; probably not an enclosure; may be late Iron Age
Childwick Bury	TL 128105	Hertfordshire	Strategic site overlooking Ver valley, but no clear earthworks (Hunn, 1994, p. 22)

Table 8.2. Certain and possible earlier Iron Age hillforts in the Hertfordshire area.

(Table 8.2) occur at lower levels on rather flatter terrain, and are bounded by a single bank and ditch rather than the multivallate defences common in earlier hillforts. They are almost circular and 200-300 m across, though Ravensburgh Castle is roughly rectangular and slightly larger (>5 ha in area). They were probably in use for several centuries, and some contain evidence of internal roundhouses, as at Arbury Banks (Dyer, 1981) and Wilbury Hill (Air Photography Unit of RCHME, 1992, p. 23), or of pits and graves.

Some sites once proposed as Iron Age hillforts may have different origins. Gatesbury near Puckeridge (TL 395240) is probably mediaeval. Whiteley Hill (TL 376391) (Wilkerson and Cra'ster, 1959) is probably a late Bronze Age domestic enclosure (Bryant, 1993). The Aubreys near Redbourn (TL 095112) is in a valley and has yielded no occupational debris; it is a promontory enclosure of uncertain purpose and may have been used only seasonally (Hunn, 1994, p. 22). Limlow Hill (TL 323417) in south Cambridgeshire was classed as a hillfort by Ordnance Survey (1962), but is probably a natural prominence ringed by a circular outcrop of Melbourn Rock or other hard bed in the Chalk.

There is also no concensus concerning the primary function of hillforts. Although nationally they have been regarded as military sites (Avery, 1976) or defended villages (Cunliffe, 1991), some archaeologists have emphasized their role in regional social systems, possibly as secure tribal centres for storage and redistribution of grain and stock (Gent, 1983). For those in the Hertfordshire area, Bryant (1995, p. 25) has suggested that their fairly regular spacing 7-12 km apart and the clustering of other Iron Age settlements, possibly farmsteads, around several of them (Cholesbury, Ivinghoe Beacon, Maiden Bower, Ravensburgh Castle and Wilbury Hill), support the concept of redistribution centres. The farmstead clusters are spread over areas 4-12 km across, so each farm was close enough to its hillfort for grain to be transported there after harvest, but the whole area would have been too large to farm efficiently as a single unit from the hillfort itself.

Linear earthworks. In addition to the circular or rectangular earthworks associated with hillforts, numerous linear ditch systems occur in Hertfordshire and surrounding areas (Fig. 8.12). The longest, known as Grim's Ditch, runs close to the Chiltern scarp on either side of the Tring Gap at the head of the Bulbourne valley. The section south of the valley is continuous from Cock's Hill (SP 895066) for at least 5 km north-eastwards to near Wigginton Bottom (SP 935093); short sections also survive on the shoulder of the Bulbourne valley south of Northchurch. North of the Tring Gap, it extends for at least 2 km from near Westland Farm (SP 952129) northwards to near Brook's Statnalls Wood (SP 953147). In both portions the ditch is 6-10 m wide and has a bank 1-3 m high on the eastern side, though it is not certain that they constitute a single earthwork. Parts of Grim's Ditch on either side of the Tring Gap have been investigated by Crawford (1931), Dyer (1963), Davis (1981) and Davis and Evans (1984), but little evidence was found for the function and age of the earthwork. Similar linear ditches, also often known as Grim's Ditch, extend over parts of the Chalk outcrop in Buckinghamshire, Berkshire, Oxfordshire, Hampshire and Wiltshire, and in some of these areas there is evidence for a late Bronze Age or early Iron Age date. They may represent territorial boundaries or perhaps served to control the movements of animal herds.

Shorter (<1 km) linear earthworks consisting of banks and single, double or multiple ditches, which are largely infilled but visible from the air as soil and cropmarks, occur on the eastern Chilterns (Fig. 8.12). They either cross the

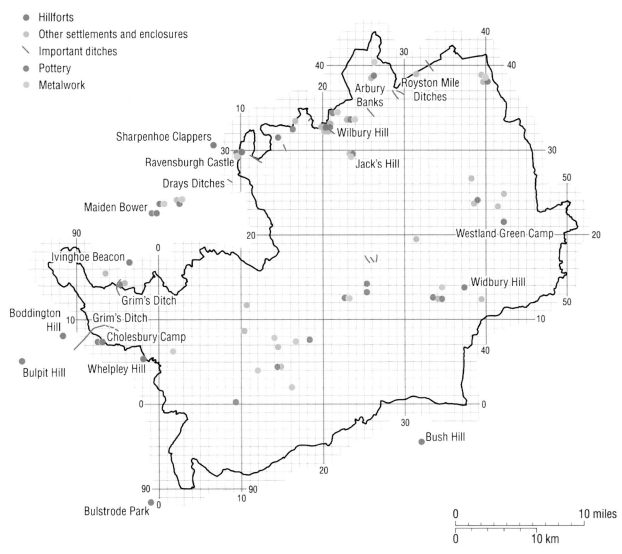

- ● Hillforts
- ● Other settlements and enclosures
- ＼ Important ditches
- ● Pottery
- ● Metalwork

Fig. 8.12. Distribution of earlier Iron Age earthworks, pottery and metalwork in the Hertfordshire area.

Icknield Way or run approximately parallel to it (Bryant and Burleigh, 1995). Similar features are present on other parts of the Chalk outcrop in eastern and southern England and also occur in the east Midlands and North Yorkshire. Some of the earliest may date from the late Bronze Age. One of these monuments, the Royston Mile Ditches (TL 3339), was originally identified by Crawford (1936) in the early days of aerial photography. Dyer (1961, 1981, p. 50) suggested that, together with rivers such as the Hiz and Ivel, the Royston Mile Ditches and others in the eastern Chilterns marked where the Icknield Way was crossed by boundaries between tribal territories, each controlled by its own major hillfort. However, later aerial photography and field survey in the Baldock-Royston area indicated more (8-9) ditches, and therefore more subdivisions of land, than known hillforts. It is of course possible that some hillforts controlled more than one territory. But excavation of at least two examples, Dray's Ditches (TL 088264) in south Bedfordshire (Dyer, 1961) and the Royston Mile Ditches (Burleigh, 1980), has indicated multiple phases of construction, so the number of ditches could reflect changes in territorial boundaries over time.

The Royston Mile Ditches eventually comprised four banks *c.* 2 m high separated by three ditches 1-2 m deep, with a total width of *c.* 30 m. A horse's jaw bone found at the base of one of the ditches gave a radiocarbon date of 2040 ± 80 BP, and infilling of the ditches by natural erosion and deposition is thought to have occurred in the late 1st or early 2nd centuries CE (Burleigh, 1995). Although they were mainly a feature of the Iron Age landscape, some of the earliest ditches may have originated in the late Bronze Age. The ditches extending nearly parallel to the Icknield Way rather than across it may have served to channel the route and prevent it from spreading.

Earlier Iron Age pottery and metalwork

Early Iron Age pottery is known from the hillforts at Maiden Bower, Ravensburgh Castle, Ivinghoe Beacon (Waugh, 1968a) and Wilbury Hill, and from minor settlements at Jack's Hill (TL 237295) near Great Wymondley (Tebbutt, 1932), Holwell (TL 163324) and Pirton (TL 145313) (Applebaum, 1934), Park Street (O'Neil, 1945, p. 73), Pitstone Hill (SP 946146) (Waugh, 1968b) and Puddlehill (Matthews, 1976, p. 143). The only metalwork items known

- Oppida
- Chieftain burials
- Metalworking sites

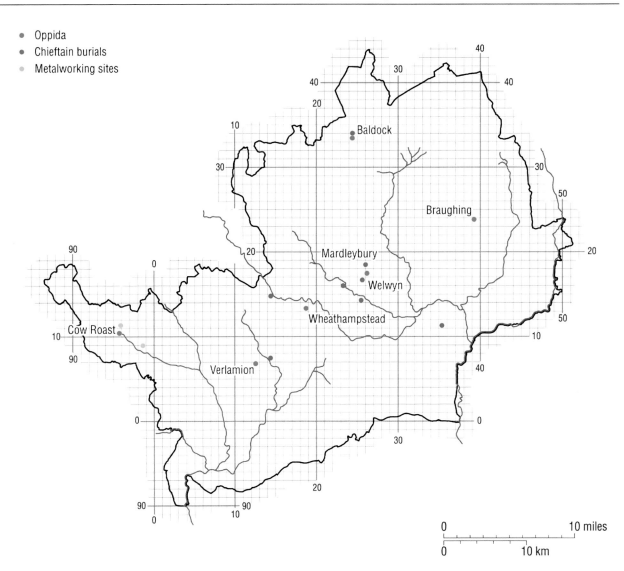

Fig. 8.13. Distribution of late Iron Age oppida, chieftain burials and metalworking sites in Hertfordshire.

from this period are a safety pin brooch, similar to those known in France as the La Tene Ib type, from Ravensburgh Castle (Dyer, 1976, p. 157), a small knife from Puddlehill (Matthews 1976, pp. 71-72), a serpentiform brooch from Pirton (Applebaum, 1934) and a bronze pendant from Jack's Hill (Burleigh, 1976).

Middle Iron Age pottery assemblages have been reported from the hillforts at Wilbury Hill and Cholesbury, and from minor settlements at Barley (Cra'ster, 1961), Puddlehill (Matthews, 1976, pp. 94-139), Blackhorse Road, Letchworth (Birley, 1988, pp. 80-83) and Foxholes Farm, Hertford (Partridge, 1989, pp. 166-170). They have also been found in minor excavations at Oaklands College (TL 1807) and Leavesden Aerodrome (TL 0900) (Niblett, 2001b, p. 35). In the Welwyn Garden City area, middle Iron Age pottery mixed with later material has been reported at Crookhams (TL 253141) (Rook, 1968), Brickwall Hill (TL 226127) (Rook, 1970a) and Grubs Barn (TL 253132) (Rook, 1970b).

Small quantities of middle Iron Age metalwork, both iron and bronze, have been found at Barley (Cra'ster, 1961, pp. 33-35), Brickwall Hill (Rook, 1970a, Fig. III) and Blackhorse Road, Letchworth (Moss-Eccardt, 1988, pp. 87-88). A small

bronze knife in the shape of a bird, found near St Albans and dated to between 300 and 100 BCE, is in the British Museum (Megaw *et al.*, 1999).

Late Iron Age changes

The late Iron Age was a period of increasing population and much more rapid social, economic and industrial change than in any earlier period of prehistory. The late Iron Age is also when Britain first appears in Greek and Roman written documents, which depict a tribal society headed by chieftains and with strong trading links with continental Europe. However, the tribal territories were not static; many changes took place between Caesar's accounts of his two invasions of Britain in 55 and 54 BCE and the Roman invasion of 43 CE. A major factor was evidently a shift in trading patterns with the continent during the 1st century BCE, when the main cross-channel route for the substantial trade in Mediterranean wine and other luxury goods via Armorica (Brittany) into the Dorset area gave way to a different route between north-eastern Gaul and Kent, Essex and Hertfordshire (Cunliffe, 2001, pp. 402-407).

Archaeology has not yet shown where the combined British forces were defeated in 54 BCE, but Caesar's account of a well-populated region with abundant pasture for cattle and horses, yet enough woodland to conceal his opponents' guerilla forces, could easily describe a part of Hertfordshire (Niblett, 1995a, p. 12). Caesar took the sons of defeated chieftains as hostages to ensure good behaviour of the tribes, and Creighton (2000, pp. 402-407) suggested that these sons, given a Roman education and a taste for Roman lifestyle before being returned to succeed as tribal chiefs, were responsible for the appearance by the late 1st century BCE of locally produced inscribed coins imitating Roman styles.

'Oppida'

In addition to numerous rural farmsteads, more extensive foci of settlement known as 'oppida' developed in the late Iron Age. The largest oppida were 20-40 km^2 in area, although this included farmsteads, fields and tracks surrounding smaller (20-40 ha) and more specialized sites dedicated to trading and the manufacture of goods.

Several oppida have been identified and others proposed (Table 8.3; Fig. 8.13), but problems in defining the nature of these agglomerations have led to the term being used less often now than it once was. There was considerable variety in layout, function and status, and some evidently acted as central places for quite extensive hinterlands (Bryant, 2007). Verlamion is later than most of the others, not appearing before the early 1st century CE. It may have developed where a route for bringing iron ore from the sources further west to the major centres in the east, including Welwyn, Braughing and Colchester in Essex, crossed the River Ver (Thompson, 2005, p. 38). This route became the Roman roads later called Akeman Street and Stane Street. Over 20 settlements and rectilinear enclosures

dated to the first half of the 1st century CE are known within a 10 km radius of Verlamion, many of them near the edges of the Chiltern plateau on either side of the Ver and upper Lea valleys (Niblett, 2001b, Fig. 17). At Ashridge, in a similar plateau-edge position north of the Bulbourne valley adjacent to the Cow Roast oppidum, there is an extensive pattern of farmsteads, banked enclosures, field systems and possible religious buildings covering approximately 20 km^2 (Morris and Wainwright, 1995). Farmsteads may have been established on the plateau edge because the nearby valley slopes could be used for arable crops and the heavier soils of the plateau for pasture. In the final decades of the late Iron Age between about 20 BCE and 40 CE, the oppidum at Braughing expanded to cover an area of at least 100 ha, including Wickham Hill (TL 391233), where pits and burials are associated with a ditched trackway (Potter and Trow, 1988), and Skeleton Green (TL 387239), where there were nine rectangular timber buildings interpreted as a trading community (Partridge, 1980b, 1981).

Burials

Large cemeteries are known at some of the 'oppida'. The usual rite was cremation, but some inhumations are known. High status cremations are often found within square enclosures. A distinctive feature at Baldock, which is on alkaline soil (Icknield series), are the numerous well preserved inhumations sited around a natural solution hollow in the Chalk, in which human bones and other offerings were placed since at least the middle Iron Age (Ashworth, 2003). In contrast, at the King Harry Lane cemetery (TL 131067) near the southern margin of the demarcated area at Verlamion, 455 cremation burials but only 17 inhumations have been excavated (Stead and Rigby, 1989). Because of the natural acidity of the soil (Carstens Association) at this site, the bones found in shallow graves

Name	Grid reference	References	Comments
Wheathampstead	TL 186134	Wheeler and Wheeler (1936), Bryant (2007)	Extensive valley site succeeding earlier bank and ditch enclosure (Devil's Dyke)
Verlamion	TL 1207	Niblett (2001b), Thompson (2005)	Central enclosure in valley by river crossing; demarcated by banks and ditch; farms outside on higher ground; cemeteries; coins minted; later major ditch system
Baldock	TL 2433	Stead and Rigby (1986), Burleigh (1995)	Many burials; possible religious focus
Braughing	TL 3923	Partridge (1981); Potter and Trow (1988)	Extensive occupation; specialist areas; coins minted
Welwyn	TL 2413	Bryant (2007)	Extensive agglomeration of farmsteads
Welches Farm	TL 260173	Rook (1974)	Widespread occupation; possible related bank and undated linear ditch system
Ashridge/Cow Roast	SP 957103	Morris and Wainwright (1995)	Extensive agglomeration of farmsteads, enclosures, field systems; ironworking in Bulbourne valley
Mardleybury	TL 260184	Andrews (1911)	'Chieftain' burial
Hertford Heath	TL 3511	Holmes and Frend (1959)	'Chieftain' burial

Table 8.3. Late Iron Age oppida in Hertfordshire.

Plate 74. The Beech Bottom earthwork on the northern side of St Albans (TL 157092).

are less well preserved and provide limited information.

Cremations with grave goods are an important feature of the late Iron Age in Hertfordshire. They range from piles of ash inside or outside single pots to richly furnished graves like the chieftain burials situated at the major centres (Fig. 8.13). The latter contained Italian amphorae and ceramic, bronze and silver vessels from Gaul and Italy. Soon after the Roman conquest in the early 50s CE, they culminated in the high status burial of Verlamion's client king at Folly Lane, St Albans (TL 142080), where the grave goods included his suit of chain mail (Niblett, 1992, 1995b, 1999), and a Roman temple was later built.

Linear earthworks of the late Iron Age

Numerous linear earthworks around Verlamion are thought to date from the late Iron Age. The largest, known as Beech Bottom, is on the north side of St Albans and is about 1.5 km long, but its precise date and purpose are unclear. Hunn (1994, p. 26) suggested that it is part of a major territorial boundary but, if true, its total length (about 1.5 km) clearly indicates it was unfinished. The most impressive part runs between the A1081 at TL 150089 on the northern side of St Albans and the St Albans-Harpenden railway line at TL 158093, where it is about 30 m wide (40-50 m with the low banks on either side) and approximately 10 m deep (Plate 74). In this part it occupies the floors of two contiguous dry valleys (Fig. 8.14), one falling south-westwards into the Ver valley near Verlamion and the other

north-eastwards through the village of Sandridge, then terminating approximately 1 km northeast of the village in a broad, shallow enclosed hollow at about 85 m OD. The Harpenden valley from the north and another from the east that contains the Devil's Dyke at Wheathampstead also terminate in this hollow. The humped longitudinal profile and the enclosed hollow northeast of Sandridge both suggest glacial influence, either by subglacial erosion or by localized deposition of glacial sediments. There are patches of Ware Till at Sandridge and east of Wheathampstead, and there is a more continuous cover in the Vale of St Albans to the south-east, but this only extends to within 1 km of Beech Bottom. As glacial deposits are not known from the humped valley occupied by the earthwork, irregular glacial deposition does not completely account for all the unusual geomorphological features associated with the earthwork. Wooldridge (1953) suggested that the valley is a marginal (subaerial) meltwater channel of the Anglian ice sheet, but its humped longitudinal profile is more likely to have resulted from subglacial erosion similar to that leading to some of the meltwater channels cut in the Chalk elsewhere in Hertfordshire (Section 6.6).

Although a shallow extension of Beech Bottom can be traced at the south-western end of its deepest section (Thompson, 2005, p. 32), there is no evidence for continuity of the earthwork between the oppida at Verlamion and Wheathampstead, as suggested by Rodwell (1976, p. 336). Bryant (2007, p. 72) suggested that, together with the Devil's Dyke at Wheathampstead, it served to guide visitors into Verlamion from the northeast, but the shortness of both

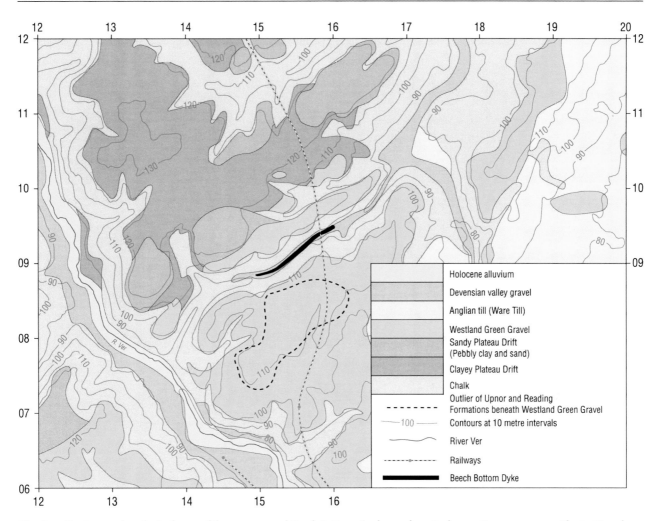

Fig. 8.14. Contour and geological map of the area around Beech Bottom, (redrawn from Ordnance Survey 1:50,000 Sheet 166 and British Geological Survey Sheet 239).

these earthworks and the gap between them make this unlikely, again unless a grander scheme was left unfinished. Neither ice-marginal meltwater nor subglacial erosion during the Anglian can explain the ditch itself, as opposed to the humped valley in which it is excavated, because they do not explain the upcast banks on either side, and it is unlikely that such a sharp-sided channel cut in Chalk bedrock would have been preserved for more than 400 ka since the Anglian glaciation. Over such a long period, it would have been severely modified or even completely obliterated by repeated periglacial erosion. We must therefore conclude that Beech Bottom is entirely a Holocene (late Iron Age?) man-made feature, modifying the floor of the earlier subglacial channel.

The only archaeological evidence for the age of Beech Bottom is provided by a coin hoard of 41 Roman denarii found in 1932 near the south-western end of the deepest part close to the road junction at TL 150089 (Wheeler and Wheeler, 1936, p. 16). The hoard was found above approximately 3 m of infill, and so post-dated construction of the dyke by an unknown period. It was buried or lost sometime after 118 CE, the date of the latest coin in the hoard.

Beech Bottom is similar in width and depth to the Devil's Dyke at Wheathampstead and other large ditches on the

edges of Verlamion. Those known as the White Dyke, Devil's Ditch and New Dyke (Fig. 8.15) are 23-26 m wide and 3.5-5 m deep, with a total length of 1850 m, and join to form three sides of a rectangle, which partially encloses a small dry valley falling north-eastwards to the River Ver. They form a large enclosure on the eastern side of a high status late Iron Age site at Gorhambury (TL 111075), which was constructed early in the 1st century CE and later became a Roman villa (Neal *et al.*, 1990). Together with other earthworks closer to Verlamion, they constitute a system evidently related to the major late Iron Age centre there, which has contemporary parallels elsewhere, for example at Colchester, Essex. The ditches were probably constructed in stages, and may have been added to or altered in the Roman period, but the archaeological work needed to clarify their exact history and purpose remains to be done.

8.8. Conclusions

The distribution of surface water, valleys and soil types, all dependent on Hertfordshire's geological history, have strongly influenced human activities in various ways in the county from the Early Palaeolithic onwards. Flint

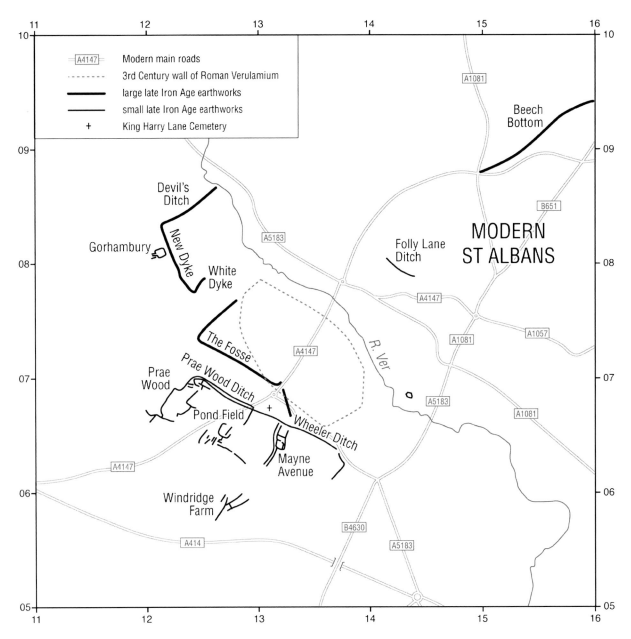

Fig. 8.15. Earthworks associated with the late Iron Age centre at Verlamion, redrawn from Niblett (2001b) and Thompson (2005, Fig. 3.1).

from upper parts of the Chalk provided an abundant raw material for tool manufacture throughout almost the entire prehistoric period, though in the last few millennia BCE it was partly replaced by other hard rock types and metal ores imported from outside the county. Rivers and even ephemeral streams flowing into swallow-holes provided other essential raw materials, not only drinking water but also food from waterside plants and animals. The distribution of human sites in the mid Holocene (Neolithic and Bronze Ages) again seems to have been strongly influenced by the suitability (drainage and cultivability) of soils for early agricultural activities.

It is with the second Roman invasion of Britain in 43 CE that we must close our survey of human activities in Hertfordshire. To quote a popular aphorism, the rest is history! However, this does not mean geology,

geomorphology, hydrogeology and soils ceased to influence the course of history in the county. As Rook (1997) has clearly explained, the distribution of many later features, including Roman sites, Domesday settlements (vills, often the forerunners of parishes) and Norman castles, the early development of industries such as malting and paper-making, and the layout of modern road and railway networks have all been influenced in varying degrees by natural geological features of the county, especially its river pattern and soil types. The distribution of mediaeval parks in the county (Rowe, 2009, Fig. 4) is also related to geomorphology and soil types; by the 13th century, large areas of woodland, important for providing timber and the essential habitat for deer and pigs, were restricted to areas of higher ground remote from valley settlements and with soils unsuitable for mediaeval agriculture. Many parish boundaries in the county, originating from those separating Saxon estates, follow interfluves between river valleys. During World War II, RAF airfields in Hertfordshire were situated on areas of flat land resulting from Quaternary processes, such as deposition of proto-Thames terraces (e.g. Leavesden airfield, Denham aerodrome) or from smoothing of the glaciated Anglian landscape by later periglacial erosion (e.g. Radlett, Hatfield, Hunsdon, Panshanger and Nuthampstead airfields).

Perhaps the most significant of the county's post-Roman settlements dates from 912-913 CE, when King Edward the Elder built a double fortified 'burh' at the confluence of several Hertfordshire rivers. After the imposition of a motte and bailey castle by the Normans, this grew into the royal borough and county town of Hertford (Cooper, 2007).

Chapter 9.

Hydrogeology: water supply, water pollution, waste disposal, engineering geology and canals

John Catt, Rob Sage, Clive Edmonds and Peter Banham

9.1. Introduction

Hydrogeology is the branch of geology concerned with water occurring either beneath the land surface (subsurface water) or in surface water bodies, such as streams, rivers, lakes, reservoirs and non-coastal wetlands. Some of the Earth's fresh (i.e. non-marine) water is also held in glaciers at high latitudes or high altitudes, and a very small part occurs in the atmosphere, but these are not usually considered in hydrogeology. Apart from glaciers, surface water bodies account globally for less than 1% of the planet's fresh water, almost all of which is subsurface water (Herschy, 1998).

Most subsurface water occurs as groundwater, which lies within deeper rocks that are permanently saturated beneath the water table. But a small proportion of it occurs above the water table, where it is either percolating slowly downwards towards the water table or is temporarily held against the force of gravity by capillary action within the smaller pores of soil horizons and fine-grained sedimentary formations. The higher parts of the earth's crust that contain water can therefore be divided into an upper unsaturated zone (or vadose zone) and a lower saturated zone (or phreatic zone). Although the saturated zone contains the exploitable resources of groundwater, the unsaturated zone is important because it controls the rate of infiltration to the water table. Also, processes within it, such as microbial degradation and cation exchange, influence the fate of potential pollutants of groundwater.

In Hertfordshire, subsurface water sources are important mainly for providing the county's public water supply and also most private domestic and industrial supplies. In contrast, the county's numerous small surface water bodies are important mainly for their ecological significance. The Chalk is almost the only major source of exploitable subsurface water in the county, and is also a major source of contributions to surface waters. Consequently, most of this chapter is concerned with water from the Chalk, though first it is necessary to explain some fundamental concepts of hydrogeology.

9.2. Definitions and basic principles – groundwater

The water table

This is defined as the level to which water rises in wells dug into the phreatic zone. However, above this level there is usually a thin layer, known as the capillary fringe, in which the rock or sediment is fully saturated, but the water cannot move laterally into a well because its molecules are more strongly attracted to mineral surfaces in the rock than to other water molecules. Fine-grained rocks and sediments tend to have finer but more numerous pores than coarser deposits. These result in a greater surface area of mineral particles attracting the water molecules, so that the capillary fringe is thicker. In gravels and coarse sands, the fringe rarely exceeds a few millimetres, and in most of the Chalk it is usually about 0.5 m thick, but in clays and silts it often extends for several metres above the water table observed in wells. For water to move out of pores laterally into the well, its pressure (the pore-water pressure) must exceed atmospheric pressure, so the water table marks the level at which the two pressure values are equal, and its height in any particular well fluctuates slightly with changing atmospheric pressure. In the unsaturated zone, pore-water pressure is less than atmospheric.

Aquifers and aquitards

The rate of water flow between pores depends on the size of the interconnecting necks between them. Water cannot flow easily where these are narrower than about 20 μm (0.02 mm), because the pore-water pressure is lowered by increased attraction between the water molecules and mineral surfaces surrounding the neck. However, flow increases as the necks between pores widen above 20 μm, because increasing proportions of the water molecules are not attracted by the mineral surfaces. Bodies of subsurface rock or sediment with large pores and wide inter-pore necks that allow the rapid transmission of large quantities of water are termed aquifers; those with predominantly finer, weakly connected pores that impede flow are termed aquitards. Aquitards rarely stop flow completely; over long periods of time, they usually transmit some water. So the distinction between aquifers and aquitards is usually determined by practical considerations, especially whether useful quantities of water can or cannot be obtained from them in a reasonable period of time. By far the most important aquifer in Hertfordshire and neighbouring parts of the Chilterns is that part of the Chalk described in Chapter 3 as the White Chalk Sub-Group. The Grey Chalk (especially the West Melbury Marly Chalk Formation) beneath transmits water much more slowly, and behaves mainly as an aquitard. The Gault Clay beneath the Chalk Marl transmits water even more slowly.

Aquifers are either unconfined or confined. In an unconfined aquifer, the water table marks the upper limit of saturation (apart from the capillary fringe) and the unsaturated zone, if present, extends above it to the ground surface. In contrast, a confined aquifer lies below an aquitard, with no unsaturated zone between. Very often the groundwater in a confined aquifer is under greater than atmospheric pressure, because of the weight of water at higher levels in the earth's crust. Consequently, in a well penetrating the overlying aquitard it will rise naturally above the base of the aquitard to what is known as the piezometric level. Sometimes it even fountains above the ground surface. Where this occurs, the well is sometimes described as artesian (from *Artois*, a region of France where confined aquifer conditions were first recognized).

The most common situation in which confined aquifers occur is where layered sequences of alternating aquifers and aquitards dip towards a synclinal fold axis or away from an anticlinal axis. For example, in Hertfordshire the White Chalk is unconfined beneath most of the Chilterns, where the rock is extensively exposed at the surface, apart from thin layers of fairly permeable superficial deposits (Plateau Drift, glacial deposits, etc), but it is confined in south-eastern parts of the county where it dips beneath the aquitard formed mainly by the London Clay Formation in the northern limb of the London Syncline. As a result, many of the wells in southeast Hertfordshire, northern and central London that take water from Chalk beneath the Palaeogene deposits were artesian in nature, at least until over-abstraction in the 19th and early 20th centuries created an artificial unsaturated layer beneath the aquitard.

Apart from the White Chalk, the only deposits in the Hertfordshire area from which groundwater has been obtained in the past include (a) fluvial gravels of the proto-Thames where these overlie aquicludes such as clays of the London and Reading Formations, (b) glacial sands and gravels overlying a till aquiclude, especially in buried channels (Section 6.6) where they are thicker than usual, and (c) the Woburn Sands in south Bedfordshire. In the 19th and early 20th centuries, Bedmond (TL 0903) was an example of situation (a), the entire water supply for the village being obtained from shallow wells in the proto-Thames Stoke Row Gravel, which here rests on clays of the Reading Formation (Gilbert, 1923). In the same period, small water supplies were obtained locally from the Pebble Gravels overlying London Clay, for example in the eastern parts of Potters Bar, and from glaciofluvial gravels between till aquicludes, i.e. situation (b), in the Hertford, Ware and Cheshunt areas (Whitaker, 1921, p. 19). The shallow groundwaters in Quaternary aquifers were often subject

to pollution from cesspits, farmyards and industrial sites, and are consequently little used today. Many of the deeper boreholes in the Hertfordshire area (Appendix 1) were drilled in the hope of obtaining water from the Woburn Sands, but most were unsuccessful because this formation is thin or absent over the London Platform.

Any water in permeable deposits immediately overlying the Chalk (e.g. Thanet Formation in east Hertfordshire, Reading Formation sands, Plateau Drift and fluvial or glaciofluvial gravels) is in hydrological continuity with, and contributes to, the Chalk aquifer. In parts of central and north London, there is also hydrological continuity with Quaternary gravels overlying the London Clay through the deep gravel-filled scour hollows (Berry, 1979), which penetrate thinner parts of the clay cover (Section 6.10). Where the Upper Greensand forms a thick bed beneath the Chalk in the area around Princes Risborough, Buckinghamshire, it is also in hydrological continuity with the Chalk.

Porosity and permeability

Porosity is the proportion by volume of a rock, sediment or soil that is occupied by pores (of any size) separated by solid mineral particles. In the saturated zone, all the pores are water-filled, but in the unsaturated zone the larger ones are filled mainly with air, though water films remain around the mineral grains. Many of the pores in fine-grained sediments are too small and too poorly connected (because of narrow necks) to transmit water. The volume of pores through which water can flow as a proportion of the total volume of a rock sample is termed the effective porosity. This property depends on particle size sorting, shape and packing, and on diagenetic changes occurring after deposition. Degree of particle sorting by size is important, because small grains can occupy spaces that otherwise would be empty pores in a well-sorted sediment composed of uniformly large particles. Particle shape is important, because platy particles can pack more closely together than spheres, thus decreasing the size of intervening pores. Packing is important, because angular particles dumped chaotically create larger intervening pores than those aligned during deposition with long axes parallel to one another. Finally, diagenetic processes may result in infilling of original pores by precipitation of mineral cements, or may dissolve soluble minerals to create large new pores.

The ability of large rock masses to transmit water, known as their permeability, depends on their effective porosity, as determined mainly by the size of necks between pores and the presence of fissures and other large cavities. Some rocks with quite large porosity values, but with mainly narrow necks and few larger cavities consequently have low permeabilities. Conversely, rocks with very small porosity values (as measured in small laboratory samples) may have high permeabilities if water can flow in fissures or large cavities formed by dissolution of soluble constituents. Chalk is an example of a dual-porosity rock, that is one with many very small pores, which contribute little to the rock's effective porosity as measured on small blocks in the laboratory, but with a very high permeability attributable to a few large fissures and dissolution cavities. The pores of typical White Chalk samples from southern England are 3-4 μm across and the necks connecting them are often no wider than 0.5-0.7 μm, much less than the minimum (~ 20 μm) required for rapid interpore flow. The main water-transporting fissures in Chalk originated as joints, which were probably formed by fracturing during tectonic deformation, particularly by extension (pulling apart). Typically there are three sets of joints in Chalk, one horizontal and approximately parallel to the bedding, and two that are sub-vertical and approximately perpendicular to one another (Price *et al.*, 1993).

Once formed, the joints become pathways for preferential water flow, many of them having been enlarged by acidic vadose water moving rapidly downwards through fissures in the unsaturated zone. In this way subsurface channels and eventually caverns and other features characteristic of karst landscapes have been created. The narrow tectonic fractures (joints) and enlarged passageways formed from them have been distinguished as microfissures and macrofissures (Reeves, 1979) or as primary and secondary fissures (Price, 1987), respectively.

Specific yield and storativity

The volume of water draining freely under gravity from an initially saturated state, for example when the water table declines, is known as the specific yield, and the volume retained after drainage is termed the specific retention. Both are calculated as percentages of the total volume of saturated rock excluding fissures. Because of the very fine matrix pores, which retain most of its saturated water content against gravity, the Chalk has a very small specific yield, usually <2% and often only 0.5%. In contrast, the Palaeogene sandy deposits overlying the Chalk have larger pores and much greater specific yields, so that they contribute large amounts of water to wells penetrating the confined Chalk aquifer. As a result, in the 1960s, when over-abstraction in east London lowered the water table in the confined aquifer to beneath the base of the Palaeogene sandy cover, the yield of wells dug into the Chalk decreased rapidly.

If the water contained in fissures below the water table is included, the concept of specific yield is extended to that of storativity. This is defined as the percentage of the aquifer by volume (including fissures), which is occupied by water that is removed when the water table declines because of abstraction from wells penetrating the saturated zone. Because the water-containing fissures in Chalk usually form a small fraction of its total volume, the storativity of Chalk is typically <5% and often only 1-2%, i.e. slightly larger than the rock's specific yield.

Recharge

Sir Edmund Halley was the first English scientist, in the late 17th century, to recognize that groundwater originates mainly from the infiltration of rain and other atmospheric water (Biswas, 1970). Apart from this meteoric water, there are some other usually very minor sources of groundwater, including water present in the pores of sediments since they were deposited (connate water) and water rising from the earth's mantle, for example by volcanic activity, or reaching the earth from outer space in meteor showers (juvenile water).

The process by which meteoric water reaches the saturated zone is known as recharge. In contrast, losses from the saturated zone, whether by artificial means (abstraction from a well) or natural processes (flow via springs into rivers), are collectively referred to as discharge. Direct recharge results from downward migration from the ground surface through the unsaturated zone. Indirect recharge occurs when water enters the unsaturated zone after an intervening episode of surface runoff, such as that contributing to flow in a river. However, some surface water bodies are fed partly by groundwater or may feed directly into the saturated zone where they are in contact with the water table. Direct recharge can also be achieved artificially, for example by pumping water from the surface into a well. This has been used to help maintain groundwater levels in areas of high abstraction rates, such as the Lea valley (Hawnt *et al.*, 1981; Flavin and Joseph, 1983).

The unconfined Chalk aquifer is recharged mainly by direct flow through the unsaturated zone, because most soils on the Chalk outcrop are moderately or very permeable. However, there is some indirect recharge through swallow-holes at the feather edge of impermeable Palaeogene strata, and in wet winter periods a little surface runoff may be generated briefly on areas of clayey Plateau Drift and reach the water table by infiltrating at their margins (Klinck *et al.*, 1998).

Precipitation (rain, snow, etc) is the ultimate source of natural recharge. Depending on the permeability and thickness of the unsaturated zone, the delay between a precipitation event and the water reaching the water table varies from a few hours to many months or even years. Also the recharge pulse is usually spread over a longer period of time than the precipitation event, and its volume is decreased by losses through evaporation, plant uptake and surface runoff. Evaporation to the atmosphere occurs from the surface of the soil or from bodies of surface water, such as rivers and lakes; the rate depends mainly on atmospheric temperature and humidity and air movement (Penman, 1948). Most of the water taken up through plant roots is returned to the atmosphere by transpiration, a process of evaporation through the stomatal openings on leaf surfaces, which also helps draw soluble nutrients into the plant from the soil. Transpiration rates also depend mainly on atmospheric temperature and humidity, air flow and solar radiation (Penman, 1949), but vary with vegetation type and leaf density (total leaf area per unit area of land).

Because it is very difficult to quantify evaporation and transpiration separately, the two are usually combined as evapotranspiration when calculating recharge (Oliver, 1998). Potential evapotranspiration is the rate at which water returns to the atmosphere by these processes, assuming there is no limit to the supply of water to plants and the soil surface. It is usually calculated on a daily basis from standard meteorological data. But, except in very wet conditions, such as periods of winter rainfall in England, the supply of water is insufficient for evapotranspiration to occur at the full potential rate. The actual evapotranspiration is then less than the potential.

Because of losses by runoff and evapotranspiration, the fraction of precipitation eventually reaching the saturated zone is often quite small. For example, the global water budget data assembled by Herschy (1998) suggest that in Europe as a whole the percentage of total precipitation reaching groundwater as recharge is only about 15%. Other reliable estimates of more local natural recharge rates range from about 5% to almost 30%. In Hertfordshire, the amount reaching the water table in the Chalk is probably in the range 150-200 mm yr⁻¹ (Rodda *et al.*, 1976), which is only 10-25% of the rainfall. Estimates such as these are usually based on changes in the height of the water table measured either in wells not used for abstraction or after allowing for the effect of known abstraction on water table decline.

Most recharge occurs in winter, when actual evapotranspiration is much less than in spring and summer. As a result, the water table rises to a maximum height in late winter (March/April), and declines over summer to a minimum in autumn or early winter (November/December). Long-term records of watertable levels in wells penetrating the unconfined Chalk aquifer show that the mean seasonal range is usually 5-8 m, but beneath interfluves (where the water table is deeper and recharge slower) the range can exceed 20 m (Fig. 9.1). Beneath valleys containing perennial streams and where the aquifer is confined by Palaeogene strata or chalky till, the seasonal variation is usually less than 2 m.

In urban areas, direct recharge is much less than in rural areas, because large amounts of surface runoff are generated by impermeable surfaces, such as roads, pavements and roofs. Hertfordshire examples were investigated by Hollis and Ovenden (1988). However, indirect recharge is often greater than in rural areas, because some of the runoff is channelled to soakaways. In addition, there can be considerable leakage from drains, sewers and water distribution pipes, much of which is also likely to reach the aquifer. Surface flooding, with damage to houses and temporary closure of roads and railways, may occur in low-lying areas when large amounts of urban storm runoff feed rapidly into streams, rivers and other surface water bodies. Fortunately, even those Hertfordshire towns sited on rivers, such as Hertford, Ware, Welwyn, Welwyn Garden City, St Albans, Hemel Hempstead, Berkhamsted, Watford, Rickmansworth and Hitchin, have low flood risks, because very few lines of communication or housing developments have been built on floodplains. Nevertheless, this is a possibility requiring consideration in future developments.

The main riverside areas subject to rapid, short-term (flash) flooding are in areas of slowly permeable soils, especially those on the London Clay (mainly Windsor Association) in south Hertfordshire. Previously the most frequently flooded houses in this part of the county were those beside the original Great North Road (now by-passed) about 1 km south of Water End (TL 231032). These houses are in the valley of the Mimmshall Brook, which has a large catchment on the London Clay around Potters Bar and Barnet, and is consequently subject to flash floods, the level of the brook rising several metres after heavy storms. The houses and adjacent road are now protected from flooding by a high concrete wall beside the brook and by floodgates, which can be closed across the road (Plate 75).

Age of groundwater

Recharge of an aquifer like the Chalk has of course continued for much of geological time, probably ever since the Chalk was uplifted above sea level in the late Cretaceous or early Palaeocene. Within the deepest parts of the confined Chalk aquifer beneath London, most of the water is probably very old. But in higher parts of the saturated zone, where the aquifer is unconfined, there has been a long and complex history of natural recharge, discharge and abstraction from wells, so that the water here has a much younger mean age. Unfortunately, attempts to date groundwater by measuring its ¹⁴C (radiocarbon) content provide only approximate indications of age, because of exchange with very ancient carbon in the carbonate of the Chalk. Nevertheless, Lloyd *et al.* (1981) reported Holocene ¹⁴C dates for groundwaters in unconfined parts of the Chalk aquifer in southern parts of East Anglia, but much greater ages (20,000 to >30,000 BP) for waters from parts of the aquifer confined beneath the London Clay Formation. The older dates suggest some recharge of the deep aquifer during the Late Pleistocene. This is supported by evidence from stable isotope ratios, such as ¹⁸O/¹⁶O, and the content of dissolved noble gases in groundwater from deeper parts of the London Basin, both of which indicate recharge with low temperature (5-6°C) water. This must have occurred during the Devensian or an earlier

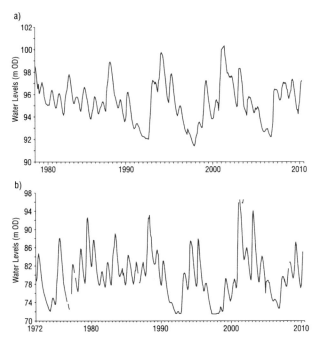

Fig. 9.1. *Records of depth of water table at a) Lilley Bottom since July 1979 and b) Therfield Rectory since January 1972 (data from Environment Agency).*

Plate 75. Flood protection scheme on the Mimmshall Brook near Water End (TL 231032).

cold stage of the Pleistocene (Downing *et al.*, 1979).

Percolation gauges

In the past direct recharge has also been estimated directly at individual sites using percolation gauges. The first percolation gauge in Hertfordshire was installed in 1835 at Nash Mills near Hemel Hempstead to provide information important for the water supply used to power Dickinson's paper mills (Mather, 2008). It consisted of a wooden cylinder, 18 inches (0.45 m) in diameter and 3 ft (0.9 m) long, which was filled with local topsoil and exposed to natural rainfall. Grass was grown on the surface. The rainfall was measured nearby, and the cylinder had facilities for collecting and measuring the volume of water percolating to the base of the column. It was assumed that this was equivalent to the amount entering the unsaturated zone and eventually moving down to the water table. The first 18 years' data from the gauge showed that a mean of 34% (range 7-52%) of the annual rainfall was likely to reach the water table, and that almost all the percolation occurred in winter (October-March), when losses by evapotranspiration were small.

A slightly different method of measuring percolation was made at Rothamsted Experimental Station, Harpenden, where John Lawes installed three 'drain gauges' in 1870 (Addiscott, 1988a). Unlike Dickinson's percolation gauge, the Rothamsted drain gauges are still in operation (Plate 76). They are more elaborate than Dickinson's percolation gauge, and consist of *in situ* (undisturbed) columns of soil (Batcombe series in Plateau Drift over Chalk) retained by brick walls. Each gauge has an area at the surface of one thousandth of an acre (4.05 m²). The columns are 20, 40 and 60 inches deep (approximately 0.5, 1.0 and 1.5 m), and

are supported beneath by perforated iron plates on girders. Water percolating through the soil columns is collected in pits beneath by galvanized funnels leading to measuring vessels. For comparison, rainfall is measured nearby in a rain gauge also with an area of one thousandth of an acre.

Over the first 35 years, the mean percentages of rainfall recovered from the three drain gauges were 46.7% (range 26.5-60.0), 49.3% (range 24.9-64.1) and 46.0% (range 18.2-61.2) for the 20-, 40- and 60-inch columns, respectively (Miller, 1906). Similar mean values but narrower ranges are obtained if the calculations are based only on the wettest 27 years between 1881 and 2001, when there are records of both rainfall and percolation for more than 300 days per year. These are 50.6% (range 36.7-63.3), 53.4% (range 39.2-67.6) and 50.2% (range 37.2-64.2) for the 20-, 40- and 60-inch gauges, respectively. In most years, maximum monthly percolation usually occurs in December and January, and the minimum in August. Because they consist of *in situ* rather than disturbed and repacked soil, the Rothamsted drain gauges should give a more accurate estimate of direct recharge than Dickinson's, but they are kept free of vegetation, and so do not take transpiration losses into account, which means they over-estimate recharge to the Chalk water table.

The percolation process

When rain falls on a dry soil, it initially forms films around particles and soil aggregates (structural units created by adhesion of numerous particles of different sizes) close to the land surface. With increasing water inputs, the films thicken and extend down the soil profile and some water moves into small pores, in which the boundaries between water and soil air form curved meniscii generated by surface

Plate 76. The Rothamsted drain gauges, built 1870 by John Lawes to study percolation through Batcombe series over Chalk.

tension. Further additions of water at the surface then fill larger pores and also percolate downwards to create films and fill pores in drier layers below. Ultimately some of this vadose water reaches the water table, causing it to rise. Continuous heavy rain creates an upper layer that for a short period reaches the saturated condition, because the rate of downward percolation is less than the rate of precipitation. When rain ceases, the pores with necks greater than about 20 μm in this saturated upper layer continue to drain under the influence of gravity until they retain only thin films held by surface tension or Van der Waals forces. At this point, the pores with smaller necks remain water-filled, and the soil or sediment moisture content is referred to as the field capacity (*FC*). *FC* is usually quoted as the water content, in volume percent, $m^3 \, m^{-3}$ or depth in mm, after drainage under gravity for 48 hours.

In most soils, more rapid downward movement of water towards the water table is achieved by flow in macropores rather than through small pores in the matrix of soils and sediments in the unsaturated zone. Macropores originate in various ways; some are biological in origin, including channels created by plant roots or burrowing animals, and others are desiccation cracks formed when clay-rich soils contract on drying. Yet others have geological origins, including for example the casts of ice-wedge polygons (Section 6.10) filled with coarse sediment, such as windblown sand. This type of flow in soils, analogous to fissure flow in the rock of an aquifer, is often referred to as by-pass flow, because the usual flow route through the small matrix pores (matrix flow) is by-passed.

FC for a given soil type can be estimated in a representative core taken through the soil or in blocks representing each soil horizon, by measuring the difference in weight between the dry condition and following 48 hours' drainage after saturation. Using laboratory apparatus for measuring suction, it can also be estimated as the water content retained at a suction of -5 kPa (-0.05 bar). But both types of estimate are only approximate, because pore characteristics vary laterally over short distances and may even vary over time because of shrink-swell processes in clay-rich soils. Water held at *FC* does not contribute to direct recharge, but rainfall in excess of that required to meet *FC* does. After a period in summer, when at least the upper part of the soil profile dries to a water content less than *FC*, most soils in southern England return to *FC* in early winter (usually October/November) and remain in this condition until March or April. Throughout this winter field capacity period, when there is very little evapotranspiration, most precipitation contributes to direct recharge, unless some is lost by surface runoff into streams and rivers. In contrast, in the summer season from March/April to October/ November, any period during which there is a return to *FC* is very short because of greatly increased evapotranspiration, so that there is almost no recharge. The amount of annual recharge is therefore approximately equal to winter rainfall in excess of that required to maintain soil *FC*.

Soil water available to plants

Although the soil water held at *FC* does not contribute to aquifer recharge, much of it is available to plants growing in the soil, as their roots can exert suctions as much as 300 times the force of gravity, i.e. approximately -1500 kPa (-15 bar). This is equivalent to water retained in pores with necks down to about 0.5 μm across. The water held between -5 and -1500 kPa suction (i.e. in pores with necks ranging from approximately 0.5 μm to 20 μm) is known as the soil's plant available water capacity (*AWC*). In a dry period when *AWC* is almost exhausted, plants wilt and grow more slowly. Wilting occurs because the guard cells surrounding leaf stomata become flaccid; this reduces the rates of transpiration and uptake of nutrients from the soil, and also limits the intake of atmospheric carbon dioxide for photosynthesis. Cell turgor can be regained, so that normal growth rate returns, if the soil's *AWC* is increased by rain or irrigation. But when *AWC* approaches zero, plants are permanently damaged and cannot recover. The soil water content at this point, known as permanent wilting point, does not correspond to a completely dry soil, because some water unavailable to plants is still held in pores less than 0.5 μm. This unavailable water is a small proportion (<5%) of the total held at *FC* in sandy, gravelly and other clay-poor soils, but increases with increasing amounts of clay (particles <2 μm), reaching approximately 40% of *FC* in British soils containing 45-80% clay (Hall *et al.*, 1977).

As the matrix pores and the necks between them in the White Chalk are slightly greater than the minimum from which plant roots are able to extract water, they can contribute to the AWC of thin chalk soils, such as the Rendzinas of the Upton (342a) and Andover (343h) Associations (Section 7.7). Consequently, in periods of drought, supplies of water from the fine pores of chalk are very important for maintaining crop growth.

Groundwater movement

Almost all groundwater is in a state of flux. When inputs to the aquifer system exceed the outputs, groundwater levels rise, water enters storage and discharge (e.g. spring flow) increases. When the inputs are less than the outputs, groundwater levels fall, water is lost from storage and discharges decrease.

Below the water table, water can move laterally by slow flow through intergranular pores contributing to the effective porosity, analogous to matrix flow in soils, or more rapidly by fissure (*cf.* by-pass) flow. The intergranular flow rate though the rock matrix is limited by the average diameter of the necks between adjacent pores, and is commonly less than a centimetre per day; in chalk it is often only 0.1-1 mm per day (Price, 1987). Such smooth, gentle movement is termed laminar flow because there is almost no mixing between vertically adjacent layers. It contrasts with the much more rapid turbulent flow typical of surface streams or subsurface fissures and caverns, which is characterized by chaotic mixing. Although there are no real physical barriers between the different layers in an aquifer,

movement by laminar flow through the rock matrix behaves as though it is separated into pipe-like layers carrying water from areas of recharge to points of discharge, such as wells or springs. The driving force for movement at any point, known as the groundwater head (or potential), is influenced by two factors: (a) the pore-water pressure at that point, and (b) the elevation of the point above a given datum (usually sea level), which determines how strongly gravity affects the flow. Groundwater always flows from points of greater to smaller head values. At the water table, as indicated by the water level in a well, head depends only on the elevation.

Hydraulic gradient and hydraulic conductivity. Spatial differences in head are quantified relative to the length of the flow pathway over which head decreases. The ratio of difference in head to the distance over which it changes is termed the hydraulic gradient (*i*). In a series of classic experiments with sand-filled cylinders, Darcy (1856) showed that the rate of water flow or specific discharge (*Q*) through the sand was proportional to the cross-sectional area of the cylinder (*A*) and the hydraulic gradient (*i*) across it. Thus,

$$Q = K . i . A \text{ (Darcy's Law)}$$

The proportionality factor (*K*) is known as the hydraulic conductivity, and is expressed in units of velocity (distance per unit time). Darcy found that *K* depends on the grain size of the sand he used, increasing in value with increasing grain size (and therefore mean pore size). Subsequent measurements of flow rates of water in a range of rocks and sediment types has shown that *K* ranges very widely, from less than 10^{-8} to more than 10^5 m day^{-1}. Sands usually have values in the range 1-10 m day^{-1}, gravels and fissured limestones (e.g. Chalk) 1-10^3 m day^{-1}, cemented sandstones 0.1-1 m day^{-1}, unfissured limestones 10^{-3} to 10^{-2} m day^{-1}, and clays (e.g. London Clay) and crystalline rocks (e.g. granite, gneiss and schist) 10^{-8} to 10^{-3} m day^{-1}. Many superficial deposits are even more variable, because they are more heterogeneous in structure and particle size distribution than bedrock formations. For example, the Plateau Drift overlying the Chalk has *K* values ranging from 4 m day^{-1} to 10^{-4} m day^{-1} (Klinck *et al.*, 1998), and in glacial deposits, such as those of the Anglian Stage in northeast Hertfordshire, it ranges from 10^{-5} to 0.1 m day^{-1}. Units of strongly bedded sediment, such as alluvial deposits with interbedded sandy, clayey and peaty layers, have *K* values that are much greater in the horizontal direction than the vertical.

Also, weathering and disturbance during soil formation (e.g. penetration by tree roots) can increase *K* values by 1-3 orders of magnitude. These factors often make it difficult to assess the performance of a particular rock as an aquifer or aquitard.

Transmissivity

Even if it has a very high *K* value, a thin aquifer or one that is saturated for a small part of its thickness will transmit only small amounts of water. From the practical perspective of the water-supplying capacity of a well or spring, it is therefore important to consider saturated thickness as well as horizontal hydraulic conductivity. The two are combined in the property known as transmissivity (*T*). Assuming hydraulic conductivity is fairly constant throughout an aquifer, transmissivity is obtained simply by multiplying *K* by the saturated thickness (*b*):

$$T = K \cdot b$$

If *K* is expressed in m day^{-1} and *b* in metres, *T* has units of m^2 day^{-1}. If hydraulic conductivity varies vertically through an aquifer, a single value for *K* in this equation is obtained by integrating measurements at several depths through the aquifer. However, as *b* can vary over time, for example if the water table in an aquifer is lowered by pumping, *T* is likely to be a time-variant property rather than constant in value.

Variations in transmissivity. Lowering of the water table in the Chalk can lead to a decrease in *K*, and therefore also in *T*. This is because the fractures in higher parts of the aquifer subject to water table fluctuation have often been greatly widened by dissolution, whereas those in the lower, permanently saturated part of the phreatic zone have not. The layer over which widening of fissures has increased transmissivity is often 50-60 m thick, encompassing the upper part of the current saturated zone and lower part of the unsaturated zone (Headworth *et al.*, 1982). Most of the enlarged fissures are near-horizontal and resemble an anastomosing network of sinuous flattened tubes rather than continuous sheet-like cavities (Price *et al.*, 1993), though in addition there is often a thin band of widened vertical fissures close to the water table. Consequently water flow in the Chalk occurs more readily along the tubes than in other horizontal or vertical directions.

Fissure enlargement in the Chalk is also more common beneath valley floors (Price, 1987), where the Chalk is often more densely fractured because of folding (Section 5.7) and where there is increased discharge by groundwater flow towards streams and increased recharge by flow in the opposite direction. Compared with other parts of the London Basin, transmissivity is especially high in the Chalk beneath the Ver, Gade and Colne valleys (Water Resources Board, 1972), where it reaches 1000-2200 m^2 day^{-1}, compared with only 15-150 m^2 day^{-1} beneath the interfluves (Fig. 9.2). An especially large cavern-like fissure, 0.1-3.7 m high, containing flowing water was recorded in the Colne valley at Watford by Whitaker (1872, pp. 50-51). Where the aquifer is confined beneath the London Basin and there has been almost no enlargement of fissures, the transmissivity is 20 m^2 day^{-1} or less. Transmissivity is also increased slightly beneath the valleys of northeast Hertfordshire and East Anglia, which have been eroded through the cover of Anglian till (Lloyd, 1993). It is also increased beneath and adjacent to the buried valleys formed subglacially during the Anglian glaciation (Section 6.6). Here the fissure enlargement probably resulted from erosion by subglacial meltwater under greatly increased pressure caused by confinement beneath a thick overlying glacier (Woodland, 1946). Increased transmissivity also occurs beneath the Plateau

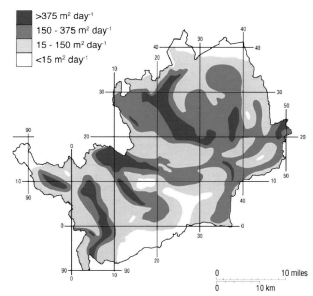

>375 m^2 day^{-1}
150 - 375 m^2 day^{-1}
15 - 150 m^2 day^{-1}
<15 m^2 day^{-1}

0   10 miles
0   10 km

Fig. 9.2. Variation in transmissivity of the Chalk of Hertfordshire, redrawn from Water Resources Board (1972).

Drift, especially near the edges of larger Palaeogene outcrops where, after entering the Chalk, aggressive runoff containing sulphuric acid from soils on the London Clay has widened fissures and created dolines.

Original variations in lithology of the Chalk can also lead to local differences in transmissivity. Hardgrounds such as the Chalk Rock often retain large (1-5 cm diameter) tubular cavities originating from animal burrows on the Late Cretaceous sea floor, and these can transmit water very rapidly in some areas. Joints in hardgrounds also have smoother faces than those in soft chalk, and this assists flow by reducing friction. The increased flow in turn erodes and widens the cavities and joints more rapidly than in other parts of the Chalk. The harder, cemented chalk in hardgrounds also prevents the formation of a skin of fine chalk paste, which can partially block the fissures in softer chalk layers. Marl bands are less permeable than other parts of the Chalk and contain fewer vertical joints. This restricts vertical flow through them, often creating a minor perched water table, which can cause dissolution cavities to develop in the immediately overlying layers (Mortimore, 1993). The presence of the Plenus Marls immediately beneath the Melbourn Rock may explain why this particular hardground shows even greater transmissivity than others, and why many springs issue along its outcrop, especially in the Hitchin area.

Finally, groundwater movement near the land surface is strongly influenced in the Chalk by the extent of physical weathering resulting from frost action during cold stages of the Pleistocene. Most notably, some near-surface layers have been reduced to a fine compact paste (known as puggy or putty chalk), which is much softer and less permeable than typical hard jointed or fissured Chalk. Locally layers of puggy chalk may even behave as aquitards. In some western parts of Stevenage where the puggy chalk is locally quite thick, its softness compared with hard, unweathered chalk has caused problems with the foundations of large industrial

Grade	Description of structure	Permeability (m s⁻¹)
V	Structureless melange (puggy chalk); unweathered and partially weathered angular blocks and fragments set in a matrix of remoulded chalk; no bedding or jointing	10^{-7} to 10^{-9}
IV	Friable to rubbly chalk; unweathered and partially weathered chalk with bedding and jointing; joints and small fractures 1-6 cm apart and up to 2 cm wide, though often infilled with fine debris	10^{-5} to 10^{-3}
III	Rubbly to blocky chalk, medium to hard with joints 6-20 cm apart and 1-2 cm wide, sometimes infilled with fine debris	Variable, related to frequency and width of fissures
II	Harder chalk with narrow (closed) joints more than 20 cm apart; when dug out, the blocks do not pull away along the joint faces, but fracture irregularly	
I	Hard, brittle chalk with joints as in Grade II. Includes hardgrounds, such as the Chalk Rock and Top Rock	

Table 9.1. The Mundford Grades for chalk structure and permeability (after Ward et al., 1968 and Mortimore, 1993). A more complex engineering classification of physically weathered chalk, based on measurements of dry density and with modified criteria for joint spacing and width, was suggested by Lord et al. (2002, Chapter 3), but is not related to groundwater movement.

buildings. In a large excavation showing progressive physical weathering of Chalk at Mundford, Norfolk, Ward *et al.* (1968) recognized five structural grades based on the progressive reduction with depth in fracture frequency and width (Table 9.1). These Mundford Grades are now used widely to assess chalk structure and permeability in civil engineering projects, such as the design of soakaways for highways and leaching of pollutants from old chalk quarries used as landfill sites.

The form of the water table

As a surface, the water table tends to follow changes in elevation of the ground surface above, but in a somewhat subdued manner, so that it is close to the surface in valleys and at greater elevations (though further below the ground surface) beneath interfluves. Within a limited area of fairly subdued relief, such as Hertfordshire, precipitation and direct recharge are fairly uniform but, because the head is greater at higher elevations, the groundwater flows from these areas towards the valleys. This accounts for why the water table is further below the land surface under the interfluves than near the valley floors. Before about 1800, many villages and larger rural houses took water supplies from their own individual wells, and sewage was collected into nearby cesspits, from which the liquid components were likely to drain towards the water table. Even then it was recognized that, because groundwater flows towards the valley floors, it was necessary to site the cesspits downhill from the supply wells.

Within the Chalk aquifer beneath Hertfordshire, the regional inclination of the water table is to the SSE (Fig. 9.3), approximately parallel to the dip of the Chalk, with a gradient of 3-4 m km⁻¹. Locally the gradients from the interfluves towards the valleys are steeper than this in directions determined by valley orientation, and near the Chiltern scarp-slope the water table is inclined steeply to the NNW. The water table may also be influenced by folds and other structures in the Chalk, rising locally over anticlines for example (Mortimore, 1993).

Where the water table intersects the ground surface near

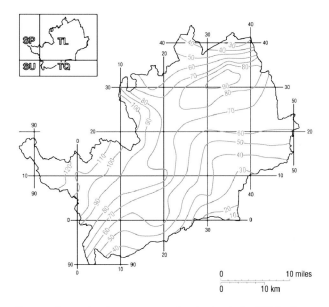

Fig. 9.3. Approximate mean groundwater levels (m OD) in the Chalk of Hertfordshire, redrawn from Lloyd (1993).

the valley floors, discharge occurs naturally to form surface water bodies, such as streams, rivers, ponds, lakes and wetlands. Springs occur where turbulent flow along fissures reaches the surface. They may form the headwaters of streams, or may contribute to other surface water bodies by upflow through their beds. Discharge outlets such as these often also influence the final directions of local groundwater flow; for example, groundwater discharging into a river bed usually flows from both opposing valley sides. The floors of Chiltern through-valleys in the direction of stream flow (or talwegs) are inclined at approximately the same angle as the water table, at least in downstream parts of the valleys. Consequently even a small increase in the height of the water table in winter period can lead to stream flow, and a small decrease in summer can temporarily terminate flow over a considerable length of the valley (Fig. 9.4).

Changes over time. Water table levels are also affected on longer time scales in response to changes in climate or

a) Winter

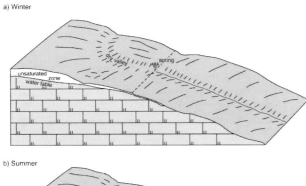

b) Summer

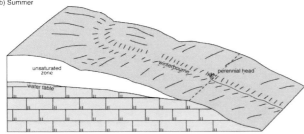

Fig. 9.4. Effect of seasonal changes in water table level on bourne flow in a typical Chiltern valley.

patterns of abstraction. In particular, over the last century or so, regional lowering of the water table by increased abstraction from the numerous wells in the area has resulted in Chiltern streams rising in much lower reaches of the valleys than before and the disappearance of other surface water bodies on the valley floors. For example, Berkhamsted

Castle (SP 995082), built on the floor of the Bulbourne valley, originally had a fairly deep protective moat but, because of progressive lowering of the local water table, the moat is now almost dry (Plate 77).

Cone of depression. When water is pumped from a well, it is taken initially from the well bore itself, so that the level in the well falls rapidly. However, a strong hydraulic gradient soon develops between the well water level and the groundwater head in surrounding parts of the aquifer, so that water flows from the aquifer into the well, and the rate of fall in well level decreases. After a long period (often months or even years), the rate of inflow from the aquifer matches the rate of water removal by pumping and the water level in the well remains constant or nearly so. In observation (unpumped) wells around the pumping well, the decline in water level (or drawdown) resulting from flow through the aquifer radially towards the pumping well decreases with distance from it. This creates a cone of depression in the water table around the well. The cone is symmetrical if the original water table is flat; but if the water table is inclined, the cone becomes asymmetrical, i.e. steeper on the downslope side of the well than on the upslope side.

Groundwater quality

The temperature of natural shallow groundwaters, at depths of about 5 m to 150 m, usually approximates to mean annual air temperature. But in the short term, temperatures

Plate 77. The moat of Berkhamsted Castle (SP 995082) in the Bulbourne valley, now almost dry because of the declining water table.

may be raised or lowered by large volumes of warm or cold water introduced by artificial recharge. Temperature influences water quality because it affects the solubility of minerals. The total content of dissolved salts is indicated by measurements of electrical conductivity, which is low in groundwater from the Hertfordshire Chalk, usually in the range 150-1000 μS cm^{-1}.

pH. Rainwater is usually very slightly acidic (pH 6-7) because it contains carbon dioxide and acidic pollutants (mainly oxides of nitrogen and sulphur) dissolved from the atmosphere. Additional CO_2 from plant and animal respiration is dissolved as the water passes through soils so that, except where the soils or underlying sediments and bedrock are strongly calcareous, the pH of recharge waters reaching the water table is usually slightly more acidic (5-6). However, because of reaction with calcium carbonate, the groundwater in the Chalk aquifer is usually slightly alkaline (pH 7.5-8.5). Much lower pH values of recharge water (2-3) may be reached if the water contains sulphuric acid derived from soils developed on deposits containing pyrite (FeS_2), such as the London Clay Formation and the Anglian till in northeast Hertfordshire. Reaction of this acid with carbonate in either the unsaturated zone or the aquifer raises the water's pH and increases the concentrations of Ca^{2+} and SO_4^- ions, often leading to precipitation of secondary gypsum ($CaSO_4.2H_2O$). For example, beneath the till in northeast Hertfordshire the Chalk groundwater contains more sulphate than usual (Lloyd *et al.*, 1981), and in the lower Lea valley, where the Chalk groundwater has been recharged with surface water originating partly from the nearby London Clay outcrop, its sulphate content is also increased (Flavin and Joseph, 1983).

In addition to ions and other substances in solution, groundwaters often also contain mineral and organic particles. Most of these are removed by passing the water through a 0.45 μm filter before it is distributed for consumption, but extremely fine (colloidal) particles of fine clay or organic macromolecules, which are often less than 0.1 μm in size, have to be removed by flocculation. This involves adding trace amounts of a solution containing the soluble salt of a trivalent cation, such as Al^{3+}, which cause the colloidal particles to aggregate electrostatically into larger groups (flocs), which can then be removed by filtration.

Groundwater types. The main cations found in uncontaminated groundwaters are calcium (Ca^{2+}), magnesium (Mg^{2+}), sodium (Na^+) and potassium (K^+). The main anions are bicarbonate (HCO_3^-), sulphate (SO_4^{2-}) and chloride (Cl^-). To facilitate chemical comparison of groundwaters, concentrations of the principal cations and anions are usually expressed in milliequivalents (meq) rather than weights (mg) per litre. Factors for converting mg L^{-1} to meq L^{-1} for ions and other components commonly found in groundwater are given by Younger (2007, Table 4.2). Groundwater types or facies are distinguished according to the dominant ions present, expressed as meq L^{-1}. For example, the Ca-HCO$_3$ type or facies is typical of

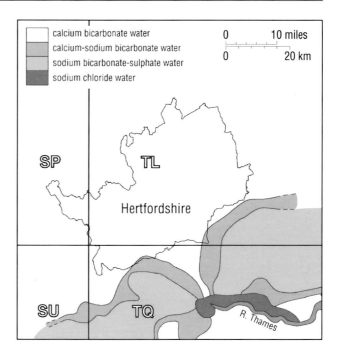

Fig. 9.5. Groundwater types in the Chalk of Hertfordshire and north London, redrawn from Water Resources Board (1972).

unconfined limestone aquifers such as that of the Chalk (Fig. 9.5), where the typical concentrations of calcium and bicarbonate are 10-150 and 200-400 mg L^{-1}, respectively.

Hardness. Calcium and magnesium together account for the hardness of water:

$$\text{total hardness} = 2.5\,[Ca^{2+}] + 4.1\,[Mg^{2+}]$$

the square brackets denoting concentrations in mg L^{-1}. Hardness is often divided into temporary hardness, which can be removed by boiling for at least 30 minutes to precipitate carbonates, and permanent hardness, which remains after boiling and results from insufficient bicarbonate ions to precipitate all the calcium and magnesium as carbonate. Hardness was previously expressed in degrees, one degree corresponding to one pound (1 lb = 0.454 kg) of carbonate in 10,000 gallons (= 45,461 litres) of water (King, 1896). As an example from Hertfordshire, Hopkinson (1896) calculated that water from the Chalk supplied to consumers in Watford then had about 20 degrees of hardness, of which 16 were temporary.

Other common components. Many groundwaters also contain variable but usually small amounts of various minor ions, including ferrous iron (Fe^{2+}), manganese (Mn^{2+}), ammonium (NH_4^+), nitrate (NO_3^-), sulphide (HS^-), fluoride (F^-) and boron (B^{3-}). High concentrations usually arise from human activities, such as mining and agriculture, and are regarded as problematic pollutants. Water from confined parts of the Chalk aquifer, which lacks oxygen, often contains large amounts of Fe^{2+} (0.5-1.0 mg L^{-1}), which probably originate naturally from pyrite in overlying aquitards, such as the London Clay or chalky till. Problems associated with nitrate originating from agriculture are discussed in detail in Section 9.5.

Salinity. The weight of total dissolved solids (TDS) remaining after evaporation, or calculated conventionally by multiplying the electrical conductivity by 0.65, is used to classify water quality very broadly as follows:

fresh water has < 1000 mg L^{-1} TDS,
brackish water has 1000-10,000 mg L^{-1} TDS,
saline water has 10,000-100,000 mg L^{-1} TDS, and
hypersaline water (brine) has >100,000 mg L^{-1} TDS.

Potable water should contain less than 2500 mg L^{-1}. Typical groundwater from the unconfined Chalk aquifer contains about 500 mg L^{-1} TDS, but values of 800 mg L^{-1} or more are common where the aquifer is confined.

Organic matter. Many groundwaters also contain small amounts (usually less than 5 mg L^{-1}) of total organic carbon (TOC), some of which is in soluble and therefore more reactive forms (dissolved organic carbon or DOC), and the remainder in colloidal particles. Most organic matter is derived from the humus in surface soils, though some may originate from industrial pollution.

Gases. Groundwaters often also contain dissolved gases, such as oxygen, carbon dioxide and methane, which may be released to the atmosphere when water under pressure comes to the surface. In the unconfined Chalk aquifer, the groundwater usually contains 5-10 mg oxygen L^{-1} but, where the aquifer is confined, oxygen is rare or absent (Edmunds *et al.*, 1984). Anaerobic bacterial decomposition of organic matter accounts for the small amounts of methane, which have been detected deep in the confined Chalk aquifer of the London Basin (Darling, 1985).

Radon. The radioactive isotope of the gas radon (^{222}Rn), a member of the ^{238}U decay series, is also present in most groundwaters, where it forms continuously by radioactive decay of radium (^{226}Ra). Its abundance in groundwater depends on the amount of uranium in the rock of the aquifer, the rate of diffusion from U-containing minerals into adjacent interstitial water, and also the hydrological properties of the aquifer, especially fracturing, which determine movement of water into wells from the rock. Chalk groundwater often contains larger amounts than many other aquifers (Cuttell *et al.*, 1986), though not as much as groundwater from granitic rocks, which are very rich in uranium. In the Chalk, uranium is contained in the crystalline structure of calcite and in phosphate minerals, and the very slow matrix flow may allow a large proportion of the radon generated from these sources to enter the groundwater. Also, the insoluble U-rich residues left after dissolution of the calcite are often concentrated in clay lining the walls of fissures, which are in frequent or continual contact with groundwater.

In Britain as a whole, radon is thought to account for about half the ionizing radiation dose received by the human population. It is carcinogenic and, second to smoking, is probably the most important cause of lung cancer, especially among those who breathe in higher concentrations because they work in poorly ventilated areas, such as mines and the basements of buildings. The half-life of ^{222}Rn is very short (3.8 days), so almost all the radioactivity is lost from the water within a few weeks once it is no longer in contact with the Chalk. The main health risks are therefore to regular consumers of fresh Chalk spring water and those working in close contact with fresh water supplies from the Chalk. The association of uranium with phosphates has also resulted in an increased risk of radon pollution in areas to the north of Hertfordshire, where coprolites are abundant in the Lower Greensand and Cambridge Greensand.

Changes in composition. Compared with rainwater, the composition of direct recharge water entering an aquifer is modified by various processes, including (a) dissolution of soluble minerals (e.g. halite, calcite) and (b) exchange of ions between the water and the electrostatically charged surfaces of organic matter, iron and manganese oxides/hydrated oxides or alumino-silicate clay particles. Warington (1887) reported that the rainwater at Harpenden in the late 19th century contained about 2 mg Cl L^{-1}, whereas uncontaminated well waters from the Chalk at depths of 20 m or more below the town contained an average of 11 mg Cl L^{-1}. He suggested that the increase resulted from leaching of the 'residue of sea salt remaining in the rock' (i.e. in connate water), and this process could explain why much greater concentrations of chloride content occur further south (e.g. 163 mg Cl L^{-1} at Harrow), where the groundwater has been in contact with the Chalk for much longer and the aquifer is confined beneath an impermeable cover of London Clay.

An important cation exchange process is replacement of Na^+ ions sorbed onto the mineral surfaces in marine sediments by the Ca^{2+} derived from groundwater percolating through limestone in the unsaturated zone. This causes incoming groundwater of Ca-HCO_3 facies to change into the Na-HCO_3 type, a process referred to as natural softening, as it partially removes the principal cause of hardness (dissolved calcium). The change has occurred in the confined Chalk aquifer beneath London, where sodium adsorbed onto the small amounts of detrital clay in the Chalk has been exchanged for calcium in water moving down from the unconfined aquifer to the north (Whitaker *et al.*, 1916, pp. 20-35; Ineson and Downing, 1963). Beneath north London and south Hertfordshire, sodium concentrations in the confined aquifer often exceed 100 mg L^{-1} because of this process (Water Resources Board, 1972), though a tongue of Ca-HCO_3 facies extends southwards down the lower Lea valley (Fig. 9.5), because excessive abstraction over the last two centuries and the southward increase in transmissivity down the valley have allowed water of this facies from the north to replace much of the Na-HCO_3 water (Flavin and Joseph, 1983). Even greater sodium concentrations in the Chalk groundwater under central and east London arise from intrusion of brackish water entering higher tidal reaches of the Thames (Fig. 9.5).

9.3. Surface water bodies

Surface water bodies include lakes, reservoirs, wetlands, rivers and streams. The water in these is derived either from rainfall and surface runoff or from discharge of groundwater. Lakes are rare in Hertfordshire, and the main reservoirs, in and near north-western parts of the county, were built to supply the Grand Union Canal where it reaches its highest point near Tring (Section 9.7). Most of the county's rivers originate as chalk streams in the valleys of the Chilterns. Chalk streams are part of a globally rare habitat, which is found only in some of the chalklands of northwest Europe and on limestone outcrops in parts of New Zealand. They are important for wildlife, including the water vole (*Arvicola terrestris/amphibius*), which is currently Britain's fastest declining mammal, and are also greatly valued by anglers, principally for their populations of brown trout, grayling and bullhead. In Hertfordshire, they are also of historic importance, having been used in the past for numerous water mills (Plate 2) and watercress beds (Plate 67). Because they are fed mainly by chalk groundwater, they are clearer and more uniform in temperature than other rivers. However, they rely strongly on winter rainfall to maintain summer flows. Flow rates are also affected by groundwater abstraction, the construction of weirs and ponds for fishing, river straightening, dredging and flood relief works. Hertfordshire's chalk streams have also been heavily modified as they pass through town centres such as Hemel Hempstead. In view of their ecological importance, it is surprising that almost no reaches of chalk streams have been recognized as Sites of Special Scientific Importance (SSSI), Local Wildlife Sites (LWS) or Regionally Important Geological Sites (RIGS).

Generation of runoff

Surface runoff is generated on slopes when rainfall exceeds the rate at which water can infiltrate the soil. This can occur when the pores in upper horizons of the soil profile that normally drain under gravity become water-filled and drain more slowly than the rainfall rate (Horton, 1933). Initial filling of drainable soil pores may occur from above by rainfall, or from below by a rise in the water table. Runoff resulting from the first is often termed infiltration-excess runoff, and that resulting from rising groundwater is known as saturation-excess runoff. As the topsoil is usually more porous than deeper soil horizons, downslope movement of water can occur by interflow within this layer before true surface runoff appears.

Surface runoff also occurs when rain falls on a soil surface which has developed an impermeable crust. Such surface soil crusts (Robinson and Woodun, 2008) are generated by a sequence of processes starting with breakage of the bonds between surface soil particles by the energy of large raindrops. The dispersed particles are then segregated, the clay and organic matter forming a thin, less porous and slowly permeable ('washed-in') layer 0.5-2 mm below the surface, leaving silt and sand particles as a thin pale-coloured surface layer. On drying, the two layers form a hard laminated crust. In any subsequent rainfall event, the sand and silt particles on the surface absorb the energy of raindrops and the less permeable lower layer severely limits infiltration, even though the soil beneath is not saturated and may indeed be quite dry. As the bonds between particles are weaker in soils containing little clay and organic matter, surface crusts and the runoff generated by their presence are more common in areas where the surface soil contains large amounts of sand or coarse silt. Also the crusts form most easily when the soil has no protective cover of vegetation. These situations occur widely in many of the soil associations in Hertfordshire (Section 7.7), especially those under arable use and derived from loess, sandy fluvial or sandy glaciofluvial deposits.

Much of the runoff generated in these ways on slopes initially flows over the soil surface as a shallow sheet of water. But as rainfall rate increases or the slope steepens, the flow is concentrated into rivulets, which frequently cause erosion of the weakly aggregated soil. Downcutting by a rivulet initially creates a shallow narrow channel known as a rill, but on longer slopes, where the surface flow rate increases and rivulets coalesce, the increasing erosive power of the runoff can result in wider, deeper channels or gullies. Rills can be removed by normal soil cultivation practices, such as harrowing or ploughing, but gullies are too large to eradicate in this way, and either have to be infilled by bulldozing or remain as semi-permanent features of the landscape. Some runoff may never enter a permanent river or other body of surface water because, on reaching more gently sloping land, it flows more slowly over the surface and consequently has more time to infiltrate as indirect recharge to the water table. If the runoff reaches a depression, surface movement may even cease, thus creating a temporary pond, which slowly soaks into the soil and eventually dries up.

Groundwater contributions to surface waters

Discharge of groundwater to create or contribute to a surface water body occurs where the water table intersects the land surface. Here it gives rise to outflow or discharge features, which are dynamic in that (a) they can be perennial (flowing semi-permanently) or intermittent (operating only at times when the water table has been elevated following a period of sustained recharge), or (b) may move their position over time. Groundwater discharge features include:

a) springs, which are point openings in the land surface through which groundwater flows fairly rapidly, usually by turbulent flow from a fissure, often acting as the source of a small surface stream
b) seepage faces, where groundwater rises slowly to the surface, mainly by laminar flow, along a fairly continuous line where the water table intersects a slope
c) lakes and wetlands fed through their beds by springs or diffuse upward flow of groundwater from an aquifer beneath. By convention, wetlands are defined as bodies of standing surface water less than 6 m in depth, whereas lakes have a maximum depth greater than 6 m. Those fed mainly by groundwater are termed phreatotrophic, those

fed mainly by rivers are termed fluviotrophic, and those fed mainly by rainwater ombrotrophic.

d) rivers and streams, many of which are partly fed by upward diffuse or point flow through their beds or banks.

Groundwater discharge is very important in maintaining the flow of rivers in periods with little or no rainfall. Without it, most rivers would stop flowing within a few days of the last large rainfall event. It provides a short-term minimum level of river flow, known as baseflow, on which are superimposed peaks resulting from surface runoff caused by heavy rainfall. However, without recharge, the groundwater head in the aquifer slowly declines and the hydraulic gradient to the river decreases; this leads to slow decline of baseflow (baseflow recession) after a period of recharge. Baseflow can therefore be estimated roughly by joining the lowest points on a long-term hydrograph, i.e. a graphical plot of river flow rate against time.

Gaining and losing rivers: bournes. Whether a river gains water from an underlying aquifer (a gaining river) or loses it to the aquifer (a losing river) depends on the permeability of the river's bank and bed deposits and on whether the groundwater head in the aquifer is higher or lower than the water level in the river. Consequently, rivers may change from one type to the other in different reaches or over time (e.g. seasonally). In chalkland areas, such as the Chilterns, parts of rivers whose flow are affected in these ways are termed bournes, or winterbournes where seasonal fluctuations in the water table (caused by greater winter recharge) result in flow in winter and early spring (gaining river) but an absence of flow in summer and autumn (losing river). All the 'through-valleys' of the Chilterns (Section 6.10) have lower (south-eastern) reaches that are permanently wet because the groundwater table is always above the valley floor, and upper (north-western) reaches that are permanently dry. But their middle reaches behave as bournes (Fig. 9.4) because the water table fluctuates around valley floor level. Often this is because the valley long profile or talweg steepens more rapidly north-westwards than does the gradient of the water table. Most of the side valleys have even steeper talwegs, and so are permanently dry, though a few, such as the Hertfordshire Bourne (described below), contain temporary streams after periods of unusually high rainfall and groundwater recharge.

Losing reaches of rivers may pass laterally into gaining reaches without any change in the height of the water table if there are significant inflows of surface water generated, for example, by tributary streams or floods resulting from large surface runoff events upstream. In these circumstances, the hydraulic gradient, initially from the aquifer into the river, is reversed; water then flows into the aquifer through the channel banks or by downward seepage from adjacent floodplains if the flood exceeds the bank-full capacity of the channel. Flow of this type from rivers to aquifers is known as bank storage. When the flood has passed and river level declines, the water in bank storage is returned to the river, because a steep hydraulic gradient develops from the aquifer or the saturated bank sediments towards the partially emptied channel. Bank storage can therefore lessen the magnitude of a flood by lowering the potential maximum water level in the river; in turn it prolongs the period over which river levels are raised. In chalkland valleys, such as those of the Chilterns, the coarse Devensian valley gravels potentially play a major role in bank storage, because they are very porous and have high storativity values.

Quality of chalk streams. As in other chalkland areas, the dominance of groundwater contributions to Chiltern streams explains why they are usually crystal clear, with almost no suspended sediment. Inputs from surface runoff, which usually bring suspended sediment, are fairly rare. However, they can occur in periods of heavy rainfall that result in brief runoff events on adjacent arable fields with little or no cover of protective vegetation. Runoff may also introduce pollutants such as agricultural pesticides and phosphate sorbed onto soil particles, which can damage fish stocks and other aquatic wildlife. Inputs of muddy polluting runoff can be restricted by the construction and careful maintenance of streamside bunds or strips of dense riparian vegetation. In the Hertfordshire area, this approach has been adopted most successfully along the River Chess.

Baseflow of the River Gade – quarrels and legal action

In the early 19th century, conflicting demands on the use of water in the River Bulbourne and its downstream continuation, the lower part of the River Gade, led to protracted arguments over how much of the river's flow arose from Chalk groundwater (Mather, 2008). At this time, John Dickinson purchased four mills on the River Gade between Hemel Hempstead and Rickmansworth using water power for the manufacture of paper. These were Apsley Mill (TL 062050), Nash Mills (TL 069045), Home Park Mill (TL 077026) and Croxley Mill (TQ 083953). Not long before this, the Grand Junction Canal had been built along the Bulbourne and lower Gade valleys, with some sections between Berkhamsted and Croxley Green actually utilizing parts of the river's course. There were also problems with the canal leaking water into the Chalk, especially near the Tring Summit (Section 9.7). Dickinson frequently complained that these aspects decreased the amount of river water available to power the paper mills, which of course the canal company denied.

Over several years, the argument led to numerous unsuccessful court actions by Dickinson against the canal company. Eventually in 1849 he successfully obtained an injunction in the Court of Chancery specifically preventing the company from pumping water from a well they had drilled in 1848 close to the river at Cow Roast to supply the canal in the upper part of the Bulbourne Valley. Dickinson argued that the large amounts of water abstracted from the Cow Roast well would lower the Chalk water table and cause the river flow to decrease even more. Initially this was confirmed by a rapid decrease in the flow of the Bulbourne a few days after pumping commenced. But in the subsequent very dry summer it became clear that it was only the well water that was maintaining the river flow that powered the mills, so the injunction was quietly forgotten!

Another threat to the water supply of the paper mills had arisen in 1839, when Sir Francis Burdett, MP for Westminster, suggested to a House of Lords committee that wells be drilled near Watford and Bushey Hall to increase the supply of water to northwest London. This proposal was supported by Robert Stephenson, who had obtained some experience of well-drilling in the Watford area while constructing the London-Birmingham railway, but it was again opposed by Dickinson. Nevertheless, the London (Watford) Spring Water Company was established in 1849 to implement the proposal. Further opposition by Dickinson (1850) was this time supported by Clutterbuck (1850) and by Dickinson's nephew and son-in-law John Evans, who wrote a series of letters on the subject to *The Times* newspaper.

Dickinson's argument was now based on new evidence from the percolation gauge, which he had installed at Nash Mills in 1835. The first 18 years' data showed that the amounts of percolation measured each year at Nash Mills could be roughly correlated with the flow of springs feeding the Gade and Bulbourne. This strongly suggested that rainwater percolating to the water table contributes to river flow, so that lowering the water table by abstraction of groundwater close to the river is likely to reduce its flow. Also, based on measurements of the water levels in numerous wells close to the Ver, Gade and Colne, Clutterbuck (1850) showed that river flow accounted for almost all the water percolating into the nearby Chalk. In contrast, Stephenson and other engineers maintained that only a small proportion of the percolation feeds Chalk springs and rivers. They postulated that most of it instead enters a large subterranean reservoir at greater depths, and eventually rises through the floor of the southern North Sea, so that groundwater beneath the Chilterns can be removed by pumping from deep wells without endangering river flow. The engineers' theory was never confirmed and has now passed into scientific mythology, whereas the ideas of Dickinson, Clutterbuck and Evans form the basis of modern Chalk hydrogeology, which recognizes that groundwater and surface water are interrelated, so that one cannot be modified without affecting the other.

The need to increase London's water supply was met initially by increasing supplies from the Thames, and later, in 1877, the Colne Valley Water Company began pumping from wells in the Bushey area. But by then any threat to Dickinson's paper mills had been minimized by converting them from water to steam power. Nevertheless, Evans continued to publish arguments countering the fallacy that large supplies of untapped water occur at depth beneath the Chilterns. He also stressed the need for legislation concerning the ownership of groundwater and the foolishness of wasting pure drinking water on flushing London's sewers and washing its streets (Evans, 1876, p. 120). Evans remained particularly concerned that, in taking groundwater supplies from the Lea and Colne catchments, London was in effect robbing Hertfordshire of its own water supply. In this he was strongly supported by Hopkinson (1892, 1901), who suggested that London would be better obtaining supplies piped from Lake Bala

and other sources in the mountains of Wales, where the rainfall is several times that of Hertfordshire and the water much softer. Because water is now used more efficiently in London, especially through development of the London Ring Main, Hopkinson's suggestion has never been implemented, but it is still revived from time to time whenever a severe drought affects southeast England.

Ecological effects of excessive groundwater abstraction

If the rate of groundwater abstraction exceeds natural aquifer recharge for any length of time, especially when pumping from wells sited close to the river is continued during a prolonged drought, the river may dry up temporarily, leading to a decline in its amenity value and to ecological issues, such as loss of fish stocks, insect and waterbird populations. Initially, the higher (head) reaches tend to dry up first, because it is here that the inclination of the valley floor is most likely to be steeper than that of the regional water table, but progressively lower reaches become dry as abstraction compounds the effect of low recharge, leading to further lowering of the water table. The reduction in stream flow and downstream migration of the seasonal heads of the Chiltern bournes persist until there has been sufficient recharge to replenish groundwater storage and raise the water table level.

Problems with the River Ver. Declining stream flow has sometimes been overcome by pumping groundwater into the river channel. River augmentation of this type has been used occasionally in the English chalklands for several decades (Downing *et al.*, 1981), and was proposed for the Ver valley in Hertfordshire (Owen *et al.*, 1991) but never fully implemented. The highest part of the Ver's course above St Albans was shortened by 10 km between 1950 and 1990, mainly because of lowering of the local Chalk water table by abstraction at seven wells in the valley. In very dry summers, such as 1975, 1976, 1997 and 1998, the dry section of the channel has even extended from the original source at Kensworth Lynch (TL 045180) to Sopwell or Park Street, more than 20 km downstream. Further downstream, groundwater abstraction near the confluence of the Ver and Colne added to the problem, though flow in the Colne has been increased since the early 1970s by inputs from a sewage treatment works constructed at Blackbirds Farm near Radlett. The effects of declining flow on aquatic mammals, fish, invertebrate populations and water-loving plants in the drying reaches of the river were of course disastrous, though subsequent restoration of flow has shown that these groups can recover given sufficient time.

In 1976 St Albans District Council sponsored formation of the Ver Valley Society to develop a riverside footpath through the city. But often with no river to walk beside, the society was soon forced to start a campaign to raise the water table and reinstate the ecological and amenity values of the river. Following publication of a report on the problem by consultants (Sir William Halcrow and Partners), the pumping station at Friar's Wash was put on standby in 1993, and is now used mainly in emergencies, though some water (about 1 ML day⁻¹) is still pumped to keep the pipes 'sweet'. The supply it provided has been replaced by a new main bringing water to the area from Grafham Reservoir in Rutland. As it had abstracted water from the Ver Valley area at a much greater rate than other wells in the Ver valley, 15 ML day⁻¹ out of a total of 45 ML day⁻¹, Friar's Wash was thought to be the main cause of water table lowering and desiccation of the Ver. However, although the river flowed slightly more strongly for a few years after 1993, problems of low flow have persisted upstream of St Albans, especially in periods of low rainfall. Some cosmetic 'compensation flow' through St Albans in periods of severe drought is provided by a low level of augmentation at St Michaels Bridge, using groundwater piped from Bow Bridge pumping station, but this does nothing to help maintain flow in the more problematic higher reaches of the valley.

Recently there have been several periods of unusually high rainfall and the flow of the Ver has increased slightly, especially in the periods January 2001-July 2003 and January 2008-May 2009. During these periods, the river has fairly consistently commenced near Flamstead (TL 0715), within about 4 km of its highest recorded source at Kensworth Lynch. However, if annual rainfall declines in the future and abstraction at the pumping stations in the valley continues at its present level, increased augmentation will become necessary, as was recognized in an official report of the Environment Agency published in October 2006.

Where the aquifer is unconfined, wells for Chalk stream augmentation need to be at least 5 km from the river (Owen *et al.*, 1991). Because of the Chalk's high transmissivity and low storativity, pumping from near the river merely lowers the water table immediately beneath, so that the water added to the river leaks all the more easily through its permeable bed. However, bringing water from a greater distance considerably increases the cost of any augmentation scheme.

The Hertfordshire Bourne

By far the most famous and most carefully studied intermittent chalk stream in Hertfordshire is the Bourne Gutter or Hertfordshire Bourne. When it flows, it usually rises south of Berkhamsted at various points between Hockeridge Bottom (SP 9706) and Bottom Farm (TL 000061), and occupies a broad sinuous valley up to 50 m deep (Plate 78), which for most of its length runs roughly parallel to the Bulbourne valley. After 6-7 km, the valley turns northwards, and any bourne flow passes through culverts beneath the recently constructed A41(T) and the old A41 (now A4251) on either side of the appropriately named hamlet of Bourne End (TL 0206), before joining the River Bulbourne.

When dry, its course on the valley floor is indicated by a narrow channel 1-2 m wide and less than 1 m deep, cut mainly in Late Devensian flinty valley gravels. In upper parts of the valley to about 0.7 km downstream of Bottom Farm, the channel coincided with a section of the original (pre-1974) county boundary between Hertfordshire and Buckinghamshire. This suggests that in the early 10th century, when Hertfordshire's county boundary was probably created (Cameron, 1996, p. 54), the bourne was a more permanent river than it has been since at least the mid-19th century, when its intermittent flow was first recorded. Unfortunately, the gravels in some parts of the valley between Bottom Farm and the A41(T) were excavated in small borrow pits during construction of this road in 1993. The pits were carefully back-filled with chalk excavated from nearby road cuttings, but the change from natural flint gravels to 'made ground' composed of chalk has almost certainly affected shallow groundwater flow. Despite this, the whole valley between the county boundary and the A41(T) is designated a RIGS.

Records of flow. Casual observations in the mid-19th century suggested that the Hertfordshire Bourne flowed regularly once every seven years, but later records by Evans (1878), Littleboy (1884), Evans and Hopkinson (1885), Hopkinson (1901, 1911a, 1915, 1917, 1923), Cox (1934), Glennie (1964a, 1964b) and other members of the Hertfordshire Natural History Society (Anon., 1882, 1884, 1898b, 1906, 1912a, 1915a, 1915b, 1917a, 1917b, 1923, 1927, 1937) showed that there is no regular interval between flow events. For over 80 years, society groups visited the valley whenever flow occurred, the numerous records indicating that this was in the late winter and spring of the following years: 1853, 1860, 1866, 1873, 1876, 1877, 1879, 1881, 1882, 1883, 1897, 1903-4, 1911, 1912, 1913, 1915, 1916, 1917, 1919, 1925, 1926, 1927-8, 1936, 1959, 1961. Since 1964, there have been no printed records of flow, though this may partly reflect less enthusiastic observation. However, the current occupier of Bottom Farm, John Marsland, took photographs during a flow event in March 2001 and a neighbour, Tanya Assarat, recorded flow west of Bottom Farm in March 2007. In each year, flow has usually begun in early-mid January and continued for a period of weeks or months, sometimes until June; flow commencing as early as November or December followed unusually wet summers and autumns.

Factors influencing flow. Hopkinson (1911b) showed that flow occurred only when annual rainfall (April 1 to March 31), measured at the two nearest meteorological stations (Berkhamsted and Nash Mills, Apsley), exceeded 32 inches (813 mm), which was presumed sufficient to raise the local water table in the Chalk to reach the valley floor. Also, by comparing periods of bourne flow with the percolation data from Dickinson's percolation gauge at Nash Mills and the drain gauges at Rothamsted Farm (Harpenden), Hopkinson (1901) showed that flow occurred only when percolation to a depth of about 1 m exceeded 26% of the annual rainfall. Winter rainfall seemed to be more important in determining flow than that of other seasons, probably because more percolates in winter when less is lost by evapotranspiration. Subsequent comparisons (Hopkinson, 1911b) showed that the amount of annual percolation required to cause bourne flow increased by 34% between 1873 and 1900, suggesting a decline in the level of the winter water table beneath the valley over this period.

One aspect of the Hertfordshire Bourne that distinguishes

Plate 78. The valley of the Hertfordshire Bourne looking up-valley towards Bottom Farm (TL 000061).

it from the more permanent chalk streams of the Chiltern 'through-valleys' (Bulbourne, Gade, Ver, etc) is that it rarely flows continuously from the various source springs to the confluence with the Bulbourne at Bourne End. Flow usually commences at the Corner Spring, a short distance up-valley from where White Hill crosses the valley (SP 991054), though other source springs have been reported above White Hill near Hockeridge Farm. However, on some occasions flow has started down-valley from White Hill, either at a diffuse area of rising groundwater in a small wetland basin known as Heathen Grove or at a stronger spring near Mount's Hill. The surface flow then terminates at various points down-valley, and has reached Bourne End only after winters with unusually high rainfall. It has often ended either in a swallow-hole close to Bottom Farm (SP 999061) or in a pond temporarily occupying a small gravel pit a short distance down-valley (TL 005061). The gravel pit acts as an artificial soakaway, because the bourne sometimes flows strongly into it but not beyond, or sometimes has reappeared a short distance down-valley.

Evans (1878) attributed the irregular appearance and disappearance of the stream down the valley to minor changes in the level of the valley floor above a more uniformly inclined water table in the Chalk beneath. However, from observations in 1959-61, Glennie (1964b) suggested that there are two independent groundwater systems in the White Hill area, one leading to flow from the Corner Spring and others above White Hill, and the other to flow at Heathen Grove and/or Mount's Hill. In the winter of 1960-61, flow from the Corner Spring began less than

a month after the groundwater level in the nearby well at Rossway Home Farm had risen above 143 m OD, and ceased when the well level had declined to about 144 m OD from a maximum of 146.3 m. In contrast, flow further down the valley from the Heathen Grove-Mount's Hill system has been recorded several days earlier or later than that from the Corner Spring, and in 1961 continued until June 6, about three weeks after flow from the Corner Spring had ceased. In early 1961, the flow from Corner Spring was fairly weak, failing to reach the culvert beneath the lane at White Hill (SP 991054), whereas that from Heathen Grove and Mount's Hill was constantly more than 80,000 gallons hr^{-1} (364,000 L hr^{-1}), some surface water reaching Bourne End.

The most likely reason for these differences in behaviour of the bourne is as follows. In the area up-valley from White Hill, where the valley floor is narrow and intersects the outcrop of the Chalk Rock, a rise in the Chalk water table, as indicated by the 143 m OD level in the Rossway well, may lead to flow from the Corner Spring and others nearby because of a downward decrease in transmissivity from the strongly fissured Chalk Rock hardground into the Lewes Nodular Chalk, which is less fissured and contains slowly permeable marl bands (the Caburn and Southerham Marls). However, down-valley from White Hill, the valley broadens and the coarse flinty valley-floor gravels overlying the Middle Chalk are more continuous, with a marked increase in width of outcrop and possibly also in thickness. As the gravels have much greater storativity than any part of the Chalk, they can act as very rapid conduits for shallow subsurface flow, so that when the water table rises into them

Plate 79. Swallow-hole on Potterells Stream at Water End.

from the Chalk below, they can supply the sudden large increases in surface flow that have often been recorded in this area.

Glennie (1964b) noted several unusual invertebrates at the Mount's Hill Spring, some of which are unknown elsewhere in Hertfordshire. They included the water beetle *Hydroporus marginatus*, the freshwater ostracod *Eucypris lilljeborgi* and the copepods *Acanthocylops venustus*, *A. gigas latipes, A. vernalis americanus and A. vernalis*. These may depend upon the constant temperature (9.6°C) of the spring water.

Further details of the Bourne Gutter and other Hertfordshire bournes, including the history of their progressive desiccation and down-valley retreat in the 19th and early 20th centuries, were given by Whitaker (1921, pp. 69-81).

Hertfordshire swallow-holes

Another hydrogeological feature for which Hertfordshire is famous are the numerous swallow-holes, through which small streams intermittently disappear underground into the Chalk. The most active, where streamflow often visibly descends into a hole, are those at the feather edge of the Palaeogene outcrop. The streams are generated by runoff over the impermeable London and Reading Beds Clays and descend into the permeable, fissured Chalk. Less spectacular are those in the floors of the Chiltern through-valleys, where either the water table in the Chalk falls below the valley floor or lithological changes in the Quaternary valley floor

deposits or in the Chalk itself cause the river bed to leak. The county has two hamlets with the name Water End, both sited close to individual swallow-holes or groups of them. One is on the edge of the Palaeogene outcrop at TL 2304 between North Mymms and Brookmans Park, and the other is at TL 039101, in the Chalk-floored Gade valley above Hemel Hempstead. There is also a Waterend in the Chalk-floored part of the upper Lea valley (TL 205137) between Wheathampstead and Lemsford.

Swallow-holes near North Mymms. Perhaps the most famous, and certainly the most intensively studied, complex of swallow-holes in Hertfordshire are those near North Mymms. Here, the Mimmshall Brook, an obsequent stream draining more than 50 km^2 of the London Clay outcrop to the south near Borehamwood, Barnet and Potters Bar (Nowell, 1994), flows down one or more swallow-holes where the Palaeogene deposits thin to a feather edge over the Chalk. Some nearby holes also take the flow of the Potterells Stream (Plate 79), which has a smaller catchment to the east on the London Clay near Brookmans Park and on the Ware Till east of Welham Green. At times of low flow, the active swallow-holes are those at the highest points on the two streams, but with increasing rainfall in the river catchments, the highest swallow-holes become flooded by the greater stream discharge, and the streams then terminate in a succession of other swallow-holes downstream. Walsh and Ockenden (1982, Fig. 2) mapped all the swallow-holes near North Mymms known in the 1970s (a total of 17), and established the sequence of hole occupation

Plate 80. Overflow channel from Water End swallow-holes, North Mymms Park.

during flooding along the Mimmshall Brook from weekly observations of the area in 1969-1970. When all the holes are overwhelmed, the surrounding area is transformed into a small lake, which then overflows through a surprisingly large but normally dry channel passing westwards beneath the A1(M) and across North Mymms Park (Plate 80). Towards Colney Heath, the overflow channel becomes a temporary headwater of the River Colne. Consequently, large changes in the area's appearance can occur between successive visits, depending on antecedent rainfall (Wooldridge and Kirkaldy, 1937). As it has become popular for demonstrating swallow-holes in the field, with frequent visits by the Hertfordshire Natural History Society (Anon., 1892a, 1912b), Geologists' Association (Whitaker, 1916; Wooldridge and Kirkaldy, 1937; Evans, 1944; Kirkaldy, 1950b) and other local and university groups, the area is designated a geological SSSI.

Wooldridge and Kirkaldy (1937) suggested that, before the Anglian glaciation, which blocked its valley with a considerable thickness of till and glaciofluvial deposits north of Water End, the Mimmshall Brook would have continued northwards, probably joining the proto-Thames near Stanborough (TL 2210). The westward course of the modern overflow channel towards Colney Heath may have originated as a marginal meltwater channel around a temporary ice lobe extending southwards from the Hatfield area.

Subsurface flow. Dye tests in 1927-1935 by Morris and Fowler (1937) showed that, from the swallow-holes near North Mymms, the water travels through the Chalk, eventually emerging as springs feeding the River Lea at various sites between Woolmers Park and Hoddesdon (TL 3808), 8-30 km NE-NNE of Water End. This direction of flow may be determined by the minor syncline mentioned in Section 5.7, whose WSW-ENE axis plunges in the same direction from Water End towards Epping Green (TL 2906) and Hoddesdon (Walsh and Ockenden, 1982). Surprisingly, there was no trace of the dye in wells SSE of Water End, i.e. in the direction of regional inclination of the water table.

The water table at Water End lies approximately 12 m below the bed of the Mimmshall Brook, and water levels in the well to the SSE fluctuate only by about 2 m, even after heavy storms. The dye tests indicated very high flow rates of approximately 5 km day^{-1} between Water End and the Lea, suggesting the presence of very wide fissures in the Chalk. Indeed, with appropriate equipment, it is possible to descend some of the swallow-holes almost to the water table and follow fissures horizontally for many metres. According to Evans (1944), a Mr R. Butler took photographs during a successful expedition into one of the holes in 1928, and John Huston, a keen speleologist from St Albans, explored others several times in the 1980s. The large recharge rate through the swallow-holes, a mean of 0.3 m^3 hr^{-1}, with a maximum of 3600 m^3 hr^{-1} before the lake overflows, and the rapid water movement away from Water End, together suggest that the water table rises in a mound beneath the area (Walsh and Ockenden, 1982). Unfortunately, the holes are easily choked with plastic and other rubbish brought by the floods, and this in turn encourages deposition of sediment within their funnel-shaped mouths. Consequently, individual holes are blocked from time to time, so that they cannot accept rapid flow, but form shallow soakaway basins from which floodwater percolates very slowly into the Chalk.

Associated deposits. Based on a geophysical (electrical resistivity) survey and several shallow boreholes, Walsh and Ockenden (1982) showed that the low-lying area enclosing the Water End swallow-holes contains four distinct deposits over the Chalk. At the surface, there is up to 2.25 m of plastic dark grey organic mud (alluvium), which has been deposited within the temporary lake during recent (late Holocene) flood episodes. This is underlain by up to 2.45 m of brown silty clay, probably also a flood deposit, but older than the overlying grey mud, and perhaps early Holocene or even late Pleistocene in age. This in turn rests on 1.5 m of greenish brown (glauconitic?) sand and clay, which is probably a thin weathered representative of the Upnor Formation. It is separated from the Chalk beneath by up to 27 cm of 'firm brown silty clay with occasional chalk fragments', possibly a layer of Clay-with-flints *sensu stricto*, similar to that described as lining fissures in the Chalk at the nearby Castle Lime Works, South Mimms (Kirkaldy, 1950a; Thorez *et al.*, 1971).

Site vegetation. The vegetation over the area of the North Mymms swallow-holes area forms three distinct zones. Beside the swallow-holes and river channels and on the floor of the flood lake, there is a central zone with a dense summer growth of persicaria (*Polygonum persicaria*). This is surrounded by an area of nettles (*Urtica dioica*) and dock (*Rumex longifolia*) on the margin of the flooded area, whereas higher ground to the north and west is covered by dense thickets of hawthorn (*Crataegus monogyna*). The persicaria, nettles and dock die down in winter to expose the swallow-holes, but in summer their dense growth conceals the holes, making the low-lying areas dangerous to explore.

Almshoe Bury. Another important Hertfordshire swallow-hole is at Almshoe Bury (TL 205246) in the Langley valley west of Stevenage. Although this is smaller and active much less frequently than the North Mymms complex, it is designated as a RIGS. In periods of unusually heavy rainfall, a normally dry depression fills with water to a depth of about 4 m, fed at least partly by a small temporary stream flowing north-westwards and originating in springs near Pigeonswick Cottage (TL 224228), southwest of Norton Green. The higher reaches of the stream are on chalky Anglian till, which is slowly permeable, but the lower reaches and the swallow-hole itself are on more permeable glaciofluvial sands and gravels forming part of the infill of the subglacial Hitchin valley, here cut in Middle Chalk. The location of the swallow-hole is more difficult to explain than the North Mymms complex, especially as the hydrogeology of the site is probably determined by the local Anglian glacial sequence, deposits which can be very variable in permeability and transmissivity.

Hertfordshire springs

Springs are another fairly common feature of the Hertfordshire landscape. Some are hidden because they rise in the beds of perennial rivers and wetlands, but many can be found by tracing brooks upstream to their sources. They are likely to arise wherever the water table in an aquifer intersects the land surface, though the actual position of the clearest examples is often determined by the existence of large fissures close to the surface within the aquifer. Where fissures carrying turbulent flow are absent, the water rises slowly to the surface by laminar flow along a seepage line, which is not usually the immediate source of a river. Instead the water from seepage lines is lost by evaporation or moves slowly downslope by interflow within the soil cover.

The commonest springs in Hertfordshire are those arising from the Chalk aquifer. They occur in two main situations: along the foot of the Chiltern escarpment in north-western parts of the county; and within valleys intersecting lower parts of the dip-slope. The former often supply streams that eventually flow into the Thame or Great Ouse basins, whereas the latter feed into the Lea and Colne catchments, and thence into lower reaches of the Thames.

Scarp-foot springs. The Chiltern scarp-foot springs often arise from the outcrop of the fissured Totternhoe Stone, which overlies the less permeable aquiclude of the West Melbury Marly Chalk Formation (Chalk Marl); examples include the main spring at Ashwell (TL 270398), which is a source of the River Rhee (or Cam), and the Burwell Springs (TL 103292) and Roaring Meg (TL 113296) near Hexton (Bloom, 1934), which are sources of the River Hiz. Small springs also emerge at slightly lower levels from the Dixoni and Doolittle Limestones within the West Melbury Marly Chalk, including those near Drayton Beauchamp (at SP 903126, SP 908126) feeding the Wilstone Reservoir. Yet others (e.g. at Tring and Baldock) emerge at higher levels from the Melbourn Rock. The water supplies provided by escarpment springs led to the establishment of many scarp-foot villages and towns, such as Wendover, Aston Clinton, Tring, Ivinghoe, Ivinghoe Aston, Barton-le-Clay, Hexton, Hitchin, Norton, Baldock, Radwell, Ashwell and Royston. Because of their importance to these early centres of habitation, the springs were often given names, such as the Well Head Spring at Wendover (SP 873072), the Wellonhead Spring at Aston Clinton (SP 888116) and the Burwell (or St Faith's) Springs at Hexton (TL 104292).

Dip-slope valley springs. Along the floors of valleys that dissect the Chalk dip-slope, numerous springs feed into the Bulbourne, Gade, Ver, Colne, Lea, Mimram, Beane, Rib and Ash rivers (Whitaker, 1921, pp. 50-64). Depending on the height of the water table, many are intermittent springs, and at times when the water table is low some even function as swallow-holes. In the 19th century, a valley floor spring at Berkhamsted known as St John's Well (SP 987082) was used as a medicinal bath (Whitaker, 1921, p. 50). Previously many of the springs were sources of water for watercress beds, but this industry has progressively declined since the late

19th century because lowering of the water table has caused many of the springs to dry up. Also agricultural pollution of the streams has periodically caused microbiological contamination. Previously watercress was grown extensively in, for example, the Bulbourne, Gade, Ver and Lea valleys, but there is now only one small stream-fed bed left in the county, at Kimpton Mill (TL 198185) in the Mimram valley (Plate 67). A larger bed (Nine Wells Watercress Farm) at Whitwell (TL 180213), also in the Mimram valley, is supplied mainly by nine artesian wells, which bring water to the surface from the Melbourn Rock at a depth of approximately 60 m below the valley floor (M. Howgate, *pers. comm.*). The artesian flow at this site suggests the presence of a major structure in the Chalk, probably the NW-SE Lilley Bottom Fault or Monocline mentioned in Sections 3.3 and 5.7.

The Chadwell and Amwell Springs. Two major groups of springs on the southern side of the lower Lea valley, the Chadwell (TL 3513) and Amwell (TL 3712) Springs, provided a source of clean water for London from 1613 until the early 20th century. Between 1609 and 1613, an aqueduct called the New River was constructed by Sir Hugh Myddelton approximately parallel to the lower Lea to carry water from these springs 27 miles (43 km) into central London. Later the New River was extended to take in water direct from the river at Kings Meads (TL 3413) and, to supplement its flow, the East London Waterworks Company, established in 1807, drilled numerous wells nearby in the Lea valley. More than 20 wells were operative in the area by about 1890, and their combined cones of depression soon began to influence the springs (Wood, 1910). Previously the two groups of springs had together provided at least 10 million gallons per day, but this decreased through the late 19th century. By then the Amwell Spring provided very little, and in autumn 1897 the Chadwell Spring failed temporarily, water from the New River flowing back into the spring basin until a dam was built (Hopkinson, 1901). The wells also affected other springs in the lower Lea valley, some of them ceasing to flow within a few hours of the start of pumping in a nearby well (Whitaker, 1921, pp. 61-62).

Other springs. Numerous small, often seasonal, springs occur where the Pebble Gravels, glaciofluvial or river terrace gravels overlie less permeable strata, such as London Clay or till. Whitaker (1921, pp. 64-66) listed examples in the Abbots Langley, St Albans, Hatfield, Colney Heath, London Colney, Lemsford, Welwyn, Digswell, Knebworth, Stevenage, Hitchin, Cheshunt, Little Hadham, Barnet, Bell Bar, Northaw and Cuffley areas. Some of these, including Lady Rachel's Well at Moat Mount and others at Barnet, Welwyn, Hitchin, Watton and Cuffley, are mineral or chalybeate springs, containing notable amounts of Fe^{2+} and SO_4^{2-} (Pryor, 1878). The chalybeate spring at Barnet Common, now disused, was said to contain enough of these ions to coagulate milk.

Where bicarbonate-rich water emerges under pressure, calcium carbonate is often deposited through loss of carbon dioxide to the atmosphere or uptake by plants, to create a petrifying spring. In the garden of Broxbourne Bury

house (TL 353073) a petrifying spring previously fed an ornamental fountain, which is now dry. There is also an early record of a petrifying spring at Clothall (Chauncy, 1826, Vol. 1, p. 12), but the only spring remaining active in this area, at Hickman's Hill (TL 269315), probably takes water from glaciofluvial gravels containing little or no carbonate. Whitaker (1921) also recorded a 'hot' spring at The Lynch (TL 379085) near Hoddesdon. In the late mediaeval period, water from springs rising where terrace gravels of the lower Lea overlie London Clay at Wormley (TL 3505) was conducted through a timber conduit more than 7 km to supply the abbey and town at Waltham Abbey (Bushby, 1934).

Numerous Hertfordshire village names indicate the presence of springs upon which early settlements depended. Chauncy (1826) suggested that various Saxon words for spring, including *well*, *wall*, *wat* and *pel*, were incorporated into Hertfordshire village names, but more recent research on the county's place names (Gover *et al.*, 1938; Cameron, 1996, Chapter 15) supports Chauncy only for names including *well* (Old English *wielle*), such as Amwell, Ashwell, Bedwell, Burwell, Causewell, Chadwell, Digswell, Holwell, Purwell, Radwell, Sopwell, Wellbury, Well End and Whitwell. Gover *et al.* (1938, p. 76) also suggested that Bedmond developed at the site of a spring (TL 097034), as it was termed Bedfunte in 1433 (*funta* = fount or spring). This spring is probably the one in the grounds of Bedmond Village School; as it is close to the birthplace of Nicholas Breakspear (Pope Adrian IV), it has often been referred to as a holy spring (Lesley Brooks, *pers. comm.*).

9.4. Groundwater usage and abstraction

As in most other parts of southern Britain, the main usage of water in Hertfordshire (>50%) is for public water supply and minor commercial purposes (offices, shops, garages, hotels). Large industrial users (manufacturing, quarrying and power stations) account for slightly less in total, and agriculture (livestock, crop irrigation, cleaning of farmyards, buildings and machinery) for only about 2%.

All abstractions above 20 m^3 day^{-1} for private use are licensed by the Environment Agency. Licences were first introduced in 1965, and existing abstractors were then given Licences of Right, which are held in perpetuity and subject to compensation should they be revoked. Later licences are time limited, and expire unless renewed. All licences attract an annual charge based on the annual permitted volume. Licences state the point of abstraction (in the case of boreholes, the depth and diameter are defined) and the purpose for which the water is to be used. They also give maximum permitted hourly, daily and annual volumes, and sometimes the maximum size of the installed pumping capacity. Some licences are restricted over which period of the year they can be used; this is particularly relevant to abstractions used for irrigation. Some contain additional clauses that control the abstraction pattern or the required monitoring. Many of these are linked to river flows or groundwater levels. They constrain the amount of water that can be abstracted under certain conditions, and are usually focused on periods of low natural flows.

There are three reasons why groundwater resources are used to provide almost the sole water supply for Hertfordshire. The first is the enormous volume available. The Chalk aquifer is continuous beneath almost the entire county, and thus covers a much greater area than the sum of the county's small surface water bodies; the depth of water involved is also much greater than any of the rivers or lakes. A second reason for using groundwater is its quality; surface waters are much more likely to be chemically and microbiologically contaminated and, although procedures of artificial purification are available, they are expensive. Third, any significant removal of water from the small surface water bodies characteristic of the county would greatly reduce their ecological role and value as landscape features.

Wells and boreholes. Groundwater is usually abstracted by the construction of a well or borehole. Wells are usually hand dug, shallow and more than 1 m in diameter, whereas boreholes are constructed by a drilling rig, and are deeper and narrower (<1 m). Construction of a new well or borehole for water supply requires consent and a licence from the Environment Agency. Hand dug wells are suitable in soft sediments, such as most of the Palaeogene and Quaternary deposits in Hertfordshire, in which they have often been brick-lined. But this method is slow in harder rocks, such as parts of the Chalk containing hardgrounds or flint layers. In the late 19th century the much faster rotary drilling methods were developed. These use a drill-bit composed of hardened steel, which is rotated at the base of the hole, the rock fragments or 'cuttings' being removed by flushing with water or compressed air. The dense muds often used for flushing when drilling oil wells are rarely used in water wells, as they block pores in the aquifer and decrease its permeability.

The modern method for construction of a chalk borehole in Hertfordshire is to drill a hole of larger diameter than that finally required down to where solid chalk is first encountered. Temporary casing is used to hold the borehole open in the upper sediments and any soft putty or puggy chalk, and is advanced as the borehole deepens. Once solid chalk is encountered, the permanent casing is installed. This is of a narrower diameter than the temporary casing, and the annulus between the two is filled with cement grout from the bottom upwards, the temporary casing being removed progressively as grouting continues. The grout forms a solid seal between the permanent casing and the surrounding upper sediments. It holds the casing in place and prevents the ingress of surface water down the annulus. Drilling in the Chalk then proceeds at a narrower diameter to the total depth of the well, usually 60-100 m below ground level, depending on the depth to the water table.

The initial flow from a well is often quite muddy because of fine particles produced during drilling. Mud smeared on the sides of the well also blocks fissures and decreases the yield of water. To remove these materials and produce clean water, the borehole is then pumped with the water agitated by compressed air. Treatment with hydrochloric acid has been used in some wells to artificially enlarge adjacent fissures (Cruse, 1986), the acid being introduced to the base of the well for a short period through a narrow pipe (Grout et al., 1992). This has been used to increase fissure flow in wells drilled, for example, in the lower Lea valley. In a well at Royston, it increased the transmissivity more than twice, allowing an increase in pumping rate from 8.6 to 18.7 L sec^{-1}, and also slowing the rate of drawdown of the water level in the well.

Pumping tests are then performed with a submersible pump to test both the capacity of the borehole and its impact on the surrounding aquifer. A step test at progressively increasing pumping rates is used to determine the performance of the borehole and assess the impact of abstraction on the aquifer and surrounding environment, including surface water features. Fluctuation of the water table is measured in one or more observation boreholes to determine the shape and extent of the cone of depression, and water levels and flow rates are measured in surface water bodies, such as nearby streams and rivers. The results of these tests are used to predict longer term impacts of the abstraction, and are used by the Environment Agency to determine licence quantities and conditions that need to be placed on the licence.

Siting of wells. Where possible, wells into the Chalk are usually dug through the floors of valleys to reach the water table where it is closest to the land surface, and thus avoid penetrating an unnecessary thickness of unsaturated zone. Valley-floor wells have the additional advantage that transmissivity and storage of water are much greater beneath the valleys than elsewhere. Examples in Hertfordshire include those at St Albans and Friar's Wash, both in the Ver Valley, and the numerous wells in the lower Lea valley. The yield of wells up to 1 m in diameter and sited near valley floors is often in the range 5000-15,000 m^3 day^{-1}, but boreholes of 0.1-0.3 m diameter on the interfluves yield only 100-1000 m^3 day^{-1}. The subsurface flow of water towards wells situated at higher levels in the landscape can be increased by digging horizontal feeder adits at depth outwards from the vertical shaft to tap the saturated zone beneath nearby rivers. This method is used, for example, at Bricket Wood Pumping Station, which is fed by two adits, one extending south-westwards beneath the River Colne and the other south-eastwards beneath the River Ver. However, feeder adits can only draw water from a limited surrounding area; the main factor limiting well yield is often the ability of the aquifer to transmit water regionally, as Grout et al. (1992) demonstrated for wells with feeder adits at Letchworth and Stevenage.

Artificial recharge. In areas where there is a consistently high demand for groundwater leading to rapid depression of the water table and thus to decreased well yields, surface water from rivers is sometimes injected down wells to raise the water table, a process known as artificial recharge. The lower Lea valley provides one of the most successful British examples of this procedure (Hawnt et al., 1981; Flavin and Joseph, 1983). Artesian conditions prevailed in central London until about 1820 AD, when over-abstraction

(abstraction at a rate exceeding the rate of natural recharge) from the confined Chalk aquifer began. By the early 1960s, when abstraction reached a peak of 1,300,000 m^3 day^{-1}, the water table had fallen by 60-95 m in central and west London. There had been two previous attempts at artificial recharge since 1890 (Boniface, 1959), but it was only in the 1970s that groundwater movement was assessed scientifically, and initially six existing wells and six new boreholes were selected within about 1 km of the River Lea for a third recharge exercise using water from the Lea and Thames. In winter, when demand is low, surplus water from the rivers is used to recharge the Chalk aquifer, but during dry summer periods water can be pumped from the replenished aquifer to meet increased demand.

Subsequently Thames Water increased the scale of the operation with a further 24 boreholes on the western side of the Lea valley, many close to the course of the New River. In addition to being used for aquifer recharge in winter, the boreholes can be used in summer to pump water from the aquifer and augment the flow of the New River, which is now carried southwards to Stoke Newington Reservoirs (TQ 3287). This scheme, known as the North London Aquifer Storage and Recovery Scheme, was introduced by Thames Water in the 1980s (Owen *et al.*, 1991) to even out supply as demand varies. A large ring main built to replace the old pipes previously used to deliver river water to different parts of the city (Keane and Kerslake, 1988) facilitated the use of excess winter water for artificial recharge.

The repeated cycles of draining and resaturating the upper parts of the aquifer in the sandy Palaeocene formations above the Chalk under north London (the 'basal sands'), have changed the quality of the groundwater. In particular, its sulphate content has increased (Fig. 9.5), because the periods of dewatering have allowed ingress of air and oxidation of pyrite in the basal sands. Sulphate concentrations as high as 2000 mg L^{-1} were recorded in water from some of the Lea valley boreholes during early recharge experiments.

Problems of rising water tables. Since the 1980s, rising groundwater under London resulting from the recharge scheme has created a range of engineering problems in structures designed and built when the water table was much lower. These have included cracking and deformation of tunnels, structural damage to buildings with deep foundations, and lateral pressure on basements, mainly through rewetting and swelling of the London Clay (Connorton, 1988; Simpson *et al.*, 1989; Wilkinson and Brassington, 1991). Also, increasing pore-water pressure in deposits around piles and deep foundations decreased their bearing capacity, and there has been an increasing risk of flooding in basements, tunnels and subways. Other problems, such as deterioration of concrete foundations and subsurface structures, arose through contact with the sulphate-rich groundwater (Mühlherr *et al.*, 1998). Perhaps the most well-known example of these problems arose when rising groundwater in the Woolwich and Reading Formations necessitated redesign of the foundations and basement retaining walls for the new British Library (TQ

299829) in Euston Road (Wilkinson and Brassington, 1991, p. 51), which delayed its opening for several years. To control the rapid water table rise, it became necessary in the 1990s to increase groundwater pumping rates, especially in eastern parts of the city, through the GARDIT initiative (Lucas and Robinson, 1995).

9.5. Water pollution and health

In Hertfordshire, many villages and towns on the Chalk outcrop originated as valley settlements, taking advantage of water supplies from local springs, streams and shallow wells as well as the easier lines of surface communication. Waste disposal was organized on a similar local basis, with cesspits, drains, soakaways and landfill sites all close to the water sources. This inadvertently created local centres of surface and groundwater pollution. Examples of early health problems in Hertfordshire arising from this type of pollution, especially where shallow groundwaters were used for local water supplies, were described by Whitaker (1921, pp. 95-99). Later, industries with polluting effluents developed in the same settlement areas, so that almost all cities, towns and even villages have become centres of groundwater pollution. In the Luton and Dunstable area, for example, groundwater in the Chalk has been contaminated with chlorinated solvents used in the local car-making, printing, paints and adhesives industries, giving local concentrations as high as 500 µg L^{-1} (Longstaff *et al.*, 1992).

In many rural areas not served by modern sewerage networks, it is still common for domestic waste to be discharged into cesspits or septic tanks, the latter sometimes overflowing into soakaways if they are not emptied frequently. These can become sources of potential pollutants, including pathogens. However, provided they are not sited close to supply wells and their density is low, less than about ten units per square kilometre, attenuation in the unsaturated zone and dilution in the aquifer are usually sufficient to prevent groundwater pollution problems.

Processes of pollutant attenuation. As recharge water percolates slowly through the soil and other parts of the unsaturated zone by intergranular (matrix) flow, many organic and inorganic pollutants are removed by processes such as microbial degradation, adsorption on the reactive surfaces of clay, organic matter and hydrated oxide particles, and physical filtering of solid particles. However, the time available for these processes of natural purification, which often depend on prolonged contact between water and soil or sediment surfaces, is greatly decreased where the soil or superficial deposits over the Chalk aquifer are thin, or where recharge occurs by fissure (by-pass) flow through coarse gravels or large cavities such as sinkholes (Banks *et al.*, 1995). Consequently, the quality of groundwater pumped from individual wells penetrating the Chalk aquifer, and the aquifer's vulnerability to future pollution, are strongly dependent on the distribution of superficial deposits (Chapters 5 and 6) and soil types (Chapter 7) surrounding well sites.

When rapid fissure flow caused by heavy rain occurs near a well, the water pumped from the Chalk is sometimes slightly cloudy, containing fine clay, organic particles and bacteria derived from surface soils. For the same reason, some spring waters, such as those of the Chadwell and Amwell Springs, also become cloudy after heavy rain. Public water supplies are sampled frequently to assess the amounts of any such chemical and microbiological contaminants that could affect human health. To remove them, water is routinely filtered through fine sand or artificial 0.45 μm filters before it is distributed for public consumption (Binnie *et al.*, 2002).

Although water of lower quality is often suitable for use in agriculture, heavy industry and cooling of power plants, all public supplies must meet the more stringent guidelines for drinking water set by law. In the United Kingdom and other parts of the European Union, these are now based on standards decided by the World Health Organization (2004). The central EU regulations have been translated into national standards by individual member states, but most national standards, such as those for the United Kingdom, closely match the WHO guideline values, particularly in terms of maximum admissable concentrations (MACs) of pathogenic microbes and the hundreds of inorganic substances and man-made organic compounds likely to be found in natural waters.

Point source and diffuse pollution. With respect to water quality in general, it is important to distinguish between point-source and diffuse pollution. The former arises from localized spillage, disposal or leakage of pollutants over a limited area, such as a farmyard, factory, cesspit or landfill site. The total losses are usually small, but the concentrations of pollutants reaching a surface water body or a small part of an aquifer are likely to be large. Beneath a point source, the pollutant is usually confined to a plume that spreads downwards and broadens laterally in accordance with groundwater flow patterns. In contrast, diffuse pollution results from activities spread over much larger areas of land, even a large part of the country, causing one or more pollutants to enter numerous surface water bodies or aquifers, usually in lower concentrations but much larger total amounts than from point sources. The commonest forms of diffuse pollution are those resulting from widespread agricultural activities, such as the application of fertilizers, manures and pesticides used in crop production.

The unconfined Chalk aquifer is vulnerable to both point-source and diffuse pollution, because in many areas the soil cover is thin and highly permeable, well developed fracture systems are widespread and the Chalk itself has limited capacity for absorption of contaminants carried in fissure flow. These hydrogeological factors constitute what has been termed an aquifer's intrinsic vulnerability, as opposed to the specific vulnerability resulting from particular pollutants, usually from point-sources. Because of both types of vulnerability, it is necessary to establish protection zones around individual water supply boreholes and wellfields. Two zones are usually recognized (Adams

and Foster, 1992). The outer protection zone corresponds to the area of land by which that part of the aquifer likely to be tapped by continuously pumped boreholes is recharged, and the inner protection zone has a perimeter equivalent to 50 days horizontal flow through the aquifer. The latter is based on a maximum known distance of pathogen transportation of 20 days in the Chalk aquifer, though subsurface pathogen survival times can exceed this value, and other pollutants may travel further, depending on rates of sorption, precipitation and biodegradation.

Pathogenic micro-organisms

Although numerous different pathogenic micro-organisms may enter groundwaters, especially in fissure flow, overall microbial water quality is usually judged simply by testing for the presence or absence of the bacterium *Escherichia coli*, which is a clear indicator of recent faecal contamination. Where the raw water pumped from an aquifer is found to contain this micro-organism, it is disinfected before distribution for public consumption by treatment with chlorine. However, some pathogenic viruses and protozoa, such as *Cryptosporidium* (Smith, 1992), are more resistant to chlorination than bacteria, and need to be assessed independently. Pollution of Chalk groundwater by coliform bacteria has been reported in eastern and southern England on several occasions when heavy rain has followed applications of farm animal slurries to shallow soils. Some of these pollution events have occurred in areas where the unsaturated zone is quite thick, so fissure flow in the Chalk may not remove pathogenic micro-organisms completely. Pathogens resistant to chlorine and other chemical disinfectants are best removed by careful filtration, exposure to ultraviolet light or prolonged boiling.

Agricultural sources of diffuse pollution

Pesticides and herbicides. Some chemical pollutants found in groundwater taken from aquifers like the Chalk, especially where they are recharged by rapid by-pass flow, originate from agriculture as diffuse pollution. Many are man-made organic chemicals used as pesticides (insecticides, fungicides, algicides and molluscicides) or herbicides (weedkillers). Previously the latter were also used in large amounts to defoliate road and railway verges, airfields and forestry breaks, but less has been used for these purposes in recent years. The current EU regulations are very strict in that they limit the amounts of an individual pesticide or herbicide in drinking water to an annual average of 0.1 μg L^{-1} (effectively zero), with a total value for all such chemicals of 0.5 μg L^{-1}. Provided they are used at the rates recommended by manufacturers, which are based on extensive testing before official accreditation, these limits should not be exceeded.

Pesticides are most frequently detected in surface waters, which can be contaminated by spray-drift from nearby fields, railways, etc or by inputs from field drains. However, pesticide contamination of rivers rarely persists for long, as it is usually related to a single event, and is rapidly diluted by cleaner water from upstream or by baseflow from groundwater. Most modern pesticides and herbicides are rapidly absorbed by clay or soil organic matter, or are degraded to less harmful compounds by soil microbial activity. As a result, in groundwaters they are detected much less frequently and in much lower concentrations than in surface waters, because they are almost completely removed during recharge by slow intergranular percolation through soils and fine superficial deposits in the unsaturated zone. Even where they do enter an aquifer by rapid by-pass and fissure flow, they continue to degrade over time, because some soil bacteria also enter the aquifer. On the few occasions when they have been found in groundwater supplies, it has usually been traced to accidental spillages near boreholes for public water supply or to runoff from arable fields into streams that recharge the Chalk aquifer (Gomme *et al.*, 1992).

All modern pesticides and herbicides have very low mammalian toxicities, and at present there are no known human health problems resulting from their use. Nevertheless, public worries persist that even trace amounts of compounds designed as lethal to invertebrates or plants may have insidious long-term detrimental effects on human health, causing perhaps cancer or reproductive problems. But there is no clear evidence for problems of this type. Some compounds are poisonous to fish and beneficial insects such as pollinating honey bees, but these effects can be avoided if the procedures recommended for application, such as not spraying in windy conditions, are carefully observed.

Two plant nutrients, nitrogen and phosphorus, also enter ground and surface waters in small amounts partly because of agricultural activities, and are widely recognized as diffuse pollutants.

Nitrate. The main form in which nitrogen enters surface and groundwater is as nitrate (NO_3^-). In soils, this may originate as nitrate fertilizer, as nitrate produced by bacterial oxidation (nitrification) of ammonium compounds or urea, also used as fertilizers, or as nitrate produced by microbial oxidation (mineralization) of soil organic matter, including organic manures applied to the soil.

Long-term field experiments on leaching of plant nutrients at Rothamsted Experimental Station, Harpenden, some dating from the middle of the 19th century (Goulding *et al.*, 2000; Addiscott, 2005, Chapter 5), have shown that organic manures (farmyard manure, slurry and sewage sludge) lead to the highest concentrations of nitrate in water draining from soil into the unsaturated zone (*i.e.* into the Plateau Drift and underlying Chalk at Rothamsted). Loss of nitrate can also be large when artificial fertilizers are used, but only if more is applied than the crop can use for optimal growth. As the nitrogen content of artificial fertilizers is known more precisely than for organic manures, amounts can be carefully matched to the expected uptake of nitrate over the growing season of crops, so that leaching losses are minimized. Nevertheless, calculations can be confounded by unexpected weather patterns or attacks by pests and diseases, which reduce a crop's ability to grow and take up nitrate from the soil.

Nitrate losses from different crops. Some crops are more efficient than others in scavenging nitrate from the soil (Macdonald *et al.*, 1997; Di and Cameron, 2002). Much depends on root density: grass or cereals have many fine roots that invade a large proportion of the soil, and thus allow less nitrate to leak below rooting depth than crops with fewer, more widely spaced roots, such as sugar beet and potatoes. Nitrate losses can be greater from winter-sown crops than spring-sown, because growth and nitrogen uptake is much slower in winter, whereas infiltration is greater. In fact, winter-sown cereals require no nitrogen fertilizer, because the amounts of nitrate remaining in the soil after the previous harvest are usually enough for initial winter growth. Consequently, any nitrogen applied as fertilizer in autumn is likely to be lost by winter leaching.

At one time, there was considerable concern that nitrate losses by leaching in winter resulted from the inefficient uptake by crops of the nitrogen applied in spring dressings of fertilizer. However, in field experiments using fertilizer labelled with the heavy isotope of nitrogen (^{15}N), Macdonald *et al.* (1989) showed that very little spring-applied nitrogen remains unchanged in the soil at harvest. Spring nitrogen is taken up so efficiently by wheat in particular that the average amounts of ^{15}N remaining in the soil at harvest after even the most generous dressing (234 kg N ha^{-1}) were no greater than where no fertilizer was applied. Where no fertilizer is applied in autumn, almost all the nitrate at risk of leaching in winter comes instead from mineralization of soil organic matter, notably the residues of previous crops (roots, straw, etc). Nitrate leached from this source in autumn and winter is probably greatest when a period of heavy rain follows a hot dry summer (Goulding *et al.*, 2000).

Nitrate losses are also large from bare unvegetated soil, as there are no roots to take up the nitrogen produced by mineralization of organic matter. Consequently, winter crops should be sown as early as possible in the autumn after harvesting the previous crop (Widdowson *et al.*, 1987), and when spring-sown crops (e.g. potatoes, sugar beet) follow an autumn harvest, the long period of bare soil over the winter should be avoided by sowing a winter cover crop (e.g. forage rape) and ploughing it in shortly before the spring crop is planted (Christian *et al.*, 1990; Catt *et al.*, 1998).

Almost no nitrate is leached from a permanent cover of unimproved (unmanured and unfertilized) grass because, without soil cultivation, the nitrogenous organic residues formed by root decay are not exposed to the atmosphere and consequently are not readily mineralized (oxidized) to release nitrate. However, ploughing up long established grassland leads to rapid mineralization of grass root residues and other soil organic matter and thus to considerable loss of nitrate by leaching (Whitmore *et al.*, 1992). Losses of nitrate under woodland are also small, though they can increase after felling, which terminates uptake of the nitrate produced by mineralization of dead leaves and other organic residues.

Careful land management is therefore important for controlling the amounts of nitrate leached from soil to an aquifer. Recommendations to minimize nitrate leaching, based on results from the Rothamsted and other field experiments, are now couched in rules laid down by the Department for Environment, Food and Rural Affairs (DEFRA) for farm management. These are especially relevant to areas known as Nitrate Vulnerable Zones, which include land with permeable soils over major aquifers such as the Chalk (Addiscott, 2005, p. 87).

Nitrate in groundwaters. Nitrate concentrations in water abstracted from the unconfined Chalk aquifer of the Chilterns are usually in the range 20-40 mg L^{-1} (Rivett *et al.*, 2007). Values near the lower end of this range are typical of the south-western Chilterns, where the Plateau Drift forms a thick widespread cover over the aquifer and many of the soils are under permanent grass or woodland rather than arable agriculture. In northeast Hertfordshire and much of East Anglia, water from the Chalk often contains slightly more (30-50 mg L^{-1}), probably because most of the land is under intensive arable cultivation using high rates of artificial fertilizer, and also because much of the soil cover over the aquifer is thinner and more permeable, thus allowing more nitrate to leach below the root zone into the Chalk before it is taken up by crops.

In Hertfordshire and many other parts of England, nitrate concentrations in groundwater have increased slowly over recent decades, certainly since about 1970. For the Chalk aquifer over the country as a whole, the average increase has been 0.38 mg NO_3 L^{-1} yr^{-1} (Stuart *et al.*, 2007), though some of the wells monitored in the Chiltern area have shown smaller increases (<0.25 mg NO_3 L^{-1} yr^{-1}), and in others nitrate concentrations have even decreased slightly. Over the same period, the amounts of artificial nitrogenous fertilizers applied to cereals and other crops have increased, but it would be wrong to attribute the increasing nitrate levels in groundwater simply to increased use of fertilizers. Another possible explanation is that, for many decades during and after World War II, the total acreage for arable crop production was increased by ploughing up extensive areas of old grassland and by removing woodland and hedgerows (Addiscott, 1988b). This led to release of abundant nitrate by mineralization of the organic matter that had accumulated in the soil under these traditional land uses. For the future, nitrate losses from farmland to groundwater are most likely to be minimized by measuring the amount of mineral nitrogen present in the soil when crops are sown and then matching applications of additional fertilizer nitrogen to the predicted requirement of the crop, using a computer-based model of crop growth. However, this exercise can be confounded by atypical weather conditions, such as a heavy rainfall causing rapid leaching in the period between fertilizer application and uptake of nitrate by the crop. Other strategies for limiting losses of nitrate to water supplies were listed by Fullen and Catt (2004, pp. 92-93).

Denitrification. Within poorly drained (anaerobic) soils and sediments, nitrate is often reduced by the process known as denitrification. This involves a sequence of microbial reactions, progressively removing oxygen from the nitrate (NO_3^-) ion, to produce first nitrite (NO_2^-), followed by the gases nitric oxide (NO), nitrous oxide (N_2O) and finally nitrogen (N_2). Denitrification occurs when the oxygen normally required for aerobic microbial degradation of organic matter becomes depleted, so that facultative anaerobic bacteria (those capable of respiring with or without gaseous oxygen) are forced to obtain their oxygen from nitrate. Initially they obtain oxygen by the denitrification sequence, but when this source is also depleted, they can extract it from iron and manganese oxides, from sulphate to produce sulphide, or even from carbon dioxide to produce methane (Christensen *et al.*, 2000).

Denitrifying micro-organisms are widespread in soils and surface waters. They have also been found within aquifers at depths of 40-60 m (Francis *et al.*, 1989; Clark *et al.*, 1991) so that, where there is some dissolved organic carbon (DOC) present but little oxygen, they can remove nitrate from groundwater. Water in the Chalk usually contains rather little DOC (a national mean of approximately 0.73 mg L^{-1}) and, where the aquifer is unconfined, the water also contains too much oxygen for denitrification to occur. However, in southern Hertfordshire and north London, where the Chalk aquifer is less aerobic because it is confined beneath the Palaeogene clay formations, the water contains very little nitrate (<10 mg L^{-1}), and denitrifying bacteria have been identified, for example in a borehole at Enfield (Parker *et al.*, 1990). So the lack of nitrate in the confined aquifer could result from this process, though it has also been explained by dilution of the modern nitrate-contaminated water by mixing with ancient nitrate-free water deep in the confined aquifer (Rivett *et al.*, 2007).

The denitrifying bacteria are generally too large (typical diameter 1 μm) to move through the matrix pores of Chalk (~0.5 μm). Where they occur in confined parts of the aquifer, they must have entered through, and live on the walls of, the fissures that also permit fairly rapid water flow. Where they have been studied in detail, their characteristics are typical of *Pseudomonas fluorescens*, suggesting derivation from soil (Parker and James, 1985). Enhanced populations of denitrifying bacteria have also been observed where the Chalk's DOC content has been increased by leachate from landfill containing domestic waste (Towler *et al.*, 1985), or by contamination with petroleum hydrocarbons, for example following a large escape from an underground petroleum storage tank at an urban retail filling station (Spence *et al.*, 2005). In the latter instance, the denitrifying bacteria were an important part of the indigenous bacterial population able to biodegrade various hydrocarbons, including benzene.

Some denitrification probably occurs in poorly drained, oxygen-depleted soils within the unsaturated zone. In Hertfordshire, some of the soils on the Plateau Drift, such as those in the Batcombe (582a), Hornbeam 1 (582b) and Hornbeam 2 (582c) Associations (Section 7.7), may fall into this category. But the main soils in which denitrification is likely to attenuate the nitrate content of recharge water entering the Chalk aquifer are those of the Hanslope Association (411d) developed on chalky till in eastern parts of the county. In addition to denitrifying bacteria present in the poorly drained soils of this Association, minerals containing Fe^{2+} (e.g. siderite, pyrite) present in unoxidized layers of the till may also facilitate denitrification (Rivett *et al.*, 2007, p. 340), because Fe^{2+} accelerates the chemical reduction of NO_2^- to NO and N_2O to N_2 (Moraghan and Buresh, 1977).

Alluvial soils, such as those of the Frome (812a), Fladbury 1 (813b), Fladbury 3 (813d) and Thames (814a) Associations, play an important role in removing nitrate from surface runoff before it enters rivers and other surface water bodies. The nitrate is removed partly by denitrification in the poorly drained alluvial soils and partly through uptake by the lush riparian vegetation (Burt *et al.*, 2007).

Nitrate peaks in the unsaturated zone. Monitoring the nitrate content of water in the matrix of the Chalk at different levels in dry boreholes penetrating the unsaturated zone has shown the existence of one or more fairly discrete nitrate peaks that move downwards quite slowly, at rates ranging from about 20 cm yr^{-1} to over 80 cm yr^{-1}. As the very narrow pore necks in the Chalk matrix normally prevent drainage under gravity, the movement is thought to result from a process termed piston displacement, in which the weight of water added to the unsaturated zone by each new major rainfall event forces the water from earlier events downwards by matrix flow until each reaches the water table. The slow descent of nitrate was earlier taken to indicate that, where the unsaturated zone above the Chalk aquifer is several tens of metres thick, as it often is, it takes many decades for nitrate originating in the soil to reach the water table, so that potentially large amounts are stored for many years in the unsaturated zone. As little denitrification occurs in the unsaturated zone, this led to the concern that excess soil nitrate resulting from changes in farming methods since World War II, such as the increased use of fertilizers or the extensive ploughing of long-established pastures, may in future decades cause a sudden increase in groundwater nitrate when the peak reaches the water table (Young *et al.*, 1976). This possibility was even described as a 'chemical time bomb'.

However, the nitrate moving slowly by intergranular matrix flow through the unsaturated zone may be only a small part of the total leached from the soil. It is likely that much more has already reached the saturated zone in rapid, though episodic, by-pass and fissure flow after periods of heavy rain (Downing *et al.*, 1978). This type of flow is thought to occur once the rate of infiltration from the soil into the unsaturated zone exceeds about 2 mm day^{-1}, and probably accounts for 15-30% of the total downward water movement. However, some of the nitrate in such episodes of fissure flow may have diffused into the Chalk matrix in the upper part of the unsaturated zone, and it is probably this fraction of the leached nitrate that has subsequently moved downwards by matrix flow (Foster, 1975; Young *et al.*, 1976). The rate of downward movement of the nitrate peak is in fact similar to the rate (80 cm yr^{-1}) calculated by Smith *et al.* (1970) for intergranular matrix flow through the unsaturated zone of the Chalk, based on the downward migration of tritium (^3H) at a site in Berkshire following the testing of thermonuclear devices in the 1950s. So the nitrate peaks are probably a rather imperfect temporal record of nitrate leaching from the soil, and when they eventually reach the water table they may have little impact on the total nitrate concentration in the groundwater.

Nitrate and human health. The MAC for nitrate in drinking water has long been set at 50 mg NO_3 L^{-1}, because the World Health Authority believed that higher concentrations can lead to gastric cancer in adults and methaemoglobinaemia or 'blue-baby syndrome' (inability of the blood to absorb and transmit oxygen in infants up to about six months old). However, no links between nitrate in drinking water and these health problems have ever been unambiguously demonstrated (Addiscott, 2005, Chapter 10). This is partly because fresh green vegetables, such as lettuce and spinach, are often very rich in nitrate, so that more may be ingested from these than from drinking nitrate-rich water. But in addition Beresford (1985) and Van Loon *et al.* (1998) found no correlation between cancer and the nitrate content of drinking water, and Al-Dabbagh *et al.* (1986) showed that workers in fertilizer factories, who must be exposed to nitrate for long periods, acquired stomach cancer no more frequently than those in other occupations. Hegesh and Shiloah (1982) and Avery (1999) have also questioned the link with 'blue-baby syndrome', though this problem may have been eliminated by the recommendation that infants consume bottled water containing little or no nitrate.

In contrast, recent medical research has demonstrated that some nitrate in the adult human diet is essential for several important aspects of good health, including regulation of blood pressure and the prevention of thrombosis, bacterial infections causing gastroenteritis and fungal skin infections (L'Hirondel and L'Hirondel, 2002; Addiscott and Benjamin, 2004; Addiscott, 2005, Chapter 9). Its antibacterial effect in the gut depends upon reduction to nitrite by bacteria (probably *Lactobacillus* or *Streptococcus mutans*) living on the tongue, followed by production of the bactericidal gas nitric oxide (NO) when the nitrite swallowed in saliva reacts with hydrochloric acid in the stomach. The bactericidal effect of nitric oxide has long been exploited by the use of nitrite to preserve meat; without such treatment, in which nitric oxide is produced by reaction of the nitrite with organic acids, the bacterium *Clostridium botulinum* is able to multiply in the meat and produce the highly poisonous botulinum toxin. Nitric oxide produced in response to gastrointestinal infections is probably the main cause of blue-baby syndrome, as it binds to haemoglobin and prevents it absorbing oxygen; adults can easily reverse this reaction, but infants do not develop the same ability until several months after birth.

The 50 mg L^{-1} MAC for drinking water therefore seems to have no medical justification and is almost certainly unnecessary, though it is still enshrined in the drinking water regulations. Hitherto, nitrate has often been chemically removed from drinking water, but the national cost is currently over £30 million per year. So it is not surprising that L'Hirondel and L'Hirondel (2002) concluded: 'The history of nitrate is that of a world-scale scientific error that has lasted more than 50 years. The time has now come to rectify this regrettable and costly misunderstanding'. Alternatively, nitrate-rich water is often diluted with low-nitrate water from a different source (e.g. confined parts of the Chalk aquifer), but the necessity for this has not been proved.

Phosphorus and eutrophication. The other major plant nutrient causing diffuse pollution of water supplies, usually occurs in soils in lower concentrations than nitrate, because it is less soluble and, as a fertilizer, is used in smaller quantities (10-35 kg P ha^{-1} yr^{-1}, compared with 100-200 kg N ha^{-1} yr^{-1}). It causes no direct problems with human or animal health. Instead, its main environmental impact is eutrophication of surface water bodies. Together with the usual amounts of nitrate present in surface waters, concentrations of phosphorus even as low as 0.02 mg P L^{-1} (OECD, 1982) can lead to rapid growth of aquatic weeds and green algal blooms on the surfaces of reservoirs, lakes and wetlands (Sharpley and Rekolainen, 1997). The algae are produced in very large numbers, and when they die their decomposition in the stagnant water uses up almost all the dissolved oxygen. This leads to anaerobic water conditions and the death by asphyxiation of freshwater animals, such as fishes. The abundance of algae, lack of oxygen and production of toxins during decomposition of dead algae also impair the quality of water for recreational and industrial purposes, and make it unsuitable for drinking.

Sources of phosphorus. Most of the phosphorus entering surface water bodies does so by gentle erosion of soil, which transfers phosphorus attached to finer soil particles, such as clay, iron oxides and organic matter. The organic matter partly originates from animal manures, which are often very rich in phosphorus. This fine particulate-P is transferred mainly in shallow sheet runoff or even lateral interflow within the topsoil rather than in the more erosive surface flows that create rills and gullies, as the latter transport mainly coarser (silt and sand) particles, which carry much less phosphorus (Stone and Walling, 1997). In areas of more erodible (very sandy or silty) soils, such gentle erosion events are widespread during and after moderate rainfall events, so the fine particulate-P that they concentrate from the soil becomes a major source of diffuse surface water pollution. Very little of the phosphorus from arable fields is transported as soluble-P in solution. However, discharges of municipal sewage, industrial wastewaters and runoff from farmyards into surface water bodies are important point sources of soluble-P, locally supplementing the diffuse inputs from arable fields. Also, artificial land drains can transport both fine particulate- and soluble-P from clay-rich soils into minor surface water bodies (ditches and small streams) at field margins, and drainwaters from soils that have received frequent superphosphate applications consequently often exceed the OECD minimum for eutrophication (0.02 mg P L^{-1}).

Phosphorus in groundwaters. The amounts of fine particulate-P and even soluble-P entering groundwaters by direct recharge through soils or by indirect recharge from contaminated surface waters are usually quite small.

This is probably because P is sorbed onto iron oxides, clays and organic matter in the unsaturated zone above the aquifer (Leinweber *et al.*, 1997). However, the capacity to absorb P may be exceeded if concentrations of soluble-P in percolating water exceed a certain value. In drainwaters from plots of the Broadbalk Winter Wheat Experiment at Rothamsted, the concentrations of soluble-P are virtually constant (<0.15 mg L^{-1}) where the soil has received low annual rates of superphosphate since 1843, but increase to >1.5 mg L^{-1} at greater application rates (Heckrath *et al.*, 1995). It seems that this particular soil (Batcombe series on Plateau Drift over Chalk) can effectively retain soluble and other plant available P up to a maximum of about 60 mg kg^{-1} soil, but is likely to lose P by leaching to the groundwater where the 60 mg P kg^{-1} limit has been exceeded because of repeated large superphosphate applications.

Phosphorus in river waters. Riparian vegetation can remove some of the soluble-P from surface runoff and interflow before it enters surface water bodies. But once the particulate-P in surface runoff from soils enters the different physico-chemical environment of surface water bodies as part of the fine sediment load, much of it becomes soluble and thus available to aquatic algae living beyond the riparian zone. Together with inputs from point sources, such as sewage outfalls, this accounts for the heavy soluble-P contamination of most large rivers in Britain (Muscutt and Withers, 1996). The few long-term records of phosphorus concentrations in English chalk rivers usually show rapid increases from the 1950s to at least the late 1970s (Environment Agency, 2004). In the early 1980s, there was a decrease in use of household and industrial detergents containing phosphorus, some of which previously entered the rivers through sewage outfalls. However, even after this source was minimized, amounts of P sufficient to cause eutrophication of surface waters have been maintained, largely because of increased use of P fertilizers and increased runoff and erosion of arable soils.

Controls on phosphorus losses. Although the importance of phosphorus as a plant nutrient has been known probably for several centuries, the small amounts required for moderate growth of grass and most arable crops were originally met from natural soil resources (organic matter and minerals such as apatite), supplemented by animal manures and pulverized animal bones (bonemeal). However, experiments begun at Rothamsted Experimental Station in the mid 19th century by Lawes and Gilbert demonstrated that more soluble forms of phosphorus, obtained by treating bones or rock phosphates with sulphuric acid (later also phosphoric acid), had very beneficial effects, especially on the growth of root crops. By about 1880, Lawes had amassed a small fortune from the sale of the artificial phosphate fertilizers (superphosphate) produced in this way at a factory in Deptford, East London (Dyke, 1993). During the 20th century, the widespread use of superphosphate in arable farming led to increases in the total phosphorus content of most arable soils in Britain. This happened because it is more difficult to match superphosphate application rates with crop requirements than it is with inorganic sources of nitrate, and farmers consequently erred on the generous side. Also, as with nitrate, large amounts of phosphorus were often also added to the soil in animal manures, mainly farmyard manure and slurry, but were not taken into account when considering crop requirements. Withers *et al.* (2001) estimated that the average surplus phosphorus added to UK soils, but not taken up by crops, consequently increased from about 7 kg ha^{-1} yr^{-1} before World War II to over 20 kg ha^{-1} yr^{-1} in the 1970s. The surplus phosphorus is temporarily retained in the soil by sorption on iron oxide, clay and organic particles. But as it is the transfer of these particles during gentle erosion events that leads to much of the diffuse phosphorus pollution, it is very likely that the increasing use of superphosphate fertilizer has been a major cause of the rising levels of soluble-P and of eutrophication of surface water bodies.

Since about 1990, eutrophication in Britain has been reduced by a range of measures (Withers and Jarvis, 1998), including (a) decreasing application rates of phosphorus fertilizers, taking careful account of the phosphorus applied in animal manures so that supplies are better matched to crop requirements, (b) developing better analytical methods for assessing the amounts of soil phosphorus available to plants, (c) avoiding soil erosion and (d) treatment to remove much of the phosphorus from municipal sewage outfalls and industrial effluent.

Nevertheless, there are some parts of Hertfordshire where surface water bodies remain at risk of eutrophication. These include areas where (a) sandy and silty soils are likely to suffer gentle erosion, especially because of surface crusting, and the runoff from them is likely to be delivered to lakes, wetlands or water-courses, and (b) drainage water from artificially drained and heavily fertilized clay-rich soils enters ditches at field margins. Delivery of P-containing runoff to surface water bodies depends on their proximity and the presence of either connecting channels (drains, ditches, culverts, gateways, roads, etc) or barriers (hedges, bunds, temporary ponds, etc) in the landscape. Winter is often a critical season, because both surface runoff and flow from artificial field drains are likely to be greater than at other times. Also crop growth and uptake of nutrients are much slower in winter, so it is important to delay applying P fertilizers until late winter or spring when growth rate increases. As with nitrate, minimizing the effects of phosphorus pollution therefore depends upon farm management practices in relation to geomorphological features and the distribution of soil types.

A particular eutrophication problem has arisen in the River Ver and lake in Verulamium Park in St Albans, where large numbers of Canada Geese and other birds are fed throughout the year by visitors to the park. The bird droppings enrich the water in both nitrogen and phosphorus. In summer, these nutrients are partly removed by riparian vegetation, but this is less effective in winter when there is less plant growth and the birds are fed more generously by sympathetic visitors.

Industrial sources of water pollution

Hydrocarbons. Spillage, leakage or casual disposal of hydrocarbons, especially petroleum products and chlorinated solvents, are a common threat to Chalk groundwater resources, especially where the soil cover is thin and coarse-textured, or where there is rapid entry to the unsaturated zone through dolines. Potential point sources of pollution include fuel storage sites, military installations, airfields and sites for metal-working, electronics, automobile production, pharmaceutical, photographic and dry-cleaning industries. Soakaways for disposal of drainage from urban streets, roads and motorways on the Chalk outcrop can also introduce petrol, oil and other contaminants, though these should now be retained in interceptor tanks, through which the drainage water passes before entering soakaways. The MACs for most hydrocarbons in drinking water are very low (<1 mg L^{-1}), so small amounts of such compounds can contaminate large volumes of groundwater. The most toxic are the BTEX compounds (i.e. benzene, toluene, ethylbenzene and xylene) and methyl tertiary butyl ether (MTBE), which are carcinogenic and consequently have MAC values as low as 10 μg L^{-1}.

A few hydrocarbons (e.g. MTBE) are miscible with water, but most are only slightly soluble or immiscible. The latter, known in the water industry as non-aqueous phase liquids (NAPLs), move mainly in fissures, but in the unsaturated zone of the Chalk they are partly absorbed into the fine matrix pores, so that the volume of a plume from a surface spillage steadily decreases as it moves downwards. If the spill is small or the unsaturated zone thick, the plume may never reach the saturated zone. Water soluble compounds are more likely to reach the water table, mainly by fissure flow, but may also enter the slow moving matrix water by diffusion. With both NAPLs and water-soluble compounds, entry into matrix pores prolongs their persistence, especially if they are not readily biodegradable. Lateral movement of pollutants may also occur by fissure flow in the direction of the hydraulic gradient, thus spreading the pollution zone at depth beyond the original limits of any surface spillage.

Petrol and diesel oil are lighter than water and only slightly soluble in it. Consequently, they float and spread laterally if they reach the water table. Any indigenous bacteria in the aquifer with access to oxygen can often adapt, multiply and, over years or decades, degrade such hydrocarbons to harmless compounds (Lloyd *et al.*, 1991). In contrast, chlorinated hydrocarbons, such as dichloroethane, dichlorethene, trichlorethylene, trichlorethane, tetrachloroethylene, carbon tetrachloride, trichloro-fluorethene and other common industrial solvents, are toxic to bacteria and therefore resist biodegradation. They are also heavier than water, and can persist for decades after sinking into the oxygen-depleted saturated zone of the Chalk (Lawrence and Foster, 1991), perhaps even reaching the base of the aquifer and then migrating down its slope. Unless they are removed or encapsulated within an impermeable membrane, both very difficult and expensive operations, the pools of chlorinated hydrocarbons in these situations slowly degrade anaerobically over centuries or even millennia to release a range of toxic or even carcinogenic volatile organic compounds into the groundwater (Mackay, 1998). If this happens, water supply wells or boreholes exploiting affected parts of the aquifer have to be permanently shut down and replacement supplies sought by drilling new wells some distance from the source of pollution.

It is therefore important that planning applications for storage, use or sale of hydrocarbons are assessed very strictly, especially where they relate to sites over an unconfined aquifer. For example, industrial sites using large quantities of chlorinated hydrocarbons and sited on thin Chalk soils, such as the Rendzinas and Brown calcareous earths widespread in north Hertfordshire, should have multi-layered barriers able to contain any leakage from storage tanks. In the Luton and Dunstable areas, where the unconfined Chalk aquifer beneath thin permeable soils has been widely polluted over decades by a range of local industries, the only viable cleanup system has been expensive water treatment at each abstraction point (Longstaff *et al.*, 1992).

A group of compounds known as polychlorinated biphenyls (PCBs), widely used in the electrical industry, are also resistant to microbial degradation, but often do not reach the groundwater because they are strongly sorbed on organic matter and clay in the soil.

The Buncefield disaster. Probably the largest potential incident of industrial pollution of the Chalk aquifer in Hertfordshire resulted from the fire in December 2005 at the Buncefield depot (TL 0808) of Hertfordshire Oil Storage Ltd, owned jointly by Total and Chevron, on the eastern side of Hemel Hempstead. Following a massive explosion caused by accidental ignition of escaping petroleum vapour, an enormous fire involving several fuel storage tanks persisted for several days, leading to a plume of black smoke that closed the nearby M1 and extended downwind for several tens of kilometres. The explosion and fire were the largest ever recorded in peacetime Britain. Because of site containment, little or no petroleum entered the aquifer through the overlying cover of Plateau Drift (Soil Association 582a). However, there was considerable concern that pollution of both surface and groundwater might result from the large amounts of foam that were eventually used to extinguish the fire. As a result, some local wells down-gradient from the site, for example in the nearby Ver valley, were immediately shut down as a precaution to prevent possible pollution of water supplies.

Bromate. For over a decade, a large section of the Chalk aquifer under central Hertfordshire has been contaminated by bromate, a man-made chemical used in various industries and known to be carcinogenic. This was first detected in May 2000 at two of the groundwater sources of Three Valleys Water Company (now Veolia Water Central), one at Hatfield where the initial concentration was 138 μg L⁻¹, and another at Essendon, where it was 7 μg L⁻¹. The MAC for bromate in ozone based water treatment processes, introduced in 2001, is 10 μg L⁻¹. The Hatfield source, then supplying 9 ML day⁻¹, was immediately taken out of supply, and an investigation

initiated to locate the source of the contamination. Analyses of samples from private water supply wells and existing observation boreholes soon established the source as a former chemical works at Sandridge, about 10 km up-gradient of Hatfield, which had been redeveloped in the 1980s as a residential site. New observation boreholes established that the plume extended at least 20 km eastwards into the lower Lea valley (Fig. 9.6), where it affected some groundwater sources of Thames Water. It is thought to be the largest pollution plume from a point source in the UK. The eastward direction of the plume is similar to that of groundwater flow in the area suggested by dye tests at the North Mymms swallow-holes (Section 9.3), and may be related to the WSW-ENE syncline mentioned in Section 5.7.

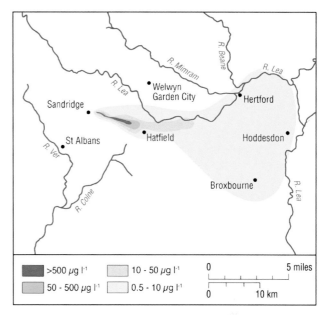

Fig. 9.6. *Bromate plume in Chalk groundwater originating from former chemical works at Sandridge.*

Ongoing monitoring by the Environment Agency showed that up-gradient from Hatfield concentrations remained fairly stable, but there was a trend of increasing concentrations down-gradient, which was superimposed on an annual fluctuation that was probably influenced by seasonal recharge patterns. In 2005 a scavenge pump was installed to abstract contaminated water from the Hatfield source; the water was treated with ferrous chloride to reduce the bromate to bromide and was then discharged to a trunk sewer for normal treatment at a sewerage works before being discharged into the River Colne. This decreased the down-gradient concentrations of bromate, but periods of non-pumping led to rapid increases at the down-gradient sources. However, the sewer capacity restricted the volumes that could be abstracted, so modifications were made to the sewer in 2006, and in 2007 the Environment Agency issued an abstraction licence to Veolia Water Central for the purpose of aquifer remediation. By the end of 2009, 2020 kg of bromate and 4667 kg of bromide had been removed from the aquifer and safely disposed of.

In June 2002, the Sandridge site was designated contaminated land by St Albans District Council, and in 2005 the Environment Agency served Remediation Notices on two 'appropriate persons', requiring them to undertake assessment of the pollution though no remediation. However, after a Public Inquiry in April 2007, the Remediation Notices were changed to require the 'appropriate persons' to meet the costs of (a) the scavenge pumping by Veolia Water Central and Thames Water, (b) the Environment Agency's monitoring of the plume, (c) determining the amount of pollutant remaining at the source and (d) the flux of pollutant leaving the site. Yet ten years after it was first discovered, there has been no attempt to clean up the source, and the only beneficial effect has been the action by the two water companies to protect their own assets and ensure that their public supply water meets the regulatory guidelines and is safe to drink.

Pollution from landfill sites

Despite increasing efforts to recycle domestic waste, Hertfordshire currently disposes of over 300,000 t yr^{-1} in landfill sites. Most of this now goes to sites outside the county, but there are still a few active sites within Hertfordshire and also many closed sites, including disused chalk quarries and pits in gravel over Chalk, from which leachate can drain directly into the Chalk aquifer. As well as the contaminants present in commercial and industrial wastes, the domestic waste included in landfill decomposes under aerobic and anaerobic conditions to produce surprisingly polluting leachates, which are often acidic, saline and rich in metals and organic compounds. Unlike many other point sources, which are temporary in nature, landfill sites can often persist as sources of groundwater pollution for many decades.

Minimizing leachates. The unsaturated zone of the Chalk aquifer can attenuate many of the contaminants in landfill leachates, provided they are released in small amounts and the unsaturated zone is thick (Blakey and Towler, 1988; Williams *et al.*, 1991). The acidic components are of course rapidly neutralized by reaction with chalk, though this often leads to precipitation of heavy metals on fissure walls. The increase in pH allows the survival of bacteria, which would otherwise die in the original acidic environment and, in the presence of oxygen and some DOC, these are able to degrade most organic compounds, though small amounts of more resistant compounds such as phenols may reach the water table. Ammonia formed by decomposition of organic matter is oxidized (nitrified) to nitrate, also by aerobic bacterial activity. However, the salinity of landfill leachates, which often contain Na$^+$, K$^+$, Cl$^-$ and SO$_4^{2-}$, is not diluted and may even be increased in the unsaturated zone. Where the unsaturated zone is thin or absent, most of the attenuation processes (other than acid neutralization) are much less effective, and it is necessary to exercise greater care in containing the effluent or collecting it for special treatment and disposal off-site.

Before the 1970s, landfills were constructed without any impermeable liner, on the assumption that any leachates would be dispersed and diluted to safe levels in the large volumes of groundwater beneath. But after numerous infamous cases of groundwater pollution resulting from this approach, landfill sites have been developed with increasingly elaborate systems for containment, collection and treatment of leachate. Initially a thin layer of clay or puddled chalk was laid on the floor of a quarry destined for landfill (Mather and Young, 1980), but this method was often unsuccessful because the layer did not remain sufficiently impermeable. Synthetic polymeric geomembranes such as butyl rubber and high density polyethylene sheeting have also been used as impermeable liners, but physical puncturing during installation or slow chemical degradation resulting from the strongly acidic and saline nature of many industrial and domestic wastes can result in leakage (Seymour, 1992).

The system now preferred, as at the Wapsey's Wood Landfill Site (SU 9789) near Gerrards Cross, is a thick (1-2 m) basal layer of puddled and compacted imported clay (e.g. London Clay) beneath heat-welded geomembrane sheets, and also a thick capping of absorbent clay (bentonite) sandwiched between geotextiles to restrict ingress of rainwater. Finally, the whole site is covered with 1 m of subsoil and a layer of topsoil, so that it can be restored to agriculture or forestry within a few years. The waste is compacted during infill to reduce contact with any infiltrating water, and the small amounts of leachate produced are collected in sumps and removed periodically through pre-installed vertical pipes for treatment and disposal off-site.

Methane. Compaction of infill and an impermeable capping together can delay the generation of significant leachate for several years, but often result in the production of large amounts of methane by anaerobic decomposition of putrescible organic matter. This must be carefully vented to the atmosphere, where it is oxidized to carbon dioxide. A completely impermeable capping that prevents gas from escaping to the atmosphere may cause it to migrate laterally off-site, where it can accumulate and cause a fire or explosion. Alternatively, as methane is a valuable fuel, recently constructed landfill sites often have wells for collecting and using it to heat buildings or generate electricity. For example, methane collected from the Wapsey's Wood site is fed to a power station capable of generating 8 megawatts of electricity.

Restoration. Completely encapsulating waste and limiting the rate of decomposition may be less satisfactory in the long run than encouraging rapid breakdown under controlled conditions, so that the landfill becomes inert and unpolluting more quickly, perhaps within a few decades. Modern management of landfill sites is therefore based on (a) careful siting, for example avoiding areas where recharge occurs within the catchment of water supply wells (Leeson *et al.*, 2003), (b) the provision of a semi-permeable capping and facilities for collection of methane, and (c) either sumps for collection of leachate for treatment off-site or slow controlled release of leachate through a semi-permeable liner, such as a thick layer of either artificial fine-grained absorbents or natural loamy sediment containing organic matter and a range of clay minerals, which encourages the necessary attenuation reactions to occur beneath the landfill. To prevent surface erosion, which might expose the infill, the topsoil is stabilized by a grass cover for a few years, followed by establishment of annual arable crops or woodland.

Remediation of contaminated groundwater

Once groundwater is known to be polluted, there are various remediation techniques available. The first, as adopted with the bromate plume at Hatfield, is known as pump and treat. This involves pumping the polluted water to the surface and then removing contaminants by one or more treatments depending on the pollutants present (Nyer, 1992), before distributing the cleaned water into the public supply system, discharging it to a surface water body or returning it to the aquifer by artificial recharge. Second, some volatile organic pollutants can be lost to the vapour phase by the process of air-stripping, which involves mixing the water with air by cascading it down a tower containing numerous baffles. The contaminated air is then further cleaned by passing it through activated charcoal. These techniques have been used very effectively to decontaminate the Chalk groundwater polluted with chlorinated hydrocarbons in the Luton/Dunstable area (Longstaff *et al.*, 1992). Some dissolved metallic ions, such as Fe^{2+} and Mn^{2+}, can also be removed by enhanced exposure to air, so that they are precipitated as the much less soluble Fe^{3+} and Mn^{3+} or Mn^{4+}. Third, sorption on a charcoal filter is also a very effective but rather expensive method of removing other pollutants directly from water, including less volatile organic compounds, pesticides, herbicides, metals and metalloids (e.g. As).

Apart from these *ex situ* methods, there are also various *in situ* techniques for decontaminating the water before it is pumped to the surface. The activity of aerobic bacteria in decomposing harmful pollutants within the aquifer can be stimulated both by pumping air into the saturated zone, a process known as air sparging, and by injecting organic nutrients, such as lactate or acetate. Air sparging has proved very successful in removing MTBE from groundwater, and organic nutrients have been used to stimulate bacterial sulphate reduction, so that metallic ions are precipitated as sulphides. Repeated treatment of groundwater by these methods can be achieved by recirculating it in specially engineered wells until decontamination is complete.

9.6. Landslides, ground heave and subsidence

These civil engineering problems are worth including in a chapter on hydrogeology, because they are caused principally by local increases in the water content and pore-water pressure in soils and soft unconsolidated sediments. Rising pore-water pressure is important with both landslides and subsidence because it forces the constituent particles apart, thus reducing the friction between them and allowing

movement relative to one another under the influence of gravity.

Landslides. These are rapid movements of these wet materials down previously stable slopes. They occur when the pore-water pressure in slowly permeable materials (e.g. clays or silts) on slopes is increased by intense rainfall, poor drainage or the groundwater table rising close to the land surface. Another critical factor is often steepening of the slope by erosion or excavation of its toe, and sometimes the increased weight of material dumped at the head of the slope can trigger movement. Initial landslipping may rupture water or drain pipes, and inputs of water from these may then increase the fluidity of already mobile material.

On the more extensive outcrops of major clay formations, such as the Gault Clay in northern parts of Hertfordshire, the London Clay in the south of the county, and the chalky tills in the east, landslides occur on quite gentle slopes (2-8°), most commonly by reactivation of the widespread clay-rich head deposits or periglacial mudflows (Hutchinson, 1991), which originally formed during the Loch Lomond or Dimlington Stadials of the Late Devensian (Section 6.10). The slip plane at the base of these slides is either between the head deposit (i.e. the previously mobile active layer) and the *in situ* clay beneath, or within a buried soil developed on the underlying clay during the Windermere or an earlier Interstadial. Each is a potential zone of increased pore-water pressure, because the compact underlying clay is likely to contain less water than either (a) the head deposit, which often includes some additional material coarser than clay, or (b) the humus-enriched, aggregated and therefore more porous buried soil. Reactivation can be triggered by various factors, including those leading to increased pore-water pressure (rainfall, inadequate drainage) and those influencing forces applied to the slope. Shallow excavations, such as those for a road, railway or foundations for a large building, can be sufficient to initiate a landslip by removing support from the toe of a slope.

On river banks or lake shores, minor landslips can occur in almost any deposits, even where there is no previous slip plane, as a result of large changes in surface water levels. A prolonged rise in water level leads to increased pore-water pressures in the deposits forming the bank, and a subsequent abrupt fall removes the weight of water that was previously supporting the slope, whereas the pore-water pressure within the bank decreases much more slowly. River bank collapses resulting from this sequence of events, and perhaps induced also by undercutting during the period of increased flow, may partially dam the river, divert its course or create a temporary lake, and cause overbank flooding.

Thick loess deposits, such as those present in many of the river valleys of Hertfordshire, are especially prone to minor landslipping when pore-water pressure is increased by rapid water inputs and drainage is slow (Northmore *et al.*, 1996). This is because loess has a very open structure, giving a low bulk density (often <2.0 g cm^3) and high total porosity (usually 45-55%). In its original periglacial condition, the constituent silt particles are not closely packed, as in a waterlain deposit, but are often propped apart by clay bridges. This structure probably originated by formation and expansion of ice lenses within the aeolian sediment by freezing of interstitial water during or soon after deposition. When the interstitial ice melted, the water gradually evaporated in the dry atmosphere, first retreating to form meniscii between silt particles. The small amounts of clay dispersed in the water were drawn into the meniscii, thus forming the bridges between the silt particles when the water finally evaporated. As the clay bridges are easily dispersed when the pores again become water-filled, the sediment can collapse, losing as much as a third of its original porosity. Much of the loess in river valleys has been reworked by water, and has consequently suffered this structural collapse already, making it more stable. But deposits lying above Holocene water levels, as on river terraces, may retain the original open (metastable) structure, which makes them more susceptible to landslips.

Countermeasures. The main way of preventing landslips in clay cuttings involves digging drainage trenches at 6-20 m spacing, so as to lead surface and groundwater away from the area (Hutchinson, 1984). The main cut-off trench is dug a short distance back from the slope crest. Other trenches are dug to form a diagonal network on the slope itself, so as to intercept any surface runoff or shallow interflow and carry it into a toe trench. The trenches are usually dug deep enough to intercept any slip surfaces and are back-filled with gravel. Where the slip surface is no deeper than about 2 m, it is sometimes possible to inject cement grouting into it, or the landslip toe can be supported with walls constructed of sheet steel or reinforced concrete piling. Potential zones of waterlogging can also be drained by drilling horizontal galleries in from the toe of the slope. Gravel-filled interceptor trenches and galleries have been used to stabilize cuttings through the London Clay for the M25 in south Hertfordshire, such as the Ridgehill cutting (TL 204025), which suffered a small landslip soon after the road was constructed. They have also been used, though less successfully, in the cutting on one side of the M1 near the London Gateway Service Area near Scratch Wood (TQ 2094) in north London.

Ground heave. This is another engineering problem related to changes in the water content of clay-rich sediments and the surface soils formed from them. In Hertfordshire, the most susceptible deposits are the Gault Clay, Reading Beds clay, London Clay, Plateau Drift and chalky tills, and soils developed directly on them without thick horizons in coarser overlying deposits. Clays swell on wetting because some of the layer-silicate minerals they contain, such as smectite and vermiculite, take up interlayer water, forcing the layers apart. The resultant swelling can be sufficient to cause heaving of the ground surface or of cut surfaces beneath foundations for buildings and other structures. The main problems are associated with large seasonal changes of water content, heave occurring because of swelling in wet autumn and winter periods after shrinkage resulting from prolonged water loss in dry summers. Shrinkage causes a polygonal pattern of near-vertical cracks to develop; on rewetting,

initially these are closed by horizontal expansion, but further swelling is translated into a strong upward force. Vertical ground surface movements up to 50 mm have been recorded on London Clay soils as a result of annual changes in moisture content (Building Research Establishment, 1996).

The main process of water loss leading to shrinkage is not evaporation but transpiration through plant leaves. The largest transpiration losses per unit area of land are through trees, which have very large leaf areas and root systems that extract water from considerable depths (often 5 m or more) below the land surface. The most problematic are deciduous species adapted to wet conditions, such as willow, elm, alder and poplar (Skempton, 1954), which transpire at high rates in hot dry periods, then lose their leaves and cease transpiring when rainfall increases in autumn. The near uniform distribution of heave resulting from a dense stand of trees is often less damaging than the localized ground movements adjacent to single large specimens, which can reach 100 mm. For this reason, trees that may eventually achieve a considerable size should not be planted close to (within 30 m of) buildings with foundations on clays. However, the extent of ground heave is related to the proportion of swelling minerals in the clay. For example, in Hertfordshire, the London Clay usually contains less than 40% swelling clay minerals (almost entirely smectite), so that ground heave is not recognized as a major problem (Burnett and Fookes, 1974). The same is true of the Gault Clay, but the Reading Beds clay, the Plateau Drift derived from Reading Beds and the chalky till in north-eastern parts of the county are more variable and sometimes contain a greater proportion of smectite, even reaching 100% of the <2 µm fraction in some parts of the Reading Beds (Perrin, 1971).

The desiccation cracks formed during summer in clay-rich soils can provide pathways assisting the rapid penetration of autumn rain to depths of 1-4 m. This may lead to sudden landslip movements by elevating porewater pressures close to slip surfaces, or may pollute surface water bodies by rapidly transferring nitrate, pesticides, etc from the topsoil to land drains that feed into ditches or streams.

Subsidence. Subsidence occurs when a cover of unconsolidated sediments collapses into cavities beneath, which have been created either naturally by slow dissolution of soluble bedrock (e.g. Chalk) or artificially by mining operations. Again, the trigger is usually an increase in pore-water pressure in the cover sediments as a result either of heavy rain or of inputs of water from surface runoff, leaking drains or artificial channels.

Most examples of severe subsidence in Hertfordshire have arisen from collapse into cavities formed originally by chalk mining for production of agricultural lime or bricks (Section 10.3). Over the last 25 years, Peter Brett Associates (PBA) have compiled a national Mining Cavities Database from field observations, commercial projects involving subsidence investigations and a comprehensive literature review (Edmonds, 2008). It contains over 16,000 records of mine locations (excluding coal mines). Within Hertfordshire there are currently 107 records of known chalk mine cavities

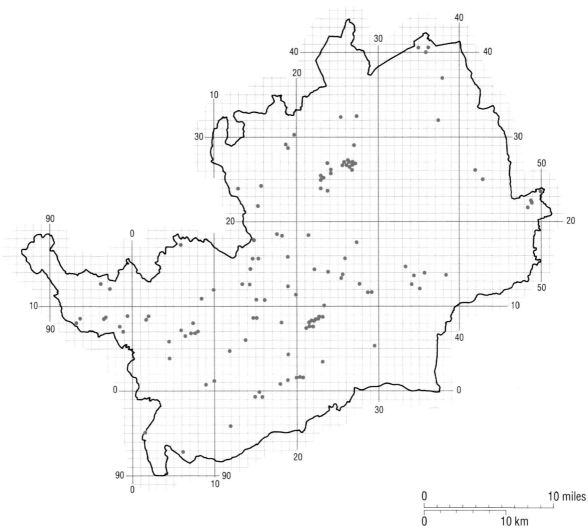

Fig. 9.7. Distribution of known chalk mines in Hertfordshire.

(Fig. 9.7), many in urban areas, such as Hemel Hempstead, Stevenage, Hatfield, St Albans, Radlett, Welwyn Garden City and Berkhamsted. Many mines are not shown on Ordnance Survey maps, and in any case many predate such maps because they are 150-200 years old, so records are very incomplete. There are probably at least 50 others yet to be located with the county.

Most chalk mines are typically at depths of 10-20 m below the ground surface. When first dug, the roof and walls were strong and self-supporting and not usually affected by building or other activities on the surface. However, over time some have become unstable and liable to collapse. In particular, the shaft entry can be disturbed by overloading, vibration or escapes of water, leading to local subsidence. Wooden or metal cappings to shafts tend to become undercut and weakened with time, or may simply rot or rust. The collapse of mine tunnels at depth is associated with either pillar or roof breakdown, which result from weakening of the exposed chalk with time and the effects of percolating water. Roof collapse aided by percolating water can also occur where a solution pipe filled with loose deposits is intersected by a mine tunnel. Consequently,

heavy rain or the presence of soakaways or leaking water mains or drains above a mine can accelerate subsidence.

Recent subsidence problems associated with chalk mines in Hertfordshire. The depressions formed by collapse into chalk mines are often termed crown holes. A recent example, in June 2007 at Nash Mills (TL 071048) near Hemel Hempstead, was 4+ m deep and 6 m across and undermined a semi-detached house (Plate 81), the walls of which suffered diagonal cracks. Although the house was built only on shallow strip foundations, it survived further damage until 2008 when the crown hole was filled with concrete mixed with a foaming agent. On drying, this mixture sets to form a porous, but strong and inexpensive supporting material. As there is no historical evidence for lime or brick kilns nearby, this mine was probably dug to extract chalk for whiting used in the manufacture of paper at Dickinsons Nash Mills works.

Damaging collapses into chalk mines in Hertfordshire have occurred over the last 30 years in the Briars Lane area of Roe Green, part of Hatfield (TL 223083). In May 1978, a hole measuring 4.6 m × 3.6 m opened suddenly in the grounds of Briars Lane Infants School, and further collapses

Plate 81. Crown hole undermining house foundations at Highbarns, Hemel Hempstead, 2007.

nearby led to the demolition of four pairs of semi-detached council houses (Anon., 2007). Boreholes, geophysical (microgravity) and CCTV and laser underground surveys in 2004-2005 indicated a network of mines 7-20 m deep and with volumes of 50 m³ to 1000 m³ in Chalk overlain by till and glaciofluvial sands and gravels. The school was closed in 2006, and the voids have subsequently been filled with foamed concrete. The mines here are thought to date from periods between the 18th century and World War II.

In 1990, similar ground subsidence affected five houses, a road and car park at Southwark Close, Stevenage (TL 255265). The properties were evacuated, the extent of the mine was investigated and the ground stabilized by grouting with a sand-cement mixture. The hole that appeared below the gable end wall of one house was about 5 m across and several metres deep. Another notable subsidence affected the Student Union Bar at the University of Hertfordshire (TL 215073) in 1993, and caused the floor to drop by more than 1 m over a collapsing chalk mine. In rural areas, the passage of farm machinery has often caused the collapse of chalk mine entry shafts. Edmonds (1987) recorded examples on farmland near Markyate (TL 061177) and Kimpton (TL 184181).

Natural chalk cavities. Solution pipes, dolines or sinkholes are much more common than chalk mines, with 1276 currently known in Hertfordshire (Edmonds, 2008) (Fig. 9.8). They are concentrated at the feather edge of the Upnor and Reading Formations, where they probably originated as swallow-holes (Section 9.3), transmitting water from streams flowing over impermeable Palaeogene deposits into the Chalk beneath. Others occur where the Chalk is directly

overlain by proto-Thames or glaciofluvial sands and gravels. There are also many beneath the edges of the Plateau Drift on the Chiltern dip-slope, and a few small examples occur beneath Devensian coombe deposits or fluvial gravels on the floors of Chiltern dry valleys. These situations mainly reflect the permeability of the overlying deposits, but aggressive acidic runoff from the London Clay is also important close to the Palaeogene outcrop. Higginbottom and Fookes (1971) suggested that elsewhere solution pipes are inherited mainly from cold stages of the Pleistocene, because cold water can contain more carbon dioxide in solution than warmer water and is therefore more active in dissolving chalk.

Over much of northeast Hertfordshire, there are fewer sinkholes than in other parts of the county (Fig. 9.8), perhaps because many of those formed before the Anglian Stage were removed by subglacial erosion. They seem to have been lost mainly from buried valleys, such as those of the Hitchin and Stevenage areas. However, the numerous large pipes filled with Reading Beds sand, which were exposed in the long cutting for the A505 Baldock by-pass across the Weston Hills (Plate 28), shows that some of the glaciated areas suffered little or no erosion at this time.

The subsidence problems created by naturally formed cavities are probably more common than those resulting from chalk mines, but are less severe because most have been at least partially infilled with sediment that has slumped into them or has been introduced by inflowing surface water over long periods. Most solution pipes are 1-5 m across and, although they may reach depths of 20-50 m, the sediment infill restricts vertical collapse at the surface during any subsidence event to less than 3 m (usually <1 m). As a result, damage to buildings is usually

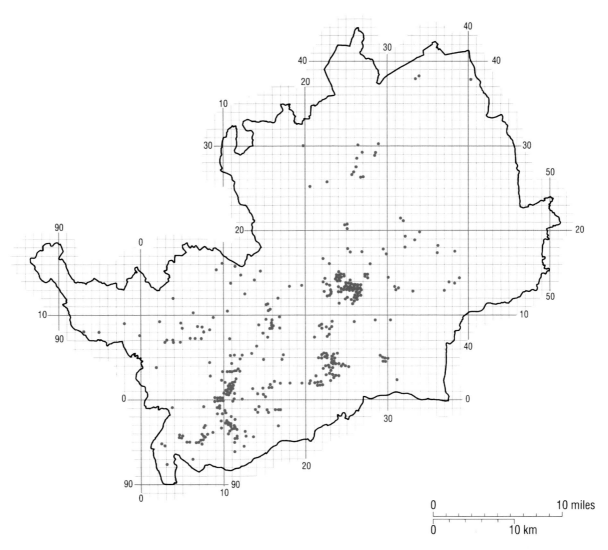

Fig. 9.8. Distribution of natural solution cavities in the Chalk of Hertfordshire.

less than that resulting from chalk mines. Minor subsidence is nevertheless very common in areas where chalk lies close to the surface beneath any permeable deposit. It has been recorded most frequently where damage to buildings has resulted, as in Berkhamsted, Hemel Hempstead, Hertford, London Colney, Rickmansworth, St Albans, Tewin, Watford, Welwyn and Welwyn Garden City.

In the early developmental stages of a solution pipe (Fig. 9.9), a small cavity formed by slow dissolution of chalk at the interface with the overlying permeable deposit is partially infilled with illuvial clay carried down in the percolating water. The clay is deposited together with flints and other insoluble residue of the chalk where the pH increases at the interface, thus forming a thin layer equivalent to Clay-with-flints *sensu stricto* (Section 5.3). But, because dissolution of chalk usually exceeds the accumulation of illuvial clay and insoluble chalk residue, the cavity increases in size and the resulting pipe is then filled by downward slumping (suffusion) of loose wet sediment from the base of the overlying cover. Repeated suffusion leads to progressive upward migration of the cavity through the disturbed pipe infill and cover deposit, until it reaches

the surface. Further dissolution of chalk then widens and deepens the pipe. If its base reaches the water table, the roots of the infill are likely to be dispersed and transported through horizontal fissures, tubes or caverns created by flow close to the water table (Lord *et al.*, 2002). Horizontal cavities of this type, filled with illuvial clay and inwashed sand, were previously exposed at Castle Lime Works near South Mimms (TL 230025) and were described by Kirkaldy (1950a) as sheet pipes. The movement of sediment away from the base of the pipe then accelerates downward slumping of the infill, so that the cavities migrating towards the surface increase in size and produce surface depressions (dolines) of increasing diameter and depth. Many dolines widen as they approach the surface to form funnel-shaped depressions. Consequently, the margins of the resulting areas of subsidence are less sharply defined than those of chalk mines.

Recent subsidence problems associated with natural cavities in Hertfordshire. The most damaging example of subsidence over a natural cavity in recent years was at Hutton Close, Hertford (TL 311129) in 1992, when a burst water main led

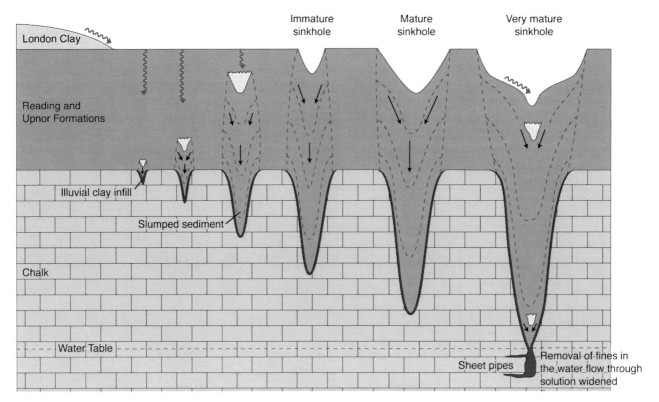

Fig. 9.9. Sequence of events leading to formation of subsidence cavities (white) and sinkholes (redrawn from Edmonds, 2008).

to subsidence of residential property and garages over an area about 30 m × 18 m. Subsequent ground investigation attributed the large area of subsidence in glaciofluvial gravel over Chalk to a cluster of solution pipes extending down to the water table about 30 m below the surface. Further subsidence damage in Hertford occurred in December 1996 at St Andrew's School in Calton Avenue (TL 309132), also on glaciofluvial gravel over Chalk. The area was about 4.5 m across, and subsidence of about 0.1 m caused settlement of a boiler house and staff toilets. The movement was probably triggered by blocked disposal drains from the toilets and a swimming pool, which caused water to flood over the surface. The buildings had to be demolished and the ground stabilized by cement grouting. In July 1997, two further properties in Tudor Way, Hertford (TL 312132), were damaged by subsidence following a heavy storm. Initially, tilting of a rear patio and garden subsidence were noted. When this was investigated, a void 12 m long, 7 m wide and 25 m deep in glaciofluvial gravels over Chalk was found extending beneath the properties and associated with the house drains. The ground was stabilized by injecting cement grout to depth through vertical and inclined holes, which were drilled beside and below the properties to strengthen the ground and partially fill the void.

In April 1997, cracking of the party wall and distortion of windows and doors in two properties at Longcroft Lane, Welwyn Garden City (TL 237122) occurred by subsidence over a solution pipe 4-7 m across and 25 m deep, again in glaciofluvial gravels over Chalk. The ground movement was probably triggered by leakage of water from cracked drains, and the properties were stabilized by cement grouting.

Properties in the Mill End district of Rickmansworth (TL 0494), where proto-Thames gravels overlie Chalk, have also been subject to subsidence damage.

Subsidence over solution cavities is also common in rural areas, causing holes to appear suddenly in fields, which can be dangerous to farm animals or machinery. For example, in 1986 a steep-sided sinkhole, 9 m wide and 9 m deep, appeared close to the Cuffley Brook (TL 309046) at the foot of Darnicle Hill (Banks *et al.*, 1995). As the Palaeogene sequence here is about 14 m thick over the Chalk, it is likely that this cavity originated by repeated suffusion of Palaeogene deposits, possibly into a large natural cavern-like void in the Chalk beneath (Edmonds, 2008). Plate 82 shows a smaller cavity, about 2m across and 2 m deep, that formed

Plate 82. Cavity formed by collapse of thin Palaeogene deposits into a natural solution hollow in Chalk on the margin of the Cowcroft Palaeogene outlier (SP 982012).

suddenly after heavy rain in a field at the feather edge of the Reading Formation on the south-western margin of the Cowcroft outlier (SP 981012).

Prevention of subsidence. First, it is important to minimize pore-water pressures in the permeable cover deposits close to solution pipes and the entrances to chalk mines. Consequently, any seepage of surface water into the cover deposits from temporary streams, leaking drains, water supply pipes, soakaways, ornamental ponds or swimming pools should be avoided. Sites for soakaways should be chosen where the chalk surface is even and without cavities, as indicated by trial pitting or shallow boring. Where such areas are not available, bored soakaways to carry water into the chalk to a depth well below any solution pipes should be considered, though these are subject to approval by the Environment Agency because contamination of the aquifer is likely.

On building sites where chalk mines or solution pipes are identified, there are several engineering options to prevent damage by subsidence. These include infilling cavities with hardcore or foamed concrete, injection of cement grouting under pressure to compact and harden loose disturbed deposits, and bridging cavities with a concrete raft or beams supported on piles driven into stable ground nearby. The last of these techniques was used by the Romans in at least two of their buildings in Verulamium, which had archways built into their foundations to bridge solution cavities in the underlying chalk (Niblett and Thompson, 2005, p. 108). In modern buildings, all engineering options require detailed exploration of cavity dimensions and ground conditions by probing, drilling or shallow geophysical techniques, such as the electrical resistivity imaging system recommended by Rigby-Jones *et al.* (1997). Piles are subject to a range of problems where they are driven into collapsing ground, and compaction grouting is usually the most successful option (Crockford and Bell, 1996).

Where deep excavations for buildings, roads, railways, underground car-parks and quarries intersect the local water table, flooding, collapse of the excavation sides and partial infilling with loose sediment or joint-bounded blocks of hard rock are all likely. These hazards can be avoided by excluding the groundwater or by artificially lowering the groundwater table. Groundwater is often excluded by lining the excavation with interlocking sheet piles driven vertically into the ground or piles sealed with a grouting of cement or bentonite. To prevent immediate collapse before the piles are installed, the ground can be frozen or temporarily dewatered by pumping. Artificial lowering of the water table can be achieved by pumping water from a specially drilled shallow well or wellfield to create sufficient local drawdown.

9.7. The hydrogeology of Hertfordshire canals

Hertfordshire is crossed by two very different systems of navigable waterways (Fig. 9.10): in the east, the very old system based on the Rivers Lea and Stort, and in the west the much later and larger Grand Junction Canal and its several branches, which were incorporated into the Grand Union Canal system in 1929. The history of the Lea-Stort system mainly concerns the widening and deepening of a navigable waterway. By contrast, the Grand Junction Canal crosses the Chalk of the Chilterns, and from the beginning struggled to find sufficient water, a problem that exercised the minds of some of the great engineers of the 19th century.

The Lea-Stort system

These rivers have been used for transporting goods for centuries (Hadfield, 1969, p. 9). Acts of Parliament authorizing works to improve navigation on the Lea date from the 15th century onwards. By the mid-18th century, the volume of goods, mainly corn and other agricultural products into London and 'manure' and coal out to Hertfordshire and East Anglia, had increased to the point where Colonel Sir George Jackson (later Duckett) of Bishop's Stortford, Second Secretary of the Admiralty, patron of Captain Cook and a major landowner, initiated moves to improve navigation on both these rivers. By 1770, the engineers Thomas Yeoman (1700-1781) and John Smeaton (1724-1792) of Eddystone Lighthouse fame, had supervised the construction of the Lea and Stort Navigations essentially as we know them today.

Both the Lea and Stort are supplied by several tributaries on the Chalk dip-slope to the north. Below their confluence near Rye Meads (TL 391093), they are probably also fed by groundwater from Quaternary gravels and the sandy Palaeogene deposits that are in hydrological continuity with the very transmissive part of the Chalk aquifer in the lower Lea valley. Here the availability of water is indicated by the numerous lakes and reservoirs now occupying abandoned gravel workings. Thus water supply was never a significant problem for navigation on these rivers.

The Grand Junction Canal

In contrast to the Lea-Stort system, water supply was always a problem for the Grand Junction Canal in the west of Hertfordshire (Richardson, 1969; Hadfield, 1981; Faulkner and Paget-Tomlinson, 1993; Evans, 2008). Approved by Parliament in 1793 to connect the industrial Midlands with London, the main trunk canal has its highest summit (c. 120 m OD) near Tring. Here, by a flight of seven locks, it rises about 30 m from the Vale of Aylesbury to pass through the Tring Gap in the Chiltern escarpment at the village of Bulbourne. This is one of the main through gaps or wind gaps of the Chilterns, where the upper parts of two valleys back into one another, one falling north-westwards towards Marsworth (SP 9114) and the other southeastwards down the dip-slope into the Bulbourne valley at Berkhamsted (SP 9807). A cutting up to 8 m deep along the crown of the gap allows the highest lock to maintain a constant water level for about 5 km from Bulbourne (SP 928138) to Cow Roast (SP 958104). The high relief of the Chilterns and the scarcity of surface water together posed a considerable challenge to the canal engineers, especially as the Grand Junction was ambitiously built as a 'broad canal'. As such,

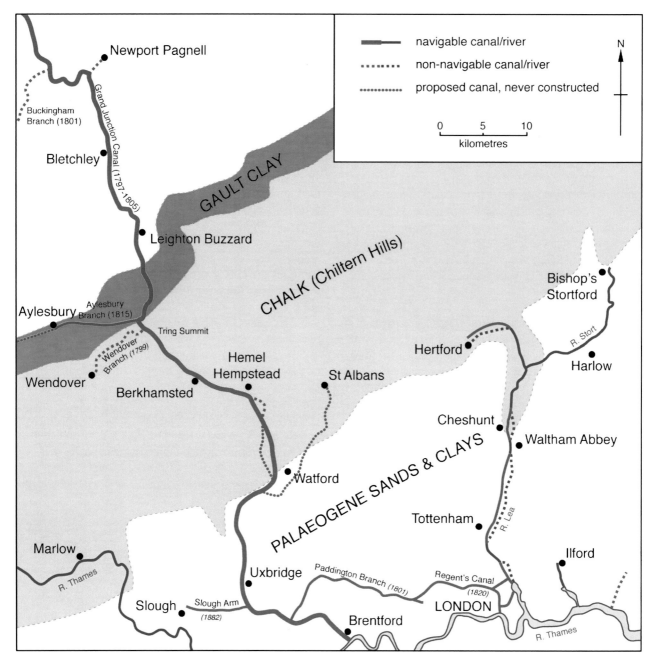

Fig. 9.10. Summary map of the canals (completed or never constructed), navigable and non-navigable rivers of the Hertfordshire area in relation to bedrock geology.

it is more than twice the normal canal width, so that large barges from the Trent and Thames basins could pass one another between locks. Given the hydrogeological context of the canal's highest summit near Tring, the requirement for more than double the normal water supply was unfortunate (Richardson, 1969; Faulkner and Paget-Tomlinson, 1993, pp. 72 & 133-145).

The Grand Junction Canal Company's proposals regarding water supply seemed acceptable to Parliament, because they provided for the Wendover Branch canal (Fig. 9.11), which has been known as the Wendover Arm since 1929. The primary purpose of this level and therefore lock-less branch canal was to feed water to the main canal, so it was cut at the same altitude (*c.* 120 m OD) as the summit lock near Tring (Plate 83). Apart from a stream fed by the Well Head Spring

at Wendover in the southwest (SP 870082), the feeder canal receives water from only two other small streams, one at Tring (SP 923128) and another at Bulbourne (SP 928138). These two streams are fed by springs arising from the Zig Zag Chalk Formation, and the large flow at Wendover is apparently from the well-jointed Totternhoe Stone (Fig. 3.2).

However, a long central section of the Wendover Branch (Fig. 9.11) receives no spring water from above, although there are several springs at lower levels than the canal, particularly near Wilstone. In consequence, despite repeated puddling with clay and even lining with asphalt, this part of the branch canal always leaked badly, and at an early stage it was closed off and left derelict (Plate 84). It is likely that this leakage was influenced by the gentle NW-SE trending Tring syncline (Moffat *et al.*, 1986, p. 341; see also Section

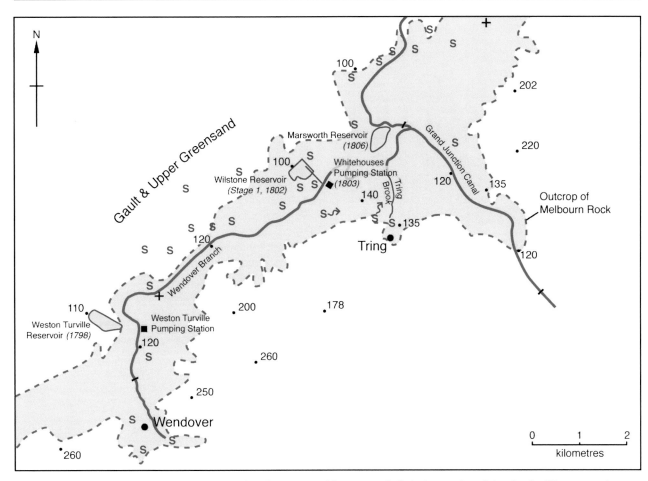

Fig. 9.11. Plan of the Wendover Branch Canal within the outcrop of the Lower Chalk (pale green), and details of William Jessop's water saving scheme 1802-1814; s = sites of springs; spot heights (m OD) in black.

Plate 83. Junction of the Wendover Arm (right) and Grand Union Canal just above the highest lock at the Tring summit (SP 928138) near Bulbourne.

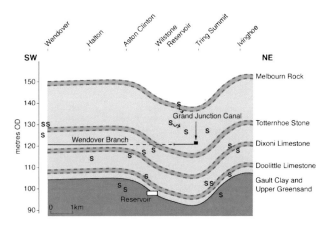

Fig. 9.12. *SW-NE section along the line of the Wendover Branch Canal, approximately parallel to the strike of the Chalk, showing the Tring Syncline and positions of nearby springs projected onto the line of section. Springs above the Wendover Branch between Wilstone and Tring do not flow into the canal, but drain northwards into the Tring Brook (Fig. 9.11).*

5.7), which lowers Chalk horizons by as much as 15 m along its axis. Preliminary micropalaeontological analyses by Dr Haydon Bailey (Network Stratigraphic) of chalk samples indicate that the springs below the Wendover Branch near Wilstone flow from the well-jointed Dixoni and Doolittle Limestones within the West Melbury Marly Chalk Formation or Chalk Marl (Fig. 3.2), which together with the Totternhoe Stone immediately above have been lowered in the south-western limb of the Tring Syncline (Fig. 9.12). Thus the Wendover Branch was cut partly in more permeable strata of

the Zig Zag Chalk Formation rather than entirely in the less permeable West Melbury Marly Chalk.

The development of the whole Grand Junction Canal system was significantly delayed by the problem of water shortage at the Tring Summit (Evans, 2008). Despite outspoken public demand, branch canals such as those to Aylesbury and Northampton, for which parliamentary approval had been given between 1793 and 1795, were delayed for up to 21 years. Other proposed canals were never constructed, including branches to St Albans, Hemel Hempstead, Shefford and Bedford. Likewise, between 1810 and 1819, plans for a Western Junction Canal extending the Aylesbury Branch to connect with the Wiltshire and Berkshire Canal near Abingdon, were repeatedly blocked by the Grand Junction Canal Company, partly because water for that potential joint venture would have had to come from the already struggling Tring Summit.

Nevertheless, the Buckingham and Paddington Branches, which were close to the properties of the Grand Junction Canal's chief promoter (the Marquis of Buckingham) and its chairman (Sir William Praed), were completed as early as 1801. To provide the additional water required for these, the first phase of the Wilstone Reservoir (SP 9013) was opened in 1802. This reservoir is safely bottomed in the Chalk Marl close to its base above the Gault Clay, and is fed by three springs which, as mentioned earlier, probably issue from the Dixoni and Doolittle Limestones. In a scheme designed by the leading consultant engineer William Jessop (1745-1814) (Hadfield and Skempton, 1979, p. 124), the Wilstone Reservoir was connected by a horizontal underground pipe, or 'heading', to the base of a vertical shaft below a coal-fired steam pump at Whitehouses (SP 911127) beside

Plate 84. *Reconstruction work by the Wendover Arm Trust on the dry derelict part of the Wendover Arm Canal near Little Tring (SP 911129).*

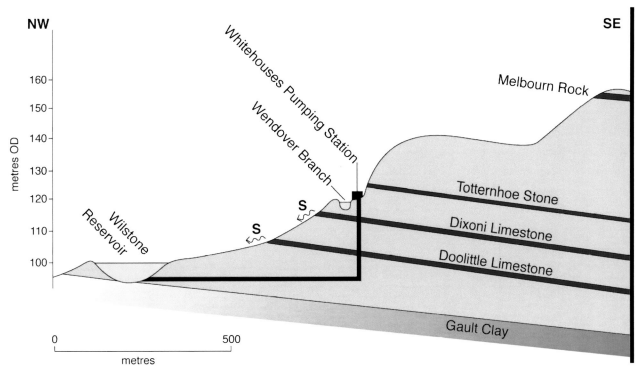

Fig. 9.13. NW-SE (down-dip) section through Wilstone Reservoir and Whitehouses Pumping Station.

the Wendover Arm (Fig. 9.13). A particular frustration for the engineers was that this and later headings were very difficult to construct owing to the large volumes of water encountered as the works cut through the permeable Dixoni and other limestones within the Chalk Marl. Nevertheless, from 1803, water from the Wilstone Reservoir could be pumped up to the Wendover Branch, and was thus made available to the Grand Junction Canal at the Tring Summit.

The Marsworth Reservoir (SP 9213) (Fig. 9.11) followed in 1806, and in 1814 another heading and pump were installed to lift water from the pre-existing Weston Turville Reservoir (SP 8609) into the Wendover Branch. This reservoir had been constructed in 1798 to compensate a water-powered corn mill, whose upstream water had been largely diverted into the Wendover Branch. However, by 1814 the corn mill had been acquired by the Grand Junction Canal Company and converted to steam power.

Thereafter, increasing canal traffic and plans for the prestigious Regent's Canal in London, eventually completed in 1820, led to an even greater demand for water from the Tring Summit. The great engineer Thomas Telford (1757-1834) had advised the Grand Junction Canal Company from time to time since 1805 and, after Jessop's death in 1814, he agreed to become the company's Chief Engineer. During the next four years, Telford worked with the Resident Engineer Benjamin Bevan (1733-1833), a surveyor and mathematician from a Leighton Buzzard brewing family, who from 1801 had been an early disciple of William Smith (1769-1839), often known as the 'Father of English Geology' (Torrens, 2003). Unlike the notoriously neglected Smith, both Telford and Bevan were early members of the Geological Society of London, founded in 1807 (Woodward, 1907). Together they developed Jessop's earlier ideas and created the basis

of the modern system to supply water to the Tring Summit (Fig 9.14).

Under the supervision of Telford and Bevan, two further spring-fed reservoirs were constructed, one at Tringford (SP 9113) and the other at Startopsend (SP 9113). The Wendover Branch was closed by a stoplock near Little Tring (SP 917129), and at Drayton Beauchamp (SP 901118) water from the south-western section was drained down to the Wilstone Reservoir. Thus the leaky central section of the Wendover Branch was isolated. By 1818, Telford had installed a powerful Boulton and Watt coal-fired steam engine at the Tringford Pumping Station above the Tringford Reservoir at Little Tring (SP 918130). By way of headings, this pump lifts water from the Wilstone, Startopsend and Tringford Reservoirs up to the north-eastern remnant of the Wendover Branch and thence to the Tring Summit (Fig. 9.15). The Wilstone Reservoir has also been able to supply water to the Aylesbury Branch (1815) simply by way of culverts and existing streams (Fig. 9.14). Telford's system worked well, and the earlier pumping stations to the southwest were not replaced; Whitehouses was closed in 1835 and Weston Turville in 1839.

After Telford's time, the Wilstone Reservoir was expanded twice more, in 1836 and 1839. Finally, in 1848 a 32 m deep borehole, which Telford had recommended in 1818, was eventually drilled at Cow Roast (SP 959103), to supply yet more water to the Tring Summit. Sited a few kilometres down-dip, this borehole abstracts water mainly from the Middle Chalk close to the axis of the Tring syncline along the Bulbourne valley (Section 5.7, Figs 5.10-5.12). Along the synclinal axis, the transmissivity of the aquifer is greatly increased and, in consequence, this and other wells and boreholes in the area are reliable providers of

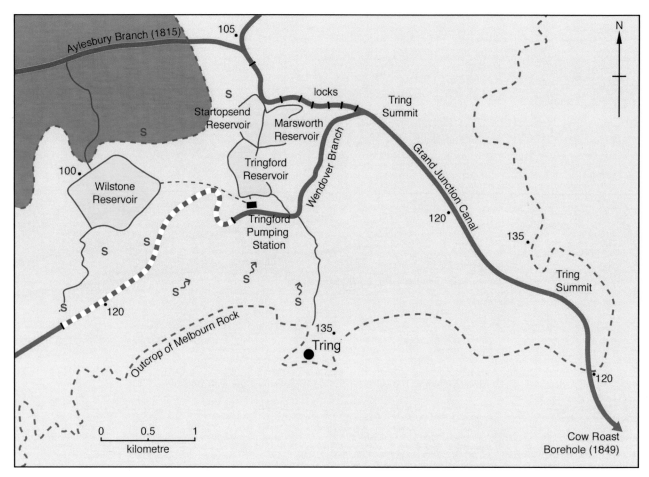

Fig. 9.14. Detailed map of the north-eastern part of the Wendover Branch showing the improvements initiated by Thomas Telford between 1814 and 1818. Wilstone Reservoir was later enlarged in 1836 and 1839.

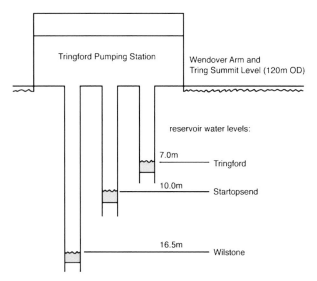

Fig. 9.15. Water levels at Tringford Pumping Station and in the three reservoirs from which it draws water (redrawn from Evans, 2008).

water in a region otherwise peppered with drilling failures (Richardson, 1969).

From as early as 1809, Dickinson's paper-making company, sited downstream on the River Gade below Hemel Hempstead, had taken legal action against the Grand Junction Canal Company alleging losses of water at their paper mills to the canal (Mather, 2008, p. 70) (Section 9.3). Eventually in 1818, the canal company agreed to return water from the canal into the River Gade above the paper mills. Nevertheless disputes continued even after the mills had changed from water to steam power, and Dickinson's had themselves sunk very productive boreholes at each of their four mills. Only a year after the Cow Roast borehole came onstream in 1849, Dickinson's secured from the Court of Chancery a 'perpetual injunction' preventing abstraction from it (Mather, 2008, p. 80) on the grounds that it was lowering the water table and decreasing the flow of the river. However, the injunction was soon overturned and the Cow Roast borehole still provides water for the Tring Summit.

Within the last few years, the Wendover Arm Trust, a group of volunteer engineers and others, with well known actor and canal boat enthusiast David Suchet as their President, have begun to re-open this largely derelict canal. Using modern techniques, particularly butyl rubber and concrete linings to prevent the notorious leaks, the navigable north-eastern portion of the Wendover Arm at Little Tring has already been extended by about 0.5 km. Another short section has been completed and water-filled near the Aston Clinton by-pass (SP 9011), and preparatory work is well advanced along other sections (Plate 84). So eventually the Wendover Branch/Arm may for the first time in over 200 years fulfil its original purpose as a navigable feeder of water to the Tring Summit of the Grand Junction/Union Canal.

Chapter 10.

Mineral resources and church building stones

John Catt, Clive Edmonds, Haydon Bailey and Chris Green

10.1. Introduction

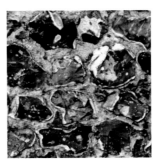

At present Hertfordshire has three main natural mineral resources – chalk, brickearth and aggregate (sand and gravel). Previously, coprolites for the manufacture of superphosphate fertilizer were an important fourth resource from the Cambridge Greensand (Sections 2.8 and 7.7), but this industry disappeared in the late 19th century. Chalk and brickearth have been extracted in the county for centuries, but the scale of current working is fairly small. Aggregate extraction started in the late 19th century and expanded rapidly in the mid-late 20th century. Since then it has declined considerably, though it is still the main mineral resource obtained within the county. Washed and screened, it is mixed with cement for the manufacture of concrete used in the construction industry. Most of the cement used in Hertfordshire is manufactured from chalk, some of which may originate in the county, though most is from other parts of England. Nationally, some cement is also produced from other limestones quarried outside Hertfordshire, such as the Carboniferous Limestone. For concrete and roadstone, crushed rock also imported from outside the county and sea-dredged gravels are increasingly used as a substitute for local aggregate.

Almost all modern construction is based on concrete, bricks, cement and steel, though some hard natural rocks (granite, gneiss, etc) are imported in polished slabs for decorative cladding of larger buildings. Prior to the production of bricks, cement and concrete, the main construction material was timber, but local rocks were also used for larger buildings such as churches and large country houses. In Hertfordshire, the main local rock used in this way was flint, a by-product of chalk extraction, and also available cheaply from arable fields in many parts of the county. Most flint was dressed and set in mortar as a facing for timber-framed buildings or garden walls. Because of the high cost of early hand-made bricks, dressed flint was also mixed with them in house construction. For the same reason, it was also mixed with ashlar (hewn masonry) in church construction. Hertfordshire builders developed considerable skills in creating attractive geometric patterns using dressed flint in these ways, including the chequerboard pattern of flint and Totternhoe Stone seen in several churches near Totternhoe (Curran, 2005, p. 21).

Before the mid-19th century, numerous small pits were opened as required for the extraction of chalk, brickearth and gravel in various parts of the county. However, increased demand in the later 19th and early 20th centuries led to fewer large extraction sites, often in areas where the deposits are thicker and more extensive. Over the last 30 years demand has decreased and almost all the previous quarries have been used for landfill, so that Hertfordshire now has very few exposures of these mineral resources. The infilled pits and quarries are shown as 'made ground' on recent BGS maps.

Hertfordshire has much smaller resources of clay suitable for brickmaking than neighbouring counties, especially Bedfordshire, which has exploited its thick deposits of Oxford, Ampthill, Kimmeridge and Gault Clays for this purpose. In the Lower Greensand of the Leighton Buzzard area, Bedfordshire is also favoured by large resources of sand, which have been exploited in the past as building and foundry sands, filtration media and even for glassmaking (Shephard-Thorn *et al.*, 1986). In the Woburn Sands and Clophill areas, the Lower Greensand also contains workable seams of fuller's earth, which were used until quite recently in numerous industries, including the manufacture of paper, cosmetics, drilling fluids and foundry sands, for refining edible oils and as pet litter. Because Mesozoic formations older than the Gault Clay are thin or absent over the Palaeozoic London Platform (Section 2.6), Hertfordshire lacks all these resources even at depth below the surface.

10.2. Aggregate

British aggregate resources have been assessed by the British Geological Survey's Mineral Assessment Unit (MAU), which operated in Hertfordshire mainly in the 1970s. Using evidence from a fairly dense array of boreholes, they defined resources of sand and gravel as aggregate according to the following criteria: deposits with less than 40% silt plus clay (<63 μm); more than 1 m thick; lying within 25 m of the ground surface; and with an overburden:aggregate thickness ratio less than 3:1. Reports on the work in Hertfordshire were written by Squirrell (1974), Hopson (1979, 1981), Gozzard (1981a, 1981b), Hopson and Samuel (1982) and Harries *et al.* (1982). The maps accompanying these reports distinguish (a) resources exposed at the surface, (b) resources forming a continuous layer beneath an overburden up to 25 m thick and (c) resources forming a discontinuous layer beneath such an overburden. However, the coverage is not quite complete because urban and some other areas were not assessed. A summary map of workable deposits occurring on the BGS Hitchin map (sheet 221), including terrace gravels in the Ivel, Purwell and Hiz valleys of north Hertfordshire, was provided by Hopson *et al.* (1996, Fig. 33).

Hertfordshire's aggregate resources originated mainly as river terrace or glaciofluvial gravels, most of which occur in the Vale of St Albans. Here, the river terrace deposits are dominantly those of the pre-Anglian proto-Thames (Section 6.3), which yield high quality aggregate because they consist almost entirely of very durable pebbles of flint, quartzite and vein quartz. However prior to extraction, it is often necessary to remove an overburden of till, Hoxnian interglacial deposits, gelifluction deposits or clay-enriched interglacial soil horizons. The last two provide an inferior type of aggregate known as hoggin, which has been used locally for surfacing farm trackways and paths. In many areas, the proto-Thames gravels are overlain by Anglian glaciofluvial gravels (Section 6.6), which have also been extensively worked as aggregate, though they are usually of lower quality because they contain slightly more silt and clay and a range of less durable, non-siliceous clasts, such as chalk, Jurassic limestones, calcareous fossil shells and phosphatic nodules. Glaciofluvial gravels, proto-Thames gravels (Kesgrave Sands and Gravels) and Red Crag have also been worked at several sites close to the Hertfordshire boundary in western Essex, for example at Elsenham (TL 550265) (Hopson, 1981).

The post-Anglian river terrace gravels of the present Hertfordshire rivers (Section 6.10) have also been extensively quarried, especially in the Colne and lower Lea valleys. These deposits underlie Holocene floodplain alluvium and also form low terraces rising a few metres above the river floodplains, which probably date from the Devensian and Wolstonian cold stages. In east Hertfordshire the post-Anglian river gravels are usually similar in composition to the glaciofluvial gravels, from which they are largely derived. In western parts of the county they are composed mainly of flint with small amounts of quartzite and vein quartz pebbles, although in unweathered form they

- ● Proto-Thames, glaciofluvial and post-Anglian river gravels
- ● Northaw Pebble Gravels
- ● Stanmore Pebble Gravels

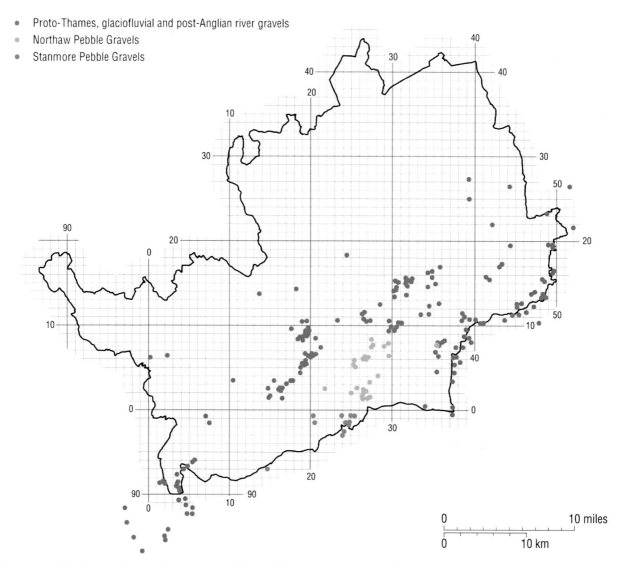

Figure 10.1. Distribution of past and present gravel pits exploiting various formations in the Hertfordshire area.

can be unsuitable as aggregate because chalk fragments are abundant.

South of the Vale of St Albans, the Pebble Gravels (both Stanmore and Northaw Pebble Gravels) were previously worked in numerous small shallow pits. As the Pebble Gravels are very thin, they have never been exploited commercially in extensive workings. All the small pits are now disused; most are overgrown with vegetation or flooded where the gravels rest on London Clay, though some have been infilled. There are numerous small dry excavations spread across Harrow Weald Common (TQ 147929), where the Stanmore Pebble Gravels rest on the sandy and fairly permeable Claygate Member of the London Clay Formation (Barrow, 1919b).

In addition to these resources of Quaternary age, sand from the Eocene Reading Formation was previously worked at a few sites in eastern Buckinghamshire for production of mortar in building. Sites most recently active included Bulstrode Park (TQ 975885), where the sand was extracted beneath a cover of proto-Thames gravels, and Chesland (SP 917060) near Dundridge Manor.

Figure 10.1 shows the numerous sites in the Hertfordshire area where aggregate is known to have been worked from these various deposits over approximately the last century. There are over 160 pits where proto-Thames, glaciofluvial and post-Anglian river gravels have been exploited, and at least a further 38 shallow pits where Stanmore and Northaw Pebble Gravels were previously worked. Some of the locations shown for Stanmore Gravels in Figure 10.1 in fact represent two or more pits; for example, Old Fold Manor Golf Course near Monken Hadley (TQ 2497) was constructed in 1910 over numerous small pits. Most of the gravel pits have been abandoned, and the only sites where clean gravel sections are visible because aggregate is currently being extracted (2010) are in the large workings at Panshanger (TL 2812), Tyttenhanger (TL 1904), Westmill (TL 3416) and Symondshyde (TL 1910). A section still exposing glaciofluvial gravels in the disused Rickney's Pit is shown in Plate 85.

Despite the enormous number of pits that have produced aggregate in the past, the decline in extraction since 1990 (Fig. 10.2) means that Hertfordshire is now a net importer of aggregate, with consumption exceeding sales by at least 300,000 t yr^{-1} (County Development Unit, 2007). The main sources outside the county are marine-dredged sand and gravel and crushed rock from quarries in both the UK and

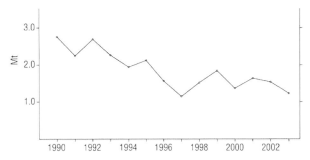

Figure 10.2. Production of aggregate in Hertfordshire 1990-2003.

Plate 85. Glaciofluvial gravels exposed in Rickney's Pit (TL 323157) near Chapmore End.

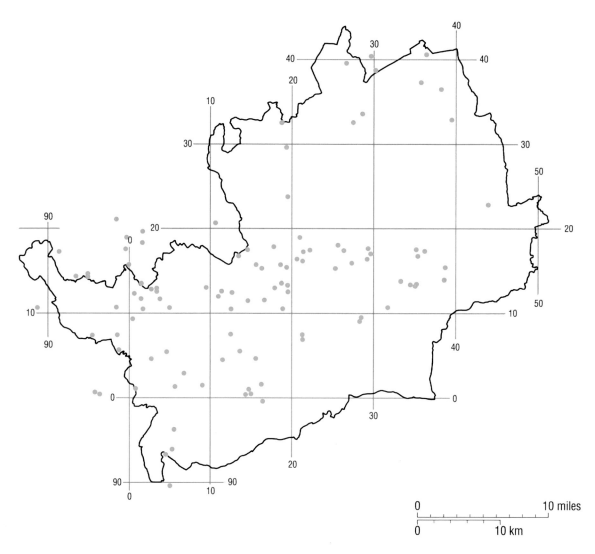

Fig. 10.3. Distribution of past and present chalk pits in and near Hertfordshire.

abroad. To meet national demand until 2016, the Aggregates Working Party for the East of England Region proposed that Hertfordshire's contribution to aggregate extraction should be 1.99 Mt yr⁻¹, which involves making planning permission available for this level of aggregate extraction (i.e. 13.93 Mt for the 7 year period 2009-2016). After a lengthy site selection process, the County Council suggested future aggregate extraction should be confined to three main areas within the county:

To the west of Hatfield on Green Belt land of the former Hatfield Aerodrome (mainly in grid squares TL 1908 and 2008); here there is an extensive but generally thin overburden of chalky till
To the north of Hertford between Sacombe Road and Wadesmill Road (B158) and south of Chapmore End (mainly in grid squares TL 3215 and TL 3216); this area has no overburden of till and is an extension of the now disused Rickneys Pit (TL 323157)
Northeast of London Colney between Junction 22 of the

M25 and Courser's Farm (mainly in grid squares TL 1903, TL 2003 and TL 2004); this area also has no overburden, and is an extension of the existing Tyttenhanger Quarry.

10.3. Chalk and flint

Quarrying and mining for chalk and flint have a long history in the Hertfordshire area. There were flint mines of possible Late Neolithic age at Pitstone Hill, Harrow and Oxhey (Section 8.5), and chalk or flint was worked in the Roman period in quarries and shallow underground mines at several sites, including those on either side of King Harry Lane on the south-eastern side of the Roman city of Verulamium (Niblett and Thompson, 2005, pp. 135-136).

As Chalk lies close to the surface over most of Hertfordshire, its outcrop is marked by numerous open and backfilled quarries (Fig. 10.3), where it has long been excavated for a wide range of uses. In addition, from the late 18th century through to the early 20th century, underground mining of chalk was common in the county (Fig. 9.7). Since at least the mediaeval period it has been used for the manufacture of agricultural lime and lime mortar and in the production of bricks, tiles and pottery. It has also been compacted to make rammed chalk floors and roads, for building foundations and as an easily carved ornamental building stone (as at Totternhoe). More recently it has also been extensively used in cement-making (as at Kensworth), and chalk from the quarries of OMYA at Steeple Morden is currently used in a wide range of commercial products, including whiting for manufacture of paper, as a filler in paints, whitewash, putty, rubber, plastics, drugs, cable sheaths and UPVC window frames, and as an additive in flour, breakfast cereals (e.g. Weetabix) and malt drinks (e.g. Horlicks).

Although flint has been used mainly as a building stone (Section 10.1), some was also utilized in the past in the manufacture of bone china or porcelain. However, little is used in this way today because the industry has greatly declined. In the 1960s, the Rugby Portland Cement Company attempted to sell flint waste to the pottery trade from their operations at Kensworth Quarry (Shephard-Thorn *et al.*, 1994), but it proved unsuitable probably because carbon dioxide was generated on firing from small amounts of included chalk, which were expensive to remove by acid pre-treatment. Flint nodules were also once used for flooring in barns and other rural buildings, and those separated from the chalk currently quarried at Anstey (TL 395329) are bound into wire containers (gabions) for use in non-load bearing construction (e.g. the exterior wall of the Roman mosaic and hypocaust museum at St Albans, TL 135069).

Chalk mines

Across southern and eastern England generally, a range of chalk mine forms are known. They include deneholes, chalkangles, bellpits, chalkwells and larger pillar-and-stall mines. Deneholes occur mainly in Kent and Essex (Pearman, 1966; Le Gear, 1979), and chalkangles are found only in Berkshire (Bennett, 1887; Money, 1906). The other three types are all found in Hertfordshire (Edmonds *et al.*, 1990), where there is also a single example of an underground folly dating from the mid-19th century: Scott's Grotto at Ware (TL 357138), created by the poet John Scott (Pearman, 1982; Clarke, 2007). Most of the chalk mine records in Hertfordshire in the Peter Brett Associates (PBA) Mining Cavities Database (Section 9.6) represent individual mines, but some bellpit and chalkwell sites are multiple mines. The depth of mining depended mainly on the thickness of cover deposits (usually Plateau Drift or Anglian till) over the chalk, so it was not unusual for mines to extend to 10 m or more below the ground surface. They were always dug in dry chalk above the water table.

Bellpits. In Hertfordshire, these have been mentioned by Sherlock (1922, p. 24) near Tring and Northchurch, by Sherlock and Pocock (1924, p. 10) at Sandridge, and by Wittering (1968). Within the PBA database, 10 are known,

but many more are likely. This form of chalk mine is the simplest and has been used for a long period of time, though not all bellpits are very old; some were excavated at Lee near Wendover in 1911 and others at Coleman's Green near Hatfield in 1913 (Sherlock and Pocock, 1924, p. 54). Circular shafts 1-3 m in diameter were dug down from the surface through the cover deposits and, after a sufficient thickness of chalk was left to form a safe roof, the shaft was widened and continued to depth as required, thus forming a bell- or bottle-shaped chamber. The chalk was then hauled to the surface in buckets by winch and rope. It was extracted mainly during summer and early autumn, and on closure of the mine, the spoil was thrown back down the shaft. A tree stump was sometimes used to help block the shaft before backfilling was completed.

Chalkwells. These have been reported in Hertfordshire by Young (1804, 1822), Sherlock (1922) and Gardner and Garner (1953), and others have been noted by members of the Chelsea Speleological Society (Pearman, 1976, 1982). In the PBA database, there are just over 60, but many more are suspected. They are similar to bellpits in having a circular shaft 1-3 m in diameter, with a woven basketwork cylinder installed to support the sides of the shaft where it passes through the cover deposits. After leaving a sufficient thickness of chalk below the cover deposits, three or four tunnels were driven outwards from the base of the shaft. These increased in height and width away from the shaft, and the tunnel floors were cut so as to slope up towards the shaft. Chalk was again hauled to the surface by winch and rope. The tunnels were 1.5-3 m wide and 2-5 m high, and extended 3-10 m from the shaft base. Chalkwells of these dimensions have been described from Kings Langley (Fisher and Walshe, 1944), Stevenage and Warrens Green (Wittering, 1968). Hayes (1908) described chalk mining activities at other sites near Hemel Hempstead, Tring and Shenley. Young (1804, 1822) suggested that chalkwells were dug from as early as 1793, and one of the last records dates from 1913 when a gang of chalk miners or chalk drawers was still operating in the Harpenden area (Gardner and Garner, 1953), including Rothamsted Farm (Plate 61).

Pillar-and-stall mines. Because of more continuous and prolonged extraction at former lime kiln and brick kiln sites, the chalkwells here usually became deeper, with tunnels extending for tens of metres, and often had interlinking side tunnels. In time, these developed into pillar-and-stall mines, which were sometimes accessed by adits dug from an adjacent valley side as well as by shafts from the plateau surface. The PBA database includes more than 20 records of such mines in the Hertfordshire area, though again it is likely that more await discovery.

Uses of mined chalk

For agricultural purposes, a season's output from a typical chalkwell was normally sufficient to spread over a 6 acre (2.4 ha) area. After spreading in autumn, the chalk lumps were shattered by winter frosts and incorporated into the topsoil by spring cultivations. Chalk improved the structure of clay-rich soils such as the Batcombe series, so that they drained more rapidly and were easier to plough, and the increase in pH improved crop yields by increasing the availability of some nutrients. Farmyard manure was often spread at the same time to improve soil structure and nutrient content. The beneficial effects of the chalk lasted 10-20 years before the land required re-chalking, so that over time multiple mines were dug in some areas. Some farms burned the chalk to produce their own quick-lime, which reacted more quickly than chalk with the soil. However, where farmers preferred to buy quick-lime rather than produce their own, lime kilns were established in association with chalk quarries, from which adits were often driven under nearby rising ground. In Hertfordshire, there were examples of this type of enterprise at Hill Farm Mine (TL 102009) near Leavesden (Kidner, 1910b), Daneswick Mine (TL 122043) near Chiswell Green (Sherlock and Pocock, 1924, p. 11), Roughdown Common Mine (TL 046056) near Boxmoor (Pearman, 1976) and the Elephant Hill Lime Works (TL 073065) at Bennetts End near Hemel Hempstead.

Dobson (1850) described how ground chalk was mixed with clay or non-calcareous brickearth to form bricks. The addition of chalk helped reduce the shrinkage of the raw bricks before firing (Gallois, 1993), and also acted as a flux during firing by combining with silicate clay minerals; this was thought to increase the frost resistance of the final bricks (Perrins, 2005). The maximum chalk content recommended was 25% (Searle, 1911). Brickworks with associated chalk mines were mainly located where Reading Formation clays overlie the Chalk, for example at Woodcock Hill (TQ 062926) near Rickmansworth. Such sites often operated a lime kiln as well, to make lime mortar and sell quick-lime for agricultural use.

According to Fisher and Walshe (1944), chalk was mined close to Nash Mills (TL 071049) near Hemel Hempstead, to produce whiting that was mixed with size (a glue solution) and used for glazing paper, probably at the nearby Dickinson's Nash Mills paperworks. They suggested that some of the chalk mined from the chalkwell near King's Langley (TL 047034) was also used for this purpose.

Some parts of the Chalk have also been mined locally in Hertfordshire for building stone. For example, there was an adit-entry mine for extraction of the Chalk Rock hardground north of Barkway (TL 383364), and a shaft-entry mine for extraction of Totternhoe Stone near Ashwell (TL 252395). However, for almost two millennia the main mining of Totternhoe Stone has been in south Bedfordshire near the village of Totternhoe (SP 9822) (Roberts, 1974; Curran, 2005).

The earliest known use of Totternhoe Stone from Totternhoe was in Roman times, when it was used for the foundations, hypocaust and floors of a Roman villa at Totternhoe (Matthews *et al.*, 1992). Even in this early period, the stone was also transported long distances, as a block was recorded by Codrington (1903, p. 68) from the Roman foundations of Edgware Road in London. For many

Plate 86. Ashridge House (SP 993122) near Little Gaddesden, rebuilt mainly of Totternhoe Stone in the early 19th century by the Bridgwater family.

centuries it was probably quarried from the outcrop near the foot of the Chalk escarpment near Totternhoe (SP 9822), but as the thickness of chalk overburden increased, the quarries had to be extended into adits and mines beneath the scarp-slope. The value accorded to the stone in the early Norman period is suggested by the motte and bailey castle that was constructed on the nearby promontory of Totternhoe Knolls (SP 979221), probably for protection of the quarries and mines.

From the mid-14th century probably until the Dissolution of Monasteries (1535-1540), at least two of the quarries/mines were owned by the Benedictine Abbey of St Albans. In the 14th century, the crown also had an interest in Totternhoe Stone, which was used extensively by Edward III at Windsor Castle, Westminster Palace, Langley Palace and the Dominican Priory at Kings Langley. In addition, in the pre-Reformation period private quarry owners supplied the stone to numerous parish churches, mainly in Hertfordshire and adjacent parts of Bedfordshire and Buckinghamshire, where its varied ornamental and construction uses can still be seen today (Section 10.5). In these periods, the stone was used for ashlar (hewn blocks for building walls) and to carve arches, parapets, door-frames, window-frames, fireplaces, ovens, stiff-leaf capitals, fonts, figurative sculptures, etc. From the mid-18th until the early 19th century, there was a resurgence in the use of Totternhoe Stone, when many wealthy landowners constructed new or remodelled existing houses. At that time it was used, for example, at Woburn Abbey and Ashridge House (Plate 86), also originally a monastery. Underground mining ceased at Totternhoe in the 1880s, and the mine entrances have since been sealed for safety reasons. However, small amounts of the stone are still extracted from a small quarry (TL 988222) when required, mainly for periodic restoration of existing stonework in churches and other nearby buildings, such as Woburn Abbey, Audley End and Dunstable Priory.

Totternhoe Stone has long been valued for its freestone qualities, which allow it to be sawn and carved easily without cracking in any direction. In a moist condition when initially quarried, it is soft and easily worked, but it hardens on drying to create a durable surface that preserves the fine detail of carvings. Used internally, the stone survives indefinitely, unless it is subject to abrasion. But externally it is very susceptible to frost and chemical weathering, with the result that exfoliation leads within a few centuries to almost complete loss of detail in carvings. Its durability in external walls depends on the protection afforded by overhanging eaves, and also on whether it is laid with the original bedding horizontal. However, the correct orientation has to be noted during quarrying, as bioturbation has often obscured the original bedding almost completely. Any macrostructure is dominated by widely-spaced vertical joints, which locally create fissures up to 15 cm wide.

The date when underground mining first began at Totternhoe is unknown, but when the Finnish visitor Pehr Kalm visited the site in April 1748 during a stay in Hertfordshire with the famous agricultural writer William Ellis, he noted in his diary that the workmen claimed the mines had existed for over 500 and possibly 1000 years

(Mead, 2003, p. 106). The tunnel of one mine that he entered was 41 poles (206 m) long, and similar measurements were made when the disused mines were re-examined by the Rugby Portland Cement Company in 1957 prior to working the White Chalk above the mines. A map of the complex pattern of underground tunnels drawn in the 1950s was given by Curran (2005, p. 2).

10.4. Brickmaking in Hertfordshire

Various deposits have been used for brickmaking in the Hertfordshire area. They have included the Lower Cretaceous Gault Clay, the Palaeogene Reading and London Clay Formations, Anglian tills and glaciolacustrine deposits, the 'true brickearth' (older loess) of Mid Pleistocene age, which mainly fills dolines penetrating the Plateau Drift of the Chiltern dip-slope, and the younger (Late Devensian) loess in the lower Lea valley.

Brickmaking was introduced to the county by the Romans, who produced large numbers of bricks, floor and roof tiles for use in the city of Verulamium in the 2nd, 3rd and 4th centuries CE. According to Niblett and Thompson (2005, p. 131), most of the Roman kilns were sited close the south-eastern part of Verulamium or beside Watling Street between Verulamium and Brockley Hill (TQ 172943), which suggests the main raw materials in use at that time were Reading Beds clay and London Clay. Following the end of the Roman occupation in the early 5th century, bricks and other building materials were purloined from the abandoned city and reused in the town and abbey of St Albans, especially in the mediaeval period. The Roman bricks are typically thinner than those produced in later periods, and are easily identified in mediaeval buildings, such as the tower of St Albans Abbey church (now St Albans Cathedral).

After the period of Roman production, the earliest known brick and tile manufacturing was in the late 13th century at London Colney and Hatfield (Perrins, 2005). Small scale mediaeval production was often by itinerant workers or local builders, farmers, architects or even clergymen. On a larger scale, it recommenced in the 16th century for the building of churches (Section 10.5) and large houses, such as Hatfield House (completed 1611) and Brocket Hall (completed 1760). Originally, Reading Beds clay (often mixed with Reading Beds sand) was probably the main raw material, but from the early 19th until the late 20th century a range of other deposits were exploited by numerous small brickmaking companies in the area. At present only two small brickmaking enterprises remain in the county, one at Ley Hill (SP 986012) using Reading Beds clay and Pleistocene doline infills, and the other at Pudds Cross (TL 004030) near Bovingdon, using brickearth from various nearby dolines, including some at Bovingdon Airfield (TL 006040). At least another 180 disused brickpits are recorded in the county (Fig. 10.4).

Gault Clay. Upper parts of the Gault Clay were dug for brickmaking at four sites in the Arlesey area (TL 185353, TL 192381, TL 160360 and TL 158372) from about 1852

- Mid-Pleistocene 'true brickearth' and Late Devensian loess
- Anglian tills and glaciolacustrine deposits
- Palaeogene deposits
- Gault clay

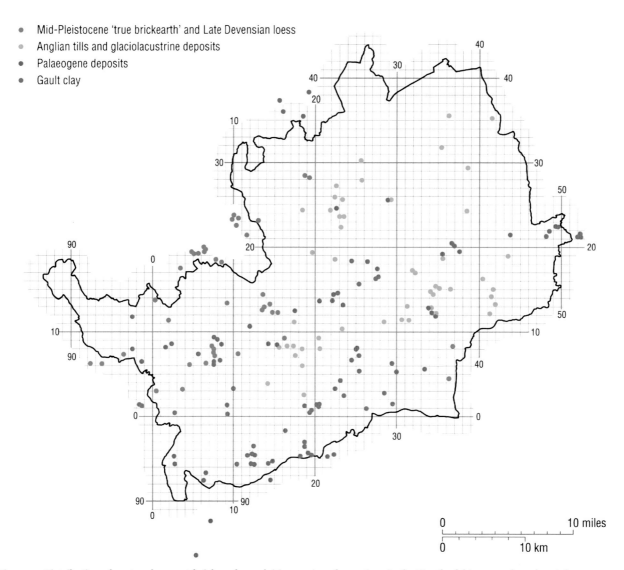

Fig. 10.4. Distribution of past and present brickworks exploiting various formations in the Hertfordshire area, based mainly on Perrins (2005).

onwards (Hopson *et al.*, 1996, pp. 118-119). The clay here is strongly calcareous, and had to be fired at about 900°C, above the temperature range over which shrinkage is caused by loss of carbon dioxide from the carbonate but below that at which fusion occurs (Cox, 1979b). The result was a hard but porous yellow brick. Two of the works were sited close to the Midland Railway line (London St Pancras to East Midlands and Yorkshire), so that coal for firing could be brought in from the north and the finished bricks transported in both directions. One of these brickworks was owned by the Great Northern Brick Company, a subsidiary of the railway company, who used the bricks to build bridges and stations in its network. Three of the works closed between 1907 and 1940, and the last remaining operational in the 1990s (at TL 185353) was owned by the Butterley Brick Company. The clay pit at this site was also used for landfill, which for a time provided methane to fire the kilns.

Palaeogene deposits. Clays from the Reading, Harwich and London Clay Formations have been used in the last few centuries for brickmaking at:

Colliers End (TL 370201 and TL 369203),
Barwick (TL 377197),
Standon Green End (TL 357193),
Ayot Green (TL 222139, TL 223145),
Woolmer Green (TL 247184)
Northaw (TL 286029),
Datchworth Green (TL 267182?),
Radlett (TQ 163984),
Ruislip (TQ 073873),
Uxbridge (TQ 056834),
Harrow Weald Common (TQ 147927) (Barrow, 1919b),
Edmonton (TQ 319923),
Bennetts End (TL 076065),
Bernards Heath (TL 153084),
Tylers Hill (SP 983012),
Bishop's Stortford (TL 439217, TL 486220 and TL 481214),
Foxholes (TL 3412),
Hatfield Park (TL 252083 and TL 251082),
Shenley (TL 202013, TL 204014 and TL 203012),
Arkley (TQ 222956),
Bushey (TQ 119953, TQ 128953 and TQ 1295),

Watford Heath (TQ 121944),
Woodcock Hill near Rickmansworth (TQ 062926),
Aldbury Common (SP 974119),
Ley Hill (SP 987012) and
Chorleywood (TQ 028953).

At many of these sites, bricks were made by mixing sand and clay from the Reading Formation. As this formation is non-calcareous, crushed chalk was often added to the sand/clay mixture. Basal parts of the London Clay were also used at Bishop's Stortford, Ayot Green, Bennetts End, Tylers Hill and Hatfield Park, mainly for the production of tiles or land drains. London Clay is not really suitable for brickmaking until it has weathered to free it from pyrites and gypsum. According to Sherlock and Pocock (1924, p. 53), London Clay dug from the Ponsbourne Tunnel during construction of the railway line south of Hertford was used to make bricks for lining the tunnel. Warren (2008) suggested that the brickworks were at Tolmers Activity Centre (TL 305038) close to the southern end of the tunnel.

Pleistocene deposits. Anglian till was used for short periods at numerous sites in the county (Fig. 10.4), including:

Weston (TL 256308),
Ware (TL 344146),
Stotfold (TL 227372),
Hill End (TL 185060) and
Preston (TL 185245).

However, the bricks were often of poor quality, because chalk clasts created cavities when carbon dioxide was generated on firing, and the remaining quick lime caused cracking by expansion on rehydration. Anglian glaciolacustrine clays were used more successfully, including for example the Watton Road Laminated Silts at Ware (TL 341149), and other deposits at:

Stonyhills (TL 320172),
Rush Green (TL 347123 and 342130),
Hertingfordbury (TL 316117),
High Heath (TL 198194),
Walkern (TL 294258,
Chipping (TL 355319) and
Hare Street (TL 387295).

The silty, loess-containing 'true brickearth' of Mid Pleistocene age obtained from small infilled dolines penetrating the Plateau Drift has been used at many Chiltern sites since at least the mid 19th century. It was probably the same brickearth in the Little Gaddesden area that was described in the 1748 diary of Pehr Kalm (Mead, 2003, p. 74). Until the early 20th century, these brickearths were hand-dug and fired at a fairly high temperature to make high quality decorative bricks of an attractive bright red colour, but at the few remaining sites near Ley Hill and Pudds Cross they are now dug by small mobile excavators. Outside the county, the main sites where similar brickearth is currently worked are near Matthews' Brickworks (SP 938062) between Bellingdon and Cholesbury in northeast Buckinghamshire. All these deposits are non-calcareous and benefit from mixing with chalk. But they contain an optimum mixture of clay (25-35%) and coarser (coarse silt and fine sand) particles, so that the bricks shrink very little on firing and do not weaken through increased porosity.

When the dolines are worked out, the irregular, funnel-shaped pits penetrating the Plateau Drift are infilled and easily returned to agricultural use, so that their previous presence is difficult or impossible to detect. However, the positions of many earlier pits were recorded in the archaeological literature because of the abundant Lower Palaeolithic artefacts found in the brickearth and overlying gelifluction deposits (Section 8.2). They include the numerous sites at:

Caddington (Fig. 8.2), and others at:
Slip End (TL 078185),
Pepperstock (TL 084181),
Gorhambury (TL 105076),
Kensworth (TL 033176),
Leverstock Green (TL 075080),
Gaddesden Row (TL 038134),
Round Green (TL 101226),
Ramridge End (TL 105233),
Stopsley Common (TL 100239) and
Mixieshill (TL 098234).

In the late 19th century, similar artefact-yielding brickearths were worked in the Hitchin area, mainly at Ransom's Pit (TL 189284) and Jeeves Pit (TL 191281). Additional brickearth sites but with no known archaeological context were recorded at Cholesbury (SP 929076), Dundridge Manor (SP 923062) and Broomfield Spring (SP 979112) by Avery *et al.* (1982), and at Old Eaton Green (TL 115216), now part of Luton Airport, by Hopson *et al.* (1996). Yet others could be located from aerial photographs taken in the 20th century during or soon after active extraction.

According to Sherlock and Pocock, 1924, p. 53), the younger (Late Devensian) brickearth deposits of the lower Lea valley were previously used for brickmaking at sites near Hailey (TL 3710) and Cheshunt (TL 3502). They also reported that Clay-with-flints (i.e. Plateau Drift) was used at Rableyheath (TL 241190), and Sherlock (1922) suggested that the same material was previously used for small brickworks at Wigginton (SP 9310) near Tring and Brockhurst Farm (SP 977028) near Chesham. However, as defined at the time, the 'Clay-with-flints' mapped by the British Geological Survey would have included the brickearth infilling dolines, and it is likely that these references were to this deposit rather than the clayey Plateau Drift.

10.5. The building materials of Hertfordshire churches

In the mid-20th century, Percy Evans and his wife Enid, both now deceased, recorded the building materials of over

500 churches in Hertfordshire and Bedfordshire (the two counties forming the Anglican Diocese of St Albans) and adjacent parts of Essex, Cambridgeshire, Buckinghamshire and north London. This section is based mainly on their records, supplemented by the later observations of Clifton Taylor (1977), Potter (1998, 1999, 2000, 2002), recent memoirs of the British Geological Survey (Millward *et al.*, 1987; Lake and Wilson, 1990; Shephard-Thorn *et al.*, 1994; Hopson *et al.*, 1996) and CPG.

Whitelaw (1990) listed 227 Anglican churches in Hertfordshire, including some that were already closed when he was writing. In the current St Albans Diocesan Directory (2009), 241 active places of worship are identified in the county, including St Albans Cathedral and several chapels of ease. The directory does not include churches no longer used as regular places of worship, several of which are mediaeval buildings. For example, five of these are in the care of the Churches Conservation Trust, and others have been converted to residential use. Thus there are at least 250 church buildings in the county, and the building materials of 216 of them were recorded by Percy and Enid Evans. They also noted the approximate age of the buildings and the extent of restoration. They recorded separately the principal building materials of the church and tower, including rubble components and materials used for surface dressings, and also noted the use of Totternhoe Stone, chequerboard construction and the extent to which the walls had been rendered. Subsequent observations by CPG have confirmed most of their records, with occasional revisions and supplementary information.

Hertfordshire churches can be separated into two main groups on the basis of age: Pre-Reformation (up to and including the early 16th century) and Post-Reformation. Among those recorded by Percy and Enid Evans, Post-Reformation foundations (114) slightly outnumber those of Pre-Reformation age (102). The principal building materials of the two groups are shown in Table 10.1, and Figure 10.5 shows the location of churches mentioned subsequently in the text and the principal materials used in building each of them.

Very few churches were built anywhere in England in the 17th and 18th centuries. In Hertfordshire, only St Peter Buntingford (1614-1626), St John Markyate (1734) and St Lawrence Ayot St Lawrence (1778-1779) were built from new in these two centuries. Consequently most of the Post-Reformation foundations date from the 19th century, many of them from the second half of the century, which was also a period of very active church restoration. This work was stimulated by the Church Building Society, established in 1818 (Port, 2006), and after 1833 also by the Oxford Movement. The Church Building Society contributed wholly or in part to the funding of 36 new churches in Hertfordshire and to the rebuilding of a further 10. Many mediaeval churches were heavily restored at this time, some being entirely rebuilt.

Clearly the factors affecting the choice of building materials in the 19th century were different from those influencing the decisions of mediaeval architects and masons, so with many mediaeval churches it is important

Building material	Pre-Reformation	Post-Reformation
Flint	71	38
Flint + Bedfordshire Lower Greensand	1	-
Flint + Totternhoe Stone	3	-
Flint + Erratics	17	-
Totternhoe Stone	3	-
Erratics	4	1
Totternhoe Stone + Erratics	3	-
Oolitic Limestone	-	7
Kentish Ragstone	-	14
Triassic Sandstone (Cheshire)	-	1
Brick	-	52
Corrugated iron	-	1
Totals	**102**	**114**

Table 10.1 Principal surviving building materials in Pre- and Post-Reformation churches of Hertfordshire.

to take into account the presence of fabric introduced much later by 19th century restoration. The main factors affecting the choice of building materials are the costs of preparing them for use and of transporting them from source to the site of construction. Readily available local materials are therefore the first choice, but Hertfordshire is not well endowed with building stones that are both versatile and durable. Consequently, various building stones from outside the county have often been used, and it is not unusual to find up to eight different building materials in a single church building. However, the decision to import stone from further afield depended on the extent and capacity of transport networks. Hertfordshire originally had few navigable waterways, and this undoubtedly affected the choice of early church building materials. But by the beginning of the 19th century, the developing canal system (Section 9.7) had begun to overcome this problem, and by the second half of the 19th century railway transport was also widely established.

Additional considerations affecting the choice of building stone have included (a) the degree of architectural refinement to which architects and, more importantly, their patrons aspired, (b) the ability to pay for these aspirations, and (c) the degree to which the required scale and level of refinement are technically possible using particular building materials. A further factor was occasionally the personal preference of certain church architects. A striking example of this in Hertfordshire is the church of All Saints Hertford, built between 1893 and 1905 and designed by the architects Paley, Austin and Paley from Lancaster. As the principal building material, they decided to use Runcorn Stone, a red sandstone from the Triassic of Cheshire, which had previously been used successfully in a number of churches in northern England, but never before or since in Hertfordshire.

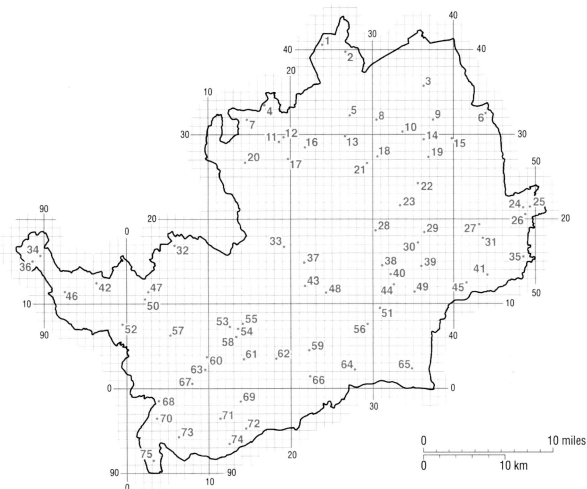

Figure 10.5. Location of churches and the building materials used in them, which are mentioned in the text. Site numbering runs from north to south.

Abbots Langley (63), Sp
Aldbury (42), F, Po
Aldenham (69), H, R
Ardeley (18), E
Ashwell (2), To
Ayot St Lawrence (33), B
Ayot St Peter (37), B
Bayford (51), K
Bedmond (60), I
Bengeo, Holy Trinity (40), K
Bishop's Stortford, Holy Trinity (26), K
Bishop's Stortford, St Michael (24), Po
Boxmoor (57), O
Buntingford (14), B
Bushey Heath (72), K
Cheshunt (65), Tr
Chorleywood (70), S

Clothall (5), O
Frogmore (61), B
Gilston (41), Tr
Great Berkhamsted (52), O, Po, F
Great Gaddesden (47), H
Great Hormead (15), F
Great Munden (22), O, C
Great Wymondley (16), E
Hatfield Hyde (48), K
Hertford, All Saints (44), Ss
High Cross (29), K
Hinxworth (1), B
Hitchin, St Mary (11), R
Hitchin, Holy Saviour (12), B
Hockerill (25), K
Holwell, (4), E
Hunsden (45), B
Langleybury (67), O, F
Lemsford (43), O
Little Amwell (49), B
Little Berkhamsted (56), K, A
Little Munden (23), C
London Colney (62), B
Long Marston old church (34), Po

Markyate (32), B
Meesden (6), B
Much Hadham (27), R
Nettleden (50), H, B
Northaw (64), O
North Mymms (59), C
Offley (20), F, B, Po
Oxhey Chapel (74), B
Perry Green (31), K
Pirton (7), To, G, C
Puttenham (36), F, Po
Reed (3), O
Rickmansworth (73), B
Rushden (8), B
St Albans Abbey (54), R, O
St Albans, St Michael (53), O
St Albans, St Peter (55), B, O
St Albans, St Stephen (58), O
St Ippollits (17), C, Tr
Sarratt (68), H
Sawbridgeworth (35), Tr, C
South Mimms (66), F, B, C
Throcking (10), B
Thundridge (30), K
Tring (46), F, To
Walkern (21), F

Ware, Christ Church (39), K
Waterford (38), K
Watton-at-Stone (28), F
West Hyde (75), F
Westmill (19), O
Weston (13), G
Wyddial (9), B

Key to building materials:
A Artificial stone
B Brick
C Cemented gravel
E Glacial erratics
F Flint
G Bedfordshire Greensand
H Hertfordshire Puddingstone
I Corrugated iron
K Kentish Ragstone
O Oolitic limestone
Po Portland Stone
R Roman brick
S Sarsenstone
Sp SPAB tile repair
Ss Sandstone
To Totternhoe Stone
Tr Travertine

309

Chalk

Although almost all the county is underlain by a considerable thickness of the White Chalk Subgroup, which is often readily accessible close to the land surface, there is little evidence that this unit has ever been quarried as a building stone for use in Hertfordshire churches. However, the Totternhoe Stone from the Grey Chalk Subgroup was used widely in Pre-Reformation Hertfordshire churches, mainly because at least two of the quarries at Totternhoe in neighbouring Bedfordshire were owned for about two centuries before the Reformation by the Benedictine Abbey of St Albans (Roberts, 1974). There is archaeological evidence that Totternhoe Stone was worked in Roman times (Section 10.3), but the earliest documentary evidence of quarries at Totternhoe itself is in a charter of *c.* 1132, in which Henry I endowed a house of Austin Canons at Dunstable with land at Totternhoe and referred specifically to a quarry there (Roberts, 1974).

As a homogeneous and easily worked 'freestone', it has been used extensively in Hertfordshire churches for complex mouldings, such as window and door frames, and for figurative sculpture. Fine examples of the work of mediaeval masons using Totternhoe Stone can be seen in many Hertfordshire church interiors. They include the stiff-leaf capitals at St Mary Magdalene Offley and several mediaeval fonts, such as the one in St Stephens St Albans (Plate 87).

However, because of its susceptibility to weathering by frost and acid rain, in many church exteriors it has been replaced in the course of restoration with more durable limestones, such as Portland Limestone from Buckinghamshire or Dorset and Middle Jurassic limestones from the south Midlands or Somerset. A recent alternative method of stabilizing weathered surfaces is by a thick coating of masonry paint subtly coloured to resemble the slightly creamy colour of fresh Totternhoe Stone; examples can be seen in the cloister arches on the south wall of the nave of St Albans Abbey.

Pre-Reformation churches in which small amounts of Totternhoe Stone are still present are numerous in Hertfordshire (Fig. 10.5), but those in which ashlar blocks are a principal component of the external fabric are few in number, and their distribution is interesting. St Mary the Virgin Ashwell (Plate 88) is probably the finest and most complete example. Others, such as St Mary Pirton and St Peter and St Paul Tring are also in the north of the county close to the outcrop of the Totternhoe Stone, suggesting that transportation cost was the main factor limiting such large scale use of the stone.

Roberts (1974) suggested that the work of Totternhoe

Plate 87. Mediaeval font constructed of Totternhoe Stone, St Stephen St Albans.

Plate 88. Extensive use of Totternhoe Stone at St Mary the Virgin Ashwell.

*Plate 89. Fragment of large ammonite (*Parapuzosia austeni*) from the Totternhoe Stone in the south wall of St Mary Pirton.*

quarry labourers can usually be recognized on stylistic grounds, though not at Ashwell or Pirton, where the stone was probably obtained from other quarries closer to hand. When Pirton church was partially rebuilt in the early 20th century, Totternhoe Stone was obtained from Glebe Pit (TL 154326) about 1 km away (M. Howgate, *pers. comm.*). This quarry was also the source of the giant ammonites (*Parapuzosia austeni*) incorporated into the south wall of the church (Plate 89), and a fossil fish (*Ctenothrissa radians*) previously displayed in the church (Newbery, 2009). It may also have been the source of a dinosaur tooth 2-3 cm long, which Newton (1892) provisionally named *Iguanodon hilli* after the finder (William Hill); this is the only dinosaur fossil known from Hertfordshire.

Flint

This is probably the most widely used of church building materials native to Hertfordshire. It is the principal component of rubble walling in Pre-Reformation churches; only 10 of those surveyed by Percy and Enid Evans did not have flint as a major building component. In addition, it has been knapped and dressed as an external facing for walls. Originally, it was probably gathered from a range of local sources, including bands exposed in chalk quarries, gravel pits and the surface of cultivated fields on flinty soils. This probably explains the diverse degrees of abrasion and patination of the flints observed in rubble walling.

Roberts (1974) included a useful section on 'building a

flint wall', in which she described the traditional methods of a family of builders, the Handys, who worked on the maintenance of flint churches in Hertfordshire for three generations. In mediaeval flintwork of superior quality, where it was not the intention to render the wall, the freshly broken faces of the most successfully knapped flints would form the outward face, but they were not usually coursed or laid in a regular pattern. Outstanding examples of such mediaeval flintwork occur at St John the Baptist Aldbury, St Nicholas Great Hormead, St Giles South Mimms, St Mary Walkern and St Andrew and St Mary Watton-at-Stone. Not all flint was dressed with such care. In many mediaeval rubble walls, the flint is a jumble of unbroken and naturally broken or crudely dressed pieces set in copious lime mortar (Plate 90). Such walls were almost certainly intended to receive a facing of render.

Flint-working skills must have experienced a considerable revival in the 19th century, when flintwork was being restored in mediaeval churches or incorporated into new church buildings. In the mainly 13th century church of St Peter Great Berkhamsted, all the flintwork except that of the tower dates from the Butterfield restoration of the 1870s. It closely resembles the method of working described by Roberts (1974), and here and there separate halves of the same piece of knapped flint can be identified (Plate 91), suggesting that the knapping took place on site as the walling was going up. Elsewhere Victorian architects called for more demanding styles of knapping. For example, at St Paul Langleybury, restored by Woodyer in 1865, the flints

Plate 90. Flint rubble walling at St Lawrence Abbots Langley, incorporating pieces of limestone, sarsenstone and Hertfordshire Puddingstone.

Plate 91. Victorian flintwork at St Peter Great Berkhamsted, incorporating two pieces recognizably from the same nodule.

Plate 92. Refined Victorian flintwork at St Paul Langleybury.

are squared and laid in regular courses (Plate 92), and at St Thomas West Hyde, restored in 1844 by Thomas Smith, each flint is knapped to present a circular outline.

Bricks and tiles

Roman bricks, such as those used in the building of Verulamium, were often re-used in mediaeval Hertfordshire churches. They are most conspicuous in the 12th century tower and other parts of St Albans Abbey, but were also noted by Percy and Enid Evans in 21 other churches in the county, including several some distance from Verulamium, such as St John the Baptist Aldenham, St Andrew Much Hadham and St Mary Hitchin.

Newly made local bricks have also been used in the fabric of many Hertfordshire churches since the Tudor period. Those made from the Gault Clay close to the northern extremities of the county do not seem to have been used in churches, but in southern parts of Hertfordshire bricks made probably from a range of other suitable materials (Reading Beds, London Clay, glacial deposits and brickearths from Chiltern dolines or the Lea valley) appear in numerous churches. The north chapel at St Giles Wyddial, dated 1532, the south porch at St Mary Meesden and the north aisle at St Giles South Mimms are rare examples of Pre-Reformation brickwork. The chapels at St Dunstan Hunsdon (Plate 93), dating from the late 16th or very early 17th century, are another example of early brickwork in the county. Other 17th century brickwork can be seen in the church of St Peter

Plate 93. Tudor brickwork forming the south chapel at St Dunstan Hunsdon.

Plate 94. 18th century brickwork forming the chancel at St Nicholas Hinxworth.

Buntingford, Oxhey Chapel (1612), the tower of St Mary Rickmansworth (1630) and the upper stages of the tower at Holy Trinity Throcking (1660). Examples of 18th and early 19th century brickwork exist in the chancel at St Nicholas Hinxworth (Plate 94), the tower of St Mary Magdalene Offley (1800) and the nave of St Lawrence Nettleden (1811).

Many Victorian churches in the county were also built using local bricks. Percy Evans identified 41 built from new since 1800 in which brick was the principal building material. Of these, 22 are of sufficient architectural merit to be mentioned by Pevsner and Cherry (1977). The earliest is St Peter London Colney, built in 1825. The work of various distinguished Victorian architects is represented, including Holy Trinity Little Amwell by Ewan Christian (Plate 95), dating from 1863, Holy Saviour Hitchin by Butterfield (1863-1865), the idiosyncratic church of St Peter Ayot St Peter by Seddon (1874-1875), and Holy Trinity Frogmore by a youthful Gilbert Scott (1842). In some of this Victorian fabric, coloured bricks were used to achieve decorative effects. For example, at Ayot St Peter, blue and yellow bricks were used as well as red. Brick was also used extensively in 19th century restoration work. Among the many examples are St Peter St Albans, largely rebuilt by Lord Grimthorpe in 1894-1895, and St Mary Rushden, where a chancel in 'white' brick has been added to an otherwise mainly 14th and 15th century church.

The Society for the Protection of Ancient Buildings (SPAB), founded in 1877 by William Morris, introduced a method of building restoration using tiles, often to repair elaborate tracery and mouldings. Most such repairs probably date from the first half of the 20th century. Examples can be seen in the church of St Lawrence Abbots Langley (Plate 96).

Puddingstone and sarsenstone

As mentioned in Section 5.11, blocks of these two forms of silcrete derived ultimately from various parts of the Palaeogene sequence, though more often found in the Plateau Drift, proto-Thames terrace gravels and other Quaternary deposits, were widely used in Pre-Reformation churches in Hertfordshire and surrounding counties. In Hertfordshire, puddingstone was used more commonly than sarsenstone (Potter, 1998). The quarries at Walters Ash, Buckinghamshire were an important 19th century commercial source of dressed sarsenstone (Watson, 1911), which was used for example by G. E. Street as dressings to buttresses when Christs Church Chorleywood was built in 1869-1870. Dressed puddingstone blocks, possibly from a pit near Radlett, were also used in the tower and buttresses of St John the Baptist Aldenham. But the principal use of both stones was by opportunistic incorporation of smaller boulders found locally in fields and gravel pits as a rare component in flint and rubble walling. There are few Pre-Reformation churches in Hertfordshire without any examples of puddingstone used in this way. Larger flat slabs, principally of puddingstone, were often used as foundation stones for buttresses, as at St Lawrence Nettleden (Plate 97), St John the Baptist Great Gaddesden and Holy Cross Sarratt.

Plate 95. Victorian brickwork at Holy Trinity Little Amwell.

Plate 96. SPAB repairs to a window at St Lawrence Abbots Langley.

Plate 97. Footings of Hertfordshire Puddingstone at St Lawrence Nettleden.

Glacial erratics

The glaciofluvial gravels of Hertfordshire contain a range of durable far-travelled boulders in addition to flint from the White Chalk and silcretes from the Palaeogene sequence. Granites, volcanic rocks, such as basalt, rhyolite and tuff, sandstones, quartzites and pre-Cretaceous limestones are among the rock types that can be seen occasionally in rubble walling, especially in churches in the eastern glaciated parts of the county. The most common in this area are the tough hard cobbles of brown or purplish quartzite derived from the Triassic Kidderminster Formation of the West Midlands

Plate 98. Rubble walling, mainly glacial erratics, at St Mary the Virgin Great Wymondley.

and the Nottingham Castle Sandstone Formation of the East Midlands (Potter, 2002). In a few churches, such as St Peter Holwell (rebuilt in 1877-1879 re-using old materials) and St Mary the Virgin Great Wymondley (Plate 98), they are the dominant component of rubble walling. Larger erratic blocks are fairly rare in Hertfordshire (Section 6.6), but Percy and Enid Evans recorded a large boulder of Carboniferous Limestone in the footings of the tower at St Lawrence Ardeley.

Cemented sands and gravels

The rubble walling of several Pre-Reformation churches in Hertfordshire contains blocks of iron oxide- or carbonate-cemented sand and gravel, which Percy and Enid Evans referred to as 'false puddingstone' because of their superficial resemblance to some forms of Hertfordshire Puddingstone. The ferruginous varieties are probably from Pleistocene river terrace deposits, as they often include flint and quartzite pebbles, though Percy did not differentiate these from sandy ironstones of the Woburn Sands in Bedfordshire. Small blocks are common in the rubble walling at St Mary North Mymms (Plate 42) and St Giles South Mimms, and larger blocks are used as footings at St Nicholas Great Munden, All Saints Little Munden, Great St Mary Sawbridgeworth and St Ippollits at the village of St Ippollits. Where the cementing agent is calcareous, as at St Mary Pirton, the blocks are probably derived from chalk-rich Anglian glaciofluvial gravels.

Travertine

In his study of travertine in the churches of the London Basin, Potter (2000) identified only four Hertfordshire churches, St Ippollits St Ippollits, Great St Mary Sawbridgeworth, St Mary Cheshunt and St Mary Gilston, where this rock has been used as a building stone. It is most abundant at St Ippollits. As in other churches of the London area, it is thought to reflect 'casual reuse from earlier sites, the majority of which were probably Roman' (Potter, 2000); for example, derivation from Roman buildings in Verulamium could explain its use in St Albans Abbey. However, the sources for some Hertfordshire churches may be local, as there are at least 43 known travertine deposits in the London Basin, including four in Hertfordshire (Hunton Bridge, Hitchin, Letchworth and Stevenage), the last three of which are fairly close to St Ippollits.

Stones from outside the county

Many building stones represented in Hertfordshire churches have originated outside the county. They fall into two groups: those from nearby sources, which could readily be used by mediaeval builders given the transport constraints of the time; and those often from further afield, which were imported by canal or rail from the 19th century onwards for new buildings or for restoration work. If we include gravestones, the frequent occurrence of Scottish, Westmoreland and Leicestershire granites and

Plate 99. An ashlar block of ferruginous Bedfordshire Greensand (Woburn Sands) in the south porch, St Mary Pirton.

Coal Measure Sandstones from the Midlands and South Yorkshire also provide widespread evidence for these forms of transportation.

Bedfordshire Greensand. In Pre-Reformation churches, sandstones from the Woburn Sands Formation of Bedfordshire have occasionally been used either as loose blocks in rubble walling, as in the north transept at Holy Trinity Weston, or less commonly as hewn ashlar blocks in dressed walls, as at St Mary Pirton (Plate 99). However, there are no Hertfordshire churches in which these sandstones are the principal building material, even in northern parts of the county close to the Woburn Sands outcrop, despite the fact that several Bedfordshire parishes adjoining the county boundary (e.g. Shillington, Stondon, Henlow) have churches in which the sandstone is used extensively. This must reflect the problem of bulk transport in the mediaeval period. Hertfordshire villages such as Holwell and Hexton were perhaps just too distant from the outcrop to make the use of these sandstones an economic proposition.

Portland Limestone. Another building stone introduced into the extreme western parts of Hertfordshire in the mediaeval period is the pale-coloured Portland Limestone, which is not unlike Totternhoe Stone but is greyer and characterized by shelly seams packed with large bivalve molluscs. Most of this probably came from outliers of Portlandian rocks near Stone and Quainton in Buckinghamshire. In the church of St Mary Puttenham (Plate 100) and in the surviving tower of the old church at All Saints Long Marston, it has been used in a chequerboard pattern alternating with flintwork. Occasional dressed blocks have also been used in churches in the west of the county, such as St John the Baptist Aldbury and the tower of St Peter Great Berkhamsted. Portland Stone from the Isle of Portland in Dorset has also been used in some Hertfordshire churches, including St Michael Bishop's Stortford and, most strikingly, in the chancel of St Mary Magdalene Offley (Plate 101), which was entirely remodelled in Portland Stone in 1777 by Sir Thomas Salusbury, chiefly to house memorials to himself and his family.

Middle Jurassic limestones. Familiar Jurassic building

Plate 100. Chequerwork of flint and Portland Limestone from Quainton at St Mary Puttenham.

Plate 101. The chancel at St Mary Magdalene Offley built for Sir Thomas Salusbury in 1777 using Portland Stone.

Plate 102. Bath Stone used by Henry Woodyer in 1865 in the south chapel at St Paul Langleybury.

Church	Architect	Date
St John the Evangelist High Cross	Anthony Salvin	1846
All Saints Hockerill *§	George Pritchett	1849-1855
St Mary Thundridge	Benjamin Ferrey	1853-1855
Holy Trinity Bengeo §	Benjamin Ferrey	1854-1856
St Thomas Perry Green §	George Pritchett	1854-1856
St Andrew Little Berkhamsted (Plate 104)	?Henry Woodyer	1857
Holy Trinity Bishop's Stortford §	Joseph Clarke	1857-1860
Christ Church Ware §	N. E. Stevens	1858
St Michael Waterford (Plate 103)	Henry Woodyer	1871-1872
St Mary Bayford	Henry Woodyer	1871-1872
St John Watford §	Christopher & White	1890-1894
St Peter Bushey Heath	James Neale	1891
St Mary Magdalene Hatfield Hyde	G. H. Fellowes Prynne	1911

* Rebuilt in 1937 by S. E. Dykes Bower after a fire in 1935
§ Original construction assisted by grant from the Church Building Society.

Table 10.2. Kentish Ragstone churches in Hertfordshire.

stones, such as the oolitic and shelly limestones of the Cotswolds and Northamptonshire, are rarely seen in the mediaeval churches of Hertfordshire, though they are important in Bedfordshire as far south as Marston Morteyne. However, Barnack Stone was used in Anglo-Saxon long-and-short work at St Mary Reed and St Mary the Virgin Westmill (Roberts, 1974), and was also identified by Percy and Enid Evans at St Mary the Virgin Clothall and in the footings of St Mary the Virgin Ashwell.

One of the consequences of the major revival of church building in the 19th century was the introduction of numerous building stones rarely or never seen before in Hertfordshire churches. The most widespread of these introductions are various Jurassic oolitic limestones, such as Ketton and Clipsham Stones from the Inferior Oolite of Northamptonshire and Bath Stone from the Great Oolite of Somerset, the coarse bioclastic limestone (Ham Hill Stone) from the Lias of the Yeovil area, Somerset and the striped Ancaster Stone from Lincolnshire. Percy and Enid Evans recorded these limestones in 186 Hertfordshire churches, though they are a major component of the fabric in only seven, including St Paul Langleybury (Plate 102), St John the Evangelist Boxmoor, St Thomas à Becket Northaw and St John the Evangelist Lemsford. Their widespread occurrence in Pre-Reformation churches is explained largely by replacement of badly weathered Totternhoe Stone. A typical example of such restoration is St Peter Great Berkhamsted, where all the external dressings – quoins, buttresses, window reveals and tracery – are oolitic limestone dating from the Butterfield restoration of the 1870s. Elsewhere oolitic limestone has also been used to replace Totternhoe Stone in door frames and parapets. Ancaster Stone and Ham Hill Stone were used extensively in Lord Grimthorpe's restoration of St Albans churches, such as the Abbey, St Peter and St Michael. The Abbey also includes a range of other imported stones, including Barnack stone, Ketton Stone, Bath Stone, Portland Limestone,

Magnesian Limestone, New Red Sandstone from Mansfield and Carboniferous Limestone from Derbyshire.

Kentish Ragstone. This also gained favour in Hertfordshire in the 19th century. Quarried from the Hythe Beds, part of

Plate 103. Kentish Ragstone used by Henry Woodyer 1871-1872 at St Michael Waterford.

Plate 104. Blocks of Pulhamite (left) and Kentish Ragstone with chert band (centre and right) at St Andrew Little Berkhamsted.

the Lower Greensand south of London, Kentish Rag has been exploited for almost two millennia, as it is common in the remains of Roman buildings in London. It is a grey sandy limestone, and thus differs from the Lower Greensand of Bedfordshire, which is a distinctive dark reddish brown sandstone. Because of its hard, often cherty nature (Plate 104), Kentish Ragstone is difficult to dress, and is used mainly for roughly dressed walls, with quoins and facings of other, more easily worked limestones. Percy and Enid Evans identified Kentish Rag as the principal building stone in 13 Hertfordshire churches (Table 10.2), the earliest, St John the Evangelist High Cross, dating from 1846.

There is also some evidence for use of Kentish Rag in Pre-Reformation churches, mainly in rubble walls or as footings. However, this is unlikely to have been transported from outcrop in the mediaeval period; instead, it is probably reused stone originally brought into the county by the Romans.

Other building materials

Many Hertfordshire churches have exterior coatings of render. Well cared for, this is an effective external facing, and the rubble walls of many smaller mediaeval churches were almost certainly originally built with the application of render in mind. In other churches, it has often been applied to check the further deterioration of decayed stonework, and then is often a patchwork of materials of different ages and compositions, ranging from soft mediaeval lime mortars to

Plate 105. The church of the Ascension, Bedmond, built of corrugated iron.

Material	Major component	Minor component
Flint	59	71
Post-Roman brick	27	43
Glacial erratics	11	19
Kentish Ragstone	7	15
Totternhoe Stone	4	50
Oolitic limestones	3	77
Other limestones	1	10
Sandstones	<1	4
Hertfordshire Puddingstone	-	14
Roman brick	-	9
Sarsenstone	-	8
Bedfordshire Lower Greensand	-	5
Cemented gravels	-	4
Travertine	-	<1
Corrugated iron	<1	-

Table 10.3. Building materials used in the external walls of Hertfordshire churches. The values are percentages of the total number of churches surveyed by Percy and Enid Evans (216) in which the materials are recorded. Because up to eight different building materials were recorded in some buildings, the values in each column do not add up to 100%.

hard modern cement mortars.

Artificial stone has also been used widely for small-scale repairs. An example of large scale use is provided by St Andrew Little Berkhamsted, which was originally built in 1857 of Kentish Ragstone. When the north aisle was added in 1894, artificial stone was used, formed and coloured to imitate the roughly dressed blocks of Ragstone. This material is probably pulhamite, a product developed by the Pulham family and produced at their works in Broxbourne in the late 19th and early 20th centuries (Banister, 2007).

Finally, no account would be complete without reference to 'tin tabernacles' – churches built of corrugated iron sheeting. In Hertfordshire, the only surviving example in regular use as an Anglican place of worship is the rather charming Church of the Ascension Bedmond (Plate 105)

Summary

A broad view of the use of different building materials in Hertfordshire churches is provided by combining the data collected by Percy and Enid Evans for both Pre-Reformation and Post-Reformation churches and distinguishing the major and minor materials used in external walls (Table 10.3). Hard local materials are dominant, mainly flint followed by post-Roman brick and glacial erratics. Other durable local materials, notably Hertfordshire Puddingstone, sarsenstone, cemented gravels, travertine and Roman brick, have also been used quite widely, though in somewhat smaller total amounts because of limited resources. Totternhoe Stone, Bedfordshire Greensand and more recently imported rocks, such as Kentish Ragstone and Jurassic limestones, have also been widely used, though usually as minor components.

Appendix 1.

Abridged logs for deep boreholes in and near Hertfordshire

Ashwell (TL 286390); BGS No. TL23NE1; surface level 59.4 m OD; Hopson *et al.* (1996)

	Thickness (m)	Depth to base (m)
Lower Chalk	51.8	51.8
Gault Clay	54.9	106.7
Lower Greensand	27.9	134.6
Cornbrash	3.8	138.4
Blisworth Clay?	0.4	138.8
Blisworth Limestone	1.4	140.2
Rutland Formation	0.7	140.9
Core loss	0.1	141.0
Grantham Formation?	11.7	152.7
Core loss	0.3	153.0
Devonian	33.5 (+)	186.5

Cambridge (TL 4316 5949); BGS No. TL45NW49; surface level 23.8 m OD; Worssam and Taylor (1969, pp. 6-7)

	Thickness (m)	Depth to base (m)
Quaternary	3.2	3.2
Gault Clay	38.9	42.1
Lower Greensand	9.6	51.7
Corallian	2.9	54.6
Oxford Clay	48.5	103.1
Kellaways Beds	3.2	106.3
Cornbrash	2.4	108.7
Great Oolite	1.3	110.0
Inferior Oolite Clay	9.5	119.5
Lower Lias	12.6	132.1
Carboniferous and Devonian (?)	130.3 (+)	262.4

Beckton (TQ 4280 8165); BGS No. TQ48SW34; surface level +3.8 m OD; Whitaker *et al.* (1916)

	Thickness (m)	Depth to base (m)
Quaternary	7.9	7.9
Woolwich and Reading Beds	13.9	21.8
Thanet Beds	17.2	39.0
Chalk	197.3	236.3
Upper Greensand	11.3	247.6
Gault Clay	49.7	297.3
Devonian	13.7 (+)	311.0

Cliffe Marshes (TQ 7185 7858); BGS No. TQ77NW43B; surface level 2.2 m OD; Whitaker (1908, 1909)

	Thickness (m)	Depth to base (m)
Quaternary	23.5	23.5
Chalk	200.0	223.5
Gault Clay	63.4	286.9
Lower Greensand	29.3	316.2
Silurian	11.3 (+)	327.5

Crossness (TQ 4827 8078); BGS No. TQ48SE74; surface level 1.8 m; Whitaker (1908)

	Thickness (m)	Depth to base (m)
Quaternary	11.9	11.9
Woolwich and Reading Beds	14.3	26.2
Thanet Sand	15.5	41.8
Chalk	?192.4	?234.2
Upper Greensand	?19.8	?254.0
Gault Clay	53.4	307.4
Devonian	15.9 (+)	323.3

Bushey (TQ 1195 9577); BGS No. TQ19NW29; surface level 59.9 m OD; Whitaker (1889, Volume 2, p. 48)

	Thickness (m)	Depth to base (m)
Soil	1.5	1.5
Upper Chalk	57.8	59.3
Middle Chalk	43.1	102.4
Lower Chalk	77.7	180.1
Gault Clay	93.9	274.0
Middle Devonian	24.7 (+)	298.7

Deanshanger (SP 7652 3880); BGS No. SP73NE2; surface level 69.7 m OD; Horton *et al.* (1974)

	Thickness (m)	Depth to base (m)
Quaternary	63.4	63.4
Lower Lias	52.7	116.1
Rhaetic?	3.3	119.4
Keuper Marl	72.2	191.6
Tremadocian (Ordovician)	67.4 (+)	259.0

Henlow (TL 164356); BGS No. TL13NE1; surface level 50.3 m OD; Smith (1992)

	Thickness (m)	Depth to base (m)
Quaternary	107.9	107.9
Lower Greensand?	10.2	118.1
Jurassic limestone?	10.8	128.9
Devonian?	10.1 (+)	139.0

Kentish Town Waterworks (TQ 2834 8612); BGS No. TQ28NE14; surface level 56.7 m OD; Whitaker (1872; 1889, Volume 2, pp. 124-127)

	Thickness (m)	Depth to base (m)
London Clay	71.9	71.9
Reading Beds	18.7	90.6
Thanet Sand	8.2	98.8
Upper Chalk	74.5	173.3
Middle & Lower Chalk	122.0	295.3
Upper Greensand	4.2	299.5
Gault Clay	39.8	339.3
Devonian	83.3 (+)	422.6

Little Chishill (TL 4528 3637); BGS No. TL43NE1; surface level 135.0 m OD; Lake and Wilson (1990)

	Thickness (m)	Depth to base (m)
Quaternary	6.1	6.1
Upper Chalk	54.9	61.0
Middle Chalk	109.7	170.7
Lower Chalk	45.7	216.4
Gault Clay	61.6	278.0
Devonian	10.6 (+)	288.6

Little Missenden (SU 9009 9818); BGS No. SU99NW9; surface level 139.9 m OD; Strahan (1916)

	Thickness (m)	Depth to base (m)
Quaternary + Chalk	249.9	249.9
Gault Clay?	21.4	271.3
Jurassic	65.0	336.3
Triassic	29.5	365.8
Silurian	19.5 (+)	385.3

Streatham Common (TQ 2956 7098); BGS No. TQ27SE33; surface level 33.5 m OD; Whitaker (1912)

	Thickness (m)	Depth to base (m)
Quaternary	3.0	3.0
London Clay	46.6	49.6
Woolwich and Reading Beds	13.3	62.9
Thanet Beds	10.7	73.6
Upper Chalk	67.5	141.1
Middle Chalk	66.8	207.9
Lower Chalk	55.6	263.5
Upper Greensand	8.7	272.2
Gault Clay	57.5	329.7
Forest Marble	11.7	341.4
Devonian	46.0 (+)	387.4

Tattenhoe (SP 8289 3437); BGS No. SP83SW1; surface level 102.4 m OD; Horton *et al.* (1974)

	Thickness (m)	Depth to base (m)
Quaternary	39.0	39.0
Oxford Clay	17.1	56.1
Kellaways Sand and Clay	0.7	56.8
Blisworth Clay	1.1	57.9
Blisworth Limestone	11.1	69.0
Inferior Oolite	10.2	79.2
Lias	70.0	149.2
Tremadocian (Ordovician)	64.0 (+)	213.2

Tottenham Court Road (TQ 2985 8145); BGS No. TQ28SE156; surface level 26.1 m OD; Whitaker (1889, Volume 2, pp. 165-168)

	Thickness (m)	Depth to base (m)
Quaternary	6.9	6.9
London Clay	19.4	26.3
Woolwich & Reading Beds	15.7	42.0
Thanet Sands	6.4	48.4
Chalk	190.1	238.5
Upper Greensand	8.5	247.0
Gault Clay	48.8	295.8
Lower Greensand/ Great Oolite	19.5	315.3
Devonian	24.4 (+)	339.7

Tring (SP 9121 1036); BGS No. SP91SW28; surface level 150.0 m OD

	Thickness (m)	Depth to base (m)
Chalk	65.5	65.5
Gault Clay	91.5	157.0
Lower Greensand	22.8	179.8
Corallian	5.0	184.8
Oxford Clay	68.8	253.6
Kellaways Beds	4.1	257.7
Cornbrash	1.7	259.4
Forest Marble	0.8	260.2
Blisworth Limestone	12.1	272.3
Inferior Oolite	3.9	276.2
Devonian	31.0 (+)	307.2

Turnford (TL 3600 0444); BGS No. TL30SE109; surface level 32.0 m OD; Whitaker (1886; 1889, Volume 2, pp. 50-52)

	Thickness (m)	Depth to base (m)
Quaternary	7.0	7.0
London Clay	9.1	16.2
Reading Beds	11.0	27.1
Thanet Sands	4.1	31.2
Upper Chalk	79.4	110.6
Middle Chalk	72.2	182.9
Lower Chalk	56.1	239.0
Upper Greensand	14.0	253.0
Gault Clay	45.9	298.9
Upper Devonian	9.0 (+)	307.9

Ware (TL 3531 1398); BGS No. TL31SE57; surface level 33.6 m OD; Etheridge (1879), Hopkinson (1880)

	Thickness (m)	Depth to base (m)
Quaternary	5.2	5.2
Upper Chalk	55.8?	61.0?
Middle Chalk	69.2?	130.2
Lower Chalk	49.6	179.8
Upper Greensand	12.2	192.0
Gault Clay	50.8	242.8
Wenlockian (Silurian)	10.6 (+)	253.4

Willesden (TQ 2086 8477); BGS No. TQ28SW88; surface level 31.4 m OD; Falcon and Kent (1960)

	Thickness (m)	Depth to base (m)
London Clay	42.4	42.4
Woolwich & Reading Beds	17.3	59.7
Upper Chalk	53.1	112.8
Middle Chalk	70.1	182.9
Lower Chalk	60.9	243.8
Upper Greensand	12.2	256.0
Gault Clay	51.9	307.9
Upper Devonian	509.0 (+)	816.9

Wyboston (TL 1759 5723); BGS No. TL15NE2; surface level 15.5 m OD; Edmonds and Dinham (1965, pp. 7-8), Moorlock *et al.* (2003)

	Thickness (m)	Depth to base (m)
Quaternary	6.1	6.1
Oxford Clay	13.5	19.6
Kellaways Beds	5.5	25.1
Cornbrash	2.4	27.5
Blisworth Limestone	5.0	32.5
Rutland Formation	9.8	42.3
Lias	68.4	110.7
Upper Old Red Sandstone/Lower Carboniferous	79.7	190.4
Upper Devonian	34.1	224.5
Cambrian	11.2 (+)	235.7

References

A

Adams, C. G. 1981. An outline of Tertiary palaeogeography. In: *The Evolving Earth* (ed. Cocks, L. R. M.). British Museum (Natural History) and Cambridge University Press, Cambridge, 221-235.

Adams, B. and Foster, S. S. D. 1992. Land-surface zoning for groundwater protection. *Journal of the Institute of Water and Environmental Management* **2**, 312-319.

Addiscott, T. M. 1988a. Long-term leakage of nitrate from bare unmanured soil. *Soil Use and Management* **4**, 91-95.

Addiscott, T. M. 1988b. Farmers, fertilizers and the nitrate flood. *New Scientist* **120**, 50-54.

Addiscott, T. M. 2005. *Nitrate, agriculture and the environment.* CABI Publishing, Wallingford.

Addiscott, T. M. and Benjamin, N. 2004. Nitrate and human health. *Soil Use and Management* **20**, 98-104.

Ager, D. V. 1975. The geological evolution of Europe. *Proceedings of the Geologists' Association* **86**, 127-154.

Aguirre, E. and Pasini, G. 1985. The Plio-Pleistocene boundary. *Episodes* **8**, 116-120.

Air Photography Unit of Royal Commission on the Historical Monuments of England 1992. *Crop Marks in Hertfordshire a report for the national mapping programme.* National Monuments Records Centre, Swindon.

Al-Dabbagh, S., Forman, D., Bryson, D., Stratton, I. and Doll, R. 1986. Mortality of nitrate fertilizer workers. *British Journal of Industrial Medicine* **43**, 507-515.

Allen, D. F. 1962. Celtic coins. In: *Map of southern Britain in the Iron Age Scale 1:625 000.* Ordnance Survey, Southampton, 19-32.

Allen, M. J. and Gardiner, J. 2009. If you go down to the woods today; a re-evaluation of the chalkland postglacial woodland; implications for prehistoric communities. In: *Land and people; papers in memory of John G. Evans* (eds Allen, M. J., Sharples, N. and O'Connor, T.). Prehistoric Society Research Paper **2**. Oxbow Books, Oxford.

Allen, P., Cheshire, D. A. and Whiteman, C. A. 1991. Glacial deposits of southern East Anglia. In: *Glacial deposits in Britain and Ireland* (eds Ehlers, J., Gibbard, P. L. and Rose, J.). A. A. Balkema, Rotterdam, 255-278.

Allen, T. J. 1978. Disposition of the terraces of the River Thames in the vicinity of Yiewsley. In: *Early man in west Middlesex* (ed. Collins, D.). HMSO, London, 5-10.

Allison, J., Godwin, H. and Warren, S. H. 1952. Late-glacial deposits at Nazeing in the Lea Valley, North London. *Philosophical Transactions of the Royal Society of London* **B236**, 169-240.

Allsop, J. M. 1985. Geophysical investigations into the extent of the Devonian rocks beneath East Anglia. *Proceedings of the Geologists' Association* **96**, 371-379.

Allsop, J. M. and Smith, N. J. P. 1988. The deep geology of Essex. *Proceedings of the Geologists' Association* **99**, 249-260.

Anderton, R., Bridges, P. H., Leeder, M. R. and Sellwood, B. W. 1979. *A dynamic stratigraphy of the British Isles.* Allen & Unwin, London.

Andrews, J. T. 1971. *Techniques of till fabric analysis. Technical Bulletin* **6**. British Geomorphological Research Group, London.

Andrews, R. T. 1911. A late Celtic cemetery at Welwyn. *Antiquity* **47**, 53-54.

Anon. 1882. Field meeting, 7th May, 1881. The Bourne Valley, Boxmoor. *Transactions of the Hertfordshire Natural History Society and Field Club* **1**, Lviii-Lxi.

Anon. 1884. Field meeting, 21st April, 1883. Berkhampstead and the valley of the Bourne. *Transactions of the Hertfordshire Natural History Society and Field Club* **2**, Lv-Lx.

Anon. 1892a. Field meeting, 19th April, 1890. North Mimms, Hatfield. *Transactions of the Hertfordshire Natural History Society and Field Club* **6**, xxix-xxxii.

Anon. 1892b. Field meeting, 9th May, 1891. Bennet's End, Hemel Hempstead. *Transactions of the Hertfordshire Natural History Society and Field Club* **6**, Lxii-Lxiii.

Anon. 1898a. Field meeting, 3rd April, 1897. Chesham and Tyler's Hill. *Transactions of the Hertfordshire Natural History Society and Field Club* **9**, Lxiv-Lxv.

Anon. 1898b. Field meeting, 24th April, 1897. The valley of the Bourne, Boxmoor. *Transactions of the Hertfordshire Natural History Society and Field Club* **9**, Lxv-Lxvii.

Anon. 1906. Field meeting, 16th April, 1904. Bourne End and the valley of the bourne. *Transactions of the Hertfordshire Natural History Society and Field Club* **12**, xLi-xLiii.

Anon. 1908a. Field Meeting, 6th April, 1907. Bushey and Croxley. *Transactions of the Hertfordshire Natural History Society and Field Club* **13**, Li-Liii.

Anon. 1908b. Field meeting, 15th June, 1907. Aldbury and Ivinghoe. *Transactions of the Hertfordshire Natural History Society and Field Club* **13**, Lvii-Lviii.

Anon. 1912a. Field meeting, 29th April, 1911. Bourne End

and Berkhamsted. *Transactions of the Hertfordshire Natural History Society and Field Club* **14**, Lxxi-Lxxii.

Anon. 1912b. Field meeting, 11th April, 1908. Mimms Hall and Potterells Park. *Transactions of the Hertfordshire Natural History Society and Field Club* **14**, xiv.

Anon. 1915a. Field meeting, 11th May, 1912. The valley of the bourne. *Transactions of the Hertfordshire Natural History Society and Field Club* **15**, xxi-xxii.

Anon. 1915b. Field meeting, 12th April, 1913. The valley of the bourne. *Transactions of the Hertfordshire Natural History Society and Field Club* **15**, xxxviii-xxxix.

Anon. 1917a. Field meeting, 24th April, 1915. The valley of the bourne. *Transactions of the Hertfordshire Natural History Society and Field Club* **16**, xviii-xix.

Anon. 1917b. Field meeting, 29th April, 1916. The valley of the bourne. *Transactions of the Hertfordshire Natural History Society and Field Club* **16**, xxxiii.

Anon. 1923. Field meeting, 12th April, 1919: Bourne End. *Transactions of the Hertfordshire Natural History Society and Field Club* **17**, Li.

Anon. 1927. Field meeting, 24th April, 1926. Bourne End and Ashley Green. *Transactions of the Hertfordshire Natural History Society and Field Club* **18**, xLi.

Anon. 1937. Field meeting, 4th April: Bourne valley. *Transactions of the Hertfordshire Natural History Society and Field Club* **20**, Part 3, ix-xi.

Anon. 1971. Ayot St Lawrence. *Hertfordshire Archaeological Review* **3**, 77-78.

Anon. 2007. Holey war. *Ground Engineering*, November 2007, 10-12.

Applebaum, E. S. 1934. An early Iron Age site at Holwell, Hertfordshire. *The Antiquaries Journal* **14**, 383-388.

Applebaum, E. S. 1949. Excavations at Wilbury Hill, an Iron Age hillfort near Letchworth, Hertfordshire. *Archaeological Journal* **106**, 12-45.

Arkell, W. J. 1947. *The geology of the country around Weymouth, Swanage, Corfe and Lulworth*. Memoirs of the Geological Survey of England and Wales. HMSO, London.

Arkell, W. J. and Oakley, K. P. 1948. The implements in the Treacher collection. In: On the ancient channel between Caversham and Henley, Oxfordshire, and its contained flint implements. *Proceedings of the Prehistoric Society* **14**, 134-154.

Arrowsmith, S. J., Kendall, M., White, N., Vandecar, J. C. and Booth, D. C. 2005. Seismic imaging of a hot upwelling beneath the British Isles. *Geology* **33**, 345-348.

Ashton, N., Lewis, S. G., Parfitt, S. A., Penkman, K. E. H. and Coope, G. R. 2008. New evidence for complex climate change in MIS 11 from Hoxne, Suffolk, UK. *Quaternary Science Reviews* **27**, 652-668.

Ashworth, H. 2003. *Land at Yeomanry Drive, Baldock, Herts.: desk-based archaeological assessment*. Unpublished Report.

Atkinson, T. C., Briffa, K. R. and Coope, G. R. 1987. Seasonal temperatures in Britain during the last 22,000 years, reconstructed using beetle remains. *Nature* **325**, 587-592.

Aubry, M. P. 1986. Palaeogene calcareous nannoplankton biostratigraphy of north-western Europe.

Palaeogeography, Palaeoclimatology, Palaeoecology **55**, 267-334.

Aubry, M. P., Hailwood, E. A. and Townsend, H. A. 1986. Magnetic and calcareous-nannofossil stratigraphy of the lower Palaeogene formations of the Hampshire and London basins. *Journal of the Geological Society, London* **143**, 729-735.

Audley-Charles, M. G. 1970. Triassic palaeogeography of the British Isles. *Quarterly Journal of the Geological Society, London* **126**, 49-89.

Avery, A. A. 1999. Infantile methaemoglobinaemia: re-examining the role of drinking water nitrates. *Environmental Health Perspectives* **107**, 583-586.

Avery, B. W. 1964. *The soils and land use of the district around Aylesbury and Hemel Hempstead Sheet 238*. Memoirs of the Soil Survey of Great Britain England and Wales. HMSO, London.

Avery, B. W. 1973. Soil classification in the Soil Survey of England and Wales. *Journal of Soil Science* **24**, 324-338.

Avery, B. W. 1980. *Soil classification for England and Wales (Higher Categories)*. Soil Survey Technical Monograph **14**. Soil Survey of England and Wales, Harpenden.

Avery, B. W. and Catt, J. A. 1983. Northaw Great Wood. In: *Diversion of the Thames. Field Guide* (ed. Rose, J.). Quaternary Research Association, Cambridge, 96-101.

Avery, B. W. and Thomasson, A. J. 1956. Field meeting in the Chilterns, 17th June, 1956. *Proceedings of the Geologists' Association* **67**, 168-171.

Avery, B. W., Bullock, P., Catt, J. A., Newman, A. C. D., Rayner, J. H. and Weir, A. H. 1972. The soil of Barnfield. *Rothamsted Experimental Station Report* **1971**, Part 2, 5-37.

Avery, B. W., Bullock, P., Catt, J. A., Rayner, J. H. and Weir, A. H. 1982. Composition and origin of some brickearths on the Chiltern Hills, England. *Catena* **9**, 153-174.

Avery, M. 1976. Hillforts of the British Isles; a student's introduction. In: *Hillforts: later prehistoric earthworks in Britain and Ireland* (ed. Harding, D. W.). Academic Press, London, 1-56.

B

Bailey, B. J. 1978. *Portrait of Hertfordshire*. Robert Hale, London.

Bailey, H. W. and Clayton, C. J. in press. Foraminiferids from flint meals and 'rotten' flints – the choice of an eclectic. Geological Society, London, Special Publication.

Bailey, H. W., Gale, A. S., Mortimore, R. N., Swiecicki, A. and Wood, C. J. 1983. The Coniacian – Maastrichtian Stages in the United Kingdom, with particular reference to southern England. *Newsletters in Stratigraphy* **12**, 19-42.

Bailey, H. W., Gale, A. S., Mortimore, R. N., Swiecicki, A. and Wood, C. J. 1984. Biostratigraphical criteria for recognition of the Coniacian to Maastrichtian stage boundaries in the chalk of north-west Europe, with particular reference to southern England. *Bulletin of the Geological Society of Denmark* **33**, 31-39.

Baker, C. A. 1976. Late Devensian periglacial phenomena

in the Upper Cam valley, north Essex. *Proceedings of the Geologists' Association* **87**, 285-306.

Baker, C. A. and Jones, D. K. C. 1980. Glaciation of the London Basin and its influence on the drainage pattern: a review and appraisal. In: *The shaping of southern England* (ed. Jones, D. K. C.). Academic Press, London, 131-175.

Banham, P. H. 1975. Glacitectonic structures: a general discussion with particular reference to the contorted drift of Norfolk. In: *Ice ages: ancient and modern* (eds Wright, A. E. and Moseley, F.). Seel House Press, Liverpool, 69-94.

Banister, K. 2007. The Pulham family of Hertfordshire and their work. In: *Hertfordshire garden history a miscellany* (ed. Rowe, A.). Hertfordshire Publications, University of Hertfordshire Press, Hatfield, 134-154.

Banks, D., Davies, C. and Davies, W. 1995. The Chalk as a karstic aquifer: evidence from a tracer test at Stanford Dingley, Berkshire, UK. *Quarterly Journal of Engineering Geology* **28**, S31-S38.

Barraud, E. M. 1951. Coprolites in Cambridgeshire. *Agriculture, London* **58**, 193-195.

Barrois, C. 1876. Récherches sur le terrain Crétacé Supérieur de l'Angleterre et de l'Irlande. *Mémoire de la Société Géologique du Nord.*

Barrow, G. 1910. Excursion to Hertingfordbury and Hertford. Saturday, March 10th, 1909. *Proceedings of the Geologists' Association* **21**, 167-171.

Barrow, G. 1915. Report of an excursion to Cowcroft Brickfield, Chesham. Saturday, July 10th, 1915. *Proceedings of the Geologists' Association* **26**, 330-340.

Barrow, G. 1917. The second excursion to Cowcroft Brickfield, Chesham. *Proceedings of the Geologists' Association* **28**, 40-43.

Barrow, G. 1918. Excursion to Chorley Wood. Saturday, June 29th, 1918. *Proceedings of the Geologists' Association* **29**, 140-148.

Barrow, G. 1919a. Some future work for the Geologists' Association. *Proceedings of the Geologists' Association* **30**, 1-48.

Barrow, G. 1919b. Excursion to Stanmore Hill and Bushey Heath. *Proceedings of the Geologists' Association* **30**, 122-126.

Barrow, G. and Green, J. F. N. 1921a. Excursion to Wendover and Buckland Common, near Cholesbury. Saturday, July 24th, 1920. *Proceedings of the Geologists' Association* **32**, 42-46.

Barrow, G. and Green, J. F. N. 1921b. Excursion to the Tring Gap and Steps Hill. Saturday, April 9th, 1921. *Proceedings of the Geologists' Association* **32**, 215-217.

Barton, N. J. 1992. *The lost rivers of London; a study of their effects upon London and Londoners, and the effects of London and Londoners upon them* (3rd edition). Historical Publications, Newbury.

Bassinot, F. E., Labayrie, L. D., Vincent, G., Quidelleur, X., Shackleton, N. J. and Lancelot, Y. 1994. The astronomical theory of climate and the Brunhes-Matuyama magnetic reversal. *Earth and Planetary Science Letters* **126**, 91-108.

Bateman, M. D. 1995. Thermoluminescence dating of the British coversand deposits. *Quaternary Science Reviews* **14**, 791-798.

Bateman, R. 1981. The Hertfordshire Orchidaceae. *Transactions of the Hertfordshire Natural History Society and Field Club* **26**, Part 4, 56-79.

Bateman, R. M. 1984. *A petrographic study of some Tertiary and Quaternary sediments of the Chiltern Hills, with particular reference to the Ayot Palaeogene outlier.* Unpublished B. Sc. Dissertation, Birkbeck College, London University.

Bateman, R. M. 1988. Relationship of the Woolwich and Reading Formation (Late Palaeocene) to the Upper Chalk (Late Cretaceous) and Clay-with-flints *sensu lato* (Quaternary) in the Chiltern Hills, southern England. *Tertiary Research* **10**, 53-63.

Bateman, R. M. and Catt, J. A. 2007. Provenance and palaeoenvironmental interpretation of superficial deposits, with particular reference to post-depositional modification of heavy mineral assemblages. In: *Heavy minerals in use* (eds Mange, M. A. and Wright, D. T.), *Developments in Sedimentology* **58**, 151-188. Elsevier, Amsterdam.

Bateman, R. M. and Moffat, A. J. 1987. Petrography of the Woolwich and Reading formation (Late Palaeocene) of the Chiltern Hills, southern England. *Tertiary Research* **8**, 75-103.

Beales, P. W. 1977. Appendix. Cladocera analysis from Fisher's Green. *New Phytologist* **78**, 520-523.

Beck, R. D., Funnell, B. M. and Lord, A. R. 1972. Correlation of Lower Pleistocene Crag at depth in Suffolk. *Geological Magazine* **109**, 137-139.

Bell, M. and Walker, M. J. C. 2005. *Late Quaternary environmental change physical and human perspectives* (2nd edition). Pearson Education Ltd, Harlow.

Bennett, F. J. 1887. On chalk wells. *Essex Naturalist* **1**, 260-265.

Beresford, S. A. 1985. Is nitrate in drinking water associated with gastric cancer in the urban UK? *International Journal of Epidemiology* **14**, 57-63.

Berry, G. F. 1979. Late Quaternary scour-hollows and related features in central London. *Quarterly Journal of Engineering Geology* **12**, 9-29.

Berggren, W. A., Kent, D. V., Swisher, C. C. and Aubry, M. P. 1995. A revised Cenozoic geochronology and chronostratigraphy. In: *Geochronology, time scales and global stratigraphic correlation* (eds Berggren, W. A., Kent, D. V., Aubry, M. P. and Hardenbol, J.). SEPM Special Publication **54**, 129-212.

Betts, R. T. and Boreham, S. 2004. Evidence for a Hoxnian Interglacial site at School Field, Tednambury, Hertfordshire. *Quaternary Newsletter* **104**, 2-11.

Billinghurst, S. A. 1927. On some new Ammonoidea from the Chalk Rock. *Geological Magazine* **64**, 511-518.

Bingley, R. M., Ashkenasi, V., Ellison, R. A., Morigi, A., Penna, N. T. and Booth, S. J. 1999. Monitoring changes in ground level, using high precision GPS. *Environment Agency R & D Report* **W210**.

Binnie, C., Kinber, M. and Smethurst, G. 2002. *Basic water treatment* (3rd edition). Thomas Telford, London.

Birley, M. 1988. Iron Age. In: Archaeological excavations in the Letchworth area, 1958-1974. Blackhorse Road, Letchworth; Norton Road, Baldock; Wilbury Hill, Letchworth (ed. Moss-Eccardt, J.). *Proceedings of the Cambridge Antiquarian Society* **77**, 79-87.

Birks, H. J. B. 1989. Holocene isochrone maps and patterns of tree-spreading in the British Isles. *Journal of Biogeography* **16**, 503-540.

Biswas, A. K. 1970. *History of hydrology*. North-Holland Publishing Company, Amsterdam.

Blake, J. F. 1895. Excursion to Elstree. Saturday, 10th November, 1894. *Proceedings of the Geologists' Association* **13**, 387.

Blake, J. F. 1900. Excursion to Bushey and Harrow Weald. Saturday, May 27th, 1899. *Proceedings of the Geologists' Association* **16**, 243-244.

Blakey, N. C. and Towler, P. A. 1988. The effect of unsaturated-saturated zone properties upon the hydrochemical and microbiological processes involved in the migration and attenuation of landfill leachate components. *Water Science and Technology* **20**, 119-128.

Blondeau, A. and Pomerol, C. 1968. A contribution to the sedimentological study of the Palaeogene of England. *Proceedings of the Geologists' Association* **79**, 441-445.

Bloom, E. F. D. 1934. Geology. In: *The natural history of the Hitchin region* (ed. Hine, R. L.). Hitchin and District Regional Survey Association, Hitchin, 26-52.

Bloom, E. F. D. and Harper, J. C. 1938. Field meeting in the Hitchin district. Saturday, 18th June, 1938. *Proceedings of the Geologists' Association* **49**, 415-419.

Bloom, E. F. D. and Wooldridge, S. W. 1930. Field meeting in the Hitchin district. Saturday, June 21st, 1929. *Proceedings of the Geologists' Association* **41**, 87-91.

Blundell, D. J. 2002. Cenozoic inversion and uplift of southern Britain. In: *Exhumation of the North Atlantic margin: timing, mechanisms and implications for petroleum exploration* (eds Doré, A. G., Cartwright, J. A., Stoker, M. S., Turner, J. P. and White, N.). Geological Society, London, Special Publication **196**, 85-101.

Bois, C., Damotte, B., Mascle, A., Cazes, M., Hirn, A. and Biju-Duval, B. 1987. Operations and main results of the ECORS project in France. *Geophysical Journal of the Royal Astronomical Society* **89**, 279-286.

Bolt, B. A. 1993. *Earthquakes and geological discovery*. Scientific American Library, New York.

Boniface, E. S. 1959. Some experiments in artificial recharge in the lower Lee valley. *Proceedings of the Institute of Civil Engineers* **14**, 325-328.

Bonney, T. G. 1874. On the Upper Greensand or Chloritic Marl of Cambridgeshire. *Proceedings of the Geologists' Association* **3**, 1-20.

Boreham, S. and Gibbard, P. L. 1995. Middle Pleistocene Hoxnian Stage interglacial deposits at Hitchin, Hertfordshire, England. *Proceedings of the Geologists' Association* **106**, 259-270.

Boreham, S. and Langford, H. 2006. The Milton Formation and late Cenozoic drainage development of the English Midlands: a comment on Belshaw, Hackney and Smith (2005). *Quaternary Newsletter* **108**, 14-23.

Boswell, P. G. H. 1952. The Pliocene-Pleistocene boundary in the east of England. *Proceedings of the Geologists' Association* **63**, 301-312.

Bott, M. H. P. and Bott, J. D. J. 2004. The Cenozoic uplift and earthquake belt of mainland Britain as a response to an underlying hot, low-density upper mantle. *Journal of the Geological Society, London* **161**, 19-29.

Bowen, D. Q. (ed.) 1999. *A revised correlation of Quaternary deposits in the British Isles*. Geological Society, London, Special Report **23**.

Bowen, D. Q., Hughes, S., Sykes, G. A. and Miller, G. H. 1989. Land-sea correlations in the Pleistocene based on isoleucine epimerization in non-marine molluscs. *Nature* **340**, 49-51.

Bowerbank, J. S. 1840. *A history of the fossil fruits and seeds of the London Clay*. John van Voorst, London.

Bradley, R. 2000. Past global changes and their significance for the future. *Quaternary Science Reviews* **19**, 391-402.

Branch Johnson, W. 1970. *The industrial archaeology of Hertfordshire*. David and Charles, Newton Abbott.

Breistroffer, M. 1947. Sur les zones d'ammonites dans l'Albien de France et d'Angleterre. *Travailles de la Laboratoire géologique de Grenoble* **26**, 17-104.

Bridgland, D. R. 1980. A reappraisal of Pleistocene stratigraphy in north Kent and eastern Essex, and new evidence concerning the former courses of the Thames and Medway. *Quaternary Newsletter* **32**, 14-24.

Bridgland, D. R. 1988. The Pleistocene fluvial stratigraphy and palaeogeography of Essex. *Proceedings of the Geologists' Association* **99**, 291-314.

Bridgland, D. R. 1994. *Quaternary of the Thames*. Geological Conservation Review **7**. Joint Nature Conservation Committee. Chapman and Hall, London.

Bridgland, D. R. 1999. 'Wealden rivers' north of the Thames: a provenance study based on gravel clast analysis. *Proceedings of the Geologists' Association* **110**, 133-148.

Bridgland, D. R. and Cheshire, D. A. 1994. Westmill Quarry (TL 344158). In: *Quaternary of the Thames* (ed. Bridgland, D. R.). Geological Conservation Review **7**. Joint Nature Conservation Committee. Chapman and Hall, London, 121-129.

Bridgland, D. R. and Harding, P. 1989. Investigations at Gaddesden Row brickpit, Hertfordshire. *Quaternary Newsletter* **59**, 2-4.

Briggs, D. J., Coope, G. R. and Gilbertson, D. D. 1985. The chronology and environmental framework of early man in the upper Thames Valley: a new model. *British Archaeological Reports* **137**, Oxford.

Bristow, C. R. 1985. *Geology of the country around Chelmsford*. Memoirs of the Geological Survey of England and Wales. HMSO, London.

Bristow, C. R., Ellison, R. A. and Wood, C. J. 1980. The Claygate Beds of Essex. *Proceedings of the Geologists' Association* **91**, 261-277.

British Geological Survey 1986. *1:625,000 Bouguer anomaly map of the British Isles, southern sheet*. British Geological Survey, Keyworth.

British Geological Survey 1990. *Great Dunmow Sheet 222. Solid and Drift Geology 1:50,000*. British Geological

Survey, Keyworth.

British Geological Survey 1993. *North London, England and Wales Sheet 256. Solid and Drift Geology 1:50,000.* British Geological Survey, Keyworth.

British Standards Institution 1975. *BS 1377. Methods of test for soils for engineering purposes.* British Standards Institution, London.

Broecker, W. S. and Denton, G. H. 1990. The role of ocean atmosphere reorganisations in glacial cycles. *Quaternary Science Reviews* **9**, 305-341.

Bromehead, C. E. N. 1912. On diversions of the Bourne near Chertsey. *Geological Survey Summary of Progress for 1911*, 74-77.

Bromehead, C. E. N. 1925. *The Geology of North London.* Memoirs of the Geological Survey England and Wales. HMSO, London.

Bromley, R. G. 1967a. Some observations on burrows of thalassinidean Crustacea in chalk hardgrounds. *Quarterly Journal of the Geological Society, London* **123**, 157-182.

Bromley, R. G. 1967b. Itinerary III. Ice-disturbed chalk south of Royston. In: *Geologists' Association Guides No 30A: The London Region (North of the Thames)* (ed. Hester, S. W.). Benham and Company, Colchester, 15-19.

Bromley, R. G. and Gale, A. S. 1982. The lithostratigraphy of the English Chalk Rock. *Cretaceous Research* **3**, 273-306.

Bromley, R. G. and Goldring, R. 1992. The palaeoburrows at the Cretaceous to Palaeocene firmground unconformity in southern England. *Tertiary Research* **13**, 95-102.

Brown, A. G. 1997. Clearances and clearings: deforestation in Mesolithic-Neolithic Britain. *Oxford Journal of Archaeology* **16**, 133-146.

Brown, E. H. 1964. Field meeting in the Chilterns, near Tring. 21 July, 1963. *Proceedings of the Geologists' Association* **75**, 341-343.

Brown, E. H. 1969. Jointing, aspect and the orientation of scarp-face dry valleys, near Ivinghoe, Buckinghamshire. *Transactions of the Institute of British Geographers* **48**, 61-73.

Brown, G., Catt, J. A., Hollyer, S. E. and Ollier, C. D. 1969. Partial silicification of Chalk fossils from the Chilterns. *Geological Magazine* **106**, 583-586.

Brown, G. M. 1970. Stone Age finds in Hatfield. *Journal of the Hatfield District Archaeological Society* **1**, Part 5, 9-12.

Brown, J. C. 1959. The sub-glacial surface in East Hertfordshire and its relation to the valley pattern. *Transactions of the Institute of British Geographers* **26**, 37-50.

Brown, J. M. B. 1953. Studies on British beechwoods. *Forestry Commission Bulletin* **20**. HMSO, London.

Brown, J. M. B. 1964. Forestry. In: Avery, B. W., *The soils and land use of the district around Aylesbury and Hemel Hempstead Sheet 238.* Memoirs of the Soil Survey of Great Britain England and Wales, pp. 191-198. HMSO, London.

Brown, N. and Murphy, P. 1997. Neolithic and Bronze Age. In: *Research and archaeology: a framework for the eastern counties. 1. Resource assessment* (ed. Glazebrook, J.). East Anglian Archaeology Occasional Paper **3**, 12-22.

Brownsell, W. 2008. *Middle Pleistocene till stratigraphy in south Bedfordshire and the Hitchin Gap.* Unpublished PhD thesis, University of Hertfordshire.

Bryant, S. 1993. Whiteley Hill, near Royston: a late Bronze Age ringwork? *Hertfordshire Archaeology* **11**, 26-29.

Bryant, S. 1995. The late Bronze Age to the middle Iron Age of the north Chilterns. In: *Chiltern archaeology recent work a handbook for the next decade* (ed. Holgate, R.). The Book Castle, Dunstable, 17-27.

Bryant, S. 2007. Central places or special places? The origins and development of '*oppida*' in Hertfordshire. In: *The later Iron Age in Britain and beyond* (eds Haselgrove, C., and Moore, T.). Oxbow Books, Oxford, 62-80.

Bryant, S. and Burleigh, G. 1995. Later prehistoric dykes of the eastern Chilterns. In: *Chiltern archaeology recent work a handbook for the next decade* (ed. Holgate, R.). The Book Castle, Dunstable, 92-95.

Bryant, S., Perry, B. and Williamson, T. 2005. A 'relict landscape' in south-east Hertfordshire: archaeological and topographic investigations in the Wormley area. *Landscape History* **27**, 5-16.

Buckingham, C. M., Roe, D. A. and Scott, K. 1996. A preliminary report on the Stanton Harcourt Channel Deposits (Oxfordshire, England): geological context, vertebrate remains and palaeolithic stone artefacts. *Journal of Quaternary Science* **11**, 397-415.

Building Research Establishment, 1996. Desiccation in clay soils. *Building Research Establishment Digest* **412**. London, HMSO.

Bujak, J. P., Downie, C. P., Eaton, G. L. and Williams, G. L. 1980. Dinoflagellate cysts and acritarchs from the Eocene of southern England. *Special Papers in Palaeontology* **24**.

Burkitt, M. C. 1926. *Our early ancestors.* Cambridge University Press, Cambridge.

Burleigh, G. R. 1976. Pipeline archaeology. *Hertfordshire's Past* **1**, 17-18.

Burleigh, G. R. 1980. Excavations at the Mile Ditches, near Royston, 1978. *Hertfordshire's Past* **8**, 24-29.

Burleigh, G. 1995. A late Iron Age oppidum at Baldock, Hertfordshire. In: *Chiltern archaeology recent work a handbook for the next decade* (ed. Holgate, R.). The Book Castle, Dunstable, 103-112.

Burnett, A. D. and Fookes, P. G. 1974. A regional engineering geological study of the London Clay in the London and Hampshire basins. *Quarterly Journal of Engineering Geology* **7**, 257-295.

Burnett, J. A. 1998. Upper Cretaceous. In: *Calcareous nannofossil stratigraphy* (ed. Bown, P. R.). British Micropalaeontological Society Publications Series. Chapman and Hall, London.

Burt, T., Hefting, M. M., Pinay, G. and Sabater, S. 2007. The role of floodplains in mitigating diffuse nitrate pollution. In: *Hydroecology and ecohydrology: past, present and future* (eds Wood, P. J., Hannah, D. M. and Sadler, J. P.). J. Wiley & Sons Ltd., Chichester, 253-268.

Busby, J. P., Kimbell, G. S. and Pharoah, T. C. 1993. Integrated geophysical/geological modelling of the Caledonian and Precambrian basement of southern Britain. *Geological Magazine* **130**, 593-604.

Bushby, G. H. 1934. The holy springs of Waltham Abbey at Wormley. *Transactions of the East Hertfordshire Archaeological Society* **8**, 176-186.

Butler, D. E. 1981. Marine faunas from concealed Devonian rocks of southern England and their reflection of the Frasnian transgression. *Geological Magazine* **118**, 679-697.

Buurman, P. 1980. Palaeosols in the Reading Beds (Paleocene) of Alum Bay, Isle of Wight. *Sedimentology* **27**, 593-606.

C

Cameron, K. 1996. *English place names*. Batsford, London.

Cameron, T. D. J., Bonny, A. P., Gregory, D. M. and Harland, R. 1984. Lower Pleistocene dinoflagellate cyst, foraminiferal and pollen assemblages in four boreholes in the southern North Sea. *Geological Magazine* **121**, 85-97.

Cameron, T. D. J., Crosby, A., Balson, P. S., Jeffery, D. H., Lott, G. K., Bulat, J. and Harrison, D. J. 1992. The geology of the southern North Sea. *United Kingdom Offshore Regional Report*. British Geological Survey, HMSO, London.

Campbell, J. B. and Hubbard, R. N. L. B. 1978. Biological investigations of the Rackley site. In: *Paleoecology and archeology of an Acheulian site at Caddington, England* (ed. Sampson, C. G.). Department of Anthropology, Southern Methodist University, Dallas, Texas, USA, 47-60.

Candy, I. and Schreve, D. 2007. Land-sea correlation of Middle Pleistocene temperate sub-stages using high-precision uranium-series dating of tufa deposits from southern England. *Quaternary Science Reviews* **26**, 1223-1235.

Carter, D. J. and Hart, M. B. 1977. Aspects of mid-Cretaceous stratigraphical micropalaeontology. *Bulletin of the British Museum (Natural History), Geology Series* **29**, 1-135.

Casey, R. 1965. Cambridge Greensand. In: *Geology of the country around Huntingdon and Biggleswade. Explanation of one-inch geological sheets 187 and 204, New Series* (eds Edmonds, E. A. and Dinham, C. H.). Memoirs of the Geological Survey of Great Britain England and Wales. HMSO, London, 54-55.

Castle, S. 1971. Archaeological survey of southwest Hertfordshire. *Watford and Southwest Hertfordshire Archaeological Society Bulletin* **14**, 1-11.

Catt, J. A. 1969. The origin and development of the soils. *Report Rothamsted Experimental Station* **1968**, Part 2, 89-93.

Catt, J. A. 1981. Quaternary history of the Hertfordshire area. *Transactions of the Hertfordshire Natural History Society and Field Club* **28**, Part 4, 27-54.

Catt, J. A. 1985. Soil particle size distribution and mineralogy as indicators of pedogenic and geomorphic history: examples from the loessial soils of England and Wales. In: *Geomorphology and soils* (eds Richards, K. S., Arnett, R. R. and Ellis, S.). G. Allen and Unwin, London, 202-218.

Catt, J. A. 1986. The nature, origin and geomorphological significance of Clay-with-flints. In: *The scientific study of flint and chert* (eds Sieveking, G. de G. and Hart, M. B.). Cambridge University Press, Cambridge, 151-159.

Catt, J. A. 2000. Aspects of English silcretes and comparison with some Australian occurrences: comment. *Proceedings of the Geologists' Association* **111**, 86-88.

Catt, J. A. and Hagen, R. E. 1978. Geological background. In: *Paleoecology and archeology of an Acheulian site at Caddington, England* (ed. Sampson, C. G.). Department of Anthropology, Southern Methodist University, Dallas, USA, pp. 17-27.

Catt, J. A. and Moffat, A. J. 1980. An occurrence of Hertfordshire Puddingstone in Reading Beds at St Albans. *Transactions of the Hertfordshire Natural History Society and Field Club* **28**, Part 3, 12-16.

Catt, J. A., Weir, A. H. and Madgett, P. A. 1974. The loess of eastern Yorkshire and Lincolnshire. *Proceedings of the Yorkshire Geological Society* **40**, 23-39.

Catt, J. A., King, D. W. and Weir, A. H. 1975. The soils of Woburn Experimental Farm. Part 1. Great Hill, Road Piece and Butt Close. *Rothamsted Experimental Station Report* **1974**, Part 2, 5-28.

Catt, J. A., Howse, K. R., Christian, D. G., Lane, P. W., Harris, G. L. and Goss, M. J. 1998. Strategies to decrease nitrate leaching in the Brimstone Farm Experiment, Oxfordshire, UK, 1988-93: the effects of winter cover crops and unfertilized grass leys. *Plant and Soil* **203**, 57-69.

Catt, J. A., Gibbard, P. L., Lowe, J. J., McCarroll, D., Scourse, J. D., Walker, M. J. C. and Wymer, J. J. 2006. Quaternary: ice sheets and their legacy. In: *The geology of England and Wales*, 2nd edition (eds. Brenchley, P. J. and Rawson, P. F.). The Geological Society, London, 429-467.

Cavalli-Sforza, L. L., Menozzi, P. and Piazza, A. 1994. *The history and geography of human genes*. Princeton University Press, Princeton.

Chadwick, R. A. 1985. Upper Jurassic: late Oxfordian to early Portlandian. In: *Atlas of onshore sedimentary basins in England and Wales. Post Carboniferous tectonics and stratigraphy* (ed. Whittaker, A.). Blackie, Glasgow, 49-51.

Chadwick, R. A. 1986. Extension tectonics in the Wessex Basin, southern England. *Journal of the Geological Society, London* **143**, 465-488.

Chadwick, R. A. 1993. Aspects of basin inversion in southern Britain. *Journal of the Geological Society, London* **150**, 311-322.

Chadwick, R. A. and Evans, D. J. 2005. *A seismic atlas of southern Britain – images of subsurface structure*. British Geological Survey Occasional Publication 7. British Geological Survey, Keyworth.

Chadwick, R. A., Pharoah, T. C. and Smith, N. J. P. 1989. Lower crustal heterogeneity beneath Britain from deep seismic reflection data. *Journal of the Geological Society, London* **146**, 617-630.

Chadwick, R. A., Kirby, G. A. and Baily, H. E. 1994. The post-Triassic structural evolution of north-west England and adjacent parts of the East Irish Sea. *Proceedings of the*

Yorkshire Geological Society **50**, 91-102.

Chandler, M. E. J. 1951. Note on the occurrence of mangroves in the London Clay. *Proceedings of the Geologists' Association* **62**, 271-272.

Chandler, R. H. 1909. On some dry chalk valley features. *Geological Magazine* Decade V, **6**, 538-539.

Chapman, F. 1903. Ostracoda from the chara-marl of Hitchin. *Transactions of the Hertfordshire Natural History Society and Field Club* **11**, 60-62.

Chauncy, H. 1826. *The historical antiquities of Hertfordshire* (2nd edition, 2 volumes). Mullinger and Holdsworth, London.

Cheshire, D. A. 1978. *The glaciation of the Lea valley between Hertford and Enfield.* Unpublished MSc Thesis. CNAA, City of London Polytechnic and Polytechnic of North London.

Cheshire, D. A. 1981. A contribution towards a glacial stratigraphy of the lower Lea Valley, and implications for the Anglian Thames. In: *Quaternary Studies* **1** (eds Bryant, R. H. and Lowe, J. J.). City of London Polytechnic, London, 27-69.

Cheshire, D. A. 1983. Hoddesdon. In: *The Diversion of the Thames. A Field Guide* (ed. Rose, J.). Quaternary Research Association, Cambridge, 140-148.

Cheshire, D. A. 1986a. *The lithology and stratigraphy of the Anglian deposits of the Lea Basin.* Unpublished PhD thesis, Hatfield Polytechnic.

Cheshire, D. A. 1986b. The use of small clast counts as a means of till differentiation in Hertfordshire and western Essex. In: *Clast lithological analysis* (ed. Bridgland, D. R). *Technical Guide* **3**, Quaternary Research Association, Cambridge, 129-143.

Cholley, A. 1943. Recherches sur les surfaces d'erosion et la morphologie de la région parisienne. *Annales de Géographie* **52**, 1-19, 81-97, 161-189.

Christensen, T. H., Bjerg, P. L., Banwart, S. A., Jakobsen, R., Heron, G. and Albrechtsen, H. -J. 2000. Characterization of redox conditions in groundwater contaminant plumes. *Journal of Contaminant Hydrology* **45**, 165-241.

Christian, D. G, Goss, M. J., Howse, K. R., Powlson, D. S. and Pepper, T. J. 1990. Leaching of nitrate through soil. *Report of Institute of Arable Crops Research for 1889.* Lawes Agricultural Trust, Harpenden, 67-68.

Clark, C. D., Gibbard, P. L. and Rose, J. 2004. Pleistocene glacial limits in England, Scotland and Wales. In: *Quaternary glaciations: extent and chronology. Part 1. Europe.* Elsevier Science, Amsterdam, 47-82.

Clark, L., Blakey, N. C., Foster, S. S. D. and West, J. M. 1991. Microbiology of aquifers. In: *Applied groundwater hydrology a British perspective* (eds Downing, R. A. and Wilkinson, W. B.). Clarendon Press, Oxford, 164-176.

Clark, M. 2001. *Mammals, amphibians and reptiles of Hertfordshire.* Hertfordshire Natural History Society and Training Publications Ltd, Watford.

Clark, M. J., Lewin, J. and Small, R. J. 1967. The sarsen stones of the Marlborough Downs and their geomorphological implications. *Southampton Research Series in Geography* **4**, 3-40.

Clark, R. 1991. Excavations at Barton Ring Ditches: landscape history and archaeology. *Bedfordshire Archaeology* **19**, 4-24.

Clarke, D. L. 1970. *Beaker pottery of Great Britain and Ireland.* Cambridge University Press, Cambridge.

Clarke, L. 2007. The influences behind the creation of John Scott's grotto. In: *Hertfordshire garden history a miscellany* (ed. Rowe, A.). Hertfordshire Publications, University of Hertfordshire Press, Hatfield, 88-105.

Clarke, M. R. and Dixon, A. J. 1981. The Pleistocene braided river deposits in the Blackwater Valley area of Berkshire and Hampshire, England. *Proceedings of the Geologists' Association* **92**, 139-158.

Clayden, B. and Hollis, J. M. 1984. Criteria for differentiating soil series. *Soil Survey Technical Monograph* **17**. Soil Survey of England and Wales, Harpenden.

Clayton, C. J. 1984. *The chemical environment of flint formation in Upper Cretaceous chalks.* Unpublished PhD Thesis, London University.

Clayton, C. J. 1986. The chemical environment of flint formation in Upper Cretaceous chalks. In: *The scientific study of flint and chert* (eds Sieveking, G. de G. and Hart, M. B.). Cambridge University Press, Cambridge, 43-54.

Clayton, K. M. 1957. Some aspects of the glacial deposits of Essex. *Proceedings of the Geologists' Association* **68**, 1-21.

Clayton, K. M. 2000. Glacial erosion of the Wash and Fen basin and the deposition of the chalky till of eastern England. *Quaternary Science Reviews* **19**, 811-822.

Clayton, K. M. and Brown, J. C. 1958. The glacial deposits around Hertford. *Proceedings of the Geologists' Association* **69**, 103-119.

Clifton Taylor, A. 1977. Building materials. In: *The Buildings of England: Hertfordshire* (eds Pevsner, N. and Cherry, B.) (2nd edition). Penguin Books, Harmondsworth.

Clutterbuck, J. C. 1850. On the periodical alternations, and progressive permanent depression, of the Chalk water level under London. *Proceedings of the Institution of Civil Engineers* **9**, 151-180.

Clutterbuck, J. 1864. Agricultural notes on Hertfordshire. *The Journal of the Royal Agricultural Society of England* **25**, 302-317.

Cocks, C. R. M. and Fortey, R. A. 1982. Faunal evidence for oceanic separations in the Palaeozoic of Britain. *Journal of the Geological Society, London* **139**, 465-478.

Codrington, T. 1903. *Roman roads in Britain.* SPCK, London.

Cogné, J. and Wright, A. E. 1980. L'Orogène cadomien. In: *Géologie de l'Europe* (eds Cogné, J. and Slansky, M.). *Mémoire du Bureau de Recherches Géologiques et Minières* **108**, 29-55.

Collins, D. and Lorimer, D. (eds). 1989. Excavations at the Mesolithic site on West Heath, Hampstead 1976-1981. *British Archaeological Reports British Series* **217**.

Collinson, M. E. 1983. *Fossil plants of the London Clay.* Palaeontological Association Field Guide to Fossils No. **1**. The Palaeontological Association, London.

Collinson, M. E., Steart, D. C., Scott, A. C., Glasspool, I. J. and Hooker, J. J. 2007. Episodic fire, runoff and deposition at the Palaeocene-Eocene boundary. *Journal of the Geological Society, London* **164**, 87-97.

Connorton, B. J. 1988. Water resources management and rising groundwater levels in the London Basin. In: *Water management and the geoenvironment Volume 1* (ed. Kozlovsky, E. A.). UNESCO, Paris, 139-148.

Cooke, N., Brown, F. and Phillpotts, C. 2008. *From hunter gatherers to huntsmen: a history of the Stansted landscape*. Framework Archaeology, Oxford.

Coope, G. R. 1977. Fossil coleopteran assemblages as sensitive indicators of climatic changes during the Devensian (Last) cold stage. *Philosophical Transactions of the Royal Society of London* **B280**, 313-337.

Coope, G. R. 1993. Late-Glacial (Anglian) and Late temperate (Hoxnian) coleoptera. In: *The Lower Palaeolithic site at Hoxne, England* (eds Singer, R., Gladfelter, B. G. and Wymer, J. J.). University of Chicago Press, Chicago, 156-162.

Coope, G. R. and Kenward, H. K. 2007. Evidence from coleopteran assemblages for a short but intense cold interlude during the latter part of the MS 11 interglacial from Quinton, West Midlands, UK. *Quaternary Science Reviews* **26**, 3276-3285.

Coope, G. R. and Tallon, P. 1983. A full glacial insect fauna from the Lea valley, Enfield, North London. *Quaternary Newsletter* **40**, 7-10.

Coope, G. R., Gibbard, P. L., Hall, A. R., Preece, R. C., Robinson, J. E. and Sutcliffe, A. J. 1997. Climatic and environmental reconstructions based on fossil assemblages from Middle Devensian (Weichselian) deposits of the River Thames at South Kensington, Central London, UK. *Quaternary Science Reviews* **16**, 1163-1195.

Cooper, J. 2007. *Hertford a history*. Phillimore, Chichester.

Cooper, J. E. 1934. Oldhaven and Thanet Sand mollusca of Herne Bay. *Journal of Conchology* **20**, 4-8.

Cooper, M. A., Williams, G. D., De Graciansky, P. C., Murphy, R. W., Needham, T., de Paor, D., Stoneley, R., Todd, S. P., Turner, J. P. and Ziegler, P. A. 1989. Inversion tectonics – a discussion. In: *Inversion tectonics* (eds Cooper, M. A. and Williams, G. D.). Geological Society, London, Special Publication **44**, 335-347.

Cope, J. C. W. 1994. A latest Cretaceous hotspot and the south-easterly tilt of Britain. *Journal of the Geological Society, London* **151**, 905-908.

Corfield, S. M., Gawthorpe, R. L., Gage, M., Fraser, A. J. and Besley, B. M. 1996. Inversion tectonics of the Variscan foreland of the British Isles. *Journal of the Geological Society, London* **153**, 17-32.

Cornwell, J. D., Royles, C. P. and Self, S. J. 1990. Interpretation of geophysical anomalies in East Anglia: a preliminary geological assessment. *British Geological Survey Technical Report* **WK/90/32**.

Costa, L. and Downie, C. 1976. The distribution of the dinoflagellate Wetzeliella in the Palaeogene of north-western Europe. *Palaeontology* **19**, 591-614.

Costa, L., Denison, C. and Downie, C. 1978. The Palaeocene/Eocene boundary in the Anglo-Paris Basin. *Journal of the Geological Society, London* **135**, 261-264.

Cotton, J. 1991. Prehistory in Greater London. *Current Archaeology* **124**, 151-154.

Cotton, M. A. and Frere, S. S. 1968. Ivinghoe Beacon excavations, 1963-65. *Records of Buckinghamshire* **18**, 187-260.

County Development Unit 2007. *Hertfordshire minerals local plan review 2002-2016*. Hertfordshire County Council, Hertford.

Cowperthwaite, I. A., Fitch, F. J., Miller, J. A., Mitchell, J. G. and Robertson, R. H. 1972. Sedimentation, petrogenesis and radio isotopic age of the Cretaceous fuller's earth of Southern England. *Clay Minerals* **9**, 309-327.

Cox, A. 1979a. Fuller's earth working in Bedfordshire. *Bedfordshire Magazine* **17**, 91-95.

Cox, A. 1979b. *Survey of Bedfordshire brickmaking: a history and gazetteer*. Bedfordshire County Council and Royal Commission on Historical Monuments, Bedford.

Cox, W. J. 1934. History of the Hertfordshire Natural History Society, 1875-1933. *Transactions of the Hertfordshire Natural History Society and Field Club* **19**, 231-242.

Cra'ster, M. D. 1961. The Aldwick Iron Age settlement, Barley, Hertfordshire. *Proceedings of the Cambridge Antiquarian Society* **54**, 22-46.

Crawford, O. G. S. 1931. The Chiltern Grim's Ditch. *Antiquity* **5**, 161-171.

Crawford, O. G. S. 1936. Field archaeology in the Royston district. *Proceedings of the Prehistoric Society of East Anglia* **35**, 97-105.

Creighton, J. 2000. *Coins and power in late Iron Age Britain*. Cambridge University Press, Cambridge.

Crockford, R. M. and Bell, A. L. 1996. Compaction grouting in the UK – a review. In: *Grouting and deep mixing. Proceedings of the 2nd International Conference on Ground Improvement Geosystems* (eds Yonekura, R., Terashi, M. and Shibazaki, M.). Balkema, Rotterdam, 279-284.

Crosskey, H. W. 1882. Ninth report of the committee, consisting of Professor Prestwich, Professor T. McK. Hughes, ... H. G. Fordham and W. Terrill, appointed for the purpose of recording the position, height above the sea, lithological characters, size and origin of the erratic blocks of England, Wales and Ireland, reporting other matters of interest connected with the same, and taking measures for their preservation. *Report of the British Association for the Advancement of Science* **1881**, 204-218.

Crosskey, H. W. 1884. Eleventh report of the committee, consisting of Professor Prestwich, W. Boyd Dawkins, ... J. Plant and R. H. Tiddeman for the purpose of recording the position, height above the sea, lithological characters, size and origin of the erratic blocks of England, Wales and Ireland, reporting other matters of interest connected with the same, and taking measures for their preservation. *Report of the British Association for the Advancement of Science* **1883**, 136-147.

Crowley, T. J. 2000. Causes of climate change over the past 1000 years. *Science* **289**, 270-277.

Cruse, P. K. 1986. Drilling and construction methods. In: *Groundwater: occurrence, development and protection* (ed. Brandon, T. W.). Institute of Water Engineers and

Scientists, London, 437-484.

Crux, J. A. 1991. Albian calcareous nannofossils from the Gault Clay of Munday's Hill (Bedfordshire, England). *Journal of Micropalaeontology* **10**, 203-222.

Culling, E. W. H. 1956a. Longitudinal profiles of the Chiltern streams. *Proceedings of the Geologists' Association* **67**, 314-345.

Culling, E. W. H. 1956b. The upper reaches of the Chiltern valleys. *Proceedings of the Geologists' Association* **67**, 346-368.

Cuming, S. 1997. *A habitat survey of Hertfordshire 1994-1997.* Unpublished Reports of Hertfordshire and Middlesex Wildlife Trust and Hertfordshire Environmental Records Centre.

Cunliffe, B. W. 1991. *Iron Age communities in Britain* (3rd edition). Routledge and Kegan Paul, London.

Cunliffe, B. W. 2001. *Facing the ocean: the Atlantic and its peoples 8000 BC–AD 1500.* Oxford University Press, Oxford.

Curran, J. 2005. *The story of Totternhoe Quarries.* Church End Publishing, Edlesborough, Dunstable.

Currant, A. P. and Jacobi, R. M. 2004. A Middle Devensian mammalian assemblage from the Hyaena Den, Wookey Hole, Somerset. In: *The Quaternary mammals of southern and eastern England* (ed. Schreve, D. C.). Quaternary Research Association, London, 87-92.

Curry, D. 1965. The Palaeogene beds of south-east England. *Proceedings of the Geologists' Association* **76**, 151-173.

Curry, D. 1982. Differential preservation of foraminiferids in the English Upper Cretaceous – consequential observations. In: *Aspects of micropalaeontology* (eds Banner, F. T. and Lord, A. R.). Allen and Unwin, London.

Curry, D., Adams, C. G., Boulter, M. C., Dilley, F. C., Eames, F. E., Funnell, B. M. and Wells, M. K. 1978. A correlation of Tertiary rocks in the British Isles. *Geological Society of London Special Report* **12**.

Curwen, E. C. 1941. More about querns. *Antiquity* **15**, 15-32.

Cuttell, J. C., Lloyd, J. W. and Ivanovich, M. 1986. A study of uranium and thorium series isotopes in Chalk groundwaters of Lincolnshire, UK. *Journal of Hydrology* **86**, 343-365.

D

Daley, B. and Balson, P. 1999. *British Tertiary stratigraphy.* Geological Conservation Review Series **15**. Joint Nature Conservation Committee, Peterborough.

Dalton, C. 2007. The gardens at Quickswood, the hunting lodge of the Earls of Salisbury. In: *Hertfordshire garden history a miscellany* (ed. Rowe, A.). University of Hertfordshire Press, Hatfield, pp. 26-40.

Darcy, H. 1856. *Les fontaines publiques de la Ville de Dijon.* Victor Dalmont, Paris.

Darling, W. G. 1985. Methane in Chalk groundwater of central London. *British Geological Survey Report* **WD/ST/85/3**.

Darwin, C. 1859. *On the origin of species by means of natural selection; or, the preservation of favoured races in the struggle for life.* J. Murray, London.

Davies, A. G. and Petchey, M. 1977. A mistaken 'Saxon' cremation at Hertford. *Hertfordshire Archaeology* **4**, 176-177.

Davies, A. G., Gibson, A. V. B. and Ashdown, R. R. 1982. A Mesolithic site at Stanstead Abbots, Hertfordshire. *Hertfordshire Archaeology* **8**, 1-10.

Davies, A. M. and Baines, A. H. J. 1953. A preliminary survey of the sarsen and puddingstone blocks of the Chilterns. *Proceedings of the Geologists' Association* **64**, 1-9.

Davis, A. G. and Elliott, G. F. 1957. The palaeogeography of the London Clay sea. *Proceedings of the Geologists' Association* **68**, 255-277.

Davis, J. 1981. Grim's Ditch in Buckinghamshire and Hertfordshire. *Records of Buckinghamshire* **23**, 23-31.

Davis, J. and Evans, J. G. 1984. Grim's Ditch, Ivinghoe. *Records of Buckinghamshire* **26**, 1-10.

Davison, C. 1924. *A history of British Earthquakes.* Cambridge University Press, Cambridge.

De Freitas, M. H. 2009. Geology; its principles, practice and potential in geotechnics. *Quarterly Journal of Engineering Geology and Hydrogeology* **42**, 397-441.

De Salis, R. F. 1914. Report of an excursion to Harefield, April 26th, 1913. *Proceedings of the Geologists' Association* **25**, 50-51.

Derricourt, R. M. and Jacobi, R. M. 1970. Mesolithic finds from Hampermill, Watford. *Hertfordshire Archaeology* **2**, 1-5.

Dewey, H. 1912. Report on an excursion to Claygate and Oxshott, Surrey. *Proceedings of the Geologists' Association* **23**, 237-242.

Dewey, H. and Bromehead, C. E. N. 1915. *The geology of the country around Windsor and Chertsey.* Memoirs of the Geological Survey England and Wales. HMSO, London.

Dewey, H. and Bromehead, C. E. N. 1921. *The geology of south London.* Memoirs of the Geological Survey of England and Wales. HMSO, London.

Di, H. J. and Cameron, K. C. 2002. Nitrate leaching in temperate agroecosystems; sources, factors and mitigating strategies. *Nutrient Cycling in Agroecosystems* **64**, 237-256.

Dickinson, J. 1850. On the supply of water from the Chalk stratum in the neighbourhood of London. *Abstracts of papers communicated to the Royal Society of London* **6**, 25-26.

Dines, H. G. and Chatwin, C. P. 1930. Pliocene sandstone from Rothamsted (Hertfordshire). *Geological Survey Summary of Progress for 1929*, 1-7.

Dines, H. G., Holmes, S. C. A. and Robbie, J. A. 1954. *Geology of the country around Chatham.* Memoirs of the Geological Survey England and Wales. HMSO, London.

Dixon, J. C., Fitton, J. G. and Frost, R. T. C. 1981. The tectonic significance of post-Carboniferous igneous activity in the North Sea Basin. In: *Petroleum geology of the continental shelf of north-west Europe* (eds Illing, L. V. and Hobson, G. D.). Heyden and Son, London.

Dobson, E. 1850. A rudimentary treatise on the manufacture of brick and tiles. Reprint with introduction, biography, notes, bibliography and index (ed. Celoria, F.). *Journal of*

Ceramic History **5**. George Street Press, Stafford.

Donovan, D. T., Horton, A. and Ivimey-Cook, H. C. 1979. The transgression of the Lower Lias over the northern flank of the London Platform. *Journal of the Geological Society, London* **136**, 165-173.

Dony, J. G. 1967. *Flora of Hertfordshire*. Hitchin Museum, Hitchin.

Downing, R. A., Smith, D. B. and Warren, S. C. 1978. Seasonal variations of tritium and other consitituents in groundwater in the Chalk near Brighton, England. *Journal of the Institute of Water Engineers and Scientists* **32**, 123-136.

Downing, R. A., Pearson, F. J. and Smith, D. B. 1979. The flow mechanism in the Chalk based on radio-isotope analyses of groundwater in the London Basin. *Journal of Hydrology* **40**, 67-83.

Downing, R. A., Ashford, P. L., Headworth, H. G., Owen, M. and Skinner, A. C. 1981. The use of groundwater for river regulation. In: *A survey of British hydrogeology* (eds Argent, C. R. and Griffin, D. J. H.). Royal Society, London, 153-171.

Dury, G. H. 1971. Relict deep weathering and duricrusting in relation to the palaeoenvironments of middle latitudes. *Geographical Journal* **137**, 511-522.

Dyer, J. F. 1959. Barrows on the Chilterns. *Archaeological Journal* **116**, 1-24.

Dyer, J. F. 1961. Dray's Ditches, Bedfordshire, and early Iron Age territorial boundaries in the eastern Chilterns. *Antiquaries Journal* **41**, 32-42.

Dyer, J. F. 1963. The Chiltern Grim's Ditch. *Antiquity* **37**, 46-49.

Dyer, J. F. 1964. A secondary Neolithic camp at Waulud's Bank, Leagrave. *Bedfordshire Archaeological Journal* **2**, 1-15.

Dyer, J. F. 1974. The excavation of two barrows on Galley Hill, Streatley. *Bedfordshire Archaeology* **9**, 13-34.

Dyer, J. F. 1976. Ravensburgh Castle, Hertfordshire. In: *Hillforts: later prehistoric earthworks in Britain and Ireland* (ed. Harding, D. W.). Academic Press, London, 153-159 and 421-423.

Dyer, J. F. 1981. *Hillforts of England and Wales*. Shire Archaeology, Aylesbury.

Dyer, J. F. 1991. The Five Knolls and associated barrows at Dunstable, Bedfordshire. *Bedfordshire Archaeology* **19**, 25-29.

Dyer, J. F. and Hales, A. J. 1961. Pitstone Hill – a study in field archaeology. *Records of Buckinghamshire* **17**, 49-56.

Dyke, G. V. 1993. *John Lawes of Rothamsted. Pioneer of science, farming and industry*. Hoos Press, Harpenden.

Dyson-Bruce, L., Bryant, S. and Thompson, I. 2006. *Historic landscape characterisation. County report for Hertfordshire*. Hertfordshire County Council and English Heritage.

E

Edmonds, C. N. 1987. *The engineering geomorphology of karst development and the prediction of subsidence risk upon the Chalk outcrop in England*. Unpublished PhD Thesis, University of London.

Edmonds, C. N. 2008. Karst and mining geohazards with particular reference to the Chalk outcrop, England. *Quarterly Journal of Engineering Geology and Hydrogeology* **41**, 261-278.

Edmonds, C. N., Green, C. P. and Higginbottom, I. E. 1990. Review of underground mines in the English Chalk: form, origin, distribution and engineering significance. In: *Chalk: Proceedings of the International Chalk Symposium, Brighton Polytechnic, 1989*. Thomas Telford, London, 511-520.

Edmonds, E. A. and Dinham, C. H. 1965. *Geology of the country around Huntingdon and Biggleswade. Explanation of of one-inch geological sheets 187 and 204 New Series*. Memoirs of the Geological Survey of Great Britain England and Wales. HMSO, London.

Edmunds, W. M., Cook, J. M. and Miles, D. L. 1984. A comparative study of sequential redox processes in three British aquifers. In: *Hydrochemical balances of freshwater systems* (ed. Eriksson, E.). International Association of Hydrological Sciences Publication **150**. IAHS Press, Wallingford, 55-70.

Edwards, F. E. and Wood, S. V. jun. 1849-1877. *A Monograph of the Eocene Cephalopoda and Univalves of England*. Palaeontographical Society Monograph, London.

Elliott, G. F. 1963. London Clay fossils from Totteridge, Herts. *Proceedings of the Geologists' Association* **74**, 259-260.

Ellison, R. A., O'B. Knox, R. W., Jolley, D. W. and King, C. 1994. A revision of the lithostratigraphical classification of the early Palaeogene strata of the London Basin and East Anglia. *Proceedings of the Geologists' Association* **105**, 187-197.

Ellison, R. A., Woods, M. A., Allen, D. J., Forster, A., Pharoah, T. C. and King, C. 2004. *Geology of London. Special Memoir for 1:50,000 Geological sheets 256 (North London), 257 (Romford), 270 (South London) and 271 (Dartford) (England and Wales)*. British Geological Survey, Keyworth, Nottingham.

Elsden, J. V. 1886. On the microscopic structure of boulders found in the north of Hertfordshire. *Transactions of the Hertfordshire Natural History Society and Field Club* **3**, 49-57.

Environment Agency, 2004. *The state of England's chalk rivers*. Environment Agency, Bristol.

Etheridge, R. 1879. Position of the Silurian rocks in Herts. *Geological Magazine* Decade II, **6**, 286-288.

Evans, J. 1876. The anniversary address of the president. *Quarterly Journal of the Geological Society, London* **32**, 53-121.

Evans, J. 1878. The Hertfordshire Bourne. *Transactions of the Watford Natural History Society and Hertfordshire Field Club* **1**, 137-140.

Evans, J. 1892. An archaeological survey of Hertfordshire. *Archaeologia* **53**, 245-262.

Evans, J. 1896. The Stone Age in Hertfordshire. *Transactions of the Hertfordshire Natural History Society and Field Club* **8**, 169-187.

Evans, J. 1897. *The ancient stone implements, weapons and ornaments of Great Britain*. Longman Green, London.

Evans, J. 1902. The prehistoric period. In: *The Victoria history of the county of Hertford* (ed. Page, W.). Vol. 1. Archibald Constable & Co. Ltd, London, 223-250.

Evans, J. 1907. On a recent Palaeolithic discovery near Rickmansworth. *Transactions of the Hertfordshire Natural History Society and Field Club* **13**, 65-66.

Evans, J. 1908. Some recent discoveries of Palaeolithic implements. *Quarterly Journal of the Geological Society, London* **64**, 1-7.

Evans, J. and Hopkinson, J. 1878. Excursion to Tyler's Hill, Chesham. *Proceedings of the Geologists' Association* **5**, 498-499.

Evans, J. and Hopkinson, J. 1885. Excursion to Berkhampstead and Bourne End. Saturday, 21st April, 1883. *Proceedings of the Geologists' Association* **8**, 117-123.

Evans, J. G. 1966. Late-glacial and post-glacial subaerial deposits at Pitstone, Buckinghamshire. *Proceedings of the Geologists' Association* **77**, 347-364.

Evans, J. G. and Valentine, K. W. G. 1974. Ecological changes induced by prehistoric man at Pitstone, Buckinghamshire. *Journal of Archaeological Science* **1**, 343-351.

Evans, K. 2008. Tring Reservoirs: Where does the water come from? Water supplies to the Tring Summit of the Grand Union Canal. *The Grebe* (Newsletter of the Friends of Tring Reservoirs) **44**, 17-27.

Evans, P. 1944. Field meeting at Water End, North Mimms, Hertfordshire. Sunday, 2nd April, 1944. *Proceedings of the Geologists' Association* **55**, 189.

Evans, P. 1947. Hertfordshire puddingstone. *Transactions of the Hertfordshire Natural History Society and Field Club* **22**, 83.

Evans, P. 1954. Field meeting in the Vale of St Albans. Sunday, 13 September, 1953. *Proceedings of the Geologists' Association* **65**, 18-22.

Evans, P. 1971. Towards a Pleistocene time-scale. In: *The Phanerozoic time-scale – a supplement*. Geological Society, London, Special Publication **5**, 123-356.

Evans, P. and Oakley, K. P. 1952. Field meeting in the central Chilterns, 7 May, 1949. *Proceedings of the Geologists' Association* **63**, 59-62.

Evershed, H. 1864. Agriculture of Hertfordshire. *The Journal of the Royal Agricultural Society of England* **25**, 269-302.

Evison, M. P. 1999. Perspectives on the Holocene in Britain; human DNA. *Journal of Quaternary Science* **14**, 615-623.

Eyers, J. 1992. Sedimentology and palaeoenvironment of the Shenley Limestone (Albian, Lower Cretaceous): an unusual shallow-water carbonate. *Proceedings of the Geologists' Association* **103**, 293-302.

Eyers, J. 2007. *Rock around Bucks! Rocks, fossils and landscape*. Bucks Earth Heritage Group, Aylesbury.

F

Fagg, C. C. 1923. The recession of the chalk escarpment. *Transactions of the Croydon Natural History and Scientific Society* **9**, 93-112.

Falcon, N. L. and Kent, P. E. 1960. Geological results of petroleum exploration in Britain 1945-1957. *Memoir of the Geological Society of London* **2**.

Farley, M. (ed.) 2010. *An illustrated history of early Buckinghamshire*. Buckinghamshire Archaeological Society, Aylesbury.

Faulkner, A. H. and Paget-Tomlinson, E. 1993. *The Grand Junction Canal*. Walker and Bros. Ltd, London.

Fegan, J. 1999. *To map the junction of the Reading Beds and the Upper Chalk along the valley of the River Ash between Little Hadham and Albury in East Hertfordshire*. Unpublished GCE AS-Level Dissertation, Hadham Hall School.

Fenner, V. E. P. 1996. *The Hertfordshire mapping project. MORPH2 data. A report for Hertfordshire County Council* (2 volumes). Air Photography Unit, National Monuments Records Centre, Swindon.

Fisher, J. F. and Walshe, J. M. 1944. An investigation into chalk mining, with reference to a shaft near King's Langley. *Transactions of the Hertfordshire Natural History Society and Field Club* **22**, 48-51.

Fisher, O. 1873. On the phosphatic nodules of the Cretaceous rocks of Cambridgeshire. *Quarterly Journal of the Geological Society, London* **29**, 52-63.

Fisher, T. G., Smith, D. G. and Andrews, J. T. 2002. Preboreal oscillation caused by a glacial Lake Agassiz flood. *Quaternary Science Reviews* **21**, 873-887.

Fitch, F. J., Hooker, P. J., Miller, J. A. and Brereton, N. R. 1978. Glauconite dating of Palaeocene-Eocene rocks from east Kent and the time-scale of the Palaeogene volcanism in the North Atlantic region. *Journal of the Geological Society, London* **135**, 499-512.

Flavin, R. J. and Joseph, J. B. 1983. The hydrogeology of the Lee valley and some effects of artificial recharge. *Quarterly Journal of Engineering Geology* **16**, 65-82.

Fletcher, B. N. 1989. Foraminifera from the Upper Albian of the Sundon Borehole. *British Geological Survey Technical Report* **WH/89/344R**.

Ford, T. D. and O'Connor, B. 2002. Coprolite mining in England. *Geology Today* **18**, 178-181.

Fordham, H. G. 1886. Notes on boulders and boulder-clay in north Hertfordshire. *Transactions of the Hertfordshire Natural History Society and Field Club* **3**, 33-46.

Fordham, H. G. 1898. The earthquake of the 17th December 1896, as it affected the county of Hertford. *Transactions of the Hertfordshire Natural History Society and Field Club* **9**, 183-208.

Foster, J. H. 2004. *Sedimentary and micropalaeontological evaluation of interglacial deposits at Hatfield, Hertfordshire, U. K.* Unpublished M. Phil thesis, University of Hertfordshire.

Foster, S. S. D. 1975. The Chalk groundwater tritium anomaly – a possible explanation. *Journal of Hydrology* **25**, 159-165.

Francis, A. J., Slater, J. M. and Dodge, C. J. 1989. Denitrification in deep sub-surface sediments. *Geomicrobiology Journal* 7, 103-116.

French, H. M. 1972. Asymmetrical slope development in the Chiltern Hills. *Biuletyn Peryglacjalny* 21, 51-73.

French, H. and Williams, P. 2007. *The periglacial environment.* J. Wiley & Sons, Chichester.

Fullen, M. A. and Catt, J. A. 2004. *Soil management problems and solutions.* Arnold, London.

Funnell, B. M. 1995. Global sea-level and the (pen)-insularity of late Cenozoic Britain. In: *Island Britain: a Quaternary perspective* (ed. Preece, R. C.). Geological Society, London, Special Publication 96, 3-13.

G

Gaffney, V., Thomson, K. and Finch, S. 2007. *Mapping Doggerland: the Mesolithic landscapes of the southern North Sea.* Archaeopress, Oxford.

Gale, A. S. 1990. A Milankovitch scale for Cenomanian time. *Terra Nova* 1, 420-425.

Gale, A. S. 1995. Cyclostratigraphy and correlation of the Cenomanian Stage in western Europe. In: *Orbital forcing timescales and cyclostratigraphy* (eds House, M. R. and Gale, A. S.). Geological Society, London, Special Publication 85, 177-197.

Gale, A. S. 1996. Turonian correlation and sequence stratigraphy of the Chalk in southern England. In: *Sequence stratigraphy in British geology* (eds Hesselbo, S. P. and Parkinson, D. N.). Geological Society, London, Special Publication 103, 177-195.

Gale, A. S., Young, Y. R., Shackleton, N. J., Crowhurst, S. J. and Wray, D. S. 1999. Orbital tuning of Cenomanian marly chalk succession: towards a Milankovitch time-scale for the Late Cretaceous. *Philosophical Transactions of the Royal Society, London* A357, 1815-1829.

Gallois, R. W. 1993. *A guide to Pinner chalk mine.* Pinner Local History Society, Pinner.

Gallois, R. W. and Morter, A. A. 1982. The stratigraphy of the Gault of East Anglia. *Proceedings of the Geologists' Association* 93, 351-368.

Gardner, H. W. 1967. *A survey of the agriculture of Hertfordshire. County Agricultural Surveys* 5. Royal Agricultural Society of England, London.

Gardner, H. W. and Garner, H. V. 1953. *The use of lime in British agriculture.* Farmer and Stockbreeder Publications Ltd, London.

Gent, H. 1983. Centralised storage in later prehistoric Britain. *Proceedings of the Prehistoric Society* 49, 243-267.

Geological Survey of Great Britain 1965. *Aeromagnetic map of Great Britain, 1:625,000 Sheet 2.* Ordnance Survey, Southampton.

Gibbard, P. L. 1974. *Pleistocene stratigraphy and vegetational history of Hertfordshire.* Unpublished PhD Thesis, University of Cambridge.

Gibbard, P. L. 1977. Pleistocene history of the Vale of St Albans. *Philosophical Transactions of the Royal Society of London* B280, 445-483.

Gibbard, P. L. 1978a. Quaternary geology and landform development of the Vale of St Albans. In: *Quaternary geology of the Vale of St Albans. Field Guide* (eds Rose, J. and Gibbard, P. L.). Quaternary Research Association, Cambridge, 9-29.

Gibbard, P. L. 1978b. Waterhall Farm. In: *Quaternary geology of the Vale of St Albans. Field Guide* (eds. Rose, J. and Gibbard, P. L.). Quaternary Research Association, Cambridge, 69-71.

Gibbard, P. L. 1979. Middle Pleistocene drainage in the Thames Valley. *Geological Magazine* 116, 35-44.

Gibbard, P. L. 1982. Terrace stratigraphy and drainage history of the plateau gravels of north Surrey, south Berkshire, and north Hampshire, England. *Proceedings of the Geologists' Association* 93, 369-384.

Gibbard, P. L. 1983a. The diversion of the Thames – a review. In: *The Diversion of the Thames. Field Guide* (ed. Rose, J.). Quaternary Research Association, Cambridge, 8-23.

Gibbard, P. L. 1983b. Hatfield Polytechnic (Roe Hyde Pit). In: *The Diversion of the Thames. Field Guide* (ed. Rose, J.). Quaternary Research Association, Cambridge, 110-119.

Gibbard, P. L. 1985. *The Pleistocene history of the Middle Thames valley.* Cambridge University Press, Cambridge.

Gibbard, P. L. 1989. The geomorphology of a part of the Middle Thames forty years on: a reappraisal of the work of F. Kenneth Hare. *Proceedings of the Geologists' Association* 100, 481-503.

Gibbard, P. L. 1994. *Pleistocene history of the Lower Thames Valley.* Cambridge University Press, Cambridge.

Gibbard, P. L. 1999. The Thames valley, its tributary valleys and their former courses. In: *A revised correlation of Quaternary deposits in the British Isles* (ed. Bowen, D. Q.). Geological Society, London, Special Report 23, 45-58.

Gibbard, P. L. 2003. Definition of the Middle-Upper Pleistocene boundary. *Global and Planetary Change* 36, 201-208.

Gibbard, P. L. and Aalto, M. M. 1977. A Hoxnian interglacial site at Fishers Green, Stevenage, Hertfordshire. *New Phytologist* 72, 505-520.

Gibbard, P. L., Bryant, I. D. and Hall, A. R. 1986. A Hoxnian interglacial doline infilling at Slade Oak Lane, Denham, Buckinghamshire, England. *Geological Magazine* 123, 27-43.

Gibbard, P. L., Wintle, A. G. and Catt, J. A. 1987. Age and origin of clayey silt 'brickearth' in west London, England. *Journal of Quaternary Science* 2, 3-9.

Gibbard, P. L., West, R. G., Zagwijn, W. H. and 14 others 1991. Early and early Middle Pleistocene correlations in the southern North Sea Basin. *Quaternary Science Reviews* 10, 23-52.

Gibbard, P. L., Smith, A. G., Zalasiewicz, J. A. and 10 others 2005. What status for the Quaternary? *Boreas* 34, 1-6.

Gibbard, P. L., Rawson, P. E. and Smith, A. G. 2006. The future: climate and sea-level change, glaciation and a northward drift. In: *The geology of England and Wales* (eds Brenchley, P. J. and Rawson, P. F.). The Geological Society, London, 469-475.

Gibbard, P. L., Head, M. J., Walker, M. J. C. and The Subcommission on Quaternary Stratigraphy 2010. Formal ratification of the Quaternary System/Period and the Pleistocene Series/Epoch with a base at 2. 58 Ma. *Journal of Quaternary Science* **25**, 96-102.

Gibson, A. V. B. 1968. Some evidence of two Mesolithic sites at Bishop's Stortford. *Hertfordshire Archaeology* **1**, 98-102.

Gilbert, C. J. 1920. On the occurrence of extensive deposits of high-level sands and gravels resting upon the Chalk at Little Heath near Berkhamsted. *Quarterly Journal of the Geological Society, London* **75**, 32-43.

Gilbert, C. J. 1923. Excursion to Bedmond, Bennett's End and Boxmoor. Saturday, September 16th, 1922. *Proceedings of the Geologists' Association* **34**, 242-243.

Gilbert, C. J. 1924. An address on local geology. *Transactions of the Hertfordshire Natural History Society and Field Club* **18**, 88-92.

Gleed-Owen, C. P. 1998. *Quaternary herpetofaunas of the British Isles: taxonomic descriptions, palaeoenvironmental reconstructions, and biostratigraphic implications.* Unpublished PhD Thesis, Coventry University.

Glennie, E. A. 1964a. The Hertfordshire Bourne in 1959. *Transactions of the Hertfordshire Natural History Society and Field Club* **25**, 105-107.

Glennie, E. A. 1964b. The Hertfordshire Bourne 1960-61. *Transactions of the Hertfordshire Natural History Society and Field Club* **25**, 200-204.

Godwin, H. 1956. *The history of the British flora: a factual basis for phytogeography.* Cambridge University Press, Cambridge.

Godwin, H. 1964. Late-Weichselian conditions in south eastern England: organic deposits at Colney Heath, Herts. *Proceedings of the Royal Society of London* **B160**, 258-275.

Gomme, J., Shurvell, S., Hennings, S. M. and Clark, L. 1992. Hydrology of pesticides in a chalk catchment: groundwaters. *Journal of the Institute of Water and Environmental Management* **6**, 172-178.

Goulding, K. W. T., Poulton, P. R., Webster, C. P. and Howe, M. T. 2000. Nitrate leaching from the Broadbalk Wheat Experiment, Rothamsted, UK, as influenced by fertilizer and manure inputs and the weather. *Soil Use and Management* **16**, 244-250.

Gover, J. E. B., Mawer, A. and Stenton, F. M. 1938. *The place-names of Hertfordshire.* English Place-name Society **15**, Cambridge University Press, Cambridge.

Gozzard, J. R. 1981a. The sand and gravel resources of the country around Hatfield and Cheshunt, Hertfordshire. Description of 1:25 000 sheets TL 20 and 30 and parts of TQ 29 and 39. *Institute of Geological Sciences Mineral Assessment Report* **67**. HMSO, London.

Gozzard, J. R. 1981b. The sand and gravel resources of the country around Welwyn Garden City, Hertfordshire. Description of 1:25 000 resource sheet TL 11 and TL 21. *Institute of Geological Sciences Mineral Assessment Report* **69**. HMSO, London.

Gradstein, F. M., Ogg, J. G., Smith, A. G. and 36 others 2005. *A geologic time scale 2004.* Cambridge University Press, Cambridge.

Grant, I. S. and Phillips, W. R. 1975. *Electromagnetism.* J. Wiley & Sons, Chichester.

Graves, T. 1980. *Dowsing and archaeology: an anthology from the Journal of the British Society of Dowsers.* Turnstone Books.

Grayson, R. F. and Oldham, L. 1987. A new structural framework for the northern British Dinantian as a basis for oil, gas and mineral exploration. In: *European Dinantian environments* (eds Miller, J., Adams, A. E. and Wright, V. P.). J. Wiley and Sons, Chichester, 33-59.

Green, C. P. 1997. Stonehenge: geology and prehistory. *Proceedings of the Geologists' Association* **108**, 1-10.

Green, C. P. 2006. Long Valley Wood – the geology. *South West Herts Archaeological and Historical Society Bulletin* **81**, 14-16.

Green, C. P. and McGregor, D. F. M. 1978a. Pleistocene gravel trains of the River Thames. *Proceedings of the Geologists' Association* **89**, 143-156.

Green, C. P. and McGregor, D. F. M. 1978b. Westwood. In: *Quaternary geology of the Vale of St Albans. Field Guide* (eds Rose, J. and Gibbard, P. L.). Quaternary Research Association, Cambridge, 91.

Green, C. P. and McGregor, D. F. M. 1999. Pre-Anglian gravel deposits of the River Thames and its tributaries between Goring and Cromer. *Proceedings of the Geologists' Association* **110**, 117-132.

Green, C. P., McGregor, D. F. M. and Evans, A. H. 1982. Development of the Thames drainage system in Early and Middle Pleistocene times. *Geological Magazine* **119**, 281-290.

Green, C. P., Coope, G. R., Currant, A. P., Holyoak, D. T., Ivanovich, M., Jones, R. L., Keen, D. H., McGregor, D. F. M. and Robinson, J. E. 1984. Evidence of two temperate episodes in late Pleistocene deposits at Marsworth, UK. *Nature* **309**, 778-781.

Green, J. F. N. 1918. Excursion to Ware. Saturday, September 15th, 1917. *Proceedings of the Geologists' Association* **29**, 42-45.

Green, P. F. 1989. Thermal and tectonic history of the East Midlands shelf (onshore UK) and surrounding regions assessed by apatite fission track analysis. *Journal of the Geological Society, London* **146**, 755-773.

Green, U. 1891. Excursion to Shenley. Saturday, July 19th, 1889. *Proceedings of the Geologists' Association* **11**, cLxix-cLxxi.

Green, U. 1895. Excursion to Harefield. Saturday, 14th April, 1894. *Proceedings of the Geologists' Association* **13**, 281-283.

Green, U. 1899. Excursion to Chesham and Cowcroft (Tyler's Hill). Saturday, April 3rd, 1897. *Proceedings of the Geologists' Association* **15**, 87-90.

Green, U. 1900. Excursion to Boxmoor. Saturday, May 12th, 1900. *Proceedings of the Geologists' Association* **16**, 501-502.

Gregory, J. W. 1894. The evolution of the Thames. *Natural Science, London* **5**, 97-108.

Gregory, J. W. 1914. The Chiltern wind gaps. *Geological*

Magazine, New Series Decade VI, **1**, 145-148.

Grey, E. 1977. *Cottage life in a Hertfordshire village.* Harpenden and District Local History Society, Harpenden.

Grout, M. W., Alexander, D. W. and Simpson, R. J. 1992. Practical aspects of yield investigations of groundwater sources. *Journal of the Institution of Water and Environmental Management* **6**, 397-407.

Grove, R. 1974. *The Cambridge coprolite mining industry.* Oleander Press, Cambridge.

Gruas Cavagnetto, C. 1976. Etude palynologique du Paléogene du sud de l'Angleterre. *Cahiers Micropaléontologique* **1**, 1-49.

Grün, R. and Schwarcz, H. P. 2000. Revised open-system U-series/ESR age calculations for teeth from Stratum C at the Hoxnian Interglacial type locality, England. *Quaternary Science Reviews* **19**, 1151-1154.

H

Hadfield, C. 1969. *Canals of south and southeast England.* David and Charles, Newton Abbot.

Hadfield, C. 1981. *The canals of the East Midlands.* David and Charles, Newton Abbot.

Hadfield, C. and Skempton, A. W. 1979. *William Jessop, Engineer.* David and Charles, Newton Abbot.

Hall, D. G. M., Reeve, M. J., Thomasson, A. J. and Wright, V. F. 1977. *Water retention, porosity and density of field soils.* Soil Survey Technical Monograph **9**. Rothamsted Experimental Station, Harpenden.

Hallsworth, C. 1993. Stratigraphic variations in the heavy minerals of the Palaeogene sandstones in the London Basin and the implications for sand provenance. *British Geological Survey Technical Report* **WH/93/304**.

Hammond, P., Morgan, A. and Morgan, A. V. 1979. On the *gibbulus* group of *Anotylus* and fossil occurrence of *Anotylus gibbulus* (Staphylinidae). *Systematic Entomology* **4**, 215-221.

Hampton, M. J., Bailey, H. W., Gallagher, L. T., Mortimore, R. N. and Wood, C. J. 2007. The biostratigraphy of Seaford Head, Sussex, southern England: an international reference section for the basal boundaries of the Santonian and Campanian Stages in Chalk facies. *Cretaceous Research* **28**, 46-60.

Hampton, M. J., Bailey, H. W. and Jones, A. D. 2010. A holostratigraphic approach to the Chalk of the North Sea Eldfisk field, Norway. In: *Petroleum geology from mature basins to new frontiers* (eds Vining, B. and Pickering, S. C.). Proceedings of the 7th Petroleum Geology Conference. Geological Society, Bath, 473-492.

Hancock, J. M. 1975. The petrology of the chalk. *Proceedings of the Geologists' Association* **86**, 499-535.

Hancock, J. M. 1989. Sea-level changes in the British region during the Late Cretaceous. *Proceedings of the Geologists' Association* **100**, 565-594.

Haq, B. U., Hardenbol, J. and Vail, P. R. 1987. Chronology of fluctuating sea levels since the Triassic (250 million years ago to present). *Science* **235**, 1156-1167.

Hardenbol, J., Thierry, J., Farley, M. B., de Graciansky, P.

-C. and Vail, P. R. 1998. Mesozoic and Cenozoic sequence chronostratigraphic framework of European basins. In: *Sequence stratigraphy of Mesozoic and Cenozoic European basins* (eds de Graciansky, P. -C., Hardenbol, J., Vail, P. R. and Jacquin, T.). SEPM Special Publication **60**, 3-13.

Harding, P. A. and Bridgland, D. R. 1999. Results of geological and archaeological observations at Switchback Road Pit, Maidenhead, Berkshire. *Proceedings of the Geologists' Association* **110**, 311-320.

Harding, P., Bridgland, D. R., Madgett, P. A. and Rose, J. 1991. Recent investigations of Pleistocene sediments near Maidenhead, Berkshire, and their archaeological content. *Proceedings of the Geologists' Association* **102**, 25-53.

Harding, P., Bridgland, D. R., Keen, D. H. and Rogerson, R. J. 1992. A Palaeolithic site rediscovered at Biddenham, Bedfordshire. *Bedfordshire Archaeology* **19**, 87-90.

Hare, F. K. 1947. The geomorphology of a part of the Middle Thames. *Proceedings of the Geologists' Association* **58**, 294-339.

Harland, W. B. and Gayer, R. A. 1972. The Arctic Caledonides and earlier oceans. *Geological Magazine* **109**, 289-314.

Harmer, F. W. 1907. On the origin of certain canyon-like valleys associated with lake-like areas of depression. *Quarterly Journal of the Geological Society, London* **63**, 470-514.

Harmer, F. W. 1928. The distribution of erratics and drift. *Proceedings of the Yorkshire Geological Society* **21**, 79-150.

Harmer, R., Peterken, G., Kerr, G. and Poulton, P. 2001. Vegetation changes during 100 years of development of two secondary woodlands on abandoned arable land. *Biological Conservation* **101**, 291-304.

Harper, J. C. 1940. A new exposure of calcareous tufa near Harpenden, Hertfordshire. *Proceedings of the Geologists' Association* **51**, 49-51.

Harries, W. J. R., Hollyer, S. E. and Hopson, P. M. 1982. The sand and gravel resources of the country around Hemel Hempstead, St Albans and Watford. Description of 1:25 000 sheets TL 00, TL 10 and parts of TQ 09 and TQ 19. *Institute of Geological Sciences Mineral Assessment Report* **71**. HMSO, London.

Harrison, S. 2003. The Icknield Way; some queries. *Archaeological Journal* **160**, 1-22.

Hart, M. B. 1973a. A correlation of the macrofaunal and microfaunal zonations of the Gault Clay in southeast England. In: *The boreal Lower Cretaceous* (eds Casey, R. and Rawson, P. F.). Geological Journal Special Issue **5**, 267-288.

Hart, M. B. 1973b. Foraminiferal evidence for the age of the Cambridge Greensand. *Proceedings of the Geologists' Association* **84**, 65-82.

Hart, M. B. 1993. *Labyrinthidoma* Adams, Knight and Hodgkinson; an unusually large foraminiferal genus from the Chalk facies (Upper Cretaceous) of southern England and northern France. In: *Proceedings of the fourth international workshop on agglutinated foraminifera, Krakow, Poland, September 12-19, 1993* (eds Kaminski,

M. A., Geroch, S. and Gasinski, M. A.). Grzybowski Foundation Special Publication **3**, 123-130.

Hart, M. B. and Carter, D. J. 1975. Some observations on the Cretaceous Foraminiferidae of south-east England. *Journal of Foraminiferal Research* **5**, 114-126.

Hart, M. B., Bailey, H. W., Crittenden, S., Fletcher, B. N., Price, R. J. and Swiecicki, A. 1989. Cretaceous. In: *Stratigraphical atlas of fossil foraminifera* (2nd edition) (eds Jenkins, D. G. and Murray, J. W.). British Micropalaeontological Society and Ellis Horwood, Chichester, 273-371.

Harwood, K. 2007. Some Hertfordshire nabobs. In: *Hertfordshire garden history a miscellany* (ed. Rowe, A.). Hertfordshire Publications, University of Hertfordshire Press, Hatfield, 49-77.

Haselgrove, C. 1987. Iron Age coinage in south-east England. *British Archaeological Reports British Series* **174**.

Hawkes, C. F. C. 1940. A site of the late Bronze Age – early Iron Age transition at Totternhoe, Beds. *Antiquaries Journal* **20**, 487-491.

Hawkes, L. 1943. The erratics of the Cambridge Greensand – their nature, provenance and mode of transport. *Quarterly Journal of the Geological Society, London* **99**, 93-104.

Hawnt, R. J. E., Joseph, J. B. and Flavin, R. J., 1981. Experience with borehole recharge in the Lee valley. *Journal of the Institution of Water Engineers and Scientists* **35**, 437-451.

Hayes, J. W. 1908. Notes on deneholes. *Journal of the British Archaeological Association, New Series* **14**, 130-135.

Hayward, J. F. 1955. Borehole records from the Lea valley between Cheshunt and Edmonton. *Proceedings of the Geologists' Association* **66**, 68-73.

Hayward, J. F. 1956. Certain abandoned channels of Pleistocene and Holocene age in the Lea Valley, and their deposits. *Proceedings of the Geologists' Association* **67**, 32-63.

Hayward, J. F. 1957. Borehole records from the Lea valley in the neighbourhood of Edmonton, Middlesex. *Proceedings of the Geologists' Association* **68**, 39-43.

Head, M. J. and Gibbard, P. L. 2005. Early-Middle Pleistocene transition: an overview and recommendation for the defining boundary. In: *Early-Middle Pleistocene Transitions – the land-ocean evidence*. Geological Society, London, Special Publication **247**, 1-18.

Headworth, H. G., Keating, T. and Packman, M. J. 1982. Evidence for a shallow highly-permeable zone in the Chalk of Hampshire, U. K. *Journal of Hydrology* **55**, 93-112.

Heckrath, G., Brookes, P. C., Poulton, P. R. and Goulding, K. W. T. 1995. Phosphorus leaching from soils containing different phosphorus concentrations in the Broadbalk Experiment. *Journal of Environmental Quality* **24**, 904-910.

Hegesh, E. and Shiloah, J. 1982. Blood nitrates and infantile methemoglobinemia. *Clinica Chimica Acta* **125**, 107-115.

Hendry, D. A. 1987. Silica and calcium carbonate replacement of plant roots in tropical dune sands, SE India. In: *Desert sediments: ancient and modern* (eds Frostick, L. R. and Reid, I.). Geological Society, London,

Special Publication **35**, 309-319.

Hepworth, J. V. 1998. Aspects of the English silcretes and comparison with some Australian occurrences. *Proceedings of the Geologists' Association* **109**, 271-288.

Herschy, R. W. 1998. World water balance. In: *Encyclopaedia of hydrology and water resources* (eds Herschy, R. W. and Fairbridge, R. W.). Kluwer Academic Publishers, Boston, 787-788.

Hertfordshire RIGS Group 2003. *A geological conservation strategy for Hertfordshire.* Hertfordshire County Council Environment Department, Hertford.

Hester, S. W. 1940. Field meeting at Harefield. *Proceedings of the Geologists' Association* **51**, 420-421.

Hester S. W. 1942. A contribution to the geology of north-west Middlesex. *Proceedings of the Geologists' Association* **52**, 304-320.

Hester, S. W. 1965. Stratigraphy and palaeogeography of the Woolwich and Reading Beds. *Bulletin of the Geological Survey of Great Britain* **23**, 117-137.

Hester, S. W. 1967. Itinerary IV. The Colne Valley from Rickmansworth to Uxbridge. In: *Geologists' Association Guides No 30A: The London Region (North of the Thames)* (ed. Hester, S. W.). Benham and Company, Colchester, 19-22.

Hey, R. W. 1965. Highly quartzose pebble gravels in the London Basin. *Proceedings of the Geologists' Association* **76**, 403-420.

Hey, R. W. 1980. Equivalents of the Westland Green Gravels in Essex and East Anglia. *Proceedings of the Geologists' Association* **91**, 279-290.

Hey, R. W. 1982. Composition of pre-Anglian gravels in Norfolk. *Bulletin of the Geological Society of Norfolk* **32**, 403-420.

Hey, R. W. 1983. Ferneux Pelham. In: *The Diversion of the Thames. Field Guide* (ed. Rose, J.). Quaternary Research Association, Cambridge, 94-95.

Hey, R. W. 1986. A re-examination of the Northern Drift of Oxfordshire. *Proceedings of the Geologists' Association* **97**, 291-301.

Hey, R. W. and Brenchley, P. J. 1977. Volcanic pebbles from Pleistocene gravels in Norfolk and Essex. *Geological Magazine* **114**, 219-225.

Hey, R. W., Krinsley, D. H. and Hyde, P. J. W. 1971. Surface textures of sand grains from the Hertfordshire pebble gravels. *Geological Magazine* **108**, 377-382.

Higginbottom, I. E. and Fookes, P. G. 1971. Engineering aspects of periglacial features in Britain. *Quarterly Journal of Engineering Geology* **3**, 85-117.

Hildreth, P. N. 1972. Upper Cretaceous and Lower Tertiary sequences in boreholes near Epping, Essex. *Bulletin of the Geological Survey of Great Britain* **38**, 67-75.

Hill, W. 1891. Our forgotten lake. *Journal of the Hitchin Natural History Club* **12**, 93-97.

Hill, W. 1908. On a deep channel of drift at Hitchin. *Quarterly Journal of the Geological Society, London* **64**, 8-26.

Hill, W. 1911a. Excursion to Arlesey and Letchworth. July 9th, 1910. *Proceedings of the Geologists' Association* **22**, 8-11.

Hill, W. 1911b. Note on a boulder near Letchworth. *Proceedings of the Geologists' Association* **22**, 120.

Hill, W. and Jukes-Browne, A. J. 1886. The Melbourn Rock and the zone of *Belemnitella plena* from Cambridge to the Chiltern Hills. *Quarterly Journal of the Geological Society, London* **42**, 216-231.

Hill, W. and Monckton, H. W. 1896. Excursion to Hitchin. Saturday, 20th June, 1896. *Proceedings of the Geologists' Association* **14**, 415-419.

Hillman, G. 1981. Crop husbandry: evidence from macroscopic remains. In: *The environment in British prehistory* (eds Simmons, I. G. and Tooley, M. J.). London, 183-191.

Hine, R. L. 1927. *The history of Hitchin* (Volume 1). Allen and Unwin, London.

Hine, R. L. 1929. *The history of Hitchin* (Volume 2). Allen and Unwin, London.

Hine, R. L. 1932. *Hitchin worthies. Four centuries of English life.* Allen and Unwin, London.

Hodge, C. A. H., Burton, R. G. O., Corbett, W. M., Evans, R. and Seale, R. S. 1984. *Soils and their use in Eastern England.* Soil Survey of England and Wales Bulletin **13**. Lawes Agricultural Trust, Harpenden.

Hodgson, J. M. (ed.) 1976. Soil Survey Field Handbook. *Soil Survey Technical Monograph* **5**. Soil Survey of England and Wales, Harpenden.

Holgate, R. 1988. Neolithic settlement of the Thames Basin. *British Archaeological Reports British Series* **194**.

Holgate, R. 1991a. Luton Museum. In: Acquisitions, enquiries, research on collections and fieldwork at Bedford and Luton Museums, 1988-89 (eds Wingfield, C. and Holgate, R.). *Bedfordshire Archaeology* **19**, 79-86.

Holgate, R. 1991b. The prehistoric pottery and flint. In: The Five Knolls and associated barrows at Dunstable, Bedfordshire (ed. Dyer, J. D.). *Bedfordshire Archaeology* **19**, 28-29.

Holgate, R. 1991c. *Prehistoric flint mines.* Shire Archaeology, Aylesbury.

Holgate, R. 1995. Early prehistoric settlement of the Chilterns. In: *Chiltern archaeology recent work a handbook for the next decade* (ed. Holgate, R.). The Book Castle, Dunstable, 3-16.

Hollis, G. E. and Ovenden, J. C. 1988. The quantity of stormwater runoff from ten stretches of road, a car park and eight roofs in Hertfordshire, England during 1983. *Hydrological Processes* **2**, 227-243.

Holloway, S. 1985. Lower Jurassic: the Lias. In: *Atlas of onshore sedimentary basins in England and Wales. Post Carboniferous tectonics and stratigraphy* (ed. Whittaker, A.). Blackie, Glasgow, 37-40.

Holmes, J. and Frend, W. H. C. 1959. A Belgic chieftain's grave on Hertford Heath. *Transactions of the East Hertfordshire Archaeological Society* **14**, 1-19.

Holmes, J. and Hayward, J. F. 1955. The Waltham Cross dugout canoe and its implications. *Transactions of the East Hertfordshire Archaeological Society* **13**, 138 & Plate 15.

Holmes, T. V. 1896. Notes on the ancient physiography of south Essex. *Essex Naturalist* **9**, 193-200.

Holyoak, D. T., Ivanovich, M. and Preece, R. C. 1983. Additional fossil and isotopic evidence for the age of the interglacial tufas at Hitchin and Icklingham. *Journal of Conchology* **31**, 260-261.

Hopkinson, J. 1873. Excursion to Watford, June 23rd, 1870. *Proceedings of the Geologists' Association* **2**, 43-44.

Hopkinson, J. 1880. On the recent discovery of Silurian rocks in Hertfordshire, and their relation to the water-bearing strata of the London Basin. *Transactions of the Watford Natural History Society and Hertfordshire Field Club* **2**, 241-248.

Hopkinson, J. 1885. Excursion to Radlett. Saturday afternoon, 12th July, 1884. *Proceedings of the Geologists' Association* **8**, 452-458.

Hopkinson, J. 1887a. Excursion to Watford and Ware. Saturday, 16th May, 1885. *Proceedings of the Geologists' Association* **9**, 182-186.

Hopkinson, J. 1887b. Excursion to Welwyn. Saturday, May 15th, 1886. *Proceedings of the Geologists' Association* **9**, 534-537.

Hopkinson, J. 1887c. Excursion to Pinner. Saturday, June 26th, 1886. *Proceedings of the Geologists' Association* **9**, 548-550.

Hopkinson, J. 1892. Water and water-supply, with special reference to the supply of London from the Chalk of Hertfordshire. *Transactions of the Hertfordshire Natural History Society and Field Club* **6**, 129-161.

Hopkinson, J. 1896. The relative advantages of hard and soft water, with special reference to the supply of Watford. *Transactions of the Hertfordshire Natural History Society and Field Club* **8**, 101-115.

Hopkinson, J. 1899. The Chadwell spring and the Hertfordshire bourne. *Transactions of the Hertfordshire Natural History Society and Field Club* **10**, 69-83.

Hopkinson, J. 1901. The Chadwell Spring and Hertfordshire Bourne. *Transactions of the Hertfordshire Natural History Society and Field Club* **10**, 69-83.

Hopkinson, J. 1908. Hertfordshire earthquakes. *Transactions of the Hertfordshire Natural History Society and Field Club* **13**, 141-172.

Hopkinson, J. 1910. Middlesex and Hertfordshire. In: *Geology in the field; the jubilee volume of the Geologists' Association (1858-1908)* (eds Monckton, H. W. and Herries, R. S.). E. Stanford, London, 1-50.

Hopkinson, J. 1911a. Excursion to the valley of the Hertfordshire Bourne. Saturday, April 29th, 1911. *Proceedings of the Geologists' Association* **22**, 234-236.

Hopkinson, J. 1911b. The Hertfordshire Bourne. *Southeastern Naturalist*, 10-19.

Hopkinson, J. (Ed.). 1911c. St Albans and its neighbourhood. *Transactions of the Hertfordshire Natural History Society and Field Club* **14**, 209-254.

Hopkinson, J. 1915. The flowing of the Hertfordshire Bourne. *Transactions of the Hertfordshire Natural History Society and Field Club* **15**, 67-70.

Hopkinson, J. 1917. The Hertfordshire Bourne in 1916. *Transactions of the Hertfordshire Natural History Society and Field Club* **16**, 169-172.

Hopkinson, J. 1923. The Hertfordshire Bourne in 1917.

Transactions of the Hertfordshire Natural History Society and Field Club **17**, 97-98.

Hopkinson, J. and Kidner, H. 1908. Excursion to Bushey and Croxley Green, Watford. Saturday, April 6th, 1907. *Proceedings of the Geologists' Association* **20**, 94-97.

Hopkinson, J. and Morison, J. 1891. Excursion to Boxmoor and Nash Mills. Saturday, 18th May, 1889. *Proceedings of the Geologists' Association* **11**, Lviii-Lxii.

Hopkinson, J. and Salter, A. E. 1899. Excursion to Ayot Green and Hatfield Hyde. Saturday, May 14th, 1898. *Proceedings of the Geologists' Association* **15**, 308-311.

Hopkinson, J. and Whitaker, W. 1892. Excursion to St Albans. Saturday, May 28th, 1892. *Proceedings of the Geologists' Association* **12**, 342-344.

Hopson, P. M. 1979. The sand and gravel resources of the country north of Harlow, Essex. Description of 1:25 000 resource sheet TL 41. *Institute of Geological Sciences Mineral Assessment Report* **46**. HMSO, London.

Hopson, P. M. 1981. The sand and gravel resources of the country around Stansted Mountfitchet, Essex. Description of 1:25,000 resources sheet TL 52. *Mineral Assessment Report of Institute of Geological Sciences* **104**.

Hopson, P. M. 1995. Chalk rafts in Anglian till in north Hertfordshire. *Proceedings of the Geologists' Association* **106**, 151-158.

Hopson, P. M. and Samuel, M. D. A. 1982. The sand and gravel resources of the country around Hertford, Hertfordshire. Description of 1:25 000 resource sheet TL 31. *Institute of Geological Sciences Mineral Assessment Report* **112**. HMSO, London.

Hopson, P. M., Aldiss, D. T. and Smith, A. 1996. *Geology of the country around Hitchin. Memoir for 1:50,000 Geological Sheet 221*. Memoir of the British Geological Survey (England and Wales). HMSO, London.

Hornett, E. 1998. *To map the junction of the Reading Beds (Tertiary) and the Upper Chalk (Cretaceous) along the valley of the River Ash between Little Hadham and Albury, near Bishop's Stortford in East Hertfordshire*. Unpublished GCE A-level Dissertation, Birchwood High School.

Horton, A. 1977. Nettlebed. In: *South East England and the Thames Valley. Guidebook for Excursion A5, X INQUA Congress, Birmingham* (eds Shephard-Thorn, E. R. and Wymer, J. J.). GeoAbstracts, Norwich, 16-18.

Horton, A. 1983. Nettlebed. In: *The Diversion of the Thames. Field Guide* (ed. J. Rose). Quaternary Research Association, Cambridge, 63-65.

Horton, A. 1989. Quinton. In: *The Pleistocene of the West Midlands. Field Guide* (ed. Keen, D. H.). Quaternary Research Association, Cambridge, 69-76.

Horton, A., Shephard-Thorn, E. R. and Thurrell, R. G. 1974. The geology of the new town of Milton Keynes. Explanation of 1:25,000 Special Geological Sheet SP93 with parts of SP73, 74, 84, 93 and 94. *Institute of Geological Sciences Report* **74/16**. HMSO, London.

Horton, A., Sumbler, M. G., Cox, B. M. and Ambrose, K. 1995. *Geology of the country around Thame. Memoir for 1:50,000 Geological Sheet 237*. Memoir of the British Geological Survey (England and Wales). HMSO, London.

Horton, R. E. 1933. The role of infiltration in the hydrologic cycle. *Transactions of the American Geophysical Union* **14**, 446-460.

House, M. R. 1995. Orbital forcing timescales: an introduction. In: *Orbital forcing timescales and cyclostratigraphy* (eds House, M. R. and Gale, A. S.). Geological Society, London, Special Publication **85**, 1-18.

House, M. R., Richardson, J. B., Chaloner, W. G., Allen, J. R. L., Holland, C. H. and Westoll, T. S. 1982. *A correlation of Devonian rocks in the British Isles*. Geological Society, London, Special Report **8**.

Hudspith, R. E. T. 1999. Fieldwalking at Pirton and Offley. *Luton Archaeological Group Report* **5**.

Huggett, J. M. and Gale, A. S. 1995. Palaeoecology and diagenesis of bored wood from the London Clay Formation of Sheppey, Kent. *Proceedings of the Geologists' Association* **106**, 119-136.

Hughes, T. McK. 1868. On the two plains of Hertfordshire and their gravels. *Quarterly Journal of the Geological Society, London* **24**, 283-287.

Hull, E. 1855. On the physical geography and Pleistocene phaenomena of the Cotteswold Hills. *Quarterly Journal of the Geological Society, London* **11**, 477-496.

Hull, E. and Whitaker, W. 1861. *The geology of parts of Oxfordshire and Berkshire*. Memoirs of the Geological Survey of the United Kingdom. HMSO, London.

Hunn, J. R. 1994. Reconstruction and measurement of landscape change. A study of six parishes in the St Albans area. *British Archaeological Reports British Series* **236**.

Hunt, C. O. 1989. The palynology and correlation of the Walton Crag (Red Crag Formation, Pliocene). *Journal of the Geological Society, London* **146**, 743-745.

Hurford, A. J. and Green, P. F. 1982. A user's guide to fission track dating calibration. *Earth and Planetary Science Letters* **59**, 343-354.

Hutchinson, J. N. 1980. Possible late Quaternary pingo remnants in central London. *Nature* **284**, 253-255.

Hutchinson, J. N. 1984. Landslides in Britain and their countermeasures. *Journal of the Japan Landslide Society* **21**, 1-24.

Hutchinson, J. N. 1991. Theme lecture: periglacial and slope processes. In: *Quaternary engineering geology* (eds Forster, A., Culshaw, M. G., Cripps, J. C., Little, J. A. and Moon, C. F.). Geological Society, London, Engineering Geology Special Publication **7**, 283-331.

Huybers, P. 2006. Early Pleistocene glacial cycles and the integrated summer insolation forcing. *Science* **313**, 508-511.

I

Ineson, J. and Downing, R. A. 1963. Changes in the chemistry of groundwaters in the Chalk passing beneath argillaceous strata. *Bulletin of the Geological Survey of Great Britain* **20**, 176-192.

Irving, A. 1899a. On the geology of the Stort valley (Herts and Essex). *Proceedings of the Geologists' Association* **15**, 224-237.

Irving, A. 1899b. Excursion to Bishop's Stortford. Saturday, July 17th, 1897. *Proceedings of the Geologists' Association* **15**, 193-197.

Isaac, K. P. 1983. Tertiary lateritic weathering in Devon, England, and the Palaeogene continental environment of south west England. *Proceedings of the Geologists' Association* **94**, 105-114.

J

Jacobi, R. M. 1966. Surface flint implements from Sandy Lodge. *Watford and Southwest Hertfordshire Archaeological Society Bulletin* **1-3**, 10-11.

Jacobi, R. M. 1973. Aspects of the 'Mesolithic Age' in Great Britain. In: *The Mesolithic in Europe* (ed. Kozlowski, S. K.). Warsaw University Press, Warsaw, 237-265.

Jacobi, R. M. 1975. *Aspects of the post-glacial archaeology of England and Wales.* Unpublished PhD thesis, University of Cambridge.

Jacobi, R. M. 1978. Northern England in the eighth millennium bc: an essay. In: *The early postglacial settlement of northern Europe. An ecological perspective* (ed. Mellars, P.). Duckworth, London, 295-332.

Jacobi, R. M. 1980a. The Upper Palaeolithic in Britain with special reference to Wales. In: *Culture and environment in prehistoric Wales* (ed. Taylor, J. A.). *British Archaeological Reports British Series* **76**, 15-99.

Jacobi, R. M. 1980b. The Mesolithic of Essex. In: *Archaeology in Essex to A. D. 1500* (ed. Buckley, D. G.). *Council for British Archaeology Research Report* **34**, 14-25.

Jacobi, R. M. 1987. The barbed bone spearhead reputedly from Royston, Hertfordshire: a suggestion. *Hertfordshire Archaeology* **9**, 176-177.

Jacobi, R. 2007. A collection of Early Upper Palaeolithic artefacts from Beedings, near Pulborough, West Sussex, and the context of similar finds from the British Isles. *Proceedings of the Prehistoric Society* **73**, 229-325.

James, T. J. 1980. The flora of Oughton Head, Hitchin. *Transactions of the Hertfordshire Natural History Society and Field Club* **28**, Part 3, 79-90.

James, T. J. 1990. The flora and vegetation of a gravel pit: Amwell Quarry. *Transactions of the Hertfordshire Natural History Society and Field Club* **30**, 371-404.

James, T. J. 1991. The plant commmunities of Hertfordshire. Part 1: Semi-natural woodlands. *Transactions of the Hertfordshire Natural History Society and Field Club* **31**, 58-85.

James, T. J. 1992. Plants and plant communities at Ashwell, Hertfordshire, 1800-1991. *Transactions of the Hertfordshire Natural History Society and Field Club* **31**, 201-218.

James, T. J. 2009. *Flora of Hertfordshire.* Hertfordshire Natural History Society, Welwyn Garden City.

Jarvis, M. G., Allen, R. H., Fordham, S. J., Hazelden, J, Moffat, A. J. and Sturdy, R. G. 1984. *Soils and their use in South East England.* Soil Survey of England and Wales Bulletin **15**. Lawes Agricultural Trust, Harpenden.

Jeans, C. V., Merriman, R. J. and Mitchell, J. G. 1977. Origin of Middle Jurassic and Lower Cretaceous fuller's earths in England. *Clay Minerals* **12**, 11-44.

Jefferies, R. P. S. 1963. The stratigraphy of the *Actinocamax plenus* Subzone (lowest Turonian) in the Anglo-Paris Basin. *Proceedings of the Geologists' Association* **74**, 1-33.

Jolley, D. W. 1992. Palynofloral association sequence stratigraphy of the Palaeocene Thanet Beds and equivalent sediments in eastern England. *Review of Palaeobotany and Palynology* **74**, 207-237.

Jones, D. K. C. 1974. The influence of the Calabrian transgression on the drainage evolution of south-east England. In: *Progress in geomorphology* (eds Brown, E. H. and Waters, R. S.). *Institute of British Geographers Special Publication* **7**, 139-157.

Jones, D. K. C. 1980. The Tertiary evolution of south-east England with particular reference to the Weald. In: *The shaping of southern England* (ed. Jones, D. K. C.). Institute of British Geographers Special Publication **11**, 13-47.

Jones, D. K. C. 1999. Evolving models of the Tertiary evolutionary geomorphology of southern England, with special reference to the chalklands. In: *Uplift, erosion and stability: perspectives on long-term landscape development* (eds Smith, B. J., Whalley, W. B. and Warke, P. A.). Geological Society, London, Special Publication **162**, 1-23.

Jones, O. T. 1938. Report of visit to the Sedgwick Museum, Cambridge, and field meeting at Royston. *Proceedings of the Geologists' Association* **49**, 405-406.

Jukes-Browne, A. J. 1875. On the relations of the Cambridge Gault and Greensand. *Quarterly Journal of the Geological Society, London* **31**, 256-316.

Jukes-Browne, A. J. and Hill, W. 1903. The *Cretaceous rocks of Britain Volume II. The Lower and Middle Chalk of England.* Memoir of the Geological Survey of the United Kingdom. HMSO, London.

Jukes-Browne, A. J. and Hill, W. 1904. *The Cretaceous rocks of Britain Volume III. The Upper Chalk of England.* Memoir of the Geological Survey of the United Kingdom. HMSO, London.

K

Kaplan, U. 1986. Ammonite stratigraphy of the Turonian of NW-Germany. *Newsletters in Stratigraphy* **17**, 9-20.

Kaplan, U. 1989. Die heteromorphe Ammonitengattung *Allocrioceras* SPATH aus dem Turon von Nordwestdeitschland. *Geologie und Paläontologie in Westfalen* **15**, 71-105.

Kaplan, U., Kennedy, W. J. and Wright, C. W. 1987. Turonian and Coniacian Scaphitidae from England and northwestern Germany. *Geologisches Jahrbuch Reihe A* **103**, 5-39.

Keane, M. A. and Kerslake, J. A. 1988. The London water ring main; an optional water supply system. *Journal of the Institution of Water and Environmental Science* **2**, 253-266.

Kearey, P. and Brooks, M. 1994. *An introduction to geophysical exploration* (2nd edition). Blackwell Science, Oxford.

Kedves, M. 1967. Spore pollen data from the London Clay. *Acta Biologica Szeged* **13**, 25-30.

Keen, D. H. 1999. The chronology of Middle Pleistocene ('Wolstonian') events in the English Midlands. In: *Late Cenozoic environments and hominid evolution: a tribute to Bill Bishop* (eds Andrews, P. and Banham, P.). Geological Society, London, 159-168.

Keen, D. H., Coope, G. R., Jones, R. L., Field, M. H., Griffiths, H. I., Lewis, S. G. and Bowen, D. Q. 1997. Middle Pleistocene deposits at Frog Hall Pit, Stretton-on-Dunsmore, Warwickshire, English Midlands, and their implications for the age of the type Wolstonian. *Journal of Quaternary Science* **12**, 183-208.

Keen, M. C. 1978. The Tertiary – Palaeogene. In: *A Stratigraphical Index of British Ostracoda* (eds Bate, R. and Robinson, E.). Seel House Press, Liverpool, 385-450.

Kellaway, G. 1971. Glaciation and the stones of Stonehenge. *Nature* **233**, 30-35.

Kellaway, G. A., Redding, J. H., Shephard-Thorn, E. R. and Destombes, J. P. 1975. The Quaternary history of the English Channel. *Philosophical Transactions of the Royal Society of London* **A279**, 189-218.

Kelly, S. R. A. and Rawson, P. F. 1983. Some late Jurassic-mid Cretaceous sections on the East Midlands Shelf, England, as demonstrated on a field meeting, 18-20 May, 1979. *Proceedings of the Geologists' Association* **94**, 65-73.

Kemp, R. A. 1987a. Genesis and environmental significance of a buried Middle Pleistocene soil in eastern England. *Geoderma* **41**, 49-77.

Kemp, R. A. 1987b. The interpretation and environmental significance of a buried Middle Pleistocene soil near Ipswich Airport, Suffolk, England. *Philosophical Transactions of the Royal Society of London* **B317**, 365-391.

Kennard, A. S. 1938. Report on the non-marine Mollusca from the Middle Gravels of the Barnfield Pit. *Journal of the Royal Anthropological Institute of London* **68**, 28-30.

Kennard, A. S. 1947. The post-Pliocene non-marine mollusca of Hertfordshire. *Transactions of the Hertfordshire Natural History Society and Field Club* **22**, 1-18.

Kennedy, W. J. and Garrison, R. E. 1975. Morphology and genesis of nodular phosphates in the Cenomanian Glauconitic Marl of south-east England. *Lethaia* **8**, 339-360.

Kennedy, W. J. and Juignet, P. 1974. Carbonate banks and slump beds in the Upper Cretaceous (Upper Turonian-Santonian) of Haute Normandie, France. *Sedimentology* **21**, 1-42.

Kerney, M. P. 1959. An interglacial tufa near Hitchin, Hertfordshire. *Proceedings of the Geologists' Association* **70**, 322-337.

Kerney, M. P. 1977. A proposed zonation scheme for Late-glacial and Post-glacial deposits using land mollusca. *Journal of Archaeological Science* **4**, 387-390.

Kerney, M. P., Brown, E. H. and Chandler, T. J. 1964. The Late-glacial and Post-glacial history of the Chalk escarpment near Brook, Kent. *Philosophical Transactions of the Royal Society of London* **B248**, 135-204.

Kerr, M. H. 1955. On the origin of silcretes in southern England. *Proceedings of the Leeds Philosophical and Literary Society (Scientific Section)* **6**, 328-337.

Khodri, M., Leclainche, Y., Ramstein, G., Braconnot, P., Marti, O. and Cortijo, E. 2001. Simulating the amplification of orbital forcing by ocean feedbacks in the last glaciation. *Nature* **410**, 570-574.

Kidner, H. 1908. Excursion to Aldbury and Ivinghoe. June 15th, 1907. *Proceedings of the Geologists' Association* **20**, 166-169.

Kidner, H. 1910a. Excursion to Northwood and Croxley Green. Saturday, July 24th, 1909. *Proceedings of the Geologists' Association* **21**, 243-246.

Kidner, H. 1910b. Notes on the geology of the neighbourhood of Watford. *Transactions of the Hertfordshire Natural History Society and Field Club* **14**, 179-180.

Kidner, H. 1915. On the strata recently exposed in the railway cutting between Oxhey and Pinner. *Transactions of the Hertfordshire Natural History Society and Field Club* **15**, 153-154.

Kidner, H. and Woodhead, J. H. 1911. Excursions to Bushey and Pinner. Saturdays, September 24th and November 5th, 1910. *Proceedings of the Geologists' Association* **22**, 152-156.

Kiln, R. J. 1970. An early Iron Age site at Moles Farm, Thundridge. *Hertfordshire Archaeology* **2**, 10-22.

Kiln, R. J. 1973. Ware. *Hertfordshire Archaeological Review* **7**, 123-124.

Kimble, D. 1933. Cholesbury Camp. *Journal of the British Archaeological Association* (New Series) **39**, 187-208.

King, A. 1896. On the advantages of a supply of soft water for the town of Watford. *Transactions of the Hertfordshire Natural History Society and Field Club* **8**, 116-124.

King, C. 1981. The stratigraphy of the London Clay and associated deposits. *Tertiary Research Special Paper* **6**. Backhuys, Rotterdam.

King, C. 1983. Cainozoic micropalaeontological biostratigraphy of the North Sea. *Institute of Geological Sciences Report* **82/7**.

King, C. 2006. Paleogene and Neogene: uplift and cooling climate. In: *The Geology of England and Wales* (eds Brenchley, P. J. and Rawson, P. F.). The Geological Society, London, 395-427.

King, D. 1986. Petrology, dating and distribution of querns and millstones. The results of research in Bedfordshire, Buckinghamshire, Hertfordshire and Middlesex. *University of London Institute of Archaeology Bulletin* **23**, 65-126.

King, D. W. 1969. *Soils of the Luton and Bedford district. A reconnaissance survey*. Soil Survey Special Publication **1**. Agricultural Research Council, Harpenden.

Kingsbury, P. 1987. Roadside hedgerows and trees in the Chilterns of north-west Hertfordshire. *Transactions of the Hertfordshire Natural History Society and Field Club* **29**, 361-368.

Kirby, R. I. 1974. Report of project meeting and field meeting to Aveley, Essex. *Tertiary Times* **2**, 102-105.

Kirkaldy, J. F. 1950a. Solution of the chalk in the Mimms Valley, Herts. *Proceedings of the Geologists' Association* **61**, 219-224.

Kirkaldy, J. F. 1950b. Field meeting at Water End, North Mimms. Saturday, 28th May, 1949. *Proceedings of the Geologists' Association* **61**, 224.

Kirkman, K. 1992. *Pinner chalk mines*. Pinner Local History Society, London.

Kitchin, F. L. and Pringle, J. 1920. On an inverted mass of Upper Cretaceous strata near Leighton Buzzard, Bedfordshire; and on an overlap of the Upper Gault in that neighbourhood. *Geological Magazine* **57**, 4-15, 52-62, 100-113.

Kitchin, F. L. and Pringle, J. 1922. Correspondence. Gault and Lower Greensand near Leighton Buzzard. *Geological Magazine* **59**, 283-287.

Klinck, B. A., Hopson, P. M., Lewis, M. A., Macdonald, D. M. J., Inglethorpe, S. D. J., Entwisle, D. C., Harrington, J. F. and Williams, L. 1998. The hydrogeological behaviour of the clay-with-flints of southern England. *British Geological Survey Technical Report* **WE/97/5**.

Knox, R. W. O'B. 1990. Thanetian and Ypresian chronostratigraphy in south-east England. *Tertiary Research* **11**, 57-64.

Knox, R. W. O'B. 1996. Tectonic controls on sequence development in the Palaeocene and earliest Eocene of southeast England: implications for North Sea stratigraphy. In: *Sequence stratigraphy in British geology* (eds Hesselbo, S. P. and Parkinson, D. N.). Geological Society, London, Special Publication **103**, 209-230.

Knox, R. W. O'B., Morigi, A. N., Ali, J. R., Hailwood, E. A. and Hallam, J. R. 1990. Early Palaeogene stratigraphy of a cored borehole at Hales, Norfolk. *Proceedings of the Geologists' Association* **101**, 145-151.

Koch, W. 1977. Biostratigraphie in der Oberkreide und taxonomie von Foraminiferen. *Geologische Jahrbuch* **A38**, 11-123.

Krauskopf, K. B. 1959. The geochemistry of silica in sedimentary environments. In: *Silica in sediments*. Society of Economic Palaeontologists and Mineralogists Special Publication **7**, 4-19.

L

Lacaille, A. D. 1961. Mesolithic facies in Middlesex and London. *Transactions of the London and Middlesex Archaeological Society* **20**, 3, 101-150.

Lake, R. D. 1975. The structure of the Weald – a review. *Proceedings of the Geologists' Association* **86**, 549-557.

Lake, R. D. and Wilson, D. 1990. *Geology of the country around Great Dunmow. Memoir for 1:50,000 geological sheet 222 (England and Wales)*. Memoirs of the Geological Survey of Great Britain. HMSO, London.

Lamplugh, G. W. 1902. Calcrete. *Geological Magazine*, New Series, Decade IV, **9**, 575.

Lamplugh, G. W. 1920. Correspondence. Gault and Lower Greensand near Leighton Buzzard. *Geological Magazine* **57**, 234-237.

Lamplugh, G. W. 1921. Correspondence. The age of the Shenley Limestone. *Geological Magazine* **58**, 140.

Lamplugh, G. W. 1922. On the junction of Gault and Lower Greensand near Leighton Buzzard (Bedfordshire). *Quarterly Journal of the Geological Society, London* **78**, 1-80.

Lamplugh, G. W. and Walker, J. F. 1903. On a fossiliferous band at the top of the Lower Greensand near Leighton Buzzard (Bedfordshire). *Quarterly Journal of the Geological Society, London* **59**, 234-265.

Lark, R. M. and Webster, R. 2006. Geostatistical mapping of geomorphic variable in the presence of trend. *Earth Surface Processes and Landforms* **31**, 862-874.

Lawrence, A. R. and Foster, S. S. D. 1991. The legacy of aquifer pollution by industrial chemicals – technical appraisal and policy implications. *Quarterly Journal of Engineering Geology* **24**, 231-239.

Lawrence, G. R. P. 1964. Some pro-glacial features near Finchley and Potters Bar. *Proceedings of the Geologists' Association* **75**, 15-29.

Lawrence, G. R. P. 1966. The geology and geography of the district. In: *The story of Potters Bar and South Mimms*. Urban District Council of Potters Bar, White Crescent Press, Luton, pp. 15-21.

Lee, J. W. C. 1977. Mesolithic and Neolithic sites at Cuffley, Herts. *Hertfordshire Archaeology* **5**, 1-12.

Lee, J. W. C. 1987. A Mesolithic site at Thorntons Farm, Cuffley. *Hertfordshire Archaeology* **9**, 1-7.

Lee, M. K., Pharoah, T. C. and Green, C. A. 1991. Structural trends in the concealed basement of eastern England from images of regional potential field data. *Annales de la Société Géologique de Belgique* **114**, 45-62.

Leeson, J., Edwards, A., Smith, J. W. N. and Potter, H. A. B. 2003. *Hydrogeological risk assessments for landfills and the derivation of groundwater control and trigger levels*. Environment Agency (England and Wales) Report No. **LFTGN01**.

Le Gear, R. F. 1979. Deneholes – part two. *Records of the Chelsea Speleological Society* **10**, 116.

Lehman, S. J. and Keigwin, L. D. 1992. Sudden changes in North Atlantic circulation during the last deglaciation. *Nature* **356**, 757-762.

Leinweber, P., Lünsmann, F. and Eckhardt, K. -U. 1997. Phosphorus sorption capacities and saturation of soils in two regions with different livestock densities in northwest Germany. *Soil Use and Management* **13**, 82-89.

Lewis, C. L. E., Green, P. F., Carter, A. and Hurford, A. J. 1992. Elevated K/T palaeotemperatures throughout northwest England : three kilometres of Tertiary erosion? *Earth and Planetary Science Letters* **112**, 131-145.

Lewis, J. S. C., Wiltshire, P. E. J. and Macphail, R. 1992. A late Devensian/early Flandrian site at Three Ways Wharf, Uxbridge: environmental implications. In: *Alluvial archaeology in Britain* (eds Needham, S. and Macklin, M. G.). Oxbow Monograph **27**, 235-247.

Lewis, S. G. 1999. Eastern England. In: *A revised correlation of Quaternary deposits in the British Isles* (ed. Bowen, D. Q.). Geological Society, London, Special Report **23**, 10-27.

Lewis, W. V. 1949. The Pegsdon dry valleys. *Compass (Cambridge University Geographical Society)* **1**, 53-70.

L'Hirondel, J. and L'Hirondel, J. -L. 2002. *Nitrate and man – toxic, harmless or beneficial?* CABI Publishing, Wallingford.

Lilwall, R. C. 1976. *Seismicity and seismic hazard in Britain.* Institute of Geological Sciences Seismology Bulletin **4**. HMSO, London.

Linton, D. L. 1956. *Sheffield and its region: a scientific and historical survey.* British Association for the Advancement of Science, Sheffield.

Little, J. A. and Atkinson, J. H. 1988. Some geological and engineering characteristics of lodgement tills from the Vale of St Albans, Hertfordshire. *Quarterly Journal of Engineering Geology* **21**, 183-199.

Littleboy, J. E. 1884. The River Bourne. *Transactions of the Hertfordshire Natural History Society and Field Club* **2**, 237.

Lloyd, J. W. 1993. The United Kingdom. In: *The hydrology of the Chalk of north-west Europe* (eds Downing, R. A., Price, M. and Jones, G. P.). Clarendon Press, Oxford, 220-249.

Lloyd, J. W., Harker, D. and Baxendale, R. A. 1981. Recharge mechanisms and groundwater flow in the Chalk and drift deposits of southern East Anglia. *Quarterly Journal of Engineering Geology* **14**, 87-96.

Lloyd, J. W., Williams, G. M., Foster, S. S. D., Ashley, R. P. and Lawrence, A. R. 1991. Urban and industrial groundwater pollution. In: *Applied groundwater hydrology a British perspective* (eds Downing, R. A. and Wilkinson, W. B.). Clarendon Press, Oxford, 134-148.

Lones, T. E. 1904. On some fossiliferous post-Tertiary beds exposed at the gas works, Watford. *Transactions of the Hertfordshire Natural History Society and Field Club* **12**, 17-20.

Lones, T. E. 1905. Some recently exposed beds in the valley of the Gade, at and near Hunton Bridge. *Transactions of the Hertfordshire Natural History Society and Field Club* **12**, 253-256.

Longstaff, S. L., Aldous, P. J., Clark, L., Flavin, R. J. and Partington, J. 1992. Contamination of the Chalk aquifer by chlorinated solvents: a case study of the Luton and Dunstable area. *Journal of the Institution of Water and Environmental Management* **6**, 541-550.

Longworth, I. 1989. The late prehistoric pottery. In: *Verulamium: the King Harry Lane site* (eds Stead, I. and Rigby, V.). *English Heritage Archaeological Report* **12**, 53-58.

Lord, J. A., Clayton, C. R. I. and Mortimore, R. N. 2002. *Engineering in Chalk.* Construction Industry Research and Information Association, Publication **C574**.

Lourens, L. J., Sluijs, A., Kroon, D., Zachos, J. C., Thomas, E., Röhl, U., Bowles, J. and Raffi, I. 2005. Astronomical pacing of late Palaeocene to early Eocene global warming events. *Nature* **435**, 1083-1087.

Loveday, J. 1962. Plateau deposits of the southern Chiltern Hills. *Proceedings of the Geologists' Association* **73**, 83-102.

Lovell, B. and Tubb, J. 2006. Ancient quarrying of rare *in situ* Palaeogene Hertfordshire Puddingstone. *Mercian Geologist* **16**, 185-189.

Lowe, J. J. and Walker, M. J. C. 1997. *Reconstructing Quaternary environments* (2nd edition). Longman, Harlow.

Lucas, H. C. and Robinson, V. K. 1995. Modelling of rising groundwater levels in the Chalk aquifer of the London Basin. *Quarterly Journal of Engineering Geology* **28**, S51-S62.

M

Macdonald, A. J., Powlson, D. S., Poulton, P. R. and Jenkinson, D. S. 1989. Unused fertiliser nitrogen in arable soils – its contribution to nitrate leaching. *Journal of the Science of Food and Agriculture* **46**, 407-419.

Macdonald, A. J., Poulton, P. R., Powlson, D. S. and Jenkinson, D. S. 1997. Effects of season, soil type and cropping on recoveries, residues and losses of ^{15}N-labelled fertilizer applied to arable crops in spring. *Journal of Agricultural Science, Cambridge* **129**, 125-154.

MacGregor, A. (ed.) 2008. *Sir John Evans 1823-1908. Antiquity, Commerce and Natural Science in the age of Darwin.* Ashmolean Museum, Oxford.

Mackay, D. M. 1998. Is cleanup of VOC contaminated groundwater feasible? In: *Contaminated land and groundwater; future directions* (eds Lerner, D. N. and Walton, N. R. G.). Geological Society, London, Engineering Geology Special Publication **14**, 3-11.

MacLennan, J. and Jones, S. M. 2006. Regional uplift, gas hydrate dissociation and the origins of the Palaeocene-Eocene Thermal Maximum. *Earth and Planetary Science Letters* **245**, 65-80.

MacRae, R. J. 1987. The great handaxe stakes. *Lithics* **8**, 15-17.

Maddy, D. 1997. Uplift driven valley incision and river terrace formation in southern England. *Journal of Quaternary Science* **12**, 539-545.

Maddy, D., Bridgland, D. R. and Green, C. P. 2000. Crustal uplift in southern England: evidence from the river terrace records. *Geomorphology* **33**, 167-181.

Maddy, D., Bridgland, D. and Westaway, R. 2001. Uplift-driven valley incision and climate-controlled river terrace development in the Thames Valley, UK. *Quaternary International* **79**, 23-36.

Maher, B. A. and Hallam, D. F. 2005. Palaeomagnetic correlation and dating of Plio-Pleistocene sediments at the southern margin of the North Sea Basin. *Journal of Quaternary Science* **20**, 67-77.

Manning, D., Lopez-Capel, E. and Renforth, P. 2009. Growth of the soil. *Geoscientist* **19**, 1, 20-23.

Marsland, A. 1977. The evaluation of the engineering design parameters for glacial clays. *Quarterly Journal of Engineering Geology* **10**, 1-26.

Maslin, M. A., Li, X. S., Loutre, M. -F. and Berger, A. 1998. The contribution of orbital forcing to the progressive intensification of northern hemisphere glaciation. *Quaternary Science Reviews* **17**, 411-426.

Mather, J. D. 2008. The hydrogeological work of Sir John Evans: his role in the battle between geologists and engineers for the water of the Chilterns. In: *Sir John Evans 1823-1908. Antiquity, commerce and natural science in the age of Darwin* (ed. MacGregor, A.). Ashmolean Museum, Oxford, 68-94.

Mather, J. D. and Young, C. P. 1980. Recent research into groundwater pollution by landfills. In: *A survey of British hydrogeology* (eds Argent, C. R. and Griffin, D. J. H.). The Royal Society, London, 33-45.

Mather, P. M. and Doornkamp, J. C. 1970. Multivariate analysis in geography with particular reference to drainage basin morphometry. *Transactions of the Institute of British Geographers* **51**, 163-187.

Mathers, S. J. and Zalasiewicz, J. A. 1988. The Red Crag and Norwich Crag Formations of southern East Anglia. *Proceedings of the Geologists' Association* **99**, 261-278.

Matthews, C. L. 1976. Occupation sites on a Chiltern ridge. Excavations at Puddlehill and sites near Dunstable, Bedfordshire. Part 1. Neolithic, Bronze Age and early Iron Age. *British Archaeological Reports British Series* **29**.

Matthews, C. L., Schneider, J. and Horne, B. 1992. A Roman villa at Totternhoe. *Bedfordshire Archaeology* **20**, 41-65.

McDonald, T. 1995. The A41 by-pass project, Hertfordshire Archaeological Trust. In: *Chiltern archaeology recent work a handbook for the next decade* (ed. Holgate, R.). The Book Castle, Dunstable, 120-123.

McDonald, T. 2004a. Archaeological excavations in advance of the A414 Cole Green By-Pass, near Hertford. *Hertfordshire Archaeology* **13**, 3-46.

McDonald, T. 2004b. Excavations at Buncefield Lane, Hemel Hempstead. *Hertfordshire Archaeology* **13**, 47-60.

McGregor, D. F. M. and Green, C. P. 1978. Gravels of the River Thames as a guide to Pleistocene catchment changes. *Boreas* **7**, 197-203.

McGregor, D. F. M. and Green, C. P. 1983a. Post-depositional modification of Pleistocene terraces of the River Thames. *Boreas* **12**, 23-33.

McGregor, D. F. M. and Green, C. P. 1983b. Lithostratigraphic subdivisions in the gravels of the proto-Thames between Hemel Hempstead and Watford. *Proceedings of the Geologists' Association* **94**, 83-85.

McGregor, D. F. M. and Green, C. P. 1983c. Gerrards Cross. In: *The Diversion of the Thames. Field Guide* (ed. Rose, J.). Quaternary Research Association, Cambridge, 80-84.

Mead, W. R. 2003. *Pehr Kalm a Finnish visitor to the Chilterns in 1748.* Published privately, Aston Clinton.

Megaw, R., Megaw, V. and Niblett, R. 1999. A decorated Iron Age copper alloy knife from Hertfordshire. *Antiquaries Journal* **79**, 379-387.

Meissner, R., Matthews, D. H. and Wever, T. H. 1986. The "Moho" in and around Great Britain. *Annaler Geophysicae* **4**, 659-664.

Meldola, R. 1888. The Great Essex earthquake of the 22nd of April, 1884. *Transactions of the Hertfordshire Natural History Society and Field Club* **4**, 23-32.

Mellars, P. and Reinhardt, S. C. 1978. Patterns of Mesolithic land-use in southern England: a geological perspective. In: *The early postglacial settlement of northern Europe. An ecological perspective* (ed. Mellars, P.). Duckworth, London, 243-293.

Miller, N. H. J. 1906. The amount and composition of the drainage through unmanured and uncropped land, Barnfield, Rothamsted. *Journal of Agricultural Science, Cambridge* **1**, 377-399.

Millward, D., Ellison, R. A., Lake, R. D. and Moorlock, B. S. P. 1987. *Geology of the country around Epping. Memoir for 1:50,000 geological sheet 240 (England and Wales).* Memoirs of the Geological Survey of Great Britain. HMSO, London.

Milnes, A. R. and Thiry, M. 1992. Silcretes. In: *Weathering, soils and palaeosols* (eds Martini, I. P. and Chesworth, W.). Developments in Earth Surface Processes **2**. Elsevier, Amsterdam, 349-377.

Mitchell, G. F., Penny, L. F., Shotton, F. W. and West, R. G. 1973. *A correlation of Quaternary deposits in the British Isles.* Geological Society, London, Special Report **4**.

Mithen, S. 1999. Mesolithic archaeology, environmental archaeology and human palaeoecology. *Journal of Quaternary Science* **14**, 477-483.

Moffat, A. J. 1980. *The Plio-Pleistocene transgression in the northern part of the London Basin – a re-examination.* Unpublished PhD Thesis, London University.

Moffat, A. J. 1986. Quartz signatures in Plio-Pleistocene gravels in the northern part of the London Basin. In: *Clast Lithological Analysis* (ed. Bridgland, D. R.). Technical Guide **3**, Quaternary Research Association, Cambridge, 117-128.

Moffat, A. J. and Bateman, R. M. 1983. The mineralogy of Palaeogene sediments in southeast England. *Proceedings of the Geologists' Association* **94**, 271-274.

Moffat, A. J. and Catt, J. A. 1982. The nature of the Pebbly Clay Drift at Epping Green, south-east Hertfordshire. *Transactions of the Hertfordshire Natural History Society and Field Club* **28**, Part 6, 16-24.

Moffat, A. J. and Catt, J. A. 1983. A new excavation in Plio-Pleistocene deposits at Little Heath. *Transactions of the Hertfordshire Natural History Society and Field Club* **29**, Part 1, 5-10.

Moffat, A. J. and Catt, J. A. 1986a. A re-examination of the evidence for a Plio-Pleistocene marine transgression on the Chiltern Hills. II. Drainage patterns. *Earth Surface Processes and Landforms* **11**, 169-180.

Moffat, A. J. and Catt, J. A. 1986b. A re-examination of the evidence for a Plio-Pleistocene marine transgression on the Chiltern Hills. III. Deposits. *Earth Surface Processes and Landforms* **11**, 233-247.

Moffat, A. J., Catt, J. A., Webster, R. and Brown, E. H. 1986. A re-examination of the evidence for a Plio-

Pleistocene marine transgression on the Chiltern Hills. I. Structures and surfaces. *Earth Surface Processes and Landforms* **11**, 95-106.

Monckton, H. W. and Herries, R. S. 1891. On some hill gravels north of the Thames. *Proceedings of the Geologists' Association* **12**, 108-114.

Monckton, H. W. and Hopkinson, J. 1906. Excursion to Ayot Green and Hatfield. Saturday, May 26th, 1906. *Proceedings of the Geologists' Association* **19**, 354-356.

Money, W. 1906. A Berkshire denehole. *Journal of the British Archaeological Association* **12-13**, 212.

Moore, J. A. 2005. *BSBI Handbook 5. Charophytes of Great Britain and Ireland.* Summerfield Books, Brough.

Moorlock, B. S. P., Sumbler, M. G., Woods, M. A. and Boreham, S. 2003. *Geology of the Biggleswade district – a brief explanation of the geological map. Explanation of the British Geological Survey 1:50,000 Sheet 204 Biggleswade (England and Wales).* British Geological Survey, Keyworth.

Moraghan, J. T. and Buresh, R. J. 1977. Chemical reduction of nitrite and nitrous oxide by ferrous iron. *Soil Science Society of America Journal* **41**, 47-49.

Morris, J. 1878. The physical structure of the London Basin, considered in its relation to the geology of the neighbourhood of Watford. *Transactions of the Watford Natural History Society and Hertfordshire Field Club* **1**, 89-107.

Morris, M. and Wainwright, A. 1995. Iron Age and Romano-British settlement, agriculture and industry in the upper Bulbourne valley, Hertfordshire: an interim interpretation. In: *Chiltern archaeology recent work a handbook for the next decade* (ed. Holgate, R.). The Book Castle, Dunstable, 68-75.

Morris, R. E. and Fowler, C. H. 1937. *The flow and bacteriology of underground water in the Lee Valley.* 32nd Annual Report of the Metropolitan Water Board, London.

Morter, A. A. and Wood, C. J. 1983. The biostratigraphy of Upper Albian-Lower Cenomanian Aucellina in Europe. *Zitteliana* **10**, 515-529.

Mortimore, R. N. 1983. The stratigraphy and sedimentation of the Turonian-Campanian in the southern province of England. *Zitteliana* **10**, 27-41.

Mortimore, R. N. 1986. Stratigraphy of the Upper Cretaceous White Chalk of Sussex. *Proceedings of the Geologists' Association* **97**, 97-139.

Mortimore, R. N. 1993. Chalk water and engineering geology. In: *The hydrogeology of the Chalk of north-west Europe* (eds Downing, R. A., Price, M. and Jones, G. P.). Clarendon Press, Oxford, 67-92.

Mortimore, R. N. in press. A Chalk revolution: what have we done to the Chalk of England? *Proceedings of the Geologists' Association*

Mortimore, R. N. and Pomerol, B. 1987. Correlation of the Upper Cretaceous White Chalk (Turonian to Campanian) in the Anglo-Paris Basin. *Proceedings of the Geologists' Association* **98**, 97-143.

Mortimore, R. N. and Pomerol, B. 1991. Upper Cretaceous tectonic disruptions in a placid Chalk sequence in the Anglo-Paris Basin. *Journal of the Geological Society, London* **148**, 391-404.

Mortimore, R. N. and Pomerol, B. 1997. Upper Cretaceous tectonic phases and end Cretaceous inversion in the Chalk of the Anglo-Paris Basin. *Proceedings of the Geologists' Association* **108**, 231-255.

Mortimore, R. N. and Wood, C. J. 1986. The distribution of flint in the English Chalk, with particular reference to the 'Brandon Flint Series' and the high Turonian flint maximum. In: *The scientific study of flint and chert* (eds Sieveking, G. de G. and Hart, M. B.). Cambridge University Press, Cambridge, 7-20.

Mortimore, R. N., Wood, C. J., Pomerol, B. and Ernst, G. 1998. Dating the phases of the Subhercynian tectonic epoch: Late Cretaceous tectonics and eustatics in the Cretaceous basins of northern Germany compared with the Anglo-Paris Basin. *Zentralblatt für Geologie und Paläontologie* Teil 1 (1996), **11/12**, 1349-1401.

Mortimore, R. N., Wood, C. J. and Gallois, R. W. 2001. British Upper Cretaceous Stratigraphy. *Geological Conservation Review Series* **23**. Joint Nature Conservation Committee, Peterborough.

Morton, A. C. 1982. The provenance and diagenesis of Palaeogene sandstones of southeast England as indicated by heavy mineral analysis. *Proceedings of the Geologists' Association* **93**, 263-274.

Moss-Eccardt, J. 1970. The ages of stone. The Mesolithic and Neolithic periods. *Hertfordshire Archaeological Council Research Report.*

Moss-Eccardt, J. (ed.) 1988. Archaeological excavations in the Letchworth area, 1958-1974. Blackhorse Road, Letchworth, Norton Road, Baldock, Wilbury Hill, Letchworth. *Proceedings of the Cambridge Antiquarian Society* **77**, 35-103.

Mühlherr, I. H., Hiscock, K. M., Dernnis, P. F. and Feast, N. A. 1998. Changes in groundwater chemistry due to rising groundwater levels in the London Basin between 1963 and 1994. In: *Groundwater pollution, aquifer recharge and vulnerability* (ed. Robins, N. S.). Geological Society, London, Special Publication **130**, 47-62.

Muir Wood, R. 1989. Fifty million years of "passive margin" deformation in North West Europe. In: *Earthquakes at North Atlantic passive margins: neotectonics and postglacial rebound* (eds Gregersen, S. and Basham, P. W.). Kluwer, Dordrecht, 393-411.

Murray, J. W. and Wright, C. A. 1974. Palaeogene Foraminiferida and palaeoecology, Hampshire and Paris Basins and the English Channel. *Special Papers in Palaeontology* **14**.

Murton, J. B., Whiteman, C. A. and Allen, P. 1995. Involutions in the Middle Pleistocene (Anglian) Barham Soil, eastern England: a comparison with thermokarst involutions from arctic Canada. *Boreas* **24**, 269-280.

Murton, J. B., Baker, A., Bowen, D. Q., Caseldine, C. J. and 16 others 2001. A late Middle Pleistocene temperate-periglacial-temperate sequence (Oxygen Isotope Stages 7-5e) near Marsworth, Buckinghamshire, UK. *Quaternary Science Reviews* **20**, 1787-1825.

Muscutt, A. D. and Withers, P. J. A. 1996. The phosphorus content of rivers in England and Wales. *Water Research* **30**, 1258-1268.

Musson, R. M. W. 1994. *A catalogue of British earthquakes*. British Geological Survey Technical Report, Seismology Series **WL/94/04**. British Geological Survey, Edinburgh.

Musson, R. M. W. 2007. British earthquakes. *Proceedings of the Geologists' Association* **118**, 305-337.

N

Nash, D. J., Thomas, D. S. G. and Shaw, P. A. 1994. Siliceous duricrusts as palaeoclimatic indicators: evidence from the Kalahari Desert of Botswana. *Palaeogeography, Palaeoclimatology, Palaeoecology* **112**, 279-295.

Nash, D. J., Shaw, P. A. and Ullyott, J. S. 1998. Drainage-line silcretes of the middle Kalahari: an analogue for Cenozoic sarsen trains? *Proceedings of the Geologists' Association* **109**, 241-254.

Neal, D. S., Wardle, A. and Hunn, J. 1990. *Excavation of the Iron Age, Roman and Medieval settlement at Gorhambury, St Albans*. English Heritage Archaeological Report **14**.

Nellist, D. R. 1989. A note on the spiders of Ridlins Mire. *Transactions of the Hertfordshire Natural History Society and Field Club* **30**, 185-187.

Newbery, M. 2009. The fossil fish mystery resolved? *St Mary's Pirton Magazine*, September 2009, 32-33.

Newton, E. T. 1892. Note on an Iguanodont tooth from the Lower Chalk ("Totternhoe Stone") near Hitchin. *Geological Magazine*, New Series, Decade III, **9**, 49-50.

Niblett, R. 1992. A Catuvellaunian chieftain's burial from St Albans. *Antiquity* **66**, 917-929.

Niblett, R. 1995a. *Roman Hertfordshire*. Dovecote Press, Wimborne.

Niblett, R. 1995b. A new site at Verulamium (St Albans). In: *Chiltern archaeology recent work a handbook for the next decade* (ed. Holgate, R.). The Book Castle, Dunstable, 96-102.

Niblett, R. 1999. *The excavation of a ceremonial site at Folly Lane, Verulamium*. Britannia Monograph **14**.

Niblett, R. 2001a. A Neolithic dugout from a multi-period site near St Albans, Herts, England. *International Journal of Nautical Archaeology* **30**, 155-195.

Niblett, R. 2001b. *Verulamium the Roman city of St Albans*. Tempus Publishing, Stroud.

Niblett, R. and Thompson, I. 2005. *Alban's buried towns. An assessment of St Albans' archaeology up to AD 1600*. Oxbow Books, Oxford.

Norden, J. 1593. *Speculum britanniae. The discription of Hartfordshire*. Eliot's Court Press, London.

Northmore, K. J., Bell, F. G. and Culshaw, M. G. 1996. The engineering properties and behaviour of the brickearth of south Essex. *Quarterly Journal of Engineering Geology* **29**, 147-161.

Nowell, D. A. G. 1991. The palaeogeography of the Hertfordshire Pebble Gravels and the Hitchin Gap. *Transactions of the Hertfordshire Natural History Society and Field Club* **31**, 41-52.

Nowell, D. A. G. 1994. A geological trail in the valley of the Mimmshall Brook, Hertfordshire. *Transactions of the Hertfordshire Natural History Society and Field Club* **32**, Part 7, 52-59.

Nowell, D. A. G. 1999. Gravity terrain corrections – an overview. *Journal of Applied Geophysics* **42**, 117-134.

Nyer, E. K. 1992. *Groundwater treatment technology* (2nd edition). J. Wiley and Sons, New York.

O

Oakley, K. P. 1936. Field meeting at Cheddington, Ivinghoe and Gubblecote. Sunday, July 7th, 1935. *Proceedings of the Geologists' Association* **47**, 38-41.

Oakley, K. P. 1947. Early man in Hertfordshire. *Transactions of the Hertfordshire Natural History Society and Field Club*, **22**, 247-257.

O'Brien, L. and Roberts, B. 2005. Excavations on Roman Ermine Street at the new restaurant facility, GlaxoSmithKline, Ware. *Hertfordshire Archaeology* **14**, 3-39.

O'Connor, A. 1997. *Finding time for the Old Stone Age. A history of Palaeolithic Archaeology and Quaternary geology in Britain, 1860-1960*. Oxford University Press, Oxford.

OECD, 1982. *Eutrophication of waters: monitoring, assessment and control*. Organisation for Economic Co-operation and Development, Paris.

Oliver, J. E. 1998. Evapotranspiration. In: *Encyclopedia of hydrology and water resources* (eds Herschy, R. W. and Fairbridge, R. W.). Kluwer Academic Publishers, Boston, 266-271.

Ollier, C. D. and Thomasson, A. J. 1956. Slumping in Reading Beds near St Leonards, Bucks. *Proceedings of the Geologists' Association* **67**, 228-231.

Ollier, C. D. and Thomasson, A. J. 1957. Asymmetrical valleys of the Chiltern Hills. *Geographical Journal* **123**, 71-80.

O'Neil, H. E. 1945. The Roman villa at Park Street, near St Albans, Hertfordshire: report on the excavations of 1943-45. *Archaeological Journal* **102**, 21-109.

Ordnance Survey, 1962. *Map of southern Britain in the Iron Age Scale 1:625 000*. Ordnance Survey, Southampton.

Osborne, E. C. and Osborne, W. 1839. *Osborne's London and Birmingham railway guide*. E. C. & W. Osborne, Birmingham.

Ovey, C. D. (ed.) 1964. The Swanscombe skull: a survey of research on a Pleistocene site. *Royal Anthropological Institute Occasional Paper* **21**.

Owen, H. G. 1972. The Gault and its junction with the Woburn Sands in the Leighton Buzzard area, Bedfordshire and Buckinghamshire. *Proceedings of the Geologists' Association* **83**, 287-312.

Owen, H. G. 1975. The stratigraphy of the Gault and Upper Greensand of the Weald. *Proceedings of the Geologists' Association* **86**, 475-498.

Owen, M., Headworth, H. G. and Morgan-Jones, M. 1991. Groundwater in basin management. In: *Applied groundwater hydrology a British perspective* (eds Downing, R. A. and Wilkinson, W. B.). Clarendon Press, Oxford, 16-34.

P

Palmer, R. 1976. Interrupted ditch enclosures in Britain: the use of aerial photography for comparative studies. *Proceedings of the Prehistoric Society* **42**, 161-186.

Parfitt, S. A., Ashton, N. M., Lewis, S. G. and 13 others 2010. Early Pleistocene human occupation at the edge of the boreal zone in northwest Europe. *Nature* **466**, 229-233.

Parker, J. M. and James, R. C. 1985. Autochthonous bacteria in the Chalk and their influence on groundwater quality in East Anglia. In: *Microbial aspects of water management* (*Journal of Applied Bacteriology Symposium Series*), 15S-25S.

Parker, J. M., Gale, I. N. and West, J. M. 1990. Investigation of in-situ bacterial denitrification in the confined Chalk aquifers in Norfolk and N. London. *British Geological Survey Technical Report* **WD/91/13C**.

Parks, D. A. and Rendell, H. M. 1992. TL geochronology of brickearths from south-east England. *Quaternary Science Reviews* **11**, 7-12.

Partridge, C. 1980a. Late Bronze Age artefacts from Hertford Heath, Hertfordshire. *Hertfordshire Archaeology* **7**, 1-9.

Partridge, C. 1980b. Excavations at Puckeridge and Braughing 1975-79. *Hertfordshire Archaeology* **7**, 28-132.

Partridge, C. 1981. *Skeleton Green, a late Iron Age and Romano-British settlement site*. Britannia Monograph **2**.

Partridge, C. 1989. *Foxholes Farm a multiperiod gravel site*. Hertfordshire Archaeological Trust, Hertford.

Paterson, K. 1977. Scarp-face dry valleys near Wantage, Oxfordshire. *Transactions of the Institute of British Geographers* New Series **2**, 192-204.

Peake, D. S. 1983. A closer look at the Merstham wind gap. *Quaternary Newsletter* **39**, 9-16.

Peake, N. B. and Hancock, J. M. 1961. The Upper Cretaceous of Norfolk. In: The Geology of Norfolk (eds Larwood, G. P. and Funnell, B. M.). *Transactions of the Norfolk and Norwich Naturalists' Society* **19**, 293-339.

Pearman, H. 1966. Deneholes. *Records of the Chelsea Speleological Society* **4**, 1-72.

Pearman, H. 1976. Caves and tunnels in south-east England – part one. *Records of the Chelsea Speleological Society* **7**, 1-42.

Pearman, H. 1982. Caves and tunnels in south-east England – part four. *Records of the Chelsea Speleological Society* **11**, 1-70.

Pearson, R. G. 1962. The coleoptera from a detritus mud of full-Glacial age at Colney Heath, near St Albans. *Proceedings of the Linnaean Society, London* **173**, 37-55.

Pemberton, S. G., MacEachern, J. A. and Frey, R. W. 1992. Trace fossil facies models: environmental and allostratigraphic significance. In: *Facies models: response to sea level change* (eds Walker, T. G. and James,

N. P.). Geological Association of Canada, St Johns, Newfoundland, 47-72.

Penman, H. L. 1948. Natural evaporation from open water, bare soil and grass. *Proceedings of the Royal Society, London* **A193**, 120-145.

Penman, H. L. 1949. The dependence of transpiration on weather and soil conditions. *Journal of Soil Science* **1**, 74-89.

Penning, W. H. and Jukes-Browne, A. J. 1881. Geology of the neighbourhood of Cambridge. *Memoir of the Geological Survey of the United Kingdom*. HMSO, London.

Penny, L. F., Coope, G. R. and Catt, J. A. 1969. Age and insect fauna of the Dimlington Silts, East Yorkshire. *Nature* **224**, 65-67.

Perrin, R. M. S. 1971. *The clay mineralogy of British sediments*. Mineralogical Society (Clay Minerals Group), London.

Perrins, L. 2005. Hertfordshire brickworks; a gazetteer. *Hertfordshire Archaeology and History* **14**, 187-206.

Pevsner, N. and Cherry, B. 1977. *The buildings of England: Hertfordshire*. Penguin Books Ltd., Harmondsworth.

Pharoah, T. C., England, R. and Lee, M. K. 1995. The concealed Caledonide basement of eastern England and the southern North Sea – a review. In: *The Trans-European suture zone. Euro-probe in Liblice 1993*. Studia Geophysica et Geodaetica **39** (eds Gee, D. G. and Beckholmen, M.), 330-346.

Phillips, C. W. 1935. A re-examination of the Therfield Heath long barrow, Royston, Herts. *Proceedings of the Prehistoric Society* **1**, 101-107.

Plant, C. W. 2008. *The moths of Hertfordshire*. Hertfordshire Natural History Society, Welwyn Garden City.

Pocock, R. W. 1914a. Excursion to Cuffley and Hertford. Saturday, July 5th, 1913. *Proceedings of the Geologists' Association* **25**, 77-78.

Pocock, R. W. 1914b. Report of an excursion to St Albans. Saturday, September 13th, 1913. *Proceedings of the Geologists' Association* **25**, 79-80.

Pocock, T. I. 1903. On the drifts of the Thames valley near London. *Geological Survey of Great Britain Summary of Progress for 1902*, 199-207.

Pomerol, C. 1989. Stratigraphy of the Palaeogene: hiatuses and transitions. *Proceedings of the Geologists' Association* **100**, 313-324.

Port, M. H. 2006. *Six hundred new churches – the Church Building Commission 1818-1856*. Spire Books Ltd, Reading.

Potter, J. F. 1998. The distribution of silcretes in the churches of the London Basin. *Proceedings of the Geologists' Association* **109**, 289-304.

Potter, J. F. 1999. The geology of London Basin churches: the Palaeogene rocks. *Tertiary Research* **19**, 117-138.

Potter, J. F. 2000. The occurrence of travertine in churches of the London Basin. *Proceedings of the Geologists' Association* **111**, 55-70.

Potter, J. F. 2002. The distribution of Bunter quartzites in the London Basin as portrayed by their occurrence in church fabrics. *Tertiary Research* **21**, 155-170.

Potter, T. W. and Trow, S. D. 1988. Puckeridge-Braughing, Herts.: the Ermine Street excavations, 1971-1972. *Hertfordshire Archaeology* **10**, 1-191.

Poulton, P. R., Pye, E., Hargreaves, P. R. and Jenkinson, D. S. 2003. Accumulation of carbon and nitrogen by old arable land reverting to woodland. *Global Change Biology* **9**, 942-955.

Powell, A. J. 1992. Dinoflagellate cysts in the Tertiary System. In: *A Stratigraphic Index of Dinoflagellate Cysts* (ed. Powell, A. J.). Chapman and Hall, London, 155-252.

Prestwich, J. 1850. On the structure of the strata between the London Clay and the Chalk in the London and Hampshire Tertiary Systems. Part I. Basement-Beds of the London Clay. *Quarterly Journal of the Geological Society, London* **6**, 252-281.

Prestwich, J. 1851. *A geological inquiry respecting the water-bearing strata of the country around London, with reference especially to the water supply of the metropolis, and including some remarks on springs.* Gurney and Jackson, London.

Prestwich, J. 1852. On the structure of the strata between the London Clay and the Chalk in the London and Hampshire Tertiary Systems. Part III. The Thanet Sands. *Quarterly Journal of the Geological Society, London* **8**, 235-264.

Prestwich, J. 1854. On the structure of the strata between the London Clay and the Chalk in the London and Hampshire Tertiary Systems. Part II. The Woolwich and Reading Series. *Quarterly Journal of the Geological Society, London* **10**, 75-157.

Prestwich, J. 1890. On the relation of the Westleton Beds, or pebbly sands of Suffolk, to those of Norfolk, and their extension inland; with some observations on the period of the final elevation and denudation of the Weald and of the Thames Valley. Part II. *Quarterly Journal of the Geological Society, London* **46**, 120-154.

Price, M. 1987. Fluid flow in the Chalk of England. In: *Fluid flow in sedimentary basins and aquifers* (eds Goff, J. C. and Williams, B. P. J.). Geological Society, London, Special Publication **34**, 141-156.

Price, M., Downing, R. A. and Edmunds, W. M. 1993. The Chalk as an aquifer. In: *The hydrogeology of the Chalk in north-west Europe* (eds Downing, R. A., Price, M. and Jones, G. P.). Clarendon Press, Oxford, 35-58.

Prince, H. 1959. The changing landscape of Panshanger. *Transactions of the East Hertfordshire Archaeological Society* **14**, 42-58.

Prince, H. 2008. *Parks in Hertfordshire since 1500.* Hertfordshire Publications, University of Hertfordshire Press, Hatfield.

Prior, S. V., Kemp, S. J., Pearce, J. M. and Inglethorpe, S. D. J. 1993. Mineralogy of the Gault from the Arlesey and Klondyke Farm boreholes. *British Geological Survey Technical Report* **WN/92/15R**. British Geological Survey, Keyworth.

Pryor, R. A. 1878. On the supposed chalybeate spring at Watford, and on other medicinal waters in Herts. *Transactions of the Watford Natural History Society and Hertfordshire Field Club* **1**, 109-11.

Q

Quine, M. and Bosence, D. 1991. Stratal geometries, facies and sea-floor erosion in Upper Cretaceous Chalk, Normandy, France. *Sedimentology* **38**, 1113-1152.

R

Rawlins, B. F. 1977. Archaeological survey of south west Hertfordshire. *Watford and Southwest Hertfordshire Archaeological Society Bulletin* **25**, 18-21.

Rawlins, B. F. 1980. Archaeological survey of south west Hertfordshire. *Watford and Southwest Hertfordshire Archaeological Society Bulletin* **32**, 14-27.

Rawson, P. F. 1992. Early Cretaceous. In: *Atlas of palaeogeography and lithofacies* (eds Cope, J. C. W., Ingham, J. K. and Rawson, P. F.). Memoir of the Geological Society, London **13**, 131-137.

Rawson, P. 2006. Cretaceous: sea levels peak as the North Atlantic opens. In: *The Geology of England and Wales*, 2nd edition (eds Brenchley, P. J. and Rawson, P. F.). The Geological Society, London, 365-393.

Rawson, P. F., Allen, P. and Gale, A. S. 2001. The Chalk Group – a revised lithostratigraphy. *Geoscientist* **11**, 21.

Raymo, M. E. and Ruddiman, W. F. 1992. Tectonic forcing of late Cenozoic climate. *Nature* **359**, 117-122.

Raynaud, D., Barnola, J. -M., Chappellaz, J., Blunier, T., Indermühle, A. and Stauffer, B. 2000. The ice record of greenhouse gases: a view in the context of future changes. *Quaternary Science Reviews* **19**, 9-17.

Rayot, V., Self, P. and Thiry, M. 1992. Transition of clay minerals to opal-CT during groundwater silicification. In: *Mineralogical and geochemical records of palaeoweathering* (eds Schmitt, J. -C. and Gall, Q.). ENSMP Mémoire Science de la Terre, Ecole des Mines de Paris **18**, 47-59.

Reeves, M. J. 1979. Recharge and pollution of the English Chalk: some possible mechanisms. *Engineering Geology* **14**, 231-240.

Reid, C. 1897. The Palaeolithic deposits at Hitchin and their relation to the glacial epoch. *Proceedings of the Royal Society of London* **61**, 40-49.

Reid, C. 1899. *The geology of the country around Dorchester.* Memoirs of the Geological Survey of Great Britain England and Wales. HMSO, London.

Reid, C. 1901. The Palaeolithic deposits at Hitchin and their relation to the glacial epoch. *Transactions of the Hertfordshire Natural History Society and Field Club* **10**, 14-22.

Reid, C. 1903. Further note on the Palaeolithic deposits at Hitchin. *Transactions of the Hertfordshire Natural History Society and Field Club* **11**, 63-64.

Reid, E. M. 1949. The late-Glacial flora of the Lea Valley. *New Phytologist* **48**, 245-252.

Reid, E. M. and Chandler, M. E. J. 1933. *The Flora of the London Clay.* British Museum (Natural History), London.

Reid, R. E. H. 1962. Sponges and the Chalk Rock. *Geological Magazine* **99**, 273-278.

Richardson, A. 1969. Water supplies to the Tring Summit. *Journal of the Railway and Canal History Society* **15**, 21-27 & 54-62.

Richardson, L., Arkell, W. J. and Dines, H. G. 1946. *Geology of the country around Witney*. Memoirs of the Geological Survey of Great Britain England and Wales. HMSO, London.

Rigby-Jones, J., Matthews, M. C. and McDowell, P. 1997. Electrical resistivity imaging systems for ground investigations, with particular reference to dissolution features in chalk areas. In: *Modern geophysics in engineering geology* (eds McCann, D. M., Eddleston, M., Fenning, P. J. and Reeves, G. M.). Geological Society, London, Engineering Geology Special Publication **12**, 235-246.

Rivett, M. O., Smith, J. W. N., Buss, S. R. and Morgan, P. 2007. Nitrate occurrence and attenuation in the major aquifers of England and Wales. *Quarterly Journal of Engineering Geology and Hydrogeology* **40**, 335-352.

Roberts, E. 1974. Totternhoe Stone and flint in Hertfordshire churches. *Mediaeval Archaeology* **18**, 66-89.

Robinson, D. A. and Woodun, J. K. 2008. An experimental study of crust development on chalk downland soils and their impact on runoff and erosion. *European Journal of Soil Science* **59**, 784-798.

Robinson, E. 1994. Hertfordshire puddingstone foray, Saturday, 5 June, 1993. *Proceedings of the Geologists' Association* **105**, 77-79.

Robinson, E. A. 1978. Ostracods from deposits in the Vale of St Albans. *Quaternary Newsletter* **25**, 8-9.

Robinson, N. D. 1986. Lithostratigraphy of the Chalk Group of the North Downs, southeast England. *Proceedings of the Geologists' Association* **97**, 141-170.

Rodda, J. C., Downing, R. A. and Law, F. M. 1976. *Systematic hydrology*. Newnes-Butterworth, London.

Rodwell, W. 1976. Coinage, oppida and the rise of Belgic power in S. E. Britain. In: *Oppida and barbarian Europe* (eds Cunliffe, B. and Rowley, T.). British Archaeological Reports Supplementary Series **11**, 181-366.

Rodwell, W. 1978. Relict landscapes in Essex. In: *Early land allotment* (eds Bowen, H. C. and Fowler, P. J.). British Archaeological Reports British Series **48**, 89-98.

Roe, D. A. 1968a. A gazetteer of British Lower and Middle Palaeolithic sites. *Council for British Archaeology Research Report* **8**.

Roe, D. A. 1968b. British Lower and Middle Palaeolithic hand-axe groups. *Proceedings of the Prehistoric Society* **34**, 1-82.

Roe, D. A. 1981. *The Lower and Middle Palaeolithic Periods in Britain*. Routledge and Kegan Paul, London.

Rook, A. G. 1968. Investigation of a Belgic occupation site at Crookhams, Welwyn Garden City. *Hertfordshire Archaeology* **1**, 51-65.

Rook, A. G. 1970a. A Belgic and Roman site at Brickwall Hill, Welwyn Garden City. *Hertfordshire Archaeology* **2**, 23-30.

Rook, A. G. 1970b. Investigation of a Belgic site at Grubs Barn, Welwyn Garden City. *Hertfordshire Archaeology* **2**, 31-36.

Rook, A. G. 1974. Welch's Farm. *Hertfordshire Archaeological Review* **9**, 170.

Rook, A. G. 1997. *A history of Hertfordshire* (2nd edition). Phillimore & Co, Chichester.

Rose, J. 1974. Small-scale spatial variability of some sedimentary properties of lodgement and slumped till. *Proceedings of the Geologists' Association* **85**, 239-258.

Rose, J. 1985. The Dimlington Stadial/Dimlington Chronozone: a proposal for naming the main glacial episode of the Late Devensian in Britain. *Boreas* **14**, 225-230.

Rose, J. 1994. Major river systems of central and southern Britain during Early and Middle Pleistocene. *Terra Nova* **6**, 435-443.

Rose, J. and Allen, P. 1977. Middle Pleistocene stratigraphy in south-east Suffolk. *Journal of the Geological Society, London* **133**, 83-102.

Rose, J., Allen, P. and Hey, R. W. 1976. Middle Pleistocene stratigraphy in southern East Anglia. *Nature* **263**, 492-494.

Rose, J., Sturdy, R. G., Allen, P. and Whiteman, C. A. 1978. Middle Pleistocene sediments and palaeosols near Chelmsford, Essex. *Proceedings of the Geologists' Association* **89**, 91-96.

Rose, J., Whiteman, C. A., Allen, P. and Kemp, R. A. 1999. The Kesgrave Sands and Gravels: pre-glacial Quaternary deposits of the River Thames in East Anglia and the Thames valley. *Proceedings of the Geologists' Association* **110**, 93-116.

Rose, J., Lee, J. A., Kemp, R. A. and Harding, P. A. 2000. Palaeoclimate, sedimentation and soil development during the Last Glacial Stage (Devensian), Heathrow Airport, London, UK. *Quaternary Science Reviews* **19**, 827-847.

Ross, B. R. M. 1932. The physiographic evolution of the Kennet-Thames. *British Association for the Advancement of Science Report of the Centenary Meeting London 1931*, 368.

Rowe, A. 2009. *Medieval parks of Hertfordshire*. Hertfordshire Publications, University of Hertfordshire Press, Hatfield.

Rowe, P. J., Atkinson, T. C. and Turner, C. 1999. U-series dating of Hoxnian interglacial deposits at Mark's Tey, Essex, England. *Journal of Quaternary Science* **14**, 693-702.

Rudge, E. A. 1994. *The lost trackway from Grime's Graves to Stonehenge* (ed. Cooper, J.). The Pudding Stone Study Group, London.

Rudge, E. A. and Rudge, E. L. 1952a. The conglomerate track. *Essex Naturalist* **29**, 17-31.

Rudge, E. A. and Rudge, E. L. 1952b. A Stone Age trade route in East Anglia. *Discovery* **13**, 207-210.

Rudge, J. F., Shaw Champion, M. E., White, N., McKenzie, D. and Lovell, B. 2008. A plume model of transient diachronous uplift at the Earth's surface. *Earth and Planetary Science Letters* **267**, 146-160.

Rundle, A. J. and Cooper, J. 1970. Some recent temporary exposures of London Clay in the London area. *London Naturalist* **49**, 113-124.

S

Sage, B. L. 1966. Geology. In: *Northaw Great Wood its history and natural history*. Hertfordshire County Council Education Department, Hertford, 22-25.

Sahni, M. R. 1929. *A monograph of the Terebratulidae of the British Chalk*. Monograph of the Palaeontographical Society, London.

Salisbury, E. J. 1916. The oak-hornbeam woods of Hertfordshire Parts I and II. *Journal of Ecology* **4**, 83-117.

Salisbury, E. J. 1918. The oak-hornbeam woods of Hertfordshire Parts III and IV. *Journal of Ecology* **6**, 14-52.

Salter, A. E. 1896. "Pebbly gravel" from the Goring Gap to the Norfolk coast. *Proceedings of the Geologists' Association* **14**, 389-404.

Salter, A. E. 1898. Pebbly and other gravels in southern England. *Proceedings of the Geologists' Association* **15**, 264-286.

Salter, A. E. 1905a. On the superficial deposits of central and parts of southern England. *Proceedings of the Geologists' Association* **19**, 1-56.

Salter, A. E. 1905b. The gravels of Hertfordshire. *Transactions of the Hertfordshire Natural History Society and Field Club* **12**, 137-144.

Salter, A. E. 1912. Sarsens and other boulders in Hertfordshire. *Transactions of the Hertfordshire Natural History Society and Field Club* **14**, 135-142.

Sampson, C. G. (ed.) 1978. *Paleoecology and archeology of an Acheulian site at Caddington, England*. Department of Anthropology, Southern Methodist University, Dallas, USA.

Sanger, F. R. 1937. Mesolithic flint flake and core implements in Hertfordshire. *Transactions of the Hertfordshire Natural History Society and Field Club* **20**, 131-132.

Saunders, C. and Havercroft, A. B. 1977. A kiln of the potter Oastrivs and related excavations at Little Munden Farm, Bricket Wood. *Hertfordshire Archaeology* **5**, 109-156.

Saunders, C. and Havercroft, A. B. 1979. Excavations in the City and District of St Albans, 1974-76. *Hertfordshire Archaeology* **6**, 1-77.

Saunders, C. and Havercroft, A. B. 1982a. Excavations at St Helen's Church, Wheathampstead. *Hertfordshire Archaeology* **8**, 102-111.

Saunders, C. and Havercroft, A. B. 1982b. Excavations on the line of the Wheathampstead by-pass 1974 and 1977. *Hertfordshire Archaeology* **8**, 11-31.

Sawford, B. 1974. The vegetation of a marsh at Norton Common, Letchworth. *Transactions of the Hertfordshire Natural History Society and Field Club* **27**, 303-306.

Sawford, B. 1990. *Wild Flower Habitats of Hertfordshire Past Present and Future?* Castlemead Publications, Ware.

Scaife, R. 2002. *St Margaret's Farm, Stanstead Abbotts (HAT 645): pollen and diatom assessment analysis (and) an examination of the plant macrofossils*. Unpublished Report.

Schmitz, B., Sundquist, B. and Andreasson, F. P. 2000. Early Paleogene warm climates and biosphere dynamics. *GFF (Geologiska Föreningens i Stockholm Förhandlingar)* **122**, 1-192.

Schreve, D. C. 2001. Differentiation of the British late Middle Pleistocene interglacials; the evidence from mammalian biostratigraphy. *Quaternary Science Reviews* **20**, 1693-1705.

Schreve, D. C. 2004. The mammalian fauna of the penultimate (MIS 7) interglacial in the Lower Thames Valley. In: *The Quaternary mammals of southern and eastern England. Field Guide* (ed. Schreve, D. C.). Quaternary Research Association, London, 69-79.

Schreve, D. C. 2006. Dating Long Valley Wood – a preliminary assessment. *South West Herts Archaeological and Historical Society Bulletin* **81**, 17-18.

Scott, K. and Buckingham, C. 1997. Quaternary fluvial deposits and palaeontology at Stanton Harcourt, Oxfordshire. In: *The Quaternary of the South Midlands and the Welsh Marches Field Guide* (eds Lewis, S. G. and Maddy, D.). Quaternary Research Association, London, 115-126.

Scott-Jackson, J. E. 2000. *Lower and Middle Palaeolithic artefacts from deposits mapped as Clay-with-flints. A new synthesis with significant implications for the earliest occupation of Britain*. Oxbow Books, Oxford.

Sealy, K. R. and Sealy, C. E. 1956. The terraces of the Middle Thames. *Proceedings of the Geologists' Association* **67**, 369-392.

Searle, A. B. 1911. *Modern brickmaking*. Scott, Greenwood and Sons, London.

Sein, M. K. 1961. *Nothofagus* pollen in the London Clay. *Nature, London* **190**, 1030-1031.

Selkirk, A. 1972. Waulud's Bank. *Current Archaeology* **30**, 173-176.

Seymour, K. J. 1992. Landfill lining for leachate containment. *Journal of the Institution of Water and Environmental Management* **6**, 389-396.

Shackleton, N. J., Berger, A. and Peltier, W. R. 1990. An alternative astronomical calibration of the Lower Pleistocene timescale based on ODL Site 677. *Transactions of the Royal Society of Edinburgh; Earth Sciences* **81**, 251-261.

Sharpley, A. N. and Rekolainen, S. 1997. Phosphorus in agriculture and its environmental implications. In: *Phosphorus loss from soil to water* (eds Tunney. H., Carton, O. T., Brookes, P. C. and Johnstone, A. E.). CAB International, Wallingford, 1-53.

Shaw, P. J. A. 1990. *Natural revegetation and soil development processes on PFA at the former Rye House power station*. National Power Research Report **ESTD/L/0124/R89**.

Shaw, P. J. A. 1992. A preliminary study of successional changes in vegetation and soil development on unamended fly ash (PFA) in southern England. *Journal of Applied Ecology* **29**, 728-736.

Shennan, I. and Horton, B. 2002. Holocene land- and sea-level changes in Great Britain. *Journal of Quaternary Science* **17**, 511-526.

Shephard-Thorn, E. R. and Wymer, J. J. 1996. An Acheulian hand-axe from St Paul's Walden. *Hertfordshire*

Archaeology **12**, 3-4.

Shephard-Thorn, E. R., Harris, P. M., Highley, D. E. and Thornton, M. H. 1986. *An outline study of the Lower Greensand of parts of south-east England*. British Geological Survey Technical Report **WF/MN/86/1**.

Shephard-Thorn, E. R., Moorlock, B. S. P., Cox, B. M., Allsop, J. M. and Wood, C. J. 1994. *Geology of the country around Leighton Buzzard. Memoir of the British Geological Survey for 1:50,000 geological sheet 220 (England and Wales)*. Memoirs of the Geological Survey of Great Britain. HMSO, London.

Sheridan, A. 2007. Green treasures from the magic mountains. *British Archaeology*, Sept-Oct, 2007, 23-27.

Sherlock, R. L. 1915. Report of an excursion to Ware. March 20th, 1915. *Proceedings of the Geologists' Association* **26**, 273-274.

Sherlock, R. L. 1919. Excursion to Codicote, Herts. Saturday, May 10th, 1919. *Proceedings of the Geologists' Association* **30**, 92-93.

Sherlock, R. L. 1922. *The geology of the country around Aylesbury and Hemel Hempstead. Explanation of Sheet 238*. Memoirs of the Geological Survey England and Wales. HMSO, London.

Sherlock, R. L. 1924. The superficial deposits of south Buckinghamshire and south Hertfordshire and the old course of the Thames. *Proceedings of the Geologists' Association* **35**, 1-28.

Sherlock, R. L. 1930. Discussion on the alleged Pliocene of Buckinghamshire and Hertfordshire. *Proceedings of the Geologists' Association* **40**, 357-370.

Sherlock, R. L. 1937. Field meeting to Welwyn and Codicote. Saturday, June 19th, 1937. *Proceedings of the Geologists' Association* **48**, 316.

Sherlock, R. L. 1947. *British Regional Geology London and the Thames Valley*. Geological Survey and Museum. HMSO, London.

Sherlock, R. L. and Noble, A. H. 1912. On the glacial origin of the Clay-with-flints of Buckinghamshire and on a former course of the Thames. *Quarterly Journal of the Geological Society, London* **68**, 199-212.

Sherlock, R. L. and Noble, A. H. 1922. *The geology of the country around Beaconsfield. Explanation of Sheet 255*. Memoir of the Geological Survey England and Wales. HMSO, London.

Sherlock, R. L. and Pocock, R. W. 1924. *The geology of the country around Hertford. Explanation of Sheet 239*. Memoir of the Geological Survey of Great Britain England and Wales. HMSO, London.

Siesser, W. G., Ward, D. J. and Lord, A. R. 1987. Calcareous nannoplankton biozonation of the Thanetian Stage (Palaeocene) in the type area. *Journal of Micropalaeontology* **6**, 85-102.

Siever, R. 1959. Petrology and geochemistry of silica cementation in some Pennsylvanian sandstones. In: *Silica in sediments*. Society of Economic Palaeontologists and Mineralogists Special Publication **7**, 55-79.

Simpson, B., Blower, T., Craig, R. N. and Wilkinson, W. B. 1989. The engineering implications of rising groundwater levels in the deep aquifer beneath London. *Special Publication* **69**. Construction Industry Research and Information Association, London.

Skelton, P. (ed.) 2003. *The Cretaceous world*. Open University and Cambridge University Press, Cambridge.

Skempton, A. W. 1954. A foundation failure due to clay shrinkage caused by poplar trees. *Proceedings of the Institution of Civil Engineers* **3**, 66-86.

Small, R. J. 1965. The role of spring sapping in the formation of Chalk escarpment valleys. *Southampton Research Series in Geography* **1**, 1-29.

Small, R. J. 1980. The Tertiary geomorphological evolution of south-east England: an alternative interpretation. In: *The shaping of southern England* (ed. Jones, D. K. C.). Institute of British Geographers Special Publication **11**. Academic Press, London, 49-70.

Smith, A. 1992. Geology of the Henlow, Stotfold and Ashwell Districts. *British Geological Survey Technical Report* **WA/92/22**. British Geological Survey, Keyworth.

Smith, A. and Rose, J. 1997. A new find of Quaternary quartzite-rich gravel near Letchworth, Hertfordshire, southeastern England. *Proceedings of the Geologists' Association* **108**, 317-326.

Smith, C. J. 1980. *Ecology of the English Chalk*. Academic Press, London.

Smith, D. B., Wearn, P. L., Richards, H. J. and Rowe, P. C. 1970. Water movement in the unsaturated zone of high and low permeability strata using natural tritium. In: *Isotope hydrology*. International Atomic Energy Agency, Vienna, 73-87.

Smith, H. V. 1992. *Cryptosporidium* and water: a review. *Journal of the Institution of Water and Environmental Management* **6**, 443-451.

Smith, I. F. 1974. The Neolithic. In: *British prehistory: a new outline* (ed. Renfrew, C.). Duckworth, London, 100-136.

Smith, N. J. P. 1985. *Map 1. Pre-Permian geology of the United Kingdom (South) Scale 1:1,000,000. Map 2. Contours on the top of the pre-Permian surface of the United Kingdom (South) Scale 1:1,000,000*. British Geological Survey 150th Anniversary Publication, Department of Energy, London.

Smith, R. A. 1919. Flint implements from the Palaeolithic 'floor' at Whipsnade, Beds. *Proceedings of the Society of Antiquaries*, Series 2, **31**, 39-50.

Smith, R. A. and Dewey, H. 1915. Researches at Rickmansworth: report on excavations made in 1914 on behalf of the British Museum. *Archaeologia* **66**, 195-224.

Smith, W. G. 1894. *Man the primeval savage. His haunts and relics from the hill-tops of Bedfordshire to Blackwall*. Edward Stanford, London.

Smith, W. G. 1904. *Dunstable: its history and surroundings*. London.

Smith, W. G. 1906. Human skeleton of Palaeolithic age. *Man* **6**, 10-11.

Smith, W. G. 1916. Notes on the Palaeolithic floor near Caddington. *Archaeologia* **67**, 49-74.

Soil Survey of England and Wales 1983. *Soil map of England and Wales Scale 1:250,000*. Soil Survey and England and Wales, Harpenden.

Sollas, W. J. 1873a. On the Ventriculidae of the Cambridge Upper Greensand. *Quarterly Journal of the Geological Society, London* **29**, 63-70.

Sollas, W. J. 1873b. On the coprolites of the Upper Greensand Formation, and on flints. *Quarterly Journal of the Geological Society, London* **29**, 76-81.

Sollas, W. J. and Jukes-Browne, A. J. 1873. On the included rock fragments of the Cambridge Upper Greensand. *Quarterly Journal of the Geological Society, London* **29**, 11-16.

Soper, N. J. 1986. The Newer Granite problem: a geotectonic view. *Geological Magazine* **123**, 227-236.

Soper, N. J., Webb, B. C. and Woodcock, N. H. 1987. Late Caledonian (Acadian) transpression in north-west England: timing, geometry and geotectonic significance. *Proceedings of the Yorkshire Geological Society* **46**, 175-192.

Sorby, H. C. 1880. Award of the Lyell Medal to John Evans. *Proceedings of the Geological Society of London* **36**, 30.

Sparks, B. W. and Lewis, W. V. 1957. Escarpment dry valleys near Pegsdon, Hertfordshire. *Proceedings of the Geologists' Association* **68**, 26-38.

Sparks, B. W., West, R. G., Williams, R. B. G. and Ransom, M. 1969. Hoxnian interglacial deposits near Hatfield, Herts. *Proceedings of the Geologists' Association* **80**, 243-267.

Spath, L. F. 1923-1943. A monograph of the Ammonoidea of the Gault, Parts 1-16. *Monograph of the Palaeontographical Society of London*.

Spath, L. F. 1932. Appendix I. Cambridge Greensand Ammonites. In: *The geology of the country near Saffron Walden. Explanation of Sheet 205* (ed. White, H. J. O.). Memoirs of the Geological Survey England and Wales. HMSO, London.

Spence, M. J., Bottrell, S. H., Thornton, S. F., Ricknow, H. H. and Spence, K. H. 2005. Hydrochemical and isotopic effects associated with petroleum fuel degradation pathways in a chalk aquifer. *Journal of Contaminant Hydrology* **79**, 67-88.

Spicer, E. C. 1905. Sarsen stones in a clay pit. *Quarterly Journal of the Geological Society, London* **61**, 39.

Squirrell, H. C. 1974. The sand and gravel resources of the country around Gerrards Cross, Buckinghamshire. Description of parts of 1:25,000 resource sheets SU 98, SU 99, TQ 08 and TQ 09. *Institute of Geological Sciences Report* **74/14**. HMSO, London.

Stageman, F. D. 1983. A Neolithic axe from Redbourn. *Hertfordshire Archaeology* **1**, 119-120.

Stainton, B. 1995. Field work by the Chess Valley Archaeological and Historical Society (CVAHS) in the Buckinghamshire Chilterns. In: *Chiltern archaeology recent work a handbook for the next decade* (ed. Holgate, R.). Book Castle, Dunstable, 124-130.

Stead, I. M. and Rigby, V. 1986. *Baldock: the excavation of a Roman and pre-Roman settlement, 1968-72.* Britannia Monograph **7**.

Stead, I. M. and Rigby, V. 1989. *Verulamium: the King Harry Lane site.* English Heritage Archaeological Report **12**.

Stephens, C. G. 1966. Origin of silcretes in central Australia. *Nature* **209**, 497.

Stephens, C. G. 1971. Laterite and silcrete in Australia: a study of the genetic relationships of laterite and silcrete and their companion materials, and their collective significance in the weathered mantle, soils, relief and drainage of the Australian continent. *Geoderma* **5**, 5-52.

Stevenson, M. G. 1987. Bronze Age funerary deposits in the Royston area. *Hertfordshire Archaeology* **9**, 8-14.

Stone, P. M. and Walling, D. E. 1997. Particle size selectivity considerations in suspended sediment budget investigations. *Water, Air and Soil Pollution* **99**, 64-70.

Stoneley, R. 1982. The structural development of the Wessex Basin. *Journal of the Geological Society, London* **139**, 543-554.

Strahan, A. 1916. On a deep boring for coal near Little Missenden in Buckinghamshire. *Summary of Progress of the Geological Survey of Great Britain for 1915*, 43-46.

Strahler, A. N. 1958. Dimensional analysis applied to fluvially eroded landforms. *Bulletin of the Geological Society of America* **69**, 279-300.

Stuart, A. J. 1974. Pleistocene history of the British vertebrate fauna. *Biological Reviews* 49, 225-266.

Stuart, M. E., Chilton, P. J., Kinniburgh, D. G. and Cooper, D. M. 2007. Screening for long-term trends in groundwater nitrate monitoring data. *Quarterly Journal of Engineering Geology* **40**, 361-376.

Stuiver, M. and Brazunias, T. 1993. Sun, ocean, climate and atmospheric $^{14}CO_2$: an evaluation of causal and spectral relationships. *The Holocene* **3**, 289-305.

Sturdy, R. G., Allen, R. H., Bullock, P., Catt, J. A. and Greenfield, S. 1979. Paleosols developed on Chalky Boulder Clay in Essex. *Journal of Soil Science* **30**, 117-137.

Sumbler, M. G. 1995. The terraces of the rivers Thame and Thames and their bearing on the chronology of glaciation in central and eastern England. *Proceedings of the Geologists' Association* **106**, 93-106.

Sumbler, M. G. 1996. *British regional geology London and Thames Valley* (4th edition). HMSO, London.

Sumbler, M. G. 2001. The Moreton Drift: a further clue to glacial chronology in central England. *Proceedings of the Geologists' Association* **112**, 13-27.

Summerfield, M. A. 1979. Origin and palaeoenvironmental interpretation of sarsens. *Nature* **281**, 137-139.

Summerfield, M. A. 1983a. Silcrete. In: *Chemical sediments and geomorphology* (eds Goudie, A. S. and Pye, K.). Academic Press, London, 59-91.

Summerfield, M. A. 1983b. Geochemistry of weathering profile silcretes, southern Cape Province, South Africa. In: *Residual deposits: surface related weathering products and materials* (ed. Wilson, R. C. L.). Geological Society, London, Special Publication **11**, 167-178.

Summerfield, M. A. 1984. Isovolumetric weathering and silcrete formation, southern Cape Province, South Africa. *Earth Surface Processes and Landforms* **9**, 135-141.

Summerfield, M. A. and Goudie, A. S. 1980. The sarsens of southern England: their palaeoenvironmental interpretation with reference to other silcretes. In: *The shaping of southern England* (ed. Jones, D. K. C.).

Institute of British Geographers Special Publication **11**, 71-100.

Sutcliffe, A. J. and Kowalski, K. 1976. Pleistocene rodents of the British Isles. *Bulletin of the British Museum (Natural History), Zoology* **27/2**, 31-147.

T

Tebbutt, C. F. 1932. Early Iron Age settlement on Jack's Hill, Great Wymondley, Herts. *Proceedings of the Prehistoric Society of East Anglia* **31**, 371-374.

Thiry, M. and Milnes, A. R. 1991. Pedogenic and groundwater silcretes at Stuart Creek opal field, South Australia. *Journal of Sedimentary Petrology* **61**, 111-127.

Thomas, A. R. A. 2007. An integrated grain-size and heavy mineral analysis of the Palaeocene strata of the London Basin. In: *Heavy minerals in use* (eds Mange, M. A. and Wright, D. T.), *Developments in Sedimentology* 58, 151-188. Elsevier, Amsterdam.

Thomas, M. F. 1994. *Geomorphology in the tropics: a study of weathering and denudation in low latitudes.* J. Wiley, Chichester.

Thomasson, A. J. 1961. Some aspects of the drift deposits and geomorphology of south-east Hertfordshire. *Proceedings of the Geologists' Association* **72**, 287-302.

Thomasson, A. J. 1969. *Soils of the Saffron Walden district. A reconnaissance survey.* Soil Survey Special Survey **2**. Agricultural Research Council, Harpenden.

Thomasson, A. J. and Avery, B. W. 1963. The soils of Hertfordshire. *Transactions of the Hertfordshire Natural History Society and Field Club* **25**, Part 6, 247-263.

Thomasson, A. J. and Avery, B. W. 1970. *The soils of Hertfordshire.* Soil Survey Special Survey **3**. Agricultural Research Council, Harpenden.

Thompson, I. 2005. Verlamion in the late pre-Roman Iron Age. In: *Alban's buried towns. An assessment of St Albans' archaeology up to AD 1600* (eds Niblett, R. and Thompson, I.). Oxbow Books, Oxford, 23-40.

Thorez, J., Bullock, P., Catt, J. A. and Weir, A. H. 1971. The petrography and origin of deposits filling solution pipes in the Chalk near South Mimms, Hertfordshire. *Geological Magazine* **108**, 413-423.

Tinsley, H. M. and Cosgrove, T. P. 1991. The peat deposits at Ridlin's Mire, Stevenage, Hertfordshire. *Transactions of the Hertfordshire Natural History Society and Field Club* **31**, 53-57.

Tomlinson, M. E. 1929. The drifts of the Stour-Evenlode watershed and their extension into the valleys of the Warwickshire Stour and upper Evenlode. *Proceedings of the Birmingham Natural History and Philosophical Society* **15**, 157-196.

Toombs, H. A. 1935. Field meeting at Leighton Buzzard, Bedfordshire. Sunday, September 30th, 1934. *Proceedings of the Geologists' Association* **46**, 432-436.

Topley, W. 1875. *The geology of the Weald.* Memoirs of the Geological Survey of Great Britain. HMSO, London.

Torrens, H. 2003. *Memoirs of William Smith, LL. D. 1844 by John Phillips.* Reprinted with *An introduction to the life and times of William Smith* and *The Geological Society William Smith Lecture 2000.* Bath Royal Literary and Scientific Institution, Bath.

Torsvik, T. H., Smethurst, M. A., Meert, J. G., Van der Voo, R., McKerrow, W. S., Brasier, M. D., Sturt, B. A. and Walderhaug, H. J. 1996. Continental break-up and collision in the Neoproterozoic and Palaeozoic – a tale of Balthica and Laurentia. *Earth-Science Reviews* **40**, 229-258.

Towler, P. A., Blakey, N. C., Irving, J. E., Clark, L., Maris, P. J., Baxter, K. M. and Macdonald, R. M. 1985. A study of the bacteria of the Chalk aquifer and the effect of landfill contamination at a site in eastern England. In: *Hydrogeology in the service of man.* Memoirs of the 18th Congress of the International Association of Hydrogeologists **3**, 84-87.

Tracey, S., Donovan, S. K., Clements, D., Jeffrey, P., Cooper, J., Rye, P. and Hensley, C. 2002. Temporary exposures of the Eocene London Clay Formation at Highgate, north London: rediscovery of a fossiliferous horizon 'lost' since the nineteenth century. *Proceedings of the Geologists' Association* **113**, 319-331.

Trümpy, R. 1973. The timing of orogenic events in the Central Alps. In: *Gravity and tectonics* (eds de Jong, K. A. and Scholten, R.). Wiley, New York, pp. 229-251.

Tucker, R. D. and Pharoah, T. C. 1991. U-Pb zircon ages for Late Precambrian igneous rocks in southern Britain. *Journal of the Geological Society, London* **148**, 435-443.

Turbitt, T. (ed.) 1987. *Bulletin of British earthquakes 1985.* Global Seismology Report **303**. British Geological Survey, Edinburgh.

Turbitt, T. (ed.) 1990. *Bulletin of British earthquakes 1988.* British Geological Survey Technical Report Global Seismology Series **WL/90/3**. British Geological Survey, Edinburgh.

Turbitt, T. (ed.) 1992. *Bulletin of British earthquakes 1990.* British Geological Survey Technical Report Global Seismology Series **WL/91/34**. British Geological Survey, Edinburgh.

Turner, C. 1970. The Middle Pleistocene deposits at Mark's Tey, Essex. *Philosophical Transactions of the Royal Society of London* **B257**, 373-440.

Turner, C. 1983. Nettlebed. In: *The Diversion of the Thames.* Field Guide (ed. Rose, J.). Quaternary Research Association, Cambridge, 66-68.

Turner, C. and West, R. G. 1968. The subdivision and zonation of interglacial periods. *Eiszeitalter und Gegenwart* **19**, 93-101.

Twidale, C. R. and Hutton, J. T. 1986. Silcrete as a palaeoclimatic indicator: discussion. *Palaeogeography, Palaeoclimatology, Palaeoecology* **52**, 351-353.

Tzedakis, P. C., Andrieu, V., de Beaulieu, J. -L. and 9 others 2001. Establishing a terrestrial chronological framework as a basis for biostratigraphical comparisons. *Earth Science Reviews* **20**, 1583-1592.

U

Ullyott, J. S. and Nash, D. J. 2006. Micromorphology and geochemistry of groundwater silcretes in the eastern South Downs, UK. *Sedimentology* **53**, 387-412.

Ullyott, J. S., Nash, D. J. and Shaw, P. A. 1998. Recent advances in silcrete research and their implications for the origin and palaeoenvironmental significance of sarsens. *Proceedings of the Geologists' Association* **109**, 255-270.

Ullyott, J. S., Wightman, C. A. and Nash, D. J. 2000. Field meeting: landscape evolution of the eastern South Downs, with particular reference to sarsens and Quaternary deposits, Saturday, 17 October, 1998. *Proceedings of the Geologists' Association* **111**, 91-96.

Underwood, G. 1968. *Pattern of the past*. Museum Press, London.

V

Vandenberghe, N., Laga, P., Steurbaut, E., Hardenbol, J. and Vail, P. R. 1998. Tertiary sequence stratigraphy at the southern border of the North Sea Basin in Belgium. In: *Sequence stratigraphy of Mesozoic and Cenozoic European basins* (eds de Graciansky, P. -C., Hardenbol, J., Vail, P. R. and Jacquin, J.). SEPM Special Publication **60**, 119-154.

Van Loon, A. J., Botterweck, A. A., Goldbohm, R. A., Brants, H. A., van Klaveren, J. D. and van den Brandt, P. A. 1998. Intake of nitrate and nitrite and the risk of gastric cancer: a prospective cohort study. *British Journal of Cancer* **78**, 129-135.

Vera, F. W. M. 2004. *Grazing ecology and forest history*. CABI Publishing, Wallingford.

W

Walder, P. S. 1964. Mineralogy of the Eocene sediments in the Isle of Wight. *Proceedings of the Geologists' Association* **75**, 291-394.

Walker, A. B. (ed.) 1995. *Bulletin of British earthquakes 1994*. British Geological Survey Technical Report Global Seismology Series **WL/95/04**. British Geological Survey, Edinburgh.

Walker, A. B. (ed.) 1997. *Bulletin of British earthquakes 1996*. British Geological Survey Technical Report Global Seismology Series **WL/97/03**. British Geological Survey, Edinburgh.

Walker, A. B. (ed.) 2000. *Bulletin of British earthquakes 1999*. British Geological Survey Technical Report Global Seismology and Geomagnetism Group **WL/00/01**. British Geological Survey, Edinburgh.

Walker, H. 1871. On the glacial drifts of north London. *Proceedings of the Geologists' Association* **2**, 289-298.

Walker, M. 2005. *Quaternary dating methods. An Introduction*. J. Wiley & Sons, Chichester.

Walker, M., Johnsen, S., Rasmussen, S. O. and 16 others 2009. Formal definition and dating of the GSSP (Global Stratotype Section and Point) for the base of the Holocene using the Greenland NGRIP ice core, and selected auxiliary records. *Journal of Quaternary Science* **24**, 3-17.

Walsh, P. T. and Ockenden, A. C. 1982. Hydrogeological observations at the Water End swallow hole complex, North Mimms, Hertfordshire. *Cave Science* **9**, 184-194.

Ward, D. J. 1975. Report of field meetings to Radlett, Herts. April 5th, 1973 and February 23rd, 1975. *Tertiary Times* **2**, 154-156.

Ward, W. H., Burland, J. B. and Gallois, R. W. 1968. Geotechnical assessment of a site at Mundford, Norfolk, for a large proton accelerator. *Geotechnique* **18**, 399-431.

Warington, R. 1887. A contribution to the study of well waters. A report of experiments made in the Rothamsted Laboratory. *Journal of the Chemical Society* **51**, 500-552.

Warren, B. 1982. Gazetteer. *Enfield Archaeological Society Newsletter* **85**.

Warren, B. 2006. Fossil gastropods and lamellibranchs from the London Clay exposed in the Potters Bar railway tunnel, 1848-1850. *Transactions of the Hertfordshire Natural History Society and Field Club* **38**, 197-203.

Warren, B. 2008. Local history – Ponsbourne Tunnel. *Update - The Newsletter of Northaw and Cuffley Parish Council* **33**, 3.

Warren, S. H. 1912. On a late glacial stage in the valley of the River Lea, subsequent to the epoch of river drift man. *Quarterly Journal of the Geological Society, London* **68**, 213-251.

Warren, S. H. 1916. Further observations on the Late Glacial or Ponder's End Stage of the Lea Valley. *Quarterly Journal of the Geological Society, London* **71**, 164-182.

Warren, S. H. 1923. The Late-glacial Stage of the Lea Valley (third report). *Quarterly Journal of the Geological Society, London* **79**, 603-605.

Warren, S. H. 1938. The correlation of the Lea Valley arctic beds. *Proceedings of the Prehistoric Society* **4**, 328-329.

Warren, S. H. 1954. The conglomerate track. Being comments on two papers by E. A. and E. L. Rudge. *Essex Naturalist* **29**, 176-177.

Warren, S. H., Clark, J. G. D., Godwin, H., Godwin, M. E. and Macfadyen, W. A. 1934. An early Mesolithic site at Broxbourne sealed under Boreal peat. *Journal of the Royal Anthropological Institute of Great Britain and Ireland* **64**, 101-128.

Water Resources Board 1972. *The hydrogeology of the London Basin*. Water Resources Board, Reading.

Watkins, A. 1925. *The old straight track*. Methuen, London.

Waton, P. V. 1982. Land snail evidence of post-glacial environmental change on the Hertfordshire chalklands. *Transactions of the Hertfordshire Natural History Society and Field Club* **28**, Part 6, 63-75.

Watson, J. 1911. *British and foreign building stones*. Cambridge University Press, Cambridge.

Watts, A. B., McKerrow, W. S. and Fielding, E. 2000. Lithospheric flexure, uplift, and landscape evolution in south-central England. *Journal of the Geological Society, London* **157**, 1169-1177.

Watts, A. B., McKerrow, W. S. and Richards, K. 2005. Localized Quaternary uplift of south-central England.

Journal of the Geological Society, London **162**, 13-24.

Waugh, B. 1970. Petrology, provenance and silica diagenesis of the Penrith Sandstone (Lower Permian) of northwest England. *Journal of Sedimentary Petrology* **40**, 1226-1240.

Waugh, H. 1968a. The pottery. In: Ivinghoe Beacon excavations 1963-65 (eds Cotton, M. A. and Frere, S. S.). *Records of Buckinghamshire* **18**, 219-234.

Waugh, H. 1968b. Pottery from Pitstone Hill. In: Ivinghoe Beacon excavations 1963-65 (eds Cotton, M. A. and Frere, S. S.). *Records of Buckinghamshire* **18**, 235-249.

Weir, A. H. and Catt, J. A. 1969. The mineralogy of Palaeogene sediments in northeast Kent (Great Britain). *Sedimentary Geology* **3**, 17-33.

Weir, A. H., Catt, J. A. and Ormerod, E. C. 1969. The mineralogy of Broadbalk soils. *Rothamsted Experimental Station Report* **1968**, Part 2, 81-89.

Wessex Archaeology 1996. *The Thames Valley and Warwickshire Avon. The English Rivers Palaeolithic Project Report 1 1994-1995*. Trust for Wessex Archaeology Limited and English Heritage, Salisbury.

West, R. G. 1956. The Quaternary deposits at Hoxne, Suffolk. *Philosophical Transactions of the Royal Society of London* **B239**, 265-356.

West, R. G. 1961. Vegetational history of the Early Pleistocene of the Royal Society borehole at Ludham, Norfolk. *Proceedings of the Royal Society of London* **B155**, 437-453.

West, R. G. 1980. Pleistocene forest history in East Anglia. *New Phytologist* **85**, 571-622.

West, R. G. and Donner, J. J. 1956. The glaciations of East Anglia and the east Midlands: a differentiation based on stone orientation measurements of the tills. *Quarterly Journal of the Geological Society, London* **112**, 69-91.

West, S. 1993. Friar's Wash A93. *St Albans Museums Evaluation Report*.

West, S. 2005. A Mesolithic and later prehistoric site in Redbourn. *Hertfordshire Archaeology* **14**, 1-2.

West, S. 2008. A multi-period landscape at Aldwickbury Golf Course, near Harpenden. *Hertfordshire Archaeology and History* **15**, 5-20.

Westaway, R. 2009. Quaternary vertical crustal motion and drainage evolution in East Anglia and adjoining parts of southern England: chronology of the Ingham River terrace deposits. *Boreas* **38**, 261-284.

Westaway, R., Maddy, D. and Bridgland, D. 2002. Flow in the lower continental crust as a mechanism for the Quaternary uplift of south-east England: constraints from the Thames terrace record. *Quaternary Science Reviews* **21**, 559-603.

Westell, W. P. 1926. Roman and pre-Roman antiquities in Letchworth Museum. *Transactions of the East Hertfordshire Archaeological Society* **7**, 258-281.

Westerby, E. 1931. Maglemose harpoons from Royston and the Thames. *Ymer*, 45-46.

Weston, A. J. S. 2006. An earthquake impact scenario for the Colchester earthquake of 1884. *Essex Naturalist* (New Series) **23**, 97-104.

Wheeler, R. E. M. and Wheeler, T. V. 1936. *Verulamium,*

a *Belgic and two Roman cities*. Research Report of the Society of Antiquaries, London **11**.

Whitaker, W. 1866. On the "Lower London Tertiaries" of Kent. *Quarterly Journal of the Geological Society, London* **22**, 404-435.

Whitaker, W. 1872. *Geology of the London Basin, Part 1: The Chalk and the Eocene Beds of the southern and western tracts*. Memoirs of the Geological Survey of England and Wales, **4**. HMSO, London.

Whitaker, W. 1886. Some Hertfordshire well sections. *Transactions of the Hertfordshire Natural History Society and Field Club* **3**, 173-180.

Whitaker, W. 1889. *The Geology of London and of part of the Thames Valley. Explanation of sheets 1, 2 and 7* (2 Volumes). Memoirs of the Geological Survey England and Wales. HMSO, London.

Whitaker, W. 1901. *Guide to the geology of London and the neighbourhood* (6th edition). Memoirs of the Geological Survey England and Wales. HMSO, London.

Whitaker, W. 1908. *The water supply of Kent, with records of sinkings and borings*. Memoirs of the Geological Survey, England and Wales. HMSO, London.

Whitaker, W. 1909. On the finding of Silurian beds in Kent. *Report of the British Association for the Advancement of Science, Dublin* **1908**, 711.

Whitaker, W. 1912. *The water supply of Surrey from underground sources, with records of sinkings and borings*. Memoirs of the Geological Survey, England and Wales. HMSO, London.

Whitaker, W. 1916. Report of excursions to the North Mymms swallow holes. *Proceedings of the Geologists' Association* **27**, 59-60.

Whitaker, W. 1921. *The water supply of Buckinghamshire and Hertfordshire from underground sources*. Memoirs of the Geological Survey, England and Wales. HMSO, London.

Whitaker, W. and Hopkinson, J. 1872. Excursion to Watford. April 13th, 1872. *Proceedings of the Geologists' Association* **3**, 65-66.

Whitaker, W. and Hopkinson, J. 1900. Excursion to Rickmansworth and Harefield. Saturday, June 10th, 1899. *Proceedings of the Geologists' Association* **16**, 244-246.

Whitaker, W., Penning, W. H., Dalton, W. H. and Bennett, F. J. 1878. *The geology of the N. W. part of Essex and the N. E. part of Herts. with parts of Cambridgeshire and Suffolk. Explanation of Sheet 47 of the map (one-inch) of the Geological Survey of England and Wales*. Memoirs of the Geological Survey England and Wales. HMSO, London.

Whitaker, W., Thresh, J. C. and Mill, H. R. 1916. *The water supply of Essex from underground sources*. Memoirs of the Geological Survey, England and Wales. HMSO, London.

White, E. I. 1923. Notes on a new species of 'Terebelloid' and other phenomena in the Great Pit at Harefield, Middlesex. With report of excursion, Saturday, May 13th, 1922. *Proceedings of the Geologists' Association* **34**, 43-46.

White, H. J. O. 1906. On the occurrence of quartzose gravel in the Reading Beds at Lane End, Bucks. *Proceedings of the Geologists' Association* **29**, 371-377.

White, H. J. O. 1907. *The geology of the country around Hungerford and Newbury*. Memoir of the Geological Survey of Great Britain, England and Wales. HMSO, London.

White, H. J. O. 1932. *The geology of the country near Saffron Walden*. Memoirs of the Geological Survey, England and Wales. HMSO, London.

White, H. J. O. and Edmunds, F. H. 1932. *The geology of the country near Saffron Walden*. Memoir of the Geological Survey of Great Britain, Sheet 205 (England and Wales). HMSO, London.

White, M. J. 1997. The earlier Palaeolithic occupation of the Chilterns (southern England): re-assessing the sites of Worthington G. Smith. *Antiquity* **71**, 912-931.

White, N. and Lovell, B. 1997. Measuring the pulse of a plume with the sedimentary record. *Nature* **387**, 888-891.

Whitelaw, J. W. 1990. *Hertfordshire churches*. Oldcastle Books, Harpenden.

Whiteman, C. A. 1992. The palaeogeography and correlation of pre-Anglian-Glaciation terraces of the River Thames in Essex and the London Basin. *Proceedings of the Geologists' Association* **103**, 37-56.

Whiteman, C. A. 1998. Preliminary report of new evidence for glaciation at Marsworth, Buckinghamshire. *Quaternary Newsletter* **85**, 1-8.

Whiteman, C. A. and Bridgland, D. R. 1995. Hornchurch railway cutting (TQ 547874). In: *The Quaternary of the lower reaches of the Thames, Field Guide* (eds. Bridgland, D. R., Allen, P. and Haggart, B. A.). Quaternary Research Association, Durham, 107-116.

Whiteman, C. A. and Rose, J. 1992. Thames river sediments of the British Early and Middle Pleistocene. *Quaternary Science Reviews* **11**, 363-375.

Whitmore, A. P., Bradbury, N. J. and Johnston, P. A. 1992. Potential contribution of ploughed grassland to nitrate leaching. *Agriculture, Ecosystems and Environment* **39**, 221-233.

Whittaker, A. 1985. *Atlas of onshore sedimentary basins in England and Wales: Post-Carboniferous tectonics and stratigraphy*. Blackie, Glasgow.

Whittle, A. 1980. Two Neolithics? *Current Archaeology* **70**, 329-334.

Widdowson, F. W., Penny, A., Darby, R. J., Bird, E. and Hewitt, M. V. 1987. Amounts of NO_3-N and NH_4-N in soil, from autumn to spring, under winter wheat and their relation to soil type, sowing date, previous crop and N uptake at Rothamsted, Woburn and Saxmundham, 1979-1985. *Journal of Agricultural Science, Cambridge* **108**, 73-95.

Wiggs, R. J. 1943. The year's palaeontology. *Journal of the Letchworth Natural History Society* **3**, 9.

Wiggs, R. J. 1944. The year's palaeontology. *Journal of the Letchworth Natural History Society* **4**, 17-18.

Wiggs, R. J. 1945. The year's palaeontology. *Journal of the Letchworth Natural History Society* **5**, 4-5.

Wilding, L. P. and Drees, L. R. 1971. Biogenic opal in Ohio soils. *Proceedings of the Soil Science Society of America* **35**, 1004-1010.

Wilkerson, J. C. and Cra'ster, M. D. 1959. Excavations at Whiteley Hill, Barley, Herts. *Proceedings of the Cambridge Antiquarian Society* **52**, 2-5.

Wilkinson, I. P. 1988. Ostracoda across the Albian/Cenomanian boundary in Cambridgeshire and western Suffolk, eastern England. In: *Evolutionary biology of Ostracoda, its fundamentals and applications* (eds Hanai, T., Ikeya, N. and Ishizaki, K.). *Developments in Palaeontology and Stratigraphy* **11**, 1229-1244.

Wilkinson, I. P. 1990a. The biostratigraphical application of Ostracoda to the Albian of eastern England. *Courier Forschungsinstitut Senckenberg* **123**, 239-258.

Wilkinson, I. P. 1990b. Foraminifera from the Anstey Chalk quarry. *British Geological Survey Technical Report* **WH/90/170R**.

Wilkinson, I. P. and Morter, A. A. 1981. The biostratigraphical zonation of the East Anglian Gault by Ostracoda. In: *Microfossils from Recent and fossil shelf seas* (eds Neale, J. W. and Brasier, M. D.). Ellis Horwood, Chichester, 163-176.

Wilkinson, W. B. and Brassington, F. C. 1991. Rising groundwater levels – an international problem. In: *Applied groundwater hydrology a British perspective* (eds Downing, R. A. and Wilkinson, W. B.). Clarendon Press, Oxford, 35-53.

Williams, A. H. 1918. Excursion to St Albans, Tyttenhanger and Hill End. Saturday, July 20th, 1918. *Proceedings of the Geologists' Association* **29**, 149.

Williams, A. H. 1921. Excursion to Tyttenhanger, Hill End, New Barns Mill Pit and St Albans. *Proceedings of the Geologists' Association* **32**, 51.

Williams, G. M., Young, C. P. and Robinson, H. D. 1991. Landfill disposal of wastes. In: *Applied groundwater hydrology* (eds Downing, R. A. and Wilkinson, W. B.). Clarendon Press, Oxford, 114-133.

Williamson, T. 1998. The Scole-Dickleburgh field system revisited. *Landscape History* **20**, 19-28.

Williamson, T. 2007. The character of Hertfordshire's parks and gardens. In: *Hertfordshire garden history a miscellany* (ed. Rowe, A.). Hertfordshire Publications, University of Hertfordshire Press, Hatfield, 1-25.

Williamson, T. and Bellamy, L. 1983. *Ley lines in question*. The Windmill Press, Tadworth, Surrey.

Winchester, A. J. L. 2000. *Discovering parish boundaries*. Shire Publications, Princes Risborough.

Wingfield, R. T. R. 1990. The origin of major incisions within the Pleistocene deposits of the North Sea. *Marine Geology* **91**, 31-52.

Wintle, A. G. 1981. Thermoluminescence dating of loesses in southern England. *Nature* **289**, 479-480.

Wishart, D. 1978. *Clustan User Manual* (3rd edition). Inter-University/Research Councils Series Report 47. Program Library Unit, Regional Computing Centre, Edinburgh.

Withers, P. J. A. and Jarvis, S. C. 1998. Mitigation options for diffuse phosphorus loss to water. *Soil Use and Management* **14**, 186-192.

Withers, P. J. A., Edwards, A. C. and Foy, R. H. 2001. Phosphorus cycling in UK agriculture and implications for phosphorus loss from soil. *Soil Use and Management* **17**, 139-149.

Wittering, W. O. 1968. Exploring a denehole. *Hertfordshire Countryside* **23**, No. 112, 34-35.

Wood, J. M. 1910. Notes on Chadwell Spring. *Proceedings of the Geologists' Association* **21**, 247-248.

Wood, R. D. 1950. Stability and zonation of Characeae. *Ecology* **31**, 642-647.

Woodcock, N. H. and Pharoah, T. C. 1993. Silurian facies beneath East Anglia. *Geological Magazine* **130**, 681-690.

Woodland, A. W. 1945. Water supply from underground sources of the Cambridge-Ipswich district. Part VIII. Well catalogues for one-inch sheets 239 (Hertford) and 240 (Epping). *Geological Survey Wartime Pamphlet* **20**. HMSO, London.

Woodland, A. W. 1946. Water supply from underground sources of Cambridge-Ipswich District. Part X. General discussion. *Geological Survey Wartime Pamphlet* **20**. HMSO, London. .

Woodland, A. W. 1970. The buried tunnel valleys of East Anglia. *Proceedings of the Yorkshire Geological Society* **37**, 521-578.

Woods, H. 1912. *A monograph of the Cretaceous Lamellibranchia of England, Volume 2, Part 8: Inoceramus.* Monograph of the Palaeontographical Society, London, 285-340.

Woods, M. A., Wilkinson, I. P. and Hopson, P. M. 1995. The stratigraphy of the Gault Formation (Middle and Upper Albian) in the BGS Arlesey Borehole, Bedfordshire. *Proceedings of the Geologists' Association* **106**, 271-280.

Woodward, H. B. 1889. Excursion to Whetstone and Finchley. Saturday, April 23rd, 1887. *Proceedings of the Geologists' Association* **10**, 145-147.

Woodward, H. B. 1903a. On some disturbances of the Chalk near Royston (Hertfordshire). *Quarterly Journal of the Geological Society, London* **59**, 362-374.

Woodward, H. B. 1903b. Excursion to Royston, Hertfordshire. May 16th, 1903. *Proceedings of the Geologists' Association* **18**, 166-170.

Woodward, H. B. 1907. *The history of the Geological Society of London.* Geological Society, London.

Woodward, H. B. and Herries, R. S. 1905. Excursion to the Chilterns. *Proceedings of the Geologists' Association* **19**, 147-149.

Woodworth, P. L., Tsimplis, M. N., Flather, R. A. and Shennan, I. 1999. A review of the trends observed in British Isles mean sea level data measured by tide gauges. *Geophysical Journal International* **136**, 651-670.

Wooldridge, S. W. 1921. Evidence for folding in the Tertiary and Cretaceous rocks near South Mimms and Ridge Hill. With report of excursion, May 28th, 1920. *Proceedings of the Geologists' Association* **32**, 227-231.

Wooldridge, S. W. 1923. The minor structures of the London Basin. *Proceedings of the Geologists' Association* **34**, 175-190.

Wooldridge, S. W. 1926. The structural evolution of the London Basin. *Proceedings of the Geologists' Association* **37**, 162-196.

Wooldridge, S. W. 1927. The Pliocene history of the London Basin. *Proceedings of the Geologists' Association* **38**, 49-132.

Wooldridge, S. W. 1928. Note on the geology of the Ayot Eocene outlier. With report of excursion, April 24th, 1926. *Proceedings of the Geologists' Association* **39**, 353-368.

Wooldridge, S. W. 1938. The glaciation of the London Basin, and the evolution of the Lower Thames drainage system. *Quarterly Journal of the Geological Society, London* **94**, 627-667.

Wooldridge, S. W. 1953. Some marginal drainage features of the chalky boulder clay ice sheet in Hertfordshire. *Proceedings of the Geologists' Association* **64**, 208-231.

Wooldridge, S. W. 1960. The Pleistocene succession in the London Basin. *Proceedings of the Geologists' Association* **71**, 113-129.

Wooldridge, S. W. and Cornwall, I. W. 1964. A contribution to a new datum for the pre-history of the Thames valley. *Bulletin of the Institute of Archaeology, University of London* **4**, 223-232.

Wooldridge, S. W. and Ewing, C. J. C. 1935. The Eocene and Pliocene deposits of Lane End, Buckinghamshire. *Quarterly Journal of the Geological Society, London* **91**, 293-317.

Wooldridge, S. W. and Gill, D. M. C. 1925. The Reading Beds of Lane End, Bucks. *Proceedings of the Geologists' Association* **36**, 146-173.

Wooldridge, S. W. and Henderson, H. C. K. 1955. Some aspects of the physiography of the eastern part of the London Basin. *Transactions of the Institute of British Geographers* **21**, 19-31.

Wooldridge, S. W. and Kirkaldy, J. F. 1937. The geology of the Mimms Valley. Together with report of the field meeting held on July 10th, 1936. *Proceedings of the Geologists' Association* **48**, 307-315.

Wooldridge, S. W. and Linton, D. L. 1955. *Structure, surface and drainage in south-east England* (2nd edition). G. Philip and Sons, London.

Wooldridge, S. W. and Smetham, D. J. 1931. The glacial drifts of Essex and Hertfordshire and their bearing upon the agricultural and historical geography of the region. *Geographical Journal* **78**, 243-265.

Wooldridge, S. W. and Wrigley, A. 1929. Excursion to Northwood and Harefield. Saturday, September 9th, 1929. *Proceedings of the Geologists' Association* **40**, 373-375.

Woolley, A. R., Bishop, A. C., Harrison, R. J. and Kinnes, I. A. 1979. European Neolithic jade implements: a preliminary mineralogical and typological study. In: *Stone axe studies: archaeological, petrological, experimental and ethnographic* (eds Clough, T. H. McK. and Cummins, W. A.). Council for British Archaeology Research Report **23**, 90-96.

World Health Organization 2004. *Guidelines for drinking water quality* (3rd edition, 3 volumes). World Health Organization, Geneva.

Worsley, P. 1987. Permafrost stratigraphy in Britain – a first approximation. In: *Periglacial processes and landforms in Britain and Ireland* (ed. Boardman, J.). Cambridge University Press, Cambridge, 89-99.

Worssam, B. C. 1963. *Geology of the country around Maidstone. Explanation of one-inch Geological Sheet 288, New Series.* Memoirs of the Geological Survey of Great

Britain England and Wales. HMSO, London.

Worssam, B. C. and Taylor, J. H. 1969. *Geology of the country around Cambridge. Explanation of One-inch Geological Sheet 188, New Series*. Memoirs of the Geological Survey of Great Britain England and Wales. HMSO, London.

Wray, D. S. 1995. Origin of clay-rich beds in Turonian chalks from Lower Saxony, Germany – a rare earth element study. *Chemical Geology* **119**, 161-173.

Wray, D. S. 1999. Identification and long-range correlation of bentonites in Turonian-Coniacian (Upper Cretaceous) chalks of northwest Europe. *Geological Magazine* **136**, 361-371.

Wray, D. S. and Gale, A. S. 1993. Geochemical correlation of marl bands in Turonian chalks of the Anglo-Paris Basin. In: *High resolution stratigraphy* (eds Hailwood, E. A. and Kidd, R. B.). Geological Society, London, Special Publication **70**, 211-226.

Wray, D. S. and Wood, C. J. 1995. Geochemical identification and correlation of tuff layers in Lower Saxony, Germany. *Berliner geowissenschaftliche Abhandlungen Reihe E* **16**(1), 215-226.

Wray, D. S. and Wood, C. J. 1998. Distinction between detrital and volcanogenic clay-rich beds in Turonian-Coniacian chalks of eastern England. *Proceedings of the Yorkshire Geological Society* **52**, 95-105.

Wright, C. W. 1979. The ammonites of the English Chalk Rock (Upper Turonian). *Bulletin of the British Museum (Natural History), Geology Series* **31**, 281-332.

Wright, C. W. and Kennedy, W. J. 1987. Ammonites. In: *Fossils of the Chalk* (ed. Smith, A. B.). Palaeontological Association (London) Field Guides to Fossils **2**, 141-182.

Wymer, J. J. 1956. Palaeoliths from the gravel of the ancient channel between Caversham and Henley at Highlands, near Henley. *Proceedings of the Prehistoric Society* **22**, 29-36.

Wymer, J. J. 1968. *Lower Palaeolithic archaeology in Britain, as represented by the Thames valley*. John Baker, London.

Wymer, J. J. (ed.) 1977. Gazetteer of Mesolithic sites in England and Wales. *Council for British Archaeology Research Report* **20**.

Wymer, J. J. 1980. The excavation of the Acheulian site at Gaddesden Row. *Bedfordshire Archaeological Journal* **14**, 2-4.

Wymer, J. J. 1982. *The Palaeolithic age*. Croom Helm, London.

Wymer, J. 1985. *The Palaeolithic sites of East Anglia*. Geo Books, Norwich.

Wyton, J., Bown, P. and Bailey, H. W. 2007. Palaeoecological trends in Turonian – Coniacian (Late Cretaceous) calcareous nannofossils from Chalk Group sections, SE England. *Journal of Nannoplankton Research* **29**, 31-37.

Y

Yates, D. T. 1999. Bronze Age field systems in the Thames valley. *Oxford Journal of Archaeology* **18**, 157-169.

Yiou, P., Fuhrer, K., Meeker, L. D., Jouzel, J., Johnsen, J. and Mayewski, P. 1997. Palaeoclimate variability inferred from the spectral analysis of Greenland and Antarctic ice cores. *Journal of Geophysical Research* **102**, 26441-26454.

Young, A. 1804. *General view of the agriculture of Hertfordshire drawn up for the consideration of the Board of Agriculture and Internal Improvement*. G. & W. Nicol, London. Reprinted 1813 by Sherwood, Neely and Jones, London, and 1971 by David and Charles, Newton Abbot.

Young, A. 1822. *The farmer's calendar* (12th edition). MacMillan, London.

Young, C. P., Oakes, D. B. and Wilkinson, W. B. 1976. Prediction of future nitrate concentrations in groundwater. *Ground Water* **14**, 426-438.

Young, G. W. 1905. The Chalk area of north-east Surrey. *Proceedings of the Geologists' Association* **19**, 188-220.

Younger, P. L. 2007. *Groundwater in the environment: an introduction*. Blackwell, Oxford.

Z

Zagwijn, W. H. 1974. The Pliocene-Pleistocene boundary in western and southern Europe. *Boreas* **3**, 75-97.

Zagwijn, W. H. 1975. Variations in climate as shown by pollen analysis, especially in the lower Pleistocene of Europe. In: *Ice ages: ancient and modern* (eds Wright, A. E. and Moseley, F.). Geological Journal Special Issue **6**, 137-152.

Zalasiewicz, J. A., Mathers, S. J., Hughes, M. J., Gibbard, P. L., Peglar, S. M., Harland, R., Nicholson, R. A., Boulton, G. S., Cambridge, P. and Wealthall, G. P. 1988. Stratigraphy and palaeoenvironments of the Red Crag and Norwich Crag formations between Aldeburgh and Sizewell, Suffolk, England. *Philosophical Transactions of the Royal Society of London* **B322**, 221-272.

Zalasiewicz, J. A., Mathers, S. J., Gibbard, P. L., Peglar, S. M., Funnell, B. M., Catt, J. A., Harland, R., Long, P. E. and Austin, T. J. F. 1991. Age and relationships of the Chillesford Clay (early Pleistocene: Suffolk, England). *Philosophical Transactions of the Royal Society of London* **B333**, 81-100.

Ziegler, P. A. 1975. North Sea Basin history in the tectonic framework of north-western Europe. In: *Petroleum and the continental shelf of north-west Europe 1. Geology* (ed. Woodland, A. W.). Applied Science Publishers, Barking, 131-148.

Ziegler, P. A. 1982. *Geological atlas of central and western Europe*. Shell Internationale Petroleum Maatschappij BV. Elsevier, Amsterdam.

Zielinski, G. A. 2000. Use of palaeo-records in determining variability within the volcanism-climate system. *Quaternary Science Reviews* **19**, 417-438.

Index

A

Abbey of St Albans   105, 305, 310. *See also* St Albans Abbey

Anticline(s)   27, 58, 98-99, 102-103, 264

Ants   197

Aptian Stage   30-31

Aquifer   56, 177, 256-259, 261-271, 275, 277-287, 293, 297, 327, 344-345, 347, 350, 353-355

Aquitard(s)   256-257, 262-263, 266

Arbury Banks   245, 247-248

Ardeley   89, 238, 242, 245, 309

Argillic

brown earths   192-193, 211, 213, 215-220

brown sands   192, 200, 217-218

gley soils   194, 206

pelosols   191, 211, 222

Arkley   75, 78, 137, 306

Arlesey   31-34, 224, 305, 339, 350, 359

Arrowheads   236, 240, 242, 245

Artesian   257, 276-277

Artificial

fertilizers   187, 280

field drainage   211, 214

recharge   266, 277-278, 287, 328, 335

Ash-Brook Channel   143

Ashlar   299, 305, 310, 317

Ashley   131, 192, 211, 215-216, 218, 221

Ashridge   19, 113-114, 251, 304-305

Ash valley   176, 206

Ashwell   10, 24, 26, 30-31, 35, 41, 43, 51, 53, 114, 157, 179, 189, 199, 208-209, 211, 214, 241-242, 245, 275-276, 304, 309-311, 319, 322

Aspen   206

Assemblage biozones   14, 32, 124, 136

Asthenosphere   21, 23

Aston Marl   58

Asymmetric dry valley   178-179

Autumn-sown crops   199, 205, 209, 218, 220-222

Axeheads   114, 236-240, 242, 247

Ayot

Green   69, 73, 306-307

St Peter   67, 75, 233, 309, 314

B

Back-to-back dry valleys   182

Bacon, Francis   19

Bacteria   40, 279-282, 284, 286-287

Badger   136, 165, 197

Bagshot Formation   62, 72, 78-79, 83, 90, 98

Baldock   10, 41, 44-46, 54-55, 59-60, 70, 89-91, 174, 184, 197, 200, 206, 209, 211-212, 220, 225, 239, 249, 251, 275, 290

by-pass   41, 44-46, 54-55, 59-60, 70, 89-91, 290

Balls

Park   242

Wood   199

Balthica   28

Bank

storage   269

structure   49

Barkway   10, 25, 46, 54, 142, 184, 208, 211, 304

Barnack Stone   319

Barnet   64, 67, 75, 137, 150, 187, 205-206, 259, 273, 276

Baseflow recession   269

Basement   5, 21, 25-29, 31, 33, 97, 105, 278

Base of the Quaternary   81, 123

Batcombe   193, 216, 219-222, 260-261, 281, 283, 304

Bayfordbury   145, 176

Beaconsfield Gravel   128, 132, 139

Beaker period   243

Beane   141, 143, 147, 150, 153-155, 174, 181, 183, 200, 206-207, 216-217, 220, 224, 244, 275

Beans   202, 209, 211, 214, 216, 218, 221

Beccles   193, 211, 218, 221

Beckton   26, 322

Bedfordshire Straits   31

Bedmond   19, 67, 115, 130, 220, 229, 238, 257, 276, 309, 320-321

Bedwell Park Quarry   41, 46, 48-49

Beech   124, 202, 220-221

Bottom   145, 252-253

Beetles   119, 124-125, 163, 165, 177, 183, 217

Belemnites   32, 40, 42, 61, 164

Bell Bar   131, 242, 276

Bellpits   303

Bengeo   141, 234, 309, 319

Bennetts End   67-68, 73, 304, 306-307

Bentonite   39, 286, 293

Berkhamsted   3, 19-20, 67, 75, 80-83, 100-101, 106, 110, 115-116, 125, 131, 136-137, 188, 193, 218-220, 222, 246, 259, 265, 269, 271, 275, 289, 291, 293, 309, 311-312, 317, 319-321

Bernard's Heath   67

Bessemer, Henry   19

Bevan, Benjamin   297

B horizon   186-187, 191, 199, 204-206

Biddenham   169

Bifurcation ratios   96-97

Bioglyphs   67

Biostratigraphy   14

Bioturbation   32, 64, 305

Birch   123, 159-160, 163, 165, 176, 183, 195-196, 205-206, 221-222, 235

Bishop's Stortford   10, 20, 24-25, 41, 65-70, 75, 106, 125, 131, 152-153, 155, 165, 221, 234, 237, 245, 293, 306-307, 309, 317, 319

Black-coated flint pebbles   64-65, 67, 70, 72-74, 87

Blackheath Beds   72-73

Black Park Gravel   128, 134, 176

Blagrove Common   199

Blattspitzen   235

Block   192, 214

Body fossils   14

Borehamwood   76, 78, 136, 273

Bottom Farm   271-272

Bouguer gravity anomalies   25

Boulders composed of Hertfordshire Puddingstone   83

Boundary markers   114

Bourne End   133, 271-272

Bournes   265, 269-273

Bovingdon   115, 196, 233, 305

Bow Bridge   271

Box   198

rampart   245

Boxmoor   176, 198, 207, 223, 304, 309, 319

Trust   176

E

Eakring-Denton Fault   29
Early temperate period   123, 230
Earthquake(s)   21, 23, 62-63, 105-106
Earthworms   197
Earthy
eu-fibrous peat soils   194, 207
eutro-amorphous peat soils   194, 207, 223-224
man-made humus soils   194, 207
peat soils   194, 207
Eastend Green Till   150, 156, 169
Eastern Avalonia   27-28
Eastwick   74, 141, 146, 238
Echinoid(s)   32, 34, 40-41, 49, 53-54, 60, 65, 76, 86
Elder   163, 195, 199, 207
Electrical conductivity   266-267
Elm   123, 160, 163, 183, 202, 206-207, 288
Elstree   75-76, 78, 187, 222
railway tunnel   76
Embankments   240
Eocene   11-12, 61-63, 68-69, 73, 76-78, 110-111, 301
Epochs   11-12, 61, 79, 119
Epping
Forest Ridge   149
Green   98, 137-140, 221, 274
Ermine Street   9, 157
Erratics   35, 89, 116, 118, 140, 157-158, 164, 174, 309, 315-316, 321
Essendon   41, 46, 49, 75, 108, 125, 131, 136, 194, 218, 222-223, 285
Etchplains   90
Eustatic   32, 36, 39, 62-63, 104-105, 136, 160, 236
Eutrophication   283-284
Evans,
John   19, 226, 238, 270
Percy   3, 129, 307, 314
Evapotranspiration   187, 258-261, 271
Evenlode valley   132
Evesham
2   210, 214
3   211

F

Faecal pellets   14
Fairfield Hospital   31, 147, 149
False puddingstone   115, 316
Farmsteads   248, 251
Feeder adits   277
Ferns   77, 160
Ferricrete   72, 108
Fertigation   217

Festoons   166, 173
Field
capacity   261
maple   199, 202-203, 221
Filler   31, 303
Finchley   78, 98, 106, 132, 139, 145, 149-150, 158
Fir Wood   221
Fishers Green   159-161, 166, 233
Fission tracks   104
Fissure
enlargement   263
flow   261, 277, 279-280, 282, 284
Five Knolls   239, 243
Fladbury
1   224, 239, 282
3   224, 282
Flasers   51
Flint   36, 40, 43, 45-46, 48-49, 51, 53-56, 58, 64-67, 69-74, 78, 80-82, 85, 87, 89, 91, 93, 109-112, 114-115, 125, 127, 130-137, 139, 143, 146-147, 152-154, 156, 161, 164, 166, 168, 172--175, 186-187, 200, 207, 210, 213-214, 217, 219, 226-227, 229-233, 235-236, 239-240, 242-243, 245-247, 271, 277, 299-300, 302-303, 311, 313-317, 321
bands   36, 43, 46, 48-49, 53-54, 56
meal   51
mines   242, 302
Flint-tempered   246-247
Flocculation   266
Flooding   116, 184, 214, 224-225, 259, 274, 278, 287, 293
Flow
structures   86
till   121
Foamed concrete   290, 293
Folly
Farm   173, 213
Lane   252
Path   162
Font(s)   305, 310
Foraminifera(l)   3, 15, 32, 34, 36-37, 40, 46, 48, 51, 58, 61-62, 64, 76-77, 121, 159
Formation of flint   40
Formations   13-16, 18, 21, 23, 27, 29-31, 37-38, 61-64, 66-68, 72-75, 78-79, 81, 87-88, 93, 97-98, 104, 106, 108-112, 118, 130, 134, 137, 141, 143, 166, 171, 174, 177, 187, 195, 198, 205, 220, 256, 262, 278, 281, 287, 299-300, 306
Fossil wood   74, 76
Foundation stones   115, 314
Foxholes   147, 153-154, 245, 247, 250, 306

Freestone   305, 310
Friar's Wash   212, 270-271, 277
Friars Wood   199
Frog   167, 217
Frogmore   153, 223, 309, 314
Meadow   223
Frome   194, 223, 225, 282
Frost-heaving   108, 116
Fuller's earth   31, 299
Furneux Pelham   66, 130-131
Furze Platt   135

G

Gabions   303
Gaddesden Row   91, 114, 166, 232-233, 238, 307
Gade   10, 85, 103, 141, 171, 175-176, 178, 181-184, 194, 206-207, 212-213, 215, 223-225, 227, 237, 242, 245-246, 263, 269-270, 272-273, 275-276, 298
Gaining river   269
Garden
city   9
walls   114, 299
Garnets   23, 68
Gastric cancer   282
Gastroenteritis   282
Gault Clay   15, 18, 21, 26-27, 29, 31-35, 152, 166, 174, 182, 186, 198-200, 206, 208, 210-211, 214-215, 257, 287-288, 296, 299, 305, 313, 322-324
Gauss-Matuyama palaeomagnetic polarity reversal   81
Geescroft Wilderness   202
Gelifluction   72, 82, 87, 123, 126, 130, 140, 160-161, 164-166, 168, 170-175, 178-179, 181-183, 186-187, 200, 209-210, 212-215, 217, 219, 222, 230, 232, 300, 307
Gelifraction   87, 93, 173, 179
Geological time   11-13, 21, 118, 259
Geomembranes   286
Germination   197, 209
Gerrards Cross   98, 126, 128, 132-135, 138, 161, 219, 286
Glacial Gravel with Bunter Pebbles   125
Glacial-interglacial climatic cycles   79, 126
Glaciofluvial   89, 115, 121, 140, 143, 145-146, 149-150, 152, 156, 158-159, 162, 164, 166, 169, 171-172, 174, 200, 205, 216-218, 221, 257, 268, 274-276, 290, 292, 300-301, 315-316
Glacioisostatic depression   147
Glasshouse(s)   185, 217-218

Spears 235-236
Specific
  retention 258
  yield 258
Spider 207
Spillways 144-145, 149
Spilsby Sandstone 157
Sponges 11, 34, 40, 45, 54, 58, 60
Spörer Minimum 122
Spring
  frosts 213
  sapping 179-181
  Wood Silt 170, 217
Spring(s) 19, 76, 110-111, 116, 164, 167,
    176, 179-181, 184, 197, 199, 201,
    205, 207, 209, 211-225, 258-259,
    262-263, 267-276, 278-280, 284,
    294-297, 304
Springview Quarry 49
Stadials 121, 140
Stages 12, 15, 54, 61, 66, 86, 91, 97, 107-
    108, 111, 119, 121-123, 126, 128-129,
    132, 135-137, 139-140, 161, 165-166,
    169, 176-179, 182, 187, 195-196, 200,
    219, 231, 253, 263, 290-291, 300,
    314
Stagnogley
  podzols 193, 205
  soils 193-194, 205-206, 210-211, 214,
    218, 220-222
Stagnogleyic
  argillic brown earths 192, 211, 215-
    216, 218-219
  brown calcareous earths 192, 200,
    211, 214-215
  paleo-argillic brown earths 193, 200-
    202, 218-220, 222
  rendzinas 191, 209
St Albans 3-4, 9-10, 19-20, 27, 40-41,
    66-67, 69, 71-72, 78, 99, 105-106,
    108, 113-117, 125-126, 129-130, 132-
    134, 137, 140, 145-147, 149-152, 155,
    157-158, 160-161, 164-165, 169-171,
    182, 185, 188, 192, 200, 205-206,
    215, 217-221, 227-229, 237-239,
    242, 247, 250, 252, 259, 270-271,
    274, 276-277, 284, 286, 289, 291,
    296, 300-301, 303, 305, 308-310,
    313-314, 316, 319
  Abbey 242, 305, 309-310, 313, 316.
    See also Abbey of St Albans
  City Hospital 67, 71
  earthquake 105
Stanborough 140, 159, 206, 217, 224, 274
  Reed Marsh 224
Standon 10, 65, 69-70, 74-75, 109, 140,
    150, 208, 234, 237-238, 242, 306
Stanmore 64, 67, 76, 78, 106, 137, 139,
    301

Pebble Gravel 137, 139
Stanstead Abbotts 143, 174, 188, 236
Steps Coombe 179-181
Stevenage 7, 19, 24, 67, 70, 88-89, 137,
    141-143, 146, 149, 153, 156-157, 159,
    161-162, 182, 184, 187, 199, 207, 211,
    215, 217, 233, 242, 244, 263, 275-
    277, 289-290, 303, 316
  Channel 141, 143, 157
Stevenage-Hitchin Gap 137
St George's-Dollis Hill Gravel 138
Stocker's Lake 196, 224
Stockpens 245
Stokenchurch 96, 101
Stoke Row Gravel 128, 130-131, 257
Stonecross 117
Stonehenge 115-116, 140
Storativity 258, 269, 271-272
Stort 64-65, 68, 141, 143, 153, 155, 165,
    174, 176, 181, 183, 206-207, 216,
    218, 224, 237, 241, 293
Stort-Cam Channel 143
Stortford Till 146, 152-153, 155
Straight-tusked elephant 135-136, 167-
    169, 228
Stratotypes 13
Straw-plaiting 10
Streatham Common 27, 323
Stripes 172, 212
Structure contours 18, 84, 100-101
sub-Anglian surface 140-141, 145, 182
Sub-Cenomanian Surface 100-102
Subcrop(s) 13, 27-28
Subduction 23, 28-29
Subhercynian 40
Sub-
  Mesozoic surface 26
  Palaeogene Surface 41, 64-66, 90, 93,
    102-104, 106-108, 125, 142, 187
  Red Crag Surface 83-84
  Senonian Surface 100-103
Subsidence 84, 104, 126, 128, 161, 177,
    287-293
Sudbury Formation 129-130, 132-133
Suffusion 291-292
Sugar beet 172, 201, 212, 215-218, 280
Sulphide 40, 266, 281
Suncracks 83
Sundon 33, 156-157
Sunspot activity 122
Superphosphate 34-35, 208, 211, 283-
    284, 299
Superposition 12
Surface flooding 214
Surface-water gley soils 193, 200, 205
Surface water(s) 11-12, 15, 110-111, 122-
    123, 186, 253, 256, 258-259, 264-
    266, 268-270, 272, 277, 279-284,
    287-288, 290, 293

Swaffham Prior 191, 209, 211-212, 215,
    239, 242, 244
Swallow-hole(s) 90, 254, 258, 272-275,
    285, 290
Swanscombe 135-136, 164, 227, 229
Sweet vernal grass 89, 203-204
Sycamore 195, 203, 207
Symondshyde Great Wood 202, 205, 221
Syncline(s) 21, 27, 58, 62, 66, 97-103,
    257, 274, 285, 294, 296-297

T

Talweg 182, 264, 269
Taplow
  Gravel 128, 134-136, 176, 228
  Terrace 128, 134-135, 176
Tattenhoe 21, 27, 29-30, 323
Tectonic uplift 79, 126, 177, 182
Tednambury 165
Teeth 14, 34, 42, 74-76, 85, 119, 135, 163,
    165, 169, 226, 230
Telegraph Hill 198, 244
Telford, Thomas 297-298
Terrace 3, 18, 67, 86, 93, 96, 104, 125-
    135, 138-139, 169, 171-172, 174-177,
    179, 182, 192, 200, 202, 205-206,
    214-215, 217-220, 222, 225, 228,
    231, 236, 276, 300, 314, 316
  aggradations 125, 129
Terrestrial raw soils 189, 191, 196
Tertiary 5, 11-12, 61-62, 65, 88, 90, 93-
    94, 104-105, 107-108, 111, 187, 206,
    219
Tethys 29
Thalassinoides 40, 42, 56, 58, 60
Thame 169, 275
Thames 3, 9, 18, 24, 29, 39, 62, 64, 67,
    72, 74, 78, 86-87, 93, 95-99, 103-
    106, 125-141, 145-147, 149-150, 152,
    162, 165, 167, 169-171, 175-177, 182,
    194-195, 202, 211, 217-220, 222,
    224-225, 228, 231, 236, 239, 242,
    245-246, 255, 257, 267, 270, 274-
    275, 278, 282, 285-286, 290, 292,
    294, 300-301, 314
  Group 62
  Water 278, 285-286
Thanet Sand 61-65, 67-68, 72, 77, 322-
    323
Therfield 46, 142, 198, 208, 241, 244, 259
Thorley Gravel 146, 152
Thorpeness Member 81
Three Ways Wharf 235-236
Through-valleys 85, 97-103, 145, 181-183,
    200, 211, 264, 269, 273
Till 46, 74-75, 89-90, 121, 135, 138-140,
    142-143, 145-147, 149-152, 154, 156-

Hertfordshire Natural History Society promotes the study and recording of the flora and fauna of Hertfordshire and encourages a wider interest in natural history, including the conservation of wildlife, habitats and geological features.

The Society was established in Watford in January 1875 by a group of local naturalists. Its objectives included *'the investigation of the Meteorology, Geology, Botany and Zoology of the neighbourhood of Watford and the County of Hertford, and the dissemination amongst its members of information on Natural History'*. The Society expanded rapidly, and in 1879 extended its remit to the whole county, taking the name Hertfordshire Natural History Society and Field Club.

Today, members of the Society are involved with individual projects and county-wide surveys, making use of modern technology to monitor and record wildlife in the county and its changing fortunes. We co-ordinate a network of County Recorders covering most taxa. Records for individual species are made available for specific studies, analysis and to support conservation work.

Documenting and publishing the results of our studies has always been very important. The first part of the Society's *'Transactions'* was published in 1875 and the series now runs to 41 volumes. The *Transactions* provide a vital and comprehensive source of information about the county and its changing flora and fauna over the last 130 years. They are now published annually in two parts.

The Hertfordshire Bird Report contains a systematic record of all bird species found in the year, together with papers on the results, analysis of specific studies and survey work.

The Hertfordshire Naturalist covers all other wildlife groups, including fungi, flora, dragonflies, butterflies, moths and other invertebrates, amphibians, reptiles and mammals plus reports of the activities of the Society.

The Society has also published six other books:
Flora of Hertfordshire (2009)
The Moths of Hertfordshire (2008)
Dragonflies and Damselflies of Hertfordshire (2008)
Mammals, Amphibians and Reptiles of Hertfordshire (2001)
Birds at Tring Reservoirs (1996)
The Breeding Birds of Hertfordshire (1993)

All the books are available to purchase direct from HNHS.

For further information contact the HNHS secretary: Linda Smith, HNHS Secretary, 24 Mandeville Rise, Welwyn Garden City, AL8 7JU; Tel: 01707 330405, Email: secretary@hnhs.org or go to our website: www.hnhs.org.

Membership of the Hertfordshire Natural History Society is open to everyone.

HNHS is registered charity number 218418

The **Hertfordshire Geological Society** aims to foster a wider appreciation of the geology of Hertfordshire, promote geological fieldwork, encourage the conservation and recording of sites of geological interest in the county, and assist in maintaining them if necessary.

Geology and related topics were always a feature of the HNHS's work, and numerous papers and notes were published in the Society's transactions. A semi-independent Geology Section was formed in 1974, and continued to flourish. In 2002 the Geology Section separated formally from HNHS to become the Hertfordshire Geological Society as it is today.

The HGS holds monthly talks on a wide range of earth science topics. It also organises several day and weekend field trips a year and usually a longer foreign excursion. These activities are aimed at anyone interested in geology, and the HGS membership includes complete beginners, knowledgeable amateurs, geology professionals, and academics.

Members of the HGS are involved in various aspects of designation and conservation of Local Geological Sites (previously known as RIGS). "Hertfordshire Geology and Landscape" is their first publication as a society, and has been a challenging but very worth-while project.

The need for a book on the geology of Hertfordshire has long been recognised, and a great deal of background research was done under the aegis of the HNHS. However, progress came to a halt in the 1970s on the death of the principal contributor, Percy Evans. Recently the challenge was taken up once again by John Catt, with the support and encouragement of HGS. The earlier research has been consolidated, recent developments and new material incorporated, and contributions obtained on a wide range of geo-diversity topics. The resulting book is both scholarly and of wide-ranging interest.

For further information contact the Secretary: Linda Hamling, 17 Rye Hill Road, Harlow, Essex, CM18 7JF; Tel: 01279 423815; e-mail:linda@hamling.org or go to our website www.hertsgeolsoc.ology.org.uk/.